The biology of Canadian weeds

Contributions 84–102

La biologie des mauvaises herbes du Canada

Communications 84 à 102

Paul B. Cavers
Editor and compiler
Department of Plant Sciences
University of Western Ontario
London, Ontario

Publiées sous la direction
de Paul B. Cavers
Department of Plant Sciences
University of Western Ontario
London, Ontario

Reprinted from
Canadian Journal of Plant Science

Extrait du
Canadian Journal of Plant Science

Canadian Cataloguing in Publication Data

Main entry under title:

The biology of Canadian weeds : contributions
84–102 = La biologie des mauvaises herbes du Canada :
communications 84 à 102

"Reprinted from Canadian journal of plant science".
Text in English with abstracts in English and French.
Includes bibliographical references and index.
ISBN 0-9690453-7-9

1. Weeds—Canada. 2. Weeds—Canada—Geographical
distribution. 3. Weeds—Control—Canada. I. Cavers,
P.B. (Paul B.), 1938–II. Agricultural Institute
of Canada III. Canadian journal of plant science.

SB613.C2B56 2000   581.6'52'0971   C00-900755-5

Contents

Introduction

I am pleased to introduce Volume 4 of the collected accounts from the series on the "biology of Canadian weeds". This volume contains accounts of twenty-two weed species and includes detailed biological, taxonomic and economic information about each species, as well as methods of control.

Over the past 28 years the Canadian Journal of Plant Science has published more than 110 accounts on the biology of plants that are weedy in Canada. These articles have proved to be an important source of information for weed scientists in Canada and around the world. As a service for those scientists the contributions from 1 to 61 were collected and republished in two volumes by Agriculture Canada with G. A. Mulligan as the Editor. In 1995, Volume 3 (containing articles 62 to 83 and edited by P. B. Cavers), was published by the Agricultural Institute of Canada. I am pleased to report a continuing demand for the collected volumes and as a result Volume 4 is now being published.

New articles for the series have been submitted in increasing numbers over the past year. In addition, a revised format for the series was published in the April 2000 issue of the Canadian Journal of Plant Science. A format for updating accounts of species already published in the series was added and the first updated account will appear this year. Information about the series can be found on the web sites of the Expert Committee on Weeds (ECW) and the Agricultural Institute of Canada.

A similar series on the biology of Australian weeds is modeled on our publications. The second volume of collected articles from the Australian series appeared recently.

For this volume, individual papers have been reproduced by photo offset. The page numbers that appeared in the Canadian Journal of Plant Science have been replaced by the page numbers in this book. A refer-

C'est avec plaisir que je vous présente le volume 4 de la série intitulée : Biologie des mauvaises herbes canadiennes. Le volume renferme des mises au point sur vingt-deux espèces qui, au Canada, vivent à l'état adventice, apportant pour chacune une somme détaillée de renseignements d'ordre biologique, taxonomique et économique ainsi que sur les méthodes pour les combattre.

Au cours des vingts-huit dernières années, plus de 110 de ces mémoires ont été publiés dans la Revue canadienne de phytotechnie. Ces articles se sont avérés une précieuse source d'information pour les malherbologistes du Canada et du monde entier. Les contributions 1 à 61 ont eté colligées, et par la suite réimprimées, en deux volumes par le ministère de l'Agriculture du Canada, sous la direction de G.A. Mulligan. En 1995, L'Institute agricole du Canada (IAC) prenait la relève avec la parution sous la conduite de P.B. Cavers du volume 3 contenant les articles 62 à 83. Et aujourd'hui en réponse à la demande soutenue pour ces recueils, l'IAC est heureux de présenter ce quatrième volume.

Le nombre de contributions à la série s'est accru au fil des dernières années. Dans le numéro d'avril 2000 de la Revue canadienne de phytotechnie était annoncé un format révisé de presentation des mises au point. Nous y ajoutons un modèle de mise à jour des mémoires déjà publiés dans la série. La première de ces mises à jour paraîtra au cours de l'année. Les renseignements sur la série peuvent s'obtenir sur les sites internet du Comité d'experts en malherbologie (CEM) et de l'Institut agricole du Canada.

Récemment paraissait en Australie le volume deux d'une série, inspirée de notre modèle, sur la biologie des mauvaises herbes australiennes.

Pour le présent recueil, les articles originaux sont reproduits par photographie offset avec, toutefois, une pagination modifiée.

ence to the source appears just above the English Abstract on the first page of each contribution.

I wish to thank the Policy Subcommittee responsible for the Canadian Journals of Plant Science, Soil Science and Animal Science for agreeing to publish this volume. In particular, the Agricultural Institute of Canada has been supportive of the series for many years.

Thanks are also due to all of the editors and referees who ensured the high standard of the original articles. In particular, Mr. G. A. Mulligan co-published the original format for the series with me in 1972 and edited all of the early accounts, establishing the standards for the series. Management of the series rests with a subcommittee of the Expert Committee on Weeds, comprised of Dr. S. I. Warwick, Dr. D. R. Clements and myself.

Dr. Paul B. Cavers, P.Ag.

Mention de la source apparaît immédiatement au-dessus de résumé anglais, à la première page de chaque contribution.

Je tiens à remercier le sous-comité des orientations responsable des Revue canadiennes de phytotechnie, de la science des sols et de zootechnie, qui a autorisé la publication du Recueil. L'Institue agricole du Canada a d'ailleurs toujours témoigné de son constant appui envers la serie.

Je remercie aussi tous les éditeurs et les examinateurs qui ont assuré le maintien du haut calibre des articles originaux. Une mention particulière va à M. G.A. Mulligan qui en 1972 établissait avec moi la présentation originale de la série et à qui revient le mérite de la lecture critique de toutes les premières mises au point. La direction de la série incombe à un sous-comité du comité d'experts en malherbologie, formé des Drs. S. I. Warwick, D.R. Clements et de moi-même.

Dr. Paul B. Cavers, P.Ag.

THE BIOLOGY OF CANADIAN WEEDS. 84.
Oenothera biennis L.

IVAN V. HALL[1], ERICH STEINER[2], PAUL THREADGILL[3], and RICHARD W. JONES[4]

[1]Research Station, Agriculture Canada, Kentville, Nova Scotia, Canada B4N 1J5; [2] Department of Biology, University of Michigan, Ann Arbor, Michigan 48109, U.S.A.; [3]Kerr Center for Sustainable Agriculture, P. O. Box 588, Poteau, Oklahoma, 74953, U.S.A.; and [4]Daldir Rhostrehwfa Llangefni, Anglesly, Wales, U.K. Contribution no. 1871, received 11 Mar 1987, accepted 27 July, 1987.

HALL, I. V., STEINER, E., THREADGILL, P. AND JONES, R. W. 1988. The biology of Canadian weeds. 84. Oenothera biennis L. Can. J. Plant Sci. 68: 163–173.

Oenothera biennis L., the common evening-primrose, is a widespread weed of roadside and waste places commonly occuring on light sandy or gravelly soils where competition is limited. The species is native to North America and, although occurring in all 10 Canadian provinces, is more common in the east than in the west. The chief factor contributing to its success as a weed is the ability to tolerate drought. A winter annual or facultative biennial, it flowers and bears seed only once in a lifetime. The small, irregularly shaped seeds have a high oil content, and contain γ linolenic acid, an uncommon fatty acid of pharmaceutical value. Oenothera biennis is a true-breeding translocation heterozygote composed of two genomes (complexes) differing genetically as well as in chromosomal end arrangement. Populations of O. biennis consist of numerous inbreeding lines, between which limited hybridization may occur.

Key words: Common evening-primrose, Oenothera biennis, weed biology, population structure

[La biologie des mauvaises herbes canadiennes. 84. Oenothera biennis L.]
Titre abrégé: Oenothera biennis L.
Oenothera biennis L., l'onagre bisannuelle commune, est une mauvaise herbe répandue le long des routes et dans les terrains vagues qui se rencontre couramment en sols sableux légers ou graveleux où la concurrence est limitée. L'espèce est originaire d'Amérique du Nord et bien qu'elle se rencontre dans les dix provinces canadiennes, elle est plus commune dans l'Est que dans l'Ouest. Le principal facteur qui contribue à son succès comme mauvaise herbe est son aptitude à tolérer la sécheresse. Annuelle d'hiver ou bisannuelle facultative, elle fleurit et monte à la graine une seule fois au cours de son existence. Les petites graines de forme irrégulière ont une forte teneur en huile et contiennent de l'acide gamma-linolénique, acide gras rare qui présente une valeur pharmaceutique. Oenothera biennis est un hétérozygote de translocation génétiquement stable composé de deux génomes (complexes) qui diffèrent au point de vue des gènes et de l'agencement final des chromosomes. Les populations de O. biennis se composent de nombreuses lignées consanguines qui permettent une hybridation limitée.

Mots clés: Onagre bisannuelle commune, Oenothera biennis, biologie des mauvaises herbes, structure des populations

1. Name

Oenothera biennis L. - **common evening primrose** (Frankton and Mulligan 1970, yellow evening-primose (Alex et al. 1980); **onagre bisannuelle** (Alex et al. 1980). Onagraceae, evening primrose family, Onagracées.

Can. J. Plant Sci. 68: 163–173 (Jan. 1988)

1

Fig. 1. Common evening-primrose, *Oenothera biennis* L. (a) adult plant; (b) seeds. (Drawing from "Weeds of Canada" by Frankton and Mulligan (1970).

2. Description and Account of Variation

Detailed descriptions of the genus *Oenothera* and of the species *biennis* are found in several well-known floras (Fernald 1950; Gleason 1958) and texts on weeds (Frankton and Mulligan 1970; Muenscher 1955). The following brief description of *O. biennis* is based on previous accounts as well as our own observations.

Winter annual or facultative biennial reproducing from seed. Tap root thick and fleshy. Seeds germinating in summer or fall giving rise to a thick short caudex surrounded by a rosette of leaves; rosette leaves simple, recumbent, oblanceolate-ovate with acute apex and base. Flowering stalk hollow, usually developing the second year, branched or unbranched,up to 1.5 m high, bearing alternate leaves; cauline leaves simple, recumbent, 8-12 cm long, 2-3 cm wide with repand-denticulate margins, lanceolate-ovate with acute apex and cuneate base; exfoliating glabrous bark. Inflorescence a prolonged spike up to 40 cm; flowers conspicuous; hypanthium 3-6 cm; sepals 4, yellow-green, lanceolate, 20-22 mm long, 4-5 mm wide, petals 4, yellow, orbicular, 15-25 mm long; stamens 8 with filaments attached to the middle of the anthers; pistil 1 with 4 spreading stigmatic lobes. Fruit a capsule, 25-29 mm long, 6 mm wide, containing many seeds; seeds 1.5 × 0.8 × 0.6 mm with irregular, sharp and prominent angles, rugose surface, brown color and mottled (Montgomery 1977). The adult plant and seeds are shown in Fig. 1.

Plants of *O. biennis* are complete translocation heterozygotes which breed predominantly true, because of a balanced lethal system and self-pollination (Fig. 2). This leads to populations consisting of many different but intergrading biotypes, each of which is an inbreeding line (Cleland 1972; Steiner and Levin 1977). Each of the two sets of chromosomes that constitute a plant of *O. biennis* produces a distinctive and contrasting phenotype; the resulting hybrid vigor is very likely a significant factor in the success of the species as a weed (Levin et al. 1972).

Characters that distinguish the genus *Oenothera* are: flowers 4-merous; stamens 8; hypanthium conspicuously prolonged beyond the ovary and deciduous; and a many-seeded,

dehiscent capsule. In Eastern Canada, *O. biennis* closely resembles *O. parviflora* L. The latter is distinguished by thick, flat, strigose, narrow leaves, stem tips which bend down and then up in a characteristic fashion, and subterminal sepal tips (Cleland 1972). The thin, crinkly, almost hairless leaves of *biennis* are broader and the sepal tips terminal. In Western Canada, *O. biennis* has been confused with *O. villosa* Thunb. (Raven, Wagner and Dietrich, pers. commun.). Some *villosa* strains are not very different from forms of *biennis* 2 (see below). *Villosa* typically has narrow leaves with dense strigose hairs, thicker and shorter buds with flared sepal tips.

Cleland (1958) identified three cytogenetically distinct groups within *O. biennis*, which he designated *biennis* groups 1, 2 and 3. Groups 1 and 2 are difficult to distinguish morphologically and can only be identified with certainty by their breeding behavior. Group 3 differs from the other two by having broader, thinner, more crinkly rosette leaves and buds which tend to be more slender and have appressed sepal tips.

Fernald (1950) recognized four varieties within the species, but Gleason (1958), basing his treatment on the cytogenetic studies of Cleland et al. (1950), does not give these varieties taxonomic status. In the most recent treatment of the subsection *Euoenothera*

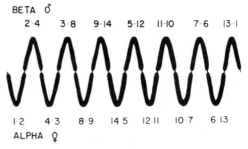

Fig. 2. Diagrammatic representation of meiosis in a complex-heterozygote of *Oenothera*. For clarity the circle of chromosomes has been broken at one point and shown in a single plane. The complex transmitted predominantly through the egg is designated as the alpha (♀); that transmitted most often through the pollen is the beta (♂) complex. The numbers indicate the chromosomal end arrangement for each complex.

(Raven et al. 1979), *O. biennis* group 3 has been recognized as a separate species, *O. austromontana*. However, according to Dietrich (pers. commun.), subsequent study has shown that the correct name for this species is *O. nutans* Atkinson. Detailed accounts of the cytogenetic structure of *Oenothera* populations are given in Cleland (1972) and Steiner (1974).

3. **Economic Importance**

(a) *Detrimental* — Terrell (1977) listed *O. biennis* as a weed affecting crop yields. It is considered a weed of meadows, hayfields, pastures, roadsides, farm yards, waste places, neglected fields and riverbanks (Muenscher 1955; Frankton and Mulligan 1970; Palfrey 1986). In Ontario, it occurs as an occasional weed in winter wheat and fall rye fields (Alex and Switzer 1976).

It has been a minor weed problem in bulb gardens in southeastern United States (Waters 1965) and in vineyards and fruit crops throughout Europe (Hanf 1983). Seedlings of this species developing late in the season interfered with potato harvesting in Florida (Shumaker 1968), and it has impaired crown-vetch establishment in Alabama (Bieber and Hoveland 1968).

(b) *Beneficial—Oenothera biennis* is an edible plant. Its young leaves can be used as a salad or cooked green and its tap root eaten as a cooked vegetable (Fernald et al. 1958; Peterson 1977; Szczawinski and Turner 1978). Mature plants with an abundance of capsules are often collected in late fall for use in dried flower arrangements. *Oenothera biennis* also has a long history of use as a medicinal plant (Ericksen-Brown 1979; Meyer 1979). It has been used to prepare an infusion effective against mental depression and coughs due to colds, and to produce an ointment for soothing rashes and skin irritations (Lust 1974). The seeds of *O. biennis* contain a large oil fraction composed of γ-linolenic acid (Wolf et al. 1983), which is the precursor of prostaglandin E_1 and its derivatives (Hudson 1984). Prostaglandin E_1 is physiologically active in animals as a potent vasodilator, an inhibitor of platelet aggregation in humans, a stimulator of renal blood flow, and an inhibitor of the basal rate of lipolysis, etc. (Moncada et al. 1985). Primrose oil appears to reduce the risk of thrombosis, to lower blood cholesterol levels, and alleviate premenstrual syndrome. Hulan et al. (1987) found that the lipid content of seeds ranged from 16 to 34% and of this approximately 10% was γ-linolenic acid. Lipid formation in the seed occurs after full seed size has been attained but shortly before the change in seed color (Palmer 1985). The seeds have a crude protein content of 16.5%. Strains with a high oil content are potential agronomic crops for north temperate climates.

(c) *Legislation* — *Oenothera biennis* is not listed as a noxious weed in any Canadian federal or provincial weed or seeds act.

4. **Geographical Distribution**

Oenothera biennis is a native North American species whose distribution extends from Newfoundland and Quebec south to Florida (Fernald 1950) and Texas, and west to southern Alberta, Washington (Gleason 1958). In Canada (Fig. 3) it has been collected from the east coast of Newfoundland to Vancouver Island; however, its occurrence in the western provinces is limited. Packer (1983) shows a wider distribution in Alberta than we report. However, his concept of *O. biennis* is more inclusive, encompassing the species *O. villosa* Thunb. and *O. parviflora* L. Specimens originally labelled *O. biennis* were obtained on loan by the senior author from the herbaria of the University of British Columbia, the University of Alberta and University of Saskatchewan. All those from the three respective provinces were of the *villosa* type rather than *biennis*. Most of the recorded collection sites are below 55° latitude. Of the two cytogenetic groups comprising *O. biennis* only the *biennis* group 2 appears to occur in Canada, as shown by maps of the distribution of the Euoenotheras in North America (Stubbe 1964; Cleland 1972). The species was introduced into Europe in the 17th century and is now widely established in Europe, Africa and Asia (Frankton and Mulligan 1970). Palmer (1985) and Cleland (1972) indicate that it has been introduced to South America and Australia, respectively.

5. Habitat

(a) *Climatic requirements* — Palmer (1985) states that *O. biennis* has long been cultivated as an ornamental plant and is now naturalized throughout the temperate regions of both hemispheres. A comparison of the distribution map of *O. biennis* (fig. 3) with a climatic map (Department of Energy, Mines and Resources 1971) reveals that the species grows where there are 2500 degree-days above 5°C.

(b) *Substratum* — *Oenothera biennis* most frequently grows on well-drained, light sandy or gravelly soils.

(c) *Communities in which the species occurs* — Some of the communities in which *O. biennis* occurs include: outwash plains, central portion of the Annapolis Valley, N.S.; gravel river banks; waste areas; roadsides; abandoned gravel pits and cropland; abandoned hayfields, central New York (Kinsman 1982); and badger mounds, Gaylor Prairie Preserve, Iowa (Platt 1975).

Seedlings of *O. biennis* establish on cultivated or disturbed land in the year the disturbance occurs, but are inconspicuous until late fall when the rosette stage is well-developed. The species is commonly found in association with early successional, biennial and perennial weed species (Gross 1980).

6. History

Oenothera biennis is native to North America (Frankton and Mulligan 1970); its present widespread distribution is undoubtedly the result of settlement and the subsequent spread to waste, disturbed or open ground (Fernald 1950). Its presence in the Ottawa area was first noted in the Transactions (No. 1, p. 51) of the Field Naturalists, Club in 1880. The earliest herbarium record in the National Museum was collected from Chatham (Ont.) in 1870.

7. Growth and Development

(a) *Morphology* — The juvenile plant consists of a tap root and a thick, fleshy caudex, the upper portion of which supports a flat leafy rosette. During the first year of development,

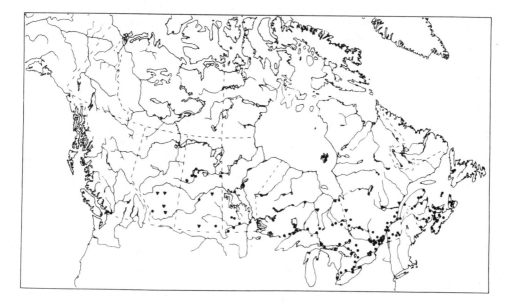

Fig. 3. Distribution of *O. biennis* in Canada based on specimens in National Museum of Natural Sciences, Ottawa, and Biosystematics Research Centre, Ottawa. Additional locations were provided by Wagner and these are represented by triangles.

the growth of a strong tap root into the soil is important in supplying a source of nutrients and moisture in light, excessively drained sandy or gravel soils.

(b) *Perennation* — *Oenothera biennis* is a hemicryptophyte. In addition to the perennating bud of the rosette, dormant seeds overwinter in the soil.

(c) *Physiological data* — A photosynthetic rate of 11.4 μmol CO_2 $m^{-2}s^{-1}$ and a dark respiration rate of 1.5 μmol CO_2 $m^{-2}s^{-1}$ were found for leaf tissue of *O. biennis* at a temperature of 24.5°C and a photosynthetic photo flux of 800 μmol $s^{-1}m^{-2}$ (Hicklenton unpubl. data). Determination of in vivo nitrate reductase activity by vaccum infiltration revealed a rate of 2.45 μmol NO_2^- g fresh $wt^{-1}L^{-1}$ in the presence of 50 mM substrate nitrate, and a rate of 2.24 μmol NO_2^- g fresh $wt^{-1}L^{-1}$ without added substrate, at a temperature of 27.5°C.

(d) *Phenology* — Seedlings emerge in summer or fall. The time of maximum root growth occurs during the early weeks of summer of the second year. New shoot growth from the overwintered rosette stage commences in late spring; in the south of Canada this is usually in late May or early June. Based on herbarium records, flowering begins mid-July to late July, with mature seeds produced by mid-August.

(e) *Mycorrhiza* — None reported.

8. Reproduction

(a) *Floral biology* — Flowers of *O. biennis*, like those of other evening primroses, open at dusk and wilt the following morning. Flowers are predominantly self-pollinated, but outcrossing does occur (Steiner 1956). Pollen is shed while the petals are convolute in the bud, thus favoring self-pollination. The pollen grains are triporate, spherical in outline, ca. 100 μm in diameter, and held together by viscin threads. In his survey of the degree of outcrossing among various races of *O. biennis* growing together in the experimental garden, Hoff (1962) found that the relative lengths of anther and style as well as the amount of pollen produced influences the degree of outcrossing. Outcrossing was negatively correlated with the additions of self-pollen applied to the stigma. Since bees and moths regularly visit the flowers, and anthers frequently fail to produce pollen, crossing is possible.

Oenothera species and hybrids show varying degrees and types of pollen sterility. These have been characterized for the hybrid between *O. biennis* and *O. villosa* by de Halac (1986).

(b) *Seed production and dispersal* — In studies in England, Ridley (1930) reported that the average *O. biennis* plant produced 140 capsules, each containing 180 seeds. The mean number of capsules per plant found in Nova Scotia was 93 $\pm$ 13 (SE), n=10 (unpublished), southwestern Ontario 19 $\pm$ 20 (SD), n=25 (Threadgill 1986), and in central New York 31 $\pm$ 20 (SD), n=22 (Kinsman 1982). The mean number of seeds per capsule found in Nova Scotia was 248 $\pm$ 0 (SE, n=10 (unpublished) and 119 $\pm$ 82 (SD), n=100 in southwestern Ontario (Threadgill 1986). The number of seeds produced per plant has been reported from England as 25 200 (Ridley 1930), from North Dakota as 118 500 (Stevens 1932) and from Michigan as 5000 – 50 000 (Gross 1980). Seed weights reported by various authors ranged from 0.2 to 0.6 mg per seed (Table 1).

Seeds of *O. biennis* possess no specialized morphological adaptations for dispersal by wind, water, or animals. When mature, the capsule dehisces longitudinally releasing the seeds. Seeds may be dispersed by wind up to 4 m from the parent plant, but most fall within 1 m (Platt 1975; Boynton 1895; Threadgill 1986). They can also be dispersed by water (Ridley 1930) and can remain floating for at least 24 h (Threadgill 1986). Since seeds of *O. biennis* are ingested and subsequently voided intact by birds (see section 14 (a)), long-range dispersal is possible. Probably the most important method of short, as well as long-range seed dispersal is by means of soil adhering to surfaces of autos, trucks, farm and construction vehicles.

(c) *Viability of seeds and germination* — Dormant seeds of *O. biennis* can remain viable

Table 1. Seed weights of *O. biennis* as reported by various authors in the United States and Canada

Location	Source	No. of samples	Mean weight (mg per seed)
North Dakota	Stevens (1932)	1†	0.3
Michigan	Gross (1980)	100	0.20±0.00 (SE)
Ohio and Michigan	Gross (1984)	100	0.29±0.08 (SD)
Ohio	Gross and Kromer (1986)	100	0.46±0.01 (SE)
SW Michigan	Mittlebach and Gross (1984)	20-25	0.41±0.08 (SE)
Ontario	Unpublished data	1‡	0.35
Nova Scotia	Unpublished data	1‡	0.6
Start of fruiting period		50	0.34±0.09 (SD)
Midpoint of fruiting period	all seeds were from London, Ont. Threadgill (1986)	50	0.53±0.24 (SD)
End of fruiting period		50	0.72±0.19 (SD)

†Sample contained 1000 seed.
‡Sample contained 2000 seed.

in soil for up to 80 y. (Darlington and Steinbauer 1961). The critical factor in seed germination under field conditions is the depth of seed in the soil; germination does not occur unless the depth is 5 mm or less (unpublished observations). Seeds of *O. biennis* exhibit skotodormancy, i.e. dark-induced, light-irreversible dormancy (Kivilaan 1975). Dormancy can be broken by low temperature, exposure to light, or wetting/drying cycles.

Threadgill (1986) found that 85.1 ± 4.9% (SD) of 1000 freshly ripened seed collected from a population of *O. biennis* growing near London, Ont. were viable. Of the viable seeds 72.2 ± 5.8% (SD) were capable of germination when placed under a regime of alternating 25/15°C and a 14-h photoperiod. When the remainder of the dormant seeds were stratified for 6 mo at 6.5°C and then placed in a 14-h photoperiod, 26.9 ± 6.4% (SD) germinated.

Anderson (1968) reviewed studies of seed germination in *O. biennis* including the works of Fawcett (1908), Toole et al. (1957) and Gardner (1921). All workers reported poor and erratic germination, although treatments such as exposure to light, abrasion and hot water improved germination. More recently Gross (1985) found that germination of *O. biennis* seeds increased with increasing irradiance to a maximum of 80% at 13 Wm⁻², with seeds requiring at least 1 h exposure to light to induce germination. Percent germination increased in direct proportion to length of exposure to a maximum of 80% after 22 h (Gross 1985). Germination of *O. biennis* seeds was strongly affected by the spectral composition of the light. Light filtered through a leaf canopy significantly reduced germination, and exposure to red, blue and especially far-red light reduced germination (Gross 1985). Gross and Kromer (1986) demonstrated that seed weight effects on seedling rosette diameter were small and did not persist beyond the fourth week after emergence.

(d) *Vegetative reproduction* — Vegetative (clonal) reproduction has not been noted in *O. biennis*.

9. **Hybrids**

The cytogenetic analysis of *Oenothera biennis* populations has clearly shown that the species is of hybrid origin, having in all likelihood arisen through the hybridization of *O. villosa* and *O. grandiflora*, or their progenitor species (Cleland 1958). A plant of *O. biennis* consists of an A and a B genotype combined with either plastome type II or III (Stubbe 1959). Although *O. biennis* populations are composed of innumerable, largely inbreeding lines, hybridization between lines does occur under circumstances described by Hoff (1962) (see Section 8 (a)). The origin of distinctive strains through hybridization in natural populations in Europe has been analyzed in detail by Renner (1942, 1951). According to Renner, *O. rubricaulis* Klebahn and *O. issleri* Renner arose from hybridization between *O. oakesiana* Robbins and *O. biennis*; further, *O. drawertii* Renner has been derived from a cross between *O. biennis* and *O. villosa*. Renner (1942) states that wherever differentiated strains of Euoenotheras coexist, hybrids readily occur. Comparable studies on natural hybridization have not been carried out in North America, although hybrids betwen *O. grandiflora* Ait. and *O. biennis* have been reported by Steiner and Stubbe (1984) in natural populations in Alabama.

10. Population Dynamics

Gross and Werner (1982) demonstrated that availability of bare ground rather than number of years since cultivation determines the occurrence of *O. biennis* in abandoned agricultural fields in southern Michigan. Thus, seeds sown in plots of 1-yr-old and 15-yr-old fields established only in the former where bare ground was abundant. When patches of bare ground were experimentally created in the 1-yr-old and 15-yr-old fields, seedlings established readily; similarly, in central New York State, Kinsman (1982) found plant density was high on newly disturbed soil, but in old fields of 15 yr, only scattered single plants occurred. Gross and Werner (1982) also found very low levels of mortality among vegetative rosettes in an old field in Michigan.

Rosettes of *O. biennis* must reach a diameter of $\geq$ 3.0 cm by the end of a growing season before vernalization and flowering the next year (Gross 1981). In old fields in southern Michigan plants could delay flowering for 1 yr, but by year 3 all plants either flowered or died (Gross 1981). All rosettes which reached a diameter of 14.0 cm by the end of a growing season flowered the following year. Flowering plants always die after seed set (Gross 1980; Kinsman 1982).

11. Response to Herbicides and Other Chemicals

Oenothera biennis is susceptible to dicamba-2,4-D mixtures (Ontario Weed Committee 1979). The standard recommendation for roadside spraying which controls this weed is dicamba/2,4-D (1:2) at 1.6 - 3.3 kg per ha in 100 - 200 L of water. *Oenothera biennis* exhibits some tolerance to the substituted triazines and herbicides of the trifluralin group in pre-emergence applications (Stringer et al. 1985). A further report on the activity of some 25 herbicides applied pre-emergence to plantings of *O. biennis* indicates that isoxaben at 0.075, trifluralin at 1.0 and tri-allate at 1.0 kg ha^{-1} were nontoxic whereas simazine at 0.25 kg ha^{-1} was toxic (Richardson and West 1986).

12. Response to Other Human Manipulations

(a) *Mowing* — For weed control, Muenscher (1955) recommends mowing before plants of *O. biennis* have set seed.

(b) *Fertilization* — On stands of cultivated plants of *O. biennis* in Nova Scotia, improved growth and yield of seed have been noted following the application of fertilizer, especially nitrogen in the range of 100 – 200 kg ha^{-1} (unpubl. obs.).

(c) *Plowing* — This destroys the rosette stage and prevents seed formation. Cultivation does, however, bring seeds to the soil surface where conditions are favorable for germination.

13. Responses to Parasites

(a) Seeds of *O. biennis* are eaten by goldfinch *Carduelis tristis* (Linneaus) and sparrows, *Spizella* spp. (Martin et al. 1951) *Aphis oenotherae* (Oestlund) attacks both wild and cultivated species of *Oenothera* in the eastern United States (Pirone 1978). *Macrosiphum gaurae* (Williams) is a host-specific aphid found in colonies on *O. biennis* in central New York and feeds on the inflorescences (Kinsman 1982). Aphids have been observed on plants of *O. biennis* in Nova Scotia, causing severely crinkled, twisted leaves and slightly twisted stem tips (Dr. H. B. Specht, pers. commun.). A number of other host-specific insect species described below are found on *O. biennis* (Kinsman 1982). Adults of *Acanthoscelidius* sp. (Coleoptera: Curcul ionidae) feed in the axils of young leaves and on flower buds; the larva develops singly within the flower bud, destroying it internally. Females of *Tyloderma foveolata* Say (Coleoptera: Curculionidae) oviposit into the stems of plants, the larvae feeding on the pith. Species of the genus *Mompha* (Lepidoptera: Momphidae) feed on stems, flower buds, and capsules. For instance, *Mompha stellella* Busck deposits eggs on or near the flower buds; the larva then feeds on the bud, destroying the floral tissues. Larvae of *M. brevivitella* (Clemens) develop within the ripening capsules, consuming varying amounts of the developing seeds. Larvae of *Conchylis oenotherana* (Riley) (Lepidoptera: Cochylidae) feed in stem tips, pulling the small leaves together with an inconspicuous web. *Schinia florida* (Guene) (Lepidoptera: Noctuidae) feeds almost exclusively on *O. biennis*. The young larva chews into the bud and feeds on the flower parts. In addition, Kinsman (1982) noted a number of generalist insects that have been observed feeding on *O. biennis*.

(b) Conners (1967) and Ginns (1986) list the following fungi as occurring on *O. biennis*: *Erysiphe cichoracearum* DC. ex Méral, powdery mildew; *E. polygoni* DC. ex Mérat, powdery mildew; *Gnomonia misella* Niessl; *Mycosphaerella tassiana* (de Not.) Johans; *Peronospora arthuri* Farl., downy mildew; *Pleospora herbarum* (Fr.) Rabh.; *Puccinia dioicae* P. Magn., rust; *P. oenotherae* Vize, rust; *Scopinella solani* (Zukal) Malloch; *Septoria oenotherae* West., leaf spot; and *Uromyces plumbarius* Pk., rust.

Downy mildew is regularly observed on plants in the experimental garden; strains vary widely in their susceptibility to mildew.

(c) No higher plant parasites have been noted on the species.

ACKNOWLEDGMENTS

We wish to thank A. T. Lightfoot for technical assistance with photographs. The loan of specimens from the Biosystematics Research Centre, the National Museum of Natural Sciences in Ottawa, the University of Saskatchewan, the University of Alberta, and the University of British Columbia is also gratefully acknowledged. We are indebted to Dr. J. M. Campbell of the Biosystematics Research Centre, Ottawa for providing the authorities for scientific names of insects cited in Section 13. For the measurements of rates of photosynthesis and dark respiration we are indebted to Dr. Peter R. Hicklenton and for information of insects feeding on *O. biennis* to Dr. H. B. Specht both of the Kentville Research Station.

Alex, J. F. and Switzer, C. M. 1976. Ontario weeds. Ministry of Agriculture and Food, University of Guelph, Guelph, Ont. Publ. **506**, 200 pp.

Alex, J. F., Cayouette, R. and Mulligan, G. A. 1980. Common and botanical names of weeds in Canada. Agriculture Canada, Ottawa, Ontario. Publ. 1397, 132 pp.

Andersen, R. N. 1968. Germination and establishment of weeds for experimental purposes. Weed Society of America, Urbana, Ill. 236 pp.

Bieber, G. L. and Hoveland, C. S. 1968. Phytotoxicity of plant materials on seed germination of crownvetch, *Coronilla varia*. Agron. J. **60**: 185–188.

Boynton, M. F. 1895. Observations on the dissemination of seeds. Bot. Gaz. **20**: 502–503.

Cleland, R. E. 1958. The evolution of the North American oenotheras of the "biennis" group. Planta **51**: 378–398.

Cleland, R. E. 1972. Oenothera cytogenetics and evolution. Academic Press, London, 370 pp.

Cleland, R. E., Preer, L. B. and Geckler, L. H. 1950. The nature and relationship of taxonomic entities in the North American euoenotheras. Indiana University Publ. Sci. **16**: 218–254.

Conners, I. L. 1967. An annotated index of plant diseases in Canada and fungi recorded on plants in Alaska, Canada and Greenland. Canada Department of Agriculture, Ottawa, Ont. Publ. 1251, 380 pp.

Darlington, H. T. and Steinbauer, G. P. 1961. The 80-year period for Dr. Beal's seed viability experiment. Am. J. Bot. **48**: 321–325.

Department of Energy, Mines and Resources. 1971. The national atlas of Canada. Folios A & B Queen's Printer, Ottawa, Ontario.

de Halac, N. 1986. Pollen sterility in hybrids and species of *Oenothera*. Centro de Microscopia Electronica, Univ. Catolica Cordoba, Trejo 323, 5000 Cordoba, Argentia. pp. 273–282.

Ericksen-Brown, C. 1979. Use of plants for the past 500 years. Breezy Creeks Press, Aurora, Ontario, pp. 429–430.

Fawcett, H. S. 1908. The viability of weed seeds

under different conditions of treatment, and a study of their dormant periods. Proc. Iowa Acad. Sci. 15: 25-45.

Fernald, M. L. 1950. Gray's manual of botany, 8th ed. American Book Co., New York, 1632 pp.

Fernald, M. L., Kinsey, A. C. and Rollins, R. C. 1958. Edible wild plants of Eastern North America. Harper & Row, Publishers, New York, 452 pp.

Frankton, C. and Mulligan, G. A. 1970. Weeds of Canada. Canada Department of Agriculture, Ottawa, Ont. Publ. 948, 217 pp.

Gardner, W. A. 1921. Effect of light on germination of light-sensitive seeds. Bot. Gaz. 71: 249-288

Ginns, J. H. 1986. Compendium of plant disease and decay fungi in Canada 1960-1980. Agriculture Canada Research Branch, Ottawa, Ont., Publ. 1813, 416 pp.

Gleason, H. A. 1958. The new Britton and Brown Illustrated flora of the northeastern United States and adjacent Canada. Vol. 2. The Choripetalous Dicotyledoneae Saururaceae to Cornaceae. Lancaster Press, Inc., Lancaster, Penn. pp. 536-544.

Gross, K. L. 1980. Ecological consequences of differences in life history characteristics among four "biennial" plant species. Ph.D. dissertation, Michigan State University, East Lansing, Mich. 120 pp.

Gross, K. L. 1981. Predictions of fate from rosette size in four "biennial" plant species: Verbascum thapsus, Oenothera biennis, Daucus carota, and Tragopogon dubius. Oecologia (Berlin): 48: 209-213.

Gross, K. L. 1984. Effects of seed size and growth form on seedling establishment of six monocarpic perennial plants. J. Ecol. 72: 369-387.

Gross, K. L. 1985. Effects of irradiance and spectral quality on the germination of Verbascum thapsus L. and Oenothera biennis L. seeds. New Phytol. 101: 531-541.

Gross, K. L. and Kromer, M. L. 1986. Seed weight effects on growth and reproduction in Oenothera biennis L. Bull. Torrey Bot. Club 113: 252-258.

Gross, K. L. and Werner, P. A. 1982. Colonizing abilities of "biennial" plant species in relation to ground cover: implications for their distributions in a successional sere. Ecology 63: 921-931.

Hanf, M. 1983. The arable weeds of Europe with their seedlings and seeds. BASF United Kingdom Limited, Suffolk, U.K. 494 pp.

Hoff, V. J. 1962. An analysis of outcrossing in certain complex heterozygous euoenotheras. I. Frequency of outcrossing. Am. J. Bot. 49: 715-721.

Hudson, B. J. F. 1984. Evening primrose (Oenothera spp.) oil and seed. J. Am. Oil Chem. Soc. 61: 540-543.

Hulan, H. W., Hall, I. V., Nash, D. M. and Proudfoot, F. G. 1987. Composition of native evening primrose seeds collected from western Nova Scotia. Crop Res. 27: 1-9.

Kinsman, Sharon. 1982. Herbivore responses to Oenothera biennis (Onagraceae): Effects of the host plant's size, genotype, and resistant conspecific neighbors. Doctoral dissertation, Cornell University, Ithaca, New York.

Kivilaan, A. 1975. Skotodormancy in Verbascum blattaria seed. Flora 164: 1-5.

Levin D. A., Howland, G. P. and Steiner, E. 1972. Protein polymorphism and genic heterozygosity in a population of the permanent translocation heterozygote, Oenothera biennis. Proc. Nat. Acad. Sci. 69: 1475-1477.

Lust, J. B. 1974. The herb book. Benedict Lust Publications, Sini Valley, Calif. 659 pp.

Martin, A. C., Zim, H. S. and Nelson, A. L. 1951. American wildlife and plants. Dover Publications, New York, 500 pp.

Meyer, D. C. 1979. The herbalist. Meyerbooks, Glenwood, Ill. p. 134.

Mittlebach, G. G. and K. L. Gross. 1984. Experimental studies of seed predation in old-fields. Oecologia (Berlin) 65: 7-13.

Moncada, S., Flower, R. J. and Vane, J. R. 1985. Prostaglandins, prostacyclin, thromboxane A_2, and leukotrienes. In Goodman and Gilman's The pharmacological basis of therapeutics. 7th ed. Macmillan Publishing Company, New York, pp. 660-673.

Montgomery, F. H. 1977. Seeds and fruits of plants of Eastern Canada and Northeastern United States. University of Toronto Press, Toronto, Ont. 232 pp.

Muenscher, W. C. 1955. Weeds. The Macmillan Company, New York. 579 pp.

Ontario Weed Committee. 1979. Guide to chemical weed control. Ontario Ministry of Agriculture and Food, Toronto, Ont. Publ. no. 75.

Packer, J. G. 1983. Flora of Alberta. Toronto, University of Toronto Press, Toronto, Ont. 687 pp.

Palfrey, G. D. 1986. Weeds of Nova Scotia, Province of Nova Scotia. 95 pp.

Palmer, J. 1985. The evening primrose — a source of essential fatty acids. N. Z. Agric. Sci. 19: 119-212.

Peterson, L. 1977. A field guide to edible wild

plants of Eastern and Central North America. Houghton Mifflin Co., Boston, Mass. 330 pp.

Pirone, P. P. 1978. Diseases and pests of ornamental plants. 5th ed. John Wiley and Sons, New York. 566 pp.

Platt, W. J. 1975. The colonization and formation of equilibrium plant species associations on badger disturbances in a tall-grass prairie. Ecol. Monogr. **45:** 285–305.

Raven, P. H., Dietrich, W. and Stubbe, W. 1979. An outline of the systematics of *Oenothera* subsect. Euoenothera (Onagraceae). Syst. Bot. **4:** 242–252.

Renner, O. 1942. Europäische Wildarten von *Oenothera* I. Ber. Deut. Bot. Ges. **60:** 448–466.

Renner, O. 1951. Europäische Wildarten von Oenothera II. Ber. Deut. Bot. Ges. **63:** 129–138.

Richardson, W. G. and West, T. M. 1986. Tolerance of evening primrose *(Oenothera biennis)* and borage (Borago officinalis) to pre-emergence herbicides. Ann. Appl. Biol. **108:** 138–139.

Ridley, H. N. 1930. The dispersal of plants throughout the world. Reeve and Co., Ashford Kent, U. K. 744 pp.

Shumaker, J. R. 1968. Chemical weed control for commercial vegetable production. Res. Rep. Inst. Food Agric. Sci. University of Florida. p. 187.

Steiner, E. 1956. New aspects of the balanced lethal mechanism in *Oenothera*. Genetics. **41:** 486–500.

Steiner, E. 1974. *Oenothera*. Pages 223–245 *in* R. C. King, ed. Handbook of genetics, Vol. 2, Plenum Press, New York.

Steiner, E. and Levin, D. A. 1977. Allozyme, Si gene, cytological and morphological polymorphisms in a population of *Oenothera biennis*. Evo-lution **31:** 127–133.

Steiner, E. and Stubbe, W. 1984. A contribution to the population biology of *Oenothera grandiflora* L'Her. Am. J. Bot. **71:** 1293–1301.

Stevens, O. A. 1932. The number and weight of seeds produced by weeds. Am. J. Bot. **19:** 784–794.

Stringer, D., Parker, C. and Richardson, W. G. 1985. Tolerance of *Oenothera biennis* to various herbicide treatments. Ann. Appl. Biol. **106:** 124–125.

Stubbe, W. 1959. Genetische analyse des Zusammenwirkens von Genom und Plastom. Z. Vererbungslehre **90:** 288–298.

Stubbe, W. 1964. The role of the plastome in evolution of the genus Oenothera. Genetica **35:** 28–33.

Szczawinski, A. F. and Turner, N. H. 1978. Edible garden weeds of Canada. National Museum of Natural Sciences, Ottawa, Ont. 1984 pp. 184.

Terrell, E. E. 1977. A checklist of names for 3000 vascular plants of economic importance. USDA Agric. Handbook no. 505. 201 pp.

Threadgill, P. 1986. Variations in the biennial life history strategy among fifteen ruderal species in an abandoned gravel pit near London, Ontario. Ph.D. Dissertation. University of Western Ontario, London, Ont. 356 pp.

Toole, E. H., Toole, V. K., Hendricks, S. B. and Borthwick, H. A. 1957. Effect of temperature on the germination of light-sensitive seeds. Seed Test. Assoc. Proc. **22:** 196–204.

Waters, W. E. 1965. Effects of several herbicides on gladiolus flower and corm production. Proc. 18th sth. Weed Control Conf. pp. 237–245.

Wolf, R. B., Kleiman, R. and England, R. E. 1983. New sources of γ-linolenic acid. J. Am. Oil Chem. Soc. **60:** 1858–1860.

THE BIOLOGY OF CANADIAN WEEDS. 85.
Euphorbia cyparissias L.

A. E. STAHEVITCH[1], C. W. CROMPTON[1], and W. A. WOJTAS[1]

[1]*Biosystematics Research Centre, Agriculture Canada, Wm. Saunders Bldg., C.E.F., Ottawa, Ontario, Canada K1A 0C6. Received 10 Oct. 1986, accepted 5 Aug. 1987.*

STAHEVITCH, A. E., CROMPTON, C. W. AND WOJTAS, W. A. 1988. The biology of Canadian Weeds. 85. *Euphorbia cyparissias* L. Can. J. Plant Sci. **68**: 175–191.

A review of the biology of *Euphorbia cyparissias* L. (cypress spurge) is presented. A key is provided for identifying those members of the *Esula* complex which occur in Canada. Cypress spurge is more abundant in eastern than western Canada. In North America, two cytotypes are found, namely a sterile diploid ($2n = 2x = 20$) and a fertile tetraploid ($2n = 4x = 40$); however, in Europe there is also a fertile diploid. Sterile diploids do not set seed. Fertile diploids have little or no capacity for vegetative reproduction. Fertile tetraploids have abundant seed set; in addition, they produce more shoots than the sterile diploids. Consequently, the tetraploids are the most weedy. Cypress spurge is commonly found on limestone or gravel substrates. Methods for achieving control are presented.

Key words: *Euphorbia cyparissias* L., cypress spurge, graveyard weed, weed biology

[Biologie des mauvaises herbes canadiennes — *Euphorbia cyparissias* L.]
Titre abrégé: *Euphorbia cyparissias* L.
Les auteurs présentent une étude de la biologie de *Euphorbia cyparissias* L. (euphorbe cyprès). Une clé d'identification est fournie pour les membres du complexe *Esula* qui se rencontrent au Canada. L'euphorbe cyprès est plus abondante dans l'est que dans l'ouest du pays. En Amérique du Nord, deux cytotypes se rencontrent, notamment un diploïde stérile ($2n = 2x = 20$) et un tétraploïde fertile ($2n = 4x = 40$); mais en Europe, on rencontre également un diploïde fertile. Les diploïdes stériles ne montent pas à graine. Les diploïdes fertiles ne sont pratiquement pas capables de reproduction végétative. Les tétraploïdes fertiles forment de nombreuses graines et produisent plus de pousses que les diploïdes fertiles. Par conséquent, les tétraploïdes sont les plus nuisibles. L'euphorbe cyprès se rencontre habituellement sur substrats de pierre à chaux ou de gravier. Les auteurs présentent des moyens de lutte.

Mots clés: *Euphorbia cyparissias* L., euphorbe cyprès, biologie des mauvaises herbes

1. Name

Euphorbia cyparissias L. — **cypress spurge** (Alex et al. 1980), graveyard spurge, graveyard week (Frankton and Mulligan 1970), Irish moss (Boivin 1967); **euphorbe cyprès** (Alex et al. 1980), euphorbe a feuille de cyprès, euphorbe faux-cyprès, euphorbe petit cyprès, rhubarbe des pauvres, rhubarbe du paysan, tithy-male (Ferron and Cayouette 1975); Euphorbiaceae, spurge family, Euphorbiacées.

Can. J. Plant Sci. 68: 175–191 (Jan. 1988)

2. Description and Account of Variation

Small-statured, semi-woody perennial (Fig. 1), superficially resembling young conifer (hence the specific epithet). Plants have milky latex throughout. Perennation is by seed or by adventitious buds on the roots. Main stems are erect, to about 4 dm in height, glabrous, often with persistent bud scales near the base. Following the onset of flowering, numerous bristle-like lateral branches arise near the apex of the main stem; these are sterile. The leaves are

Fig. 1. *Euphorbia cyparissias* L. (A) and (B) habit. (C) pseudo-cyme with numerous inflorescences (cyathia) at the center. (D) and (E) fruit capsule (schizocarp) in polar and equatorial view respectively. (F) seed.

alternate, without stipules, sessile, with pinnate venation, linear to oblanceolate in shape with acute bases and rounded apices with short tips. Leaf margins are entire to slightly wavy, and turned under. The leaf blade is rough and sparingly glandular on both the upper and lower surface. Leaves of the main stem are 5.0–32.0 mm long, and 1.0–2.6 mm wide; the lower ones are deciduous, leaving prominent, dark brown, lenticular scars on the stem. The leaves of the lateral branches are 2.0–9.0 mm long, and 0.3–0.5 mm wide; these are persistent.

Both the inflorescences and flowers of *Euphorbia* species are highly modified, which has led to considerable confusion in the literature concerning their description. What appears to be a flower is in fact an inflorescence (termed a cyathium) and what appears to be a cymous inflorescence is in fact a cluster of inflorescences (termed a pseudo-cyme). The inflorescence or cyathium of *E. cyparissias* consists of a pistillate flower surrounded by several staminate ones, enclosed by an involucre which, in turn, is subtended by two bracts (except in the case of the central cyathium). The flowers are minute, lacking perianth parts, and very inconspicuous. The female flower is merely a pistil consisting of three fused carpels and three free styles each with two branches. Each male flower is a single pedicelled stamen. The involucre is a cup-shaped structure, 1.5–2.0 mm in diameter, whose lobed and ciliated rim bears four (or occasionally five) horned glands. The glands are initially yellow-green, but turn orange-brown with age. The involucral bracts are cordate, and 2.0–6.2 mm at the widest point. Each plant has 25–60 of these inflorescences or cyathia. The oldest cyathium, which is central, usually aborts; the remaining cyathia develop in a cluster around it to form the mock inflorescence or pseudo-cyme. The pseudo-cyme consists of 5–22 rays, ranging between 8.7 and 39.4 mm in length. At the apex of each ray is a pair of cordate bractioles, which measure from 4.0 to 7.00 mm in width. Each pair of bractioles subtends a pair of peduncles.

Each of these peduncles is terminated by a pair of cordate bracts, 2.0–6.2 mm at the widest point. Each pair of bracts encloses a cyathium. The entire pseudo-cyme is subtended by a whorl of 10–18, linear to lanceolate ray leaves, which are 5.6–21.2 mm long and 1.2–4.9 mm wide.

The fruit of *Euphorbia* (technically termed the regma) is an explosively dehiscent capsule or schizocarp which splits into three, one-seeded carpels. The seeds are quadrate-subglobular, smooth and to 1 mm in diameter at maturity. The seedling cotyledons are oblanceolate, about 1 cm long and 2 mm broad. Together with the hypocotyl, the cotyledons are usually markedly tinged with purple, presumably due to the presence of anthocyanins. In contrast, the epicotyl and young leaves are green.

Chromosome numbers in both Europe and North America are $2n = 20, 40$ (Moore and Lindsay 1953; Pritchard 1961; Stahevitch et al. unpub.). Three cytogenetic variants are known to occur in *E. cyparissias*, namely a fertile and a sterile diploid (both with $2n = 2x = 20$) and a fertile tetraploid ($2n = 4x = 40$). Meiosis is normal in the sterile diploid and the cause of pollen sterility is not known (Moore and Lindsay 1953). The sterile diploid and fertile tetraploid do not cross. We have carried out 570 crosses using 6 diploids as female parents and 19 tetraploids as males; no projeny were recovered. In contrast, three tetraploid plants crossed easily with each other (Stahevitch and Wojtas, unpubl.) Although very similar in gross morphology, the three forms differ in geographic distribution, reproductive strategy and cellular characters (Moore and Lindsay 1953; Pritchard 1958; Table 1).

In Canada, *E. cyparissias* can be confused with several other introduced spurges of the *Esula* complex. The various taxa of this group can be distinguished as follows:

A. Cauline leaves cordate at base
. . . . *E.   agraria*

A. Cauline leaves not cordate at base. . .B

   B. Cauline leaves greater than 4 mm

Table 1. Characteristics of *Euphorbia cyparissias* cytotypes

Character	Fertile diploid (2n = 20)	Sterile diploid (2n = 20)	Fertile tetraploid (2n = 40)	Reference
Distribution				
(a) Eurasia	France to W. Yugoslavia (excluding Alps)	Mainly Britain	Throughout range	Pritchard (1961)
(b) North America	Absent	N.E. North America	N.E. North America	Muenscher (1936), Moore and Lindsay (1953)
Pollen diameter (μm)				
(a) Eurasia	30.9–31.5	22.6–23.0	33.9–36.0	Pritchard (1958)
(b) Canada	—	22–26	35–40 20–25†	Muenscher (1936)
Epidermal cell area (μm²)				
(a) Eurasia	432–609	242–519	621–942	Pritchard (1958)
(b) Canada	—	280–525	680–925	Muenscher (1936)
Seed production	Present	Absent	Present	Muenscher (1936), Pritchard (1958)
Vegetative propagation	Little/none	Moderate	Prolific	Muenscher (1936), Pritchard (1958)

†A few pollen fall in the smaller range

broad; lateral branches none, or a few with scattered leaves only...*E. esula*
B. Cauline leaves less than 4 mm broad; lateral branches many, with numerous conjested leaves.................C
C. Cauline leaves not greater than 2.6 mm wide; terminal pseudo-cymes in compact clusters; lateral pseudo-cymes absent or few.........*E. cyparissias*
C. Cauline leaves greater than 2.6 mm wide; terminal pseudo-cymes in open clusters; lateral pseudo-cymes numerous ....*E. xpseudoesula*

All these taxa are illustrated and described in Radcliffe-Smith (1985). *Euphorbia agraria* Bieb. is found in a few locations in Alberta and Saskatchewan. *Euophorbia esula* L. is primarily western in distribution; *E. cyparissias*, primarily eastern. The hybrid of *E. cyparissias* and *E. esula*, *E. xpseudoesula* Schur, has been collected from British Columbia, Saskatchewan, and Ontario. We have excluded *E. lucida* Waldst. et Kit. (Croizat 1945; Boivin 1967) because all Canadian collections examined to date are referable to *E. agraria* Bieb. (Marschall von Bieberstein 1808), or, in one case, to *E. esula* (Turner 6489, DAO). Young cypress spurge may also be confused with preflowering yellow toadflax, *Linaria vulgaris* Hill, and goldenrod, *Solidago* spp., but these have no latex and their leaves are acute, not rounded at the apex.

3. Economic Importance

(a) Detrimental — *Euphorbia cyparissias* infestations are found primarily in eastern rather than western North America, typically on open ground used for pasture, often with a sandy or limestone substrate. In Canada, major infestations occur at Mile River, Nova Scotia; Baie St. Paul and Charteris, Quebec; and Braeside, Port Hope, Bobcaygeon, Goderich and Orangeville, Ontario (Barabé and Gagnon 1950; Lindsay 1951; Roland and Smith 1969). About 14 000 ha are infested at Braeside and another 1800 ha at Orangeville. According to Harris (1984), the proximity of these infestations to the limestone substrates of the Smiths Fall's plain and the Niagara escarpment, respectively, poses a high risk in terms of future spread of *E. cyparissias* in southern and eastern Ontario. Smaller infestations are found throughout eastern Canada. In the United States, 25 counties have infestations of more than 200 ha, and an additional 287 counties have smaller stands of up to 200 ha. Most of the large infestations are in the Northeast. There are very few infestations in the South although the largest infestation in the country is located in Bland Co., Virginia (Dunn 1979).

Under certain conditions cypress spurge may become the dominant species (Harris and Alex 1971) on a site to the exclusion of valuable forage and native plants. For example, on lightly grazed pasture at Braeside, *E. cyparissias* comprised 26% of the vegetation in wet summers and 56% in dry ones (Harris 1984). In general, cattle avoid grazing on cypress spurge, but those which accidentally ingest the plant may develop scours, collapse and eventually die (Muenscher 1948; Kingsbury 1964). The latex, which is present in all parts of the plant, produces dermatitis and blisters in susceptible individuals; even a small amount in the eyes is extremely painful (Johnston and Smoliak 1965). Ott and Hecker (1981) found that the active fractions consisted of diesters of 13-hydroxyinginol, which are the most irritating ingenane esters known.

Euphorbia cyparissias is a host of the rust *Uromyces striatus* Schroet., whose alternate hosts included many species of *Medicago*, as well as some yellow-flowered species of *Trifolium*, and *Pisum sativum* (Conners and Savile 1948; Parmelee 1962).

(b) *Beneficial* — *Euphorbia cyparissias* has been used as a ground cover, primarily in cemeteries; hence the name "graveyard spurge" (Frankton and Mulligan 1970). Occasionally, it has been planted around domiciles as well (Gray 1867; Pritchard 1958). For landscaping, the sterile diploid form was utilized because it is less aggressively weedy than the tetraploid and does not produce unsightly seed heads. Today, cypress spurge has fallen into disfavor as an ornamental (Bailey 1949; Stuckey and

Pearson 1973).

Cypress spurge has a long history as a medicinal plant, the earliest known reference to it apparently being found in Hippocrates (cf. Ott and Hecker 1981). Various parts of the plant, or more correctly the latex found in them, have been used to alleviate a variety of complaints including epidermal conditions such as face cancers, wens, hangnails, warts, freckles, calluses and corns, as well as cancers of the stomach, liver and uterus (Hartwell 1969; Usher 1974). Recently, Hokanson and Matyunas (1981) showed that cypress spurge does indeed contain an active anticarcinogenic fraction, but they were unable to determine its precise structure. The plant has also been used widely as a laxative. The vernacular names "Rhubarbe de pauvres" and "rhubarbe du paysan" (Marie-Victorin 1964) refer to its laxative properties. Roslycky (1972) found that the latex could be used to stimulate hair growth in rabbits although the results were highly variable. According to the 6th century A.D. "Geopinkia", the latex was mixed with barley and honey to prepare a rodent poison (Owen 1805).

(c) *Legislation* — Cypress surge is listed as a noxious weed in the Alberta Weed Control Act (Anonymous 1979), the Manitoba Noxious Weeds Act (Anonymous 1970), the Ontario Weed Control Act (Anonymous 1980), the Quebec Agricultural Abuses Act (Anonymous 1964) and the Nova Scotia Weed Control Act (Anonymous 1977).

4. Geographic Distribution

Euphorbia cyparissias is native to Eurasia. It is found throughout Europe except the extreme north and south, and ranges from Britain to Lake Baikal in central Siberia (Pritchard 1961; Smith and Tutin 1968). Cypress spurge is adventive in North America and in New Zealand (Fernald 1950; Connor 1977; Dunn 1979). In North America, it is most common in the east, from Nova Scotia and Maine westward to Ontario and Minnesota, reaching its southern limit in Tennessee (Chester 1975). The Canadian distribution is shown in Fig. 2; the map is based on herbarium collections at ACAD, CAN, DAO,

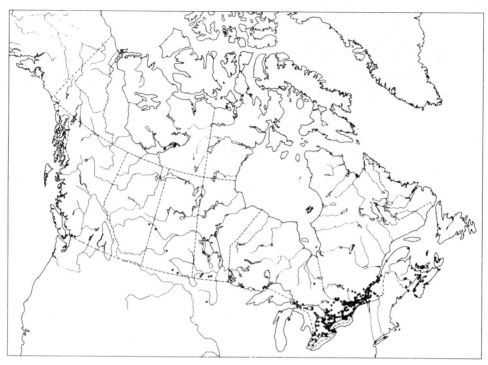

Fig. 2. Canadian distribution of *E. cyparissias*.

MTM, OAC, QFA, QK, SASK, SCC, TRT, UAC, V, WIN (acronyms according to Holmgren et al. (1981)). It should be noted that cypress spurge is recorded from only 19 sites west of Lake Huron. The east–west distribution pattern is very similar in the United States (Dunn 1979).

All three cytogenetic variants are present in Europe and these have a distinctive cytogeography (Pritchard 1961). Fertile tetraploids are the most widely distributed, being found throughout the range of the species. The fertile diploid has a relatively southern distribution (France, Italy, Switzerland, Austria and Dalmatia). Finally, the sterile diploid has managed to establish itself extensively only in Britain. Only sterile diploids and fertile tetraploids have been found in North America; no fertile diploids have been reported to date. In contrast to Eurasia where the tetraploid predominates, the sterile diploid is the most common variant in North America. There is no latitudinal pattern in the distribution of cytotypes in Ontario and Quebec (Fig. 3); we have insufficient data to comment on the situation in the rest of North America.

5. Habitat

(a) *Climatic* — *Euphorbia cyparissias* has a relatively broad ecological amplitude. It is found in both the "warm temperate" and "snow climates with equitable precipitation" as defined in the Geiger system (Strahler 1967). In Europe, its north–south range is from central Italy to central Scandinavia; and in North America, from Tennessee to the Gaspé Peninsula of Quebec. Pritchard (1958) pointed out that in Europe the tetraploid is established in areas (Britain, Scandinavia, Finland, Poland) with cooler summer

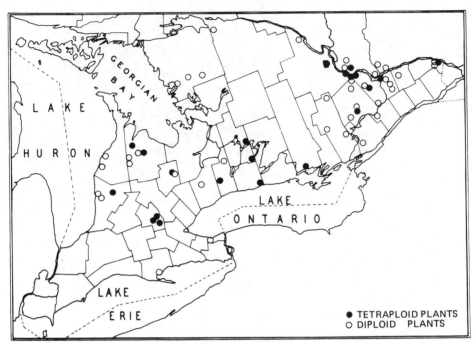

Fig. 3. Cytological map of *E. cyparissias* in Ontario and Quebec.

temperatures overall than is the fertile diploid. In its native range, cypress spurge occupies an altitudinal gradient from lowlands to the alpine zone. It has been recorded at 2200 m in Bavaria, 2400 m in the Tyrol, and 2600 m in Switzerland (Zimmermann 1924). This suggests that in North America its western limits are determined by the aridity of the prairies rather than by low winter temperatures.

(b) *Substratum* — Zimmermann (1924) and Prokhanov (1949) state that in Eurasia *Euphorbia cyparissias* occurs mainly in poor, stony, fairly dry soils. Pritchard (1958) noted its frequent occurrence on chalk downs in Britain. He found that the tetraploid was more tolerant of base-poor soils than the fertile diploid; the tolerance of the sterile diploid is not known.

Cypress spurge is found on similar substrates in Canada. Our field observations,

supplemented by herbarium data, indicate that it is a species of light sands, sandy loams, and gravels. In Ontario, it is also common on limestone (e.g. the Arnprior area). Lindsay (1951) reported that at Braeside, cypress spurge was found mostly on sandy loams or rocky soils with pH ranging from 5.6 to 7.0. Most of the sites were dry although occasionally plants were found growing along wet ditches.

(c) *Communities* — In Europe, *Euphorbia cyparissias* occurs in dry to moderately moist meadows, pastures, alpine meadows, dry heaths, in sparse woods, along forest edges, grassy hills, and stream banks. It is also found in man-made habitats including railway embankments, roadside cuts, cemeteries, gardens and vineyards (Zimmermann 1924; Pritchard 1961; Prokhanov 1949). Its habitats are very similar in North America. Cypress spurge generally does not occur on intensively cultivated soils or on heavily forested ones. Pritchard (1958) noted that the tetraploid appears to be more shade-tolerant than the fertile diploid. In Ontario, we have found that tetraploid colonies occur more frequently on wooded sites than do sterile diploid ones. Zimmermann (1924), Pritchard (1958), and Ranft and Wagner (1972) have examined the natural communities in which *E. cyparissias* is found in Europe. Apparently, there are no comparable autecological studies of cypress spurge in North America. Our observations in central Canada indicate that there are no well-developed plant communities associated with *E. cyparissias* although on a number of railroad embankments it is found with poison ivy (*Rhus radicans* L.) or staghorn sumac (*Rhus typhina* L.). These two species are indicative of the disturbed, sandy substrates often favored by cypress spurge.

6. History

The original Eurasian distribution of *E. cyparissias* is difficult to reconstruct. It is intolerant of prolonged cultivation, and so today is restricted to highlands and other marginal areas. Zimmermann (1924) maintained that in Central Europe, cypress spurge was indigenous only south of the Rhine River. In northern Germany, it apparently was introduced as an ornamental (cemeteries) or as a contaminant of grass seed (military parade grounds) or ballast (railway lines).

The cytogeographic data (Pritchard 1961) support Zimmermann's hypothesis. Fertile diploids occur throughout France and north-central Spain, and also in a narrow band across central Europe (excluding the Alps) from the Atlantic to Dalmatia. Tetraploids apparently replace the fertile diploids in Britain, the Low Countries, the central and southern Balkans, the Soviet Union, north-central Europe and Scandinavia. The two cytotypes are sympatric in southeastern France and the western Balkans. This pattern suggests that cypress spurge arose in western continental Europe in the area occupied exclusively by the fertile diploids. Later, the tetraploids arose in the eastern portions of the range of the diploids. The tetraploids, presumably being adapted to more extreme conditions (Pritchard 1958), were able to extend the range of the species to the north and east. The presence of tetraploids, but not fertile diploids, in Britain and the absence of tetraploids from adjacent portions of the continent, suggests that cypress spurge is a relatively recent addition to the British flora. However, Godwin (1975) reports seed and fruits of *E. cyparissias* from Ipswichian and Middle Weichselian interglacial deposits in Cambridgeshire. If the identification is correct, it appears that cypress spurge was present in Britain for a part of the Quaternary, became extinct, and then was reintroduced.

Finally, the sterile diploid is in almost all instances closely associated with human habitation, which suggests that this form has been propagated and disseminated strictly as an ornamental. Since it is apparently more common in Britain than elsewhere (Pritchard 1961), it may have arisen there. The earliest English reference to cypress spurge as an ornamental which we have found is Sweet (1818). Earlier, Gerard (1633) did refer to cypress spurge, but since he noted that it was a prolific seed-bearer, he presumably was referring to the tetraploid form. Cypress spurge is not mentioned in either the 6th or 8th editions of "The gardners dictionary" (Miller 1752, 1768), which suggests that the sterile diploid form had not yet appeared. It seems probable that this mutant arose between 1768 and 1818.

The sterile diploid was undoubtedly introduced from England into North America as an ornamental. The tetraploid, on the other hand, probably was introduced as an accidental contaminent. The plant described by Gray (1867) under "E. esula" is quite clearly *E. cyparissias*. It is noted as having escaped from gardens and had become naturalized in Essex County, Massachusetts. Lindsay (1951) mentioned that residents of Braeside, Ontario reported that cypress spurge was introduced as an ornamental around 1870. He believed that the present large infestation at Braeside is a result of several small infestations which spread from local cemeteries and then coalesced. Harris and Auld (unpublished) have noted that the center of the Braeside infestation coincides with the old Usborne estate, and consequently believes that it was introduced into the area for landscaping the grounds. With respect to both of these theories, it should be noted that the Braeside infestation consists of tetraploids, not sterile diploids as one would expect. Macoun (1883) recorded cypress spurge as having escaped at Halifax, Pictou, Annapolis, and Blomidon, Nova Scotia; Nashwaak, New Brunswick; Ottawa, Belleville, Picton, Trenton, Hamilton and London, Ontario. St. Cyr collected it in 1889 at Cap-Saint-Ignace, cté de Montmagny, Québec (Rousseau 1968).

7. Growth and Development

(a) *Morphology* — The root system is a major factor contributing to the success of *E. cyparissias* as a weed. It is the only means of propagation available to the sterile diploid, and a supplementary mode for the fertile diploids and tetraploids. There is little published information on root development in cypress spurge, but our observations indicate that it is similar to the pattern described in *E. esula* (Bakke 1936; Holmgren 1958; Raju et al. 1963; Myers et al. 1964). The root system of cypress spurge consists of two types of roots. The young seedling sends forth a long, vertical tap root which is persistent and indeterminate. This root eventually penetrates 3 m or more, thus facilitating survival of the plant on sand or gravel substrates. The tap root gives rise to short, horizontal laterals which are short-lived and determinate. Following initiation of cambial activity, additional long indeterminate roots are produced; but these, unlike the tap root, grow in a horizontal plane. At maturity the root system of cypress spurge consists of long, indeterminate roots, which spread both in vertical and horizontal planes, and short, determinate roots which spread in a strictly horizontal plane. Perennating buds, which give rise to new shoots, develop only on the indeterminate roots.

The fruit of *E. cyparissias* is a dehiscent capsule which explodes at maturity, dispersing the seed. Seed production occurs in two waves: one in early summer, the other in mid-fall.

The latex, which is found in all parts of the cypress spurge plant, is strongly irritating and consequently affords protection against grazing (see section (a)). The waxy cuticle is composed of alkanes, wax esters, aldehydes, primary alcohols, fatty acids and triterpenols (Hemmers and Gulz 1986). The cuticle inhibits herbicide absorption (Jaeger and Moerchen 1977) because it causes the solution to pearlize. The addition of surfactants to the herbicide mixture overcomes this problem.

(b) *Perennation* — Cypress spurge is a hemicryptophyte, which overwinters as root and crown tissue; new shoots are produced each spring. Sterile diploids produce no seed, but tetraploid cytotypes do and thus overwinter as seed as well. Szujko-Lacza and Fekete (1974) found that new buds appear by October (or even September) in several positions on the root system. Bud development is facilitated by the large buildup of assimilates which characterizes the post reproductive period. New shoots emerge soon after the snow cover melts in the spring.

(c) *Physiological data* — *Euphorbia cyparissias* and other members of the Subgenus *Esula* have a C_3 photosynthetic pathway in contrast to Subgenus *Euphorbia* which has CAM metabolism and Subgenus *Chamaesyce* which is characterized by Krantz-type photosynthesis. This pattern has been interpreted to indicate that *E. cyparissias* and its allies are primitive members of the genus (Webster et al. 1975).

Heinze et al. (1982) examined uptake of chemical elements by *E. cyparissias* growing on gypsum, carbonate and silicate substrates. Concentration of N was highest in plants found on gypsum sites; of Fe and Al on carbonate and silicate sites. Calcium concentration was highest in plants on gypsum, less on carbonate, and least on silicate sites. The concentrations of K, P, Mn were higher on silicate than on gypsum or carbonate sites.

Szujko-Lacza and Fekete (1974) studied four parameters associated with growth of *E. cyparissias* in oakwoods. Highest dry weight, net assimilation rate (NAR), and relative growth rate (RGR) occurred at the time of fruit set. Ten days later, leaf area rate (LAR) reached its maximum, at which time NAR and RGR became negative. The authors suggested that these unexpected negative values were due to the intensive respiration accompanying shoot elongation, which depleted the assimilates accumulated in the seeds. Positive values were restored later in the season, followed by negative ones again in late fall.

Lee and Starratt (1972) studied callus formation in cypress spurge to develop a bioassay for host-specificity testing. Callus formed successfully on Murashige and Skoog's medium, supplemented with auxins and cytokinin. Indoleacetic acid was less effective than naphthelenacetic acid, 2,4-D, or picloram. An exogenous supply of cytokinin enhanced growth (e.g. 5×10^{-8} M kinetin, doubled callus weight). After 18 mo, callus deteriorated despite subculturing to fresh medium. Tissues failed to produce chlorophyll even after exposure to a light intensity of 10 000 lx although many species, including the closely related *E. esula*, do so under similar experimental conditions.

Pilet (1953, 1957, 1960) carried out chromatographic studies of auxin and RNA catabolism in *E. cyparissias*. He found that tissue infected by the rust fungus *Uromyces pisi* (Pers.) de By. had higher concentrations of IAA and RNA than did uninfected controls. This suggested that the pathogen produces a toxic element which inhibits the activity of IAA-oxidases and RNase, leading to the observed IAA and RNA increases. Further analysis demonstrated that the situation involving the auxin system is more complex and is phenology dependent. There is an increase in hormone levels, stems elongate and the leaves are retained longer in infected plants.

The latex of *E. cyparissias* includes three serine proteases all of which are glycoproteins containing glucosamine. Proteolytic enzymes with serine residues are apparently rare in plants (Lynn and Clevette-Radford 1985). Those found in cypress spurge are related to the ones which occur in caper-spurge (*E. lathyris* L.) and poinsettia (*E. pulcherrima* Willd.).

(d) *Phenology* — The following description is based on our observations on populations in the Ottawa Valley and on material grown in cultivation, supplemented by herbarium records and by the study of Szujko-Lacza and Fekete (1974).

Cypress spurge seeds germinate from mid- to late May in Ontario. The first true leaves appear 6–10 d postemergence. The leaf arrangement of these is opposite; that of subsequent ones is alternate.

Shoot buds are formed in the crown by mid-autumn. Inflorescence primordia are evident by late winter (Szujko-Lacza and Fekete 1974). Shoots emerge from the perennating buds in Ontario as early as the second or third week of April. Flowering begins the first or second week of May in Ontario, but about the third week of April in Central Europe. In the initial phase of growth, the primary axes reach their full length. Then the secondary inflorescence axes elongate, and within 2 wk double their length. Following the initiation of flowering, the lateral vegetative shoots develop, usually towards the end of May. The lower leaves of the main stem begin to senesce soon afterwards. Seeds may mature as early as the third week in June. A second peak of flowering often occurs in late summer or early fall.

(e) *Mycorrhiza* — Dr. Y. Dalpé (Agriculture Canada), following the techniques of Daniels and Skipper (1985), demonstrated the presence of endomycorrhiza in cypress spurge. Material collected in Arnprior, Ontario had *Glomus constrictum* Trappe and *G. mosseae* (Nicol. & Gerd.) Gerdemann & Trappe, the former species accounting for 90% of the sample. Plants collected at Hull, Québec had only *G. constrictum*. These two species are typical endomycorrhiza in eastern Canada (Dalpé in prep.). Root colonization in both samples was 40–50%.

8. Reproductive Biology

(a) *Floral biology* — The inflorescence or cyathium of *E. cyparissias* is a highly modified unit which mimics the structure and function of an individual flower (details are provided in Section 2(a)). In contrast, the actual flowers of cypress spurge are much reduced with no obvious perianth parts. The cyathium is analogous to the capitulum of the Compositae (Mclean and Ivimey-Cook 1956). The large yellow-green subtending bracts offer a marked visual contrast to the green cyathium and thus afford a guide to prospective pollinators (Faegri and van der Pijl 1978). The nectar in the glands of the cyathium offers an additional attractant. In early spring, many colonies of cypress spurge appear to exude an extremely pleasant fragrance. Actually, the scent is given off by sweet-tasting nectar produced by the pycnia of the rust *Uromyces striatus*, infecting the plants (Parmelee 1962). Thus, rust-infested plants offer two additional stimulants to insect pollinators. *Euphorbia* species are characterized by an obturator, a plug which acts as a bridge for the pollen tube between the base of the style and the ovule thereby facilitating fertilization. *Euphorbia* species are unique among vascular plants in that they possess a 16-nucleate embryo sac (MacLean and Ivimey-Cook 1956).

Muenscher (1936) concluded that tetraploid *E. cyparissias* plants were self-incompatible while Pritchard (1958) reported that they were self-compatible. Our observations have been that tetraploid plants grown in cultivation fail to set seed if the cyathia are bagged before the flowers mature.

(b) *Seed production and dispersal* — In North America, only tetraploid plants produce seed; all diploids are sterile, but a fertile diploid cytotype is known from Europe. Based on herbarium material, individual tetraploid plants may produce between 30–900 or more seeds. The seeds weigh 0.022–0.023 g (Salisbury 1961).

The fruit of cypress spurge is a schizocarp which at maturity ejects the three-parted carpel as three one-seeded achenes. Each achene is termed a mericarp or coccus and is about 1.5 mm in diameter (Salisbury 1961). Dymes (1933) observed that ants aid in the dispersal of cypress spurge. The seed has a small swelling, termed the eliasome appendage or caruncle, near the hilum, which is rich in an oily substance which the ants use as food. According to Bewley and Black (1983), the major storage tissue is in the endosperm where oil (lipid) content ranges from 23 to 49% on a dry weight basis.

(c) *Viability of seeds and germination* — Salisbury (1961) reported germination rates of 85% in *E. cyparissias* (whether pretreatments were used is not indicated). Other studies report considerably less success. Both Crocker (1906) and Dymes (1933) found that unscarified seeds did not germinate at all. In the Dymes study, when the eliasome was scratched or removed, a 16% germination rate was achieved. Lincoln (1980) carried out germination tests using a number of temperature and light regimes. The highest percentage (53%) was achieved with a 21-d prechilling treatment at 5–8°C followed by alternating temperatures of 25°C (for 16 h) and 15°C (for 8 h) in full light. Percentage germination dropped to 40% if a prechilling period was not used. Germination was very low (4–8%) if temperatures were kept constant.

(d) *Vegetative reproduction* — *Euphorbia cyparissias* plants are capable of clonal propagation by the 10-leaf stage. The capacity for vegetative propagation differs in the three cytotypes. It is least in the fertile diploid, and greatest in the fertile tetraploid. In two natural stands, Pritchard (1958) found that tetraploid plants had 3–14 times as many shoots as fertile diploids. Even under uniform environmental conditions, the vegetative propagation of the tetraploid was 2–3 times greater. In Ontario, we found that sterile diploids produced between 2 and 4 shoots (avg. 3.3) and tetraploids, 2–10 shoots (avg. 6.6).

9. Hybrids

Both in Europe and North America, *E. cyparissias* hybridizes with its close relative *E. esula* (Moore and Lindsay 1953; Pritchard 1961). The correct name of the hybrid is *E. xpseudoesula* Schur, although it often appears in the literature under the later synonym *E. figerti* Dorfl. Morphological characters which distinguish the two parental species and the hybrid are shown in Table 2. Cytological information on the hybrid is available only for North American populations. So far, all naturally occurring hybrids have a chromosome number of $n = 25$, $2n = 50$ (Moore and Lindsay 1953; Moore and Frankton 1969; Stahevitch et al. unpubl. data). This is clearly a cross between *E. esula*, a hexaploid ($2n = 60$), and the tetraploid ($2n = 40$) race of *E. cyparissias*. Moore (1958) artifically produced this hybrid to verify the parentage. In Europe, two infraspecific variants of the hybrid (*E. figerti*) have been described (Dorfler 1902). One *forma* more closely resembles *E. cyparissias*; the other, *E. esula*. Moore and Frankton (1969) proposed that each of these *formae* might represent the cross between *E. esula* and a different ploidy level of *E. cyparissias*. Theoretically, there is no reason why *E. esula* should not hybridize with both of the diploid variants of *E. cyparissias* as long as the sterile diploid acted as the female parent in any cross. However, Pritchard (1958) was unable to produce hybrids between *E. esula* and either of the diploid forms of cypress spurge.

10. Population Dynamics

The three cytotypes of *E. cyparissias* exhibit somewhat different colonization patterns. Fertile diploid plants have little or no capacity for vegetative reproduction. Pritchard (1958) found that such plants produce only one or at most two shoots. Furthermore, the seedlings apparently can not become established in dense grass cover. Consequently, this cytotype is restricted to sites with patchy ground cover. In a 2-m^2 quadrat containing fertile diploids, 88 of 114 shoots occurred in bare ground; the remainder, where ground cover was least dense. In contrast, the sterile diploid has a greater vegetative capacity; but of course, produces no seed. In our experience, it is usually a minor element of moderately closed communities. Occasionally, under suitable conditions such as mechanical breakage of rootstocks, sterile colonies may become quite extensive as was the case near Goderich, Ontario (Moore and Lindsay 1953). Finally, the tetraploid shows the greatest sexual and vegetative capacity of the three forms. In North America, long-established tetraploid colonies usually cover much larger areas than do sterile diploid populations of similar age (Moore and Lindsay 1953). Deane (1910, 1912) attested to the rapidity with which infestation of fertile plants spread.

Colonies of each cytotype differ in overall appearance (Pritchard 1958). The sterile diploid patches tend to be continuous. Fertile diploid populations consist of plants with one or two shoots and the plants are fairly evenly spread throughout the area. Tetraploid plants tend to form circular clusters which originated from a single seed and subsequently expanded in diameter by vegetative reproduction. These patches are usually scattered throughout the area, but may eventually coalesce to form stands many square yards in extent, in which case they can be mistaken for sterile diploid stands (Moore and Lindsay 1953).

11. Response to Herbicides and other Chemicals

Control of *Euphorbia cyparissias* is difficult to achieve because of its extensive root system and highly efficient seed dispersal. Repeated applications of several chemicals bring about its control. Maltais and Bernier (1983) reported that 2,4-DB isobutyl and 2,4-D ester at rates of 1.12 and 2.24 kg active ingredient ha^{-1}, respectively, gave acceptable control of *E. cyparissias* in Concorde wheat.

Table 2. Characteristics of *E. cyparissias*, *E. esula* and their hybrid, *E. xpseudo-esula*†

Character	Taxon		
	E. cyparissias	*E. xpseudoesula*	*E. esula*
Max. height (dm)	4	5	10
Width cauline leaves (mm)	1.0–2.6	2.8–3.0	4.0–12.0
Lateral branches			
(a) Presence	Typical	Typical	Rare
(b) Spacing leaves	Congested	Congested	Sparse
Bract apex	Rounded	Mucronate/rounded	Mucronate
Pseudocyme			
(a) Terminal	Densely crowded	Open clusters	Open clusters
(b) Lateral	Few/none	Numerous	Numerous
Chromosome no.	$2n = 20, 40$	$2n = 50$	$2n = 60$
Pollen diameter (μm)	22–26 (2x)‡	40–50	42–45
	35–40 (4x)§		

† Data only available for North America.
‡ Sterile diploids.
§ Small % grains 20–25 μm (Moore and Lindsay 1953).

McLaren and Sikkema (1983) found that UC (Union Carbide) 77179 combined with glyphosate (Roundup), diuron (Karmex) or aminotriazole (Amizol) at rates of $4.5 + 2.25$, $4.5 + 6.25$, or $4.5 + 3.38$ kg ha^{-1}, respectively, controlled 92–94% of the *E. cyparissias* in non-crop land. In a follow-up to the preceding experiment, McLaren (1983) found that Dicamba 5G broadcast in 1 year (1982) at rates of 5.6 and 11.2 kg a.i. ha^{-1} resulted in 91 and 99% control, respectively, in the next year (1983). MacDonald (1983) concluded that either 2,4-D or 2,4,5T gave the best long-term control, while 2,4-DB isobutyl or 2,4-D ester provided good control of *E. cyparissias*. Gagnon (1951) reported that two applications of 2,4-D butyl ester at rates of 1.3 kg in 1 L H$_2$O to 1.6 kg in 1 L H$_2$O provided 97–99% control of *E. cyparissias*. It has been shown that *E. cyparissias* is "intermediate resistant" to 2,4-D, MCPA 2,4-DB and MCPB at rates of 1.2 kg ha^{-1} and that it is "intermediate resistant" to Dicamba applied at 422 g or less ha^{-1} (Ontario Weed Committee 1984). This suggests that higher rates or repeated applications may be necessary to effectively control infestations. Benkov (1973) reported that 2,4-D butyl ester at 1.26 L ha^{-1} or a combination of 2,4-D and Dicamba applied at 2.96 L h^{-1} gave satisfactory control of *E. cyparissias* in white clover. The white clover is initially inhibited by the treatment, but eventually fully recovers. In Germany, Argosan-sodium chlorate spot-treatment is recommended prior to fall ploughing (Roth 1971).

12. Responses to Other Human Manipulations

There is no experimental data in the literature on control of cypress spurge by such means. Extensive rhizome production, coupled with prolific seed production, make tetraploid plants of *Euphorbia cyparissias* extremely difficult to control. In Renfrew Co., Ontario, a major gravel pit operation has a severe infestation of this cytotype. As a result, the tetraploid is being introduced throughout central and southern Renfrew Co. in road ballast used for construction of culverts and other secondary road repair operations. Sterile diploid plants were introduced as ornamentals into older graveyards throughout eastern Ontario. Since local graveyard maintenence has improved this less aggressive cytotype is unable to expand on properly managed sites (personal observations). In a screened weed nursery enclosure, repeated intensive hand rouging at monthly intervals for 1 year was required to eradicate the tetraploid form from our test plots after non-selective herbicides such as glyphosate applied four times per year at approved rates did not provide control.

13. Responses to Parasites

(a) *Insects and other nondomestic animals* — The latex of *E. cyparissias* is generally effective in repelling insect attacks. Some insects have adapted to the plant and in the past 20 y, several of these have been used in attempts to control the spread of *E. cyparissias* in Canada. The first attempt involved *Hyles euphorbiae* (L.) (Lepidoptera: Sphingidae), the spurge hawkmoth, a large defoliator of *Euphorbia* species in the subgenus *Esula* in south and central Europe, northern India and central Asia. It was found that the stabilized population consumed less than 5% of the available *E. cyparissias* foliage, making the spurge hawkmoth of little use as a biological control agent.

The second attempt involved the release of two species of *Chamaesphecia* (Lepidoptera: Sesiidae), which are root-boring moths. Originally thought to be one species which attacked both cypress and leafy spurge, Naumann and Schroeder (1980) were forced to redefine their species concept, when they found differences in host specificity and various aspects of their biology. Eggs of *C. empiformis* (host specific to *E. cyparissias*) were collected from a tetraploid population in the Swiss Jura. They were released on sterile diploid populations at Belleville and Sidney, Ontario where they failed to become established. Finally, releases of *Aphthona* spp. (Chrysomelidae), a genus of root feeding beetles, show promise for the control of *Euphorbia cyparissias* and *E. esula* in Canada (Harris 1984).

Jauffret (1973) examined cecidogensis in *Euphorbia cyparissias* induced by the gall midge *Bayeria captigena* (Bre.) (Diptera). Changes observed in infected apical meristems included cellular, nuclear and nucleolar hypertrophy and marked increase in the number of ergastoplasmic processes and organelles. Compared to healthy controls, the diseased tissues exhibit markedly lower concentrations of lipids and starches. Other gall-forming Diptera which attach cypress spurge include *Dasineura schulzei* Rues. and *D. capsulae* Kieff, and *D. loewi* Mik (Solinas and Pecora 1984). Finally, there is one report of a root-boring nematode, *Meloidogyne* spp., feeding on cypress spurge (Licopoli 1875).

(b) *Microorganisms and viruses* — Parmelee (1962) discovered large stands of *E. cyparissias* infected by the fungus *Uromyces striatus* Schroet. in Ontario. This systemic fungus infects both the diploid and tetraploid cytotypes of *E. cyparissias* through the rhizome buds. The fungus causes hypertrophy of the leaves and flowers of the infected plant, resulting in a necrosis of the apices and suppression of the lower buds. In Europe, *U. pisi* (Pers.) de By, also infects cypress spurge (Pilet 1953); reports of its presence on cypress spurge in North America are erroneous, and actually refer to *U. striatus* Schroet. (Ginns 1986). A second species, *U. scutellatus* (Pers.) Lèv., has shown potential as a biocontrol agent of weedy spurges (Défago et al. 1985).

Other plant diseases reported on *E. cyparissias* include *Melampsora euphorbiae* (Schub.) Cast. which is found in Ontario, Nova Scotia and Prince Edward Island (Conners 1967; Ginns 1986) and from Maine to Pennsylvania, and Indiana to Wisconsin (Anonymous 1960), and *Cerocospora* spp., leaf spot, and *Phymatotrichum omnivorum* (Shear) Dug., root rot, both of which are reported from Texas (Anonymous 1960).

ACKNOWLEDGMENTS

We wish to express our thanks for their assistance to the curators of the various herbaria from which we borrowed specimens, to Dr. Yolande Dalpé (B.R.C.) for her assessment of the mycorrhizal flora, to Dr. Jacques Cayouette (B.R.C.) for providing plant material, to Dr. Peter Harris (Agriculture Canada Regina) for his comments on the manuscript, to Miss Valerie A. Crompton for typing the manuscript, to the Research Program Service Graphics Unit for their production of plates and to Bill Lukey of that unit for his excellent photography.

Alex, J. F., Cayouette, R. L. and Mulligan, G. A. 1980. Common and botanical names of weeds in Canada. Agriculture Canada, Ottawa, Ont. Publ. 1397, 132 pp.

Anonymous. 1960. Index of plant diseases in the United States. U.S. Dep. Agric. Crops Res. Div., Agric. Handbook **165**: 138–139.

Anonymous. 1964. Agricultural abuses act. Division IV. Noxious weeds. Government of Québec, Ministry of Argriculture, Québec. 4 pp.

Anonymous. 1970. The noxious weed act. Queen's Printer, Winnipeg, Man. 20 pp.

Anonymous. 1977. Regulations to the weed control act 1968. Nova Scotia Dep. Agric. Mark. Publ. 10. Rev. ed., 6 pp.

Anonymous. 1979. Weed control act. Weed designation regulation. Alberta regulation 138/80. Queen's Printer, Edmonton and Calgary, Alta. 2 pp.

Anonymous. 1980. Weed control act. Queen's Printer for Ontario, Toronto, Ont. 10 pp.

Bailey, L. H. 1949. Manual of cultivated plants most commonly grown in the continental United States and Canada. Rev. ed., Macmillan Publishing Co. Inc., New York. 1116 pp. illus.

Bakke, A. L. 1936. Leafy spurge, *Euphorbia esula* L. Iowa State Coll. Agric. Exp. Stan. Res. Bull. **198**: 209–246.

Barabé, R. and Gagnon L. P. 1950. Cypress spurge (*Euphorbia cyparissias* L.) in pastures at Baie St. Paul. First destruction trials by herbicides. Proc. Third Meet. Eastern Sect., Nat. Weed Comm.: 25–26.

Benkov, B. 1973. Effect of some herbicides on cypress spurge (*Euphorbia cyparissias* L.) occurring in natural pastures. Rastenievud. Nauki **10**(5): 141–146. [in Russian.]

Bewley, J. D. and Black, M. 1983. Physiology and biochemistry of seeds. 1. Development, germination and growth. Springer-Verlag, New York. 306 pp.

Boivin, B. 1967. Flora of the Prairie Provinces. Université Laval, Québec.

Chester E. W. 1975. Range extensions and first reports for some Tennessee USA vascular plants. Castanea **40**(1): 56–63.

Conners, I. L. 1967. An annotated index of plant diseases in Canada and fungi recorded on plants in Alaska, Canada and Greenland. Res. Br. Canada Department of Agriculture, Ottawa, Ont. Publ. 1251. pp. 112–113.

Conners, I. L. and Saville, D. B. O. 1948. Twenty-seventh Ann. Rept. Can. Plant Disease Survey, Canada Department of Agriculture, Ottawa, Ont. 118 pp.

Connor, H. E. 1977. The poisonous plants in New Zealand. 2nd rev. ed. E.C. Keating, Govt. Printer, Wellington, New Zealand. pp. 249. illus.

Crocker, W. 1906. Role of seed coats in delayed germination. Bot Gaz. **42**: 265–291.

Croizat, L. 1945. "Euphorbia esula" in North America. Am. Midl. Nat. **33**: 231–243.

Daniels, B. A. and Skipper, H. D. 1982. Methods for the recovery and quantitative estimation of propagules from soil. *In* N. C. Schenck, ed, Methods and principles of mycorrhizal research. Phytopath. Soc., St. Paul, Minn., pp 29–46.

Deane, W. 1910. *Euphorbia cyparissias* in fruit. Rhodora **12**: 57–61.

Deane, W. 1912. A further note on *Euphorbia cyparissias* in fruit. Rhodora **14**: 193–196.

Défago, G., Kern, H. and Sedlar, L. 1985. Potential control of weedy spurges by the rust *Uromyces scutellatus*. Weed Sci. **33**: 857–860.

Dorfler, I. 1902. Herbarium Normal n. 4295 and 4296. Vienna.

Dunn, P. H. 1979. The distribution of leafy spurge (*Euphorbia esula*) and other weedy *Euphorbia* spp. in the United States. Weed Sci. **27**(5): 509–516.

Dymes, T. A. 1933. The germination of *Euphorbia cyparissias* L. J. Bot. **71**: 321–322.

Faegri, K. and Van Der Pijl, L. 1979. The principles of pollination ecology. 3rd rev. ed. Pergamon Press, Oxford, U.K. 244 pp.

Fernald, M. L. 1950. Gray's manual of botany, 8th ed. American Book Co., New York. 1632 pp.

Ferron, M. and Cayouette, R. L. 1975. Noms des mauvaises herbes du Québec. 3rd ed. Agriculture Québec, Québec City, Qué. 113 pp.

Frankton, C. and Mulligan G. A. 1970. Weeds of Canada. Rev. ed. Queen's Printer, Ottawa, Ont. 217 pp.

Gagnon, L. P. 1951. Progress report on the destruction of cypress spurge (*Euphorbia cyparissias* L.) in pastures at Baie St. Paul, Quebec. Proc. Fourth Meeting, Eastern Sect., Nat. Weed Comm.: 72.

Gerard, J. 1633. The herbal or general history of plants. The complete 1633 edition as revised and enlarged by Thomas Johnson 1975. Dover Publications, Inc., New York. 1631 pp.

Ginns, J. H. 1986. Compendium of plant disease and decay fungi in Canada, 1960–1980. Agriculture Canada, Ottawa, Ont. Publ. 1813, 416 pp.

Godwin, H. 1975. History of the British Flora. A factual basis for phytogeography. 2nd ed. Cambridge University Press, London, U.K. 541 pp.

Gray, A. 1867. Manual of botany of the northern United States. 5th ed., Ivison, Blakeman, Taylor and Co., New York and Chicago. 703 pp. + 20 pl.

Harris, P. 1984. *Euphorbia esula-virgata* complex, leafy spurge and *E. cyparissias* L., cypress spurge. (Euphorbiaceae). *In* J. S. Kelleher, and M. A. Hulme, (eds.). Biological control programmes against insects and weeds in Canada 1969-1980: 159-169. Commonwealth Agricultural Bureaux, Slough, U.K.

Harris, P. and Alex, J. 1971. *Euphorbia esula* L., leafy spurge, and *Euphorbia cyparissias* L., cypress spurge (Euphorbiaceae). Commonwealth Inst. Biol. Contr. Tech. Commun. 4: 83-88.

Hartwell, J. J. 1969. Plants used against cancer. A survey. IV. Lloydia 32(2): 153-205.

Heinze, M., Hohne, H. and Fielder, H. J. 1982. Vergleichende Untersuchungen zum Elementgehalt von Bodenpflanzen auf Gipsstandorten. Flora 172: 493-510.

Hemmers, H. and Gulz, P. G. 1986. Chemistry and morphology of epicuticular waxes from leaves of five *Euphorbia* species. Z. Naturforsch. 41c: 521-525.

Hokanson, G. C. and Matyunas, N. J. 1981. Dry column chromatographic procedure for rapid concentration of biological activity in natural products fractionation. J. Pharm. Sci. 70(3): 329-331.

Holmgren, A. H. 1958. Weeds of Utah. Utah State University, Agric. Exp. Sta. Spec. Rep. 12. 85 pp.

Holmgren, P. K., Keuken, W. and Schofield, E. K. 1981. Index herbariorum 1. 7th ed. Dr. W. Junk B. V., Boxton, Mass. 452 pp.

Jaeger, E. J. and Moerchen, G. 1977. Morphometrische Untersuchungen zur Fremdfaktorindikation an *Cirsium acaule* und *Euphorbia cyparissias*. Wiss. Z. Univ. Halle 26(4): 115-122.

Jauffret, F. 1973. Etude ultrastructural de la transformation du méristeme apical de l'*Euphorbia cyparissias* L. en tissu nourricier sous l'action du *Bayeria capitigena* (Bre.). Acad. Sci. (Paris) C.R. Ser. D. 276(7): 1177-1180.

Johnston, A. and Smoliak, S. 1965. Plants of the prairie provinces poisonous or injurious to humans. Canada Department of Agriculture Res. Sta. Rep.. Lethbridge, Alta. 13 pp.

Kingsbury, J. M. 1964. Poisonous plants of the United States and Canada. Prentice Hall Inc., Englewood Cliffs, New Jersey. 626 pp.

Lee, T. T. and Starratt, A. N. 1972. Growth substance requirements and major lipid constituents of tissue cultures of *Euphorbia esula* and *E. cyparissias*. Can. J. Bot. 50: 723-726.

Licopoli, L. 1875. Sopra alcuni lubercoli radicellari continante anguillole. R.C. Acad. Napoli 14(2): 41-42.

Lincoln, W. C. 1980. Laboratory germination of *Euphorbia cyparissias*, cypress spurge. Newsletter of the Association of Official Seed Analysts 54(2): 31-33.

Lindsay, D. R. 1951. Biology of leaf y and cypress spurge with notes on their distribution in eastern Canada. Proc. Fourth Meeting, Eastern Sect., Nat. Weed Comm.: 68-72.

Lynn, K. R. and Clevette-Radford, N. A. 1985. Three serine proteases from the latex of *Euphorbia cyparissias*. Phytochem. 24(5): 925-928.

MacDonald, D. 1983. Perennial weeds. Res. Report Expert Comm. on Weeds, Eastern Canada: 506.

Macoun, J. 1883. Catalogue of Canadian plants. Dawson Bros., Montreal, Que. 623 pp.

Maltais, B. and Bernier, D. 1983. Decherbage chimique du blé: herbicides de postlévee. Res. Rep. Expert Comm. on Weeds, Eastern Canada: 361.

Marie-Victorin, Frère. 1964. Flore laurentienne. 2nd ed. Illus. by Frere Alexandre; edited by E. Rouleau. Les presses de L'Université de Montréal, Montréal, 925 pp. illus., maps.

Marschall Von Bieberstein, F. A. 1808. Flora taurico-caucasica. Cracow.

McLaren, R. D. 1983. Leafy spurge control. Res. Rep. Expert Comm. on Weeds, Eastern Canada: 463.

McLaren, R. D. and Sikkema, P. H. 1983. Evaluation of UC77179 for total vegetation control. Res. Rep. Expert Comm. on Weeds, Eastern Canada: 462.

McLean, R. C. and Ivimey-Cook, W. R. 1956. Textbook of theoretical botany. Volume 2, Longmans, Green and Co., Toronto, Ont. 130 pp.

Miller, P. 1752. The gardeners dictionary. 6th ed. rev., Rivington, London, U.K. 976 pp., 9 pl.

Miller, P. 1768. The gardeners dictionary. 8th ed. rev., Rivington, London, U.K. 1300 pp., 20 pl.

Moore, R. J. 1958. Cytotaxonomy of *Euphorbia esula* in Canada and its hybrid with *Euphorbia cyparissias*. Can. J. Bot. 36: 547-559.

Moore, R. J. and Frankton, C. 1969. *Euphorbia pseudo-esula* (*E. cyparissias* × *E. esula*) in Canada. Can. Field Nat. 83(3): 243-246.

Moore, R. J. and Lindsay, D. R. 1953. Fertility and polyploidy of *Euphorbia cyparissias* in Canada. Can. J. Bot. 31: 152-163.

Muenscher, W. C. 1936. The production of seed by *Euphorbia cyparissias*. Rhodora 38: 161-163.

Muenscher, W. C. 1948. Some selected

introduced noxious weeds that should receive special attention for control. Proc. Northeastern States Weed Control Conf.: pp. 157–158.

Muenscher, W. C. 1960. Poisonous plants of the United States, The Macmillan Company, New York. 277 pp.

Myers, G. A., Beasley, C. A. and Derscheid, L. A. 1964. Anatomical studies of *Euphorbia esula* L. Weeds **12**: 291–195.

Naumann, C. M. and Schroeder, D. 1980. An additional pair of twin species of central European Sesiidae, *Chamaesphecia-tenthrediniformis* and *Chamaesphecia-empiformis* Lepidoptera. Z. Arbeitsgem Oesterr. Entomol. **32**(1–2): 29–46.

Ontario Weed Committee. 1984. Guide to chemical weed control. Ministry of Agriculture and Food, Toronto, Ont. Publ. 75. 167 pp.

Ott, H. H. and Hecker, E. 1981. Highly irritant ingenane type diterpene esters from *Euphorbia cyparissias*. Exper. **37**(1): 88–91.

Owen, T. 1805. Translation of Geoponika of Cassianus. London.

Parmelee, J. A. 1962. *Uromyces striatus* Schroet. in Ontario. Can. J. Bot. **40**: 492–510.

Pilet, P. E. 1953. Etude physiologique du parasitisme de l'*Uromyces pisi* sur l'*Euphorbia cyparissias*. Experientia **8**: 300.

Pilet, P. E. 1957. Activité anti-auxines-oxydasique de l'*Uromyces pisi*, parasite d'*Euphorbia cyparissias*. Phytopath. Z. **31**: 162.

Pilet P. E. 1960. Auxin content and auxin catabolism of the stems of *Euphorbia cyparissias* L. infected by *Uromyces pisi* (Pers.) de By. Phytopathology Z. **40**: 75–90.

Pritchard, T. 1958. The genecology of weed species. Studies on *Euphorbia cyparissias* L. and *Hypericum perforatum* L. Ph. D. thesis, University of Leeds, Leeds, U.K. 201 pp. + viii.

Pritchard, T. 1961. The cytotaxonomy of the weedy species *Euphorbia cyparissias* L. and *Euphorbia esula* L. Recent Adv. Bot. (IX Int. Bot. Congr.) **1**: 866–870.

Prokhanov, Y. I. 1949. "*Euphorbia* L." *In* B. K. Shishkin, ed., Flora of the U.S.S.R. **14**: 233–378. [Translated into English, 1974, Israel Program for Scientific Translations, Jerusalem.]

Radcliffe-Smith, A. 1985. Taxonomy of North American Spurges. *In* A. K. Watson, ed. Leafy spurge. Weed Society of America, Champaign, Illinois, pp 14–25.

Raju, M. V. S., Steeves, T. A. and Coupland R. T. 1963. Developmental studies on *Euphorbia esula*. Morphology of the root system. Can. J. Bot. **41**: 579–589.

Ranft, M. and Wagner, W. 1972. Flora des kreises Freital. Ber Arbeitsgem. Sachs. Bot., NF **10**: 157–168.

Roland, A. E. and Smith, E. C. 1969. Flora of Nova Scotia. 2 parts. Nova Scotia Museum. Halifax, N.S. 743 pp. illus.

Roth, D. 1971. Studies on the control of common grassland weeds in riverside and foothill areas using herbicides. Arch. Acker. Pflanzenbau und Bodenk. D. **15**: 67–82.

Roslycky, E. B. 1972. Stimulation of hair growth by a plant factor. Can. J. Plant Sci. **52**(5): 844–845.

Rousseau, C. 1968. Histoire, habitat et distribution de 220 plantes introduites au Québec. Nat. Can. **95**: 49–169.

Salisbury, E. 1961. Weeds and aliens. Collins, London, U.K. 384 pp. illus.

Selleck, G. W., Coupland, R. T. and Frankton, C. 1962. Leafy spurge in Saskatchewan. Ecol. Monogr. **32**: 1–29.

Smith, A. R. and Tutin, T. G. 1968. "*Euphorbia* L." *In* T. G. Tutin et al. eds. Flora Europaea **2**: 213–226. Cambridge University Press, London, U.K.

Solinas, M. and Percora P. 1984. The midge complex diptera Cecidomiidae on *Euphorbia* spp. I. Entomologica v. **19**: 167–213.

Strahler, A. N. 1967. Introduction to physical geography. John Wiley and Sons, Inc., New York. 455 pp.

Stuckey, I. H. and Pearson, J. L. 1973. Cypress spurge. Ext. Circ. Univ. R.I. Coop. Ext. Serv. **165**: 1–4.

Sweet, R. 1818. Hortus suburbanus Londinensis or a catalogue of plants cultivated in the neighborhood of London. S. Gosnell Printer, London, U.K. 242 pp. + xi.

Szujko-Lacza, J. and Fekete, G. 1974. Examination of development and growth of *Brachypodium silvaticum* and *Euphorbia cyparissias* in oakwoods. Acta Bot. Hung. **20**(1–2): 147–158.

Usher, G. 1974. A Dictionary of plants used by man. Constable and Company Ltd., London, U.K. 619 pp.

Webster, G. L., Brown, W. V. and Smith, B. N. 1975. Systematics of photosynthetic carbon fixation pathways in *Euphorbia*. Taxon **24**(1): 27–33.

Zimmermann, W. 1924. "*Euphorbia* L. (=Tithymalus Tourn,). Wolfsmilch." *In* Hegi G. Illustrierte flora von mittel-Europa. **5**(1): 134–190. J. F. Lehmanns Verlag., Munich, Federal Republic of Germany.

THE BIOLOGY OF CANADIAN WEEDS. 86.
Galium aparine L. and *Galium spurium* L.

N. MALIK[1] and W. H. VANDEN BORN[2]

[1]*Research Station, Agriculture Canada, P.O. Box 1240, Melfort, Saskatchewan, Canada S0E 1A0; and* [2]*Department of Plant Science, University of Alberta, Edmonton, Alberta, Canada T6G 2P5. Received 7 Jan. 1987, accepted 30 Sept. 1987.*

MALIK, N. AND VANDEN BORN, W. H. 1988. The biology of Canadian weeds. 86. *Galium aparine* L. and *Galium spurium* L. Can. J. Plant Sci. **68**: 481–499.

Galium aparine L., cleavers, is considered to be native, as well as introduced into North America from Eurasia. It is found from southern Alaska, across the wheat belt of Canada, to Newfoundland. *Galium spurium* L., false cleavers, is solely an introduced weed. Both species have several characteristics that predispose them toward weediness. These include rapid seedling development, early flower initiation after a short period of vegetative growth, self-compatibility, "stickiness" of fruits and plant foliage which aids in dispersal and crop contamination, resistance to phenoxy acetic herbicides and seedling emergence throughout the growing season, which helps the plants escape herbicides and cultivation. Both species are found in grain fields but examination of contaminated seed so far has shown only *G. spurium* to occur in rapeseed. *Galium spurium* is the more weedy and aggressive of the two species and is better adapted to growing conditions on the prairies.

Key words: Weed biology, cleavers, false cleavers, *Galium aparine*, *Galium spurium*

[La biologie des mauvaises herbes du Canada. 86. *Galium aparine* L. et *G. spurium* L.]
Titre abrégé: *Galium aparine* L. et *G. spurium* L.
Le gaillet grateron, *Galium aparine* L., est une mauvaise herbe indigène de l'Amérique du Nord mais a également été introduit de l'Eurasie. On le trouve du sud de l'Alaska, d'un bout à l'autre de la zone de culture du blé au Canada, jusqu'à Terre-Neuve. Le gaillet bâtard, *G. spurium*, est une espèce introduite seulement. Les deux espèces affichent plusieurs caractéristiques que les prédisposent à l'envahissement. Mentionnons un développement rapide de leur semences, une floraison hâtive après une courte période de croissance végétative, l'autocompatibilité, l'adhésivité des fruits et des feuilles qui favorise leur dispersion et la contamination des cultures, leur résistance aux herbicides de phénoxy et l'émergence des jeunes plantes pendant toute la saison de croissance, ce qui les aide à échapper aux herbicides et au travail du sol. On trouve les deux espèces dans les champs de céréales mais, d'après l'examen de semences contaminées, seulement *G. spurium* contamine jusqu'à maintenant le colza. L'espèce *G. spurium* est la plus envahissante et la plus agressive et est mieux adaptée aux conditions de croissance dans les Prairies.

Mots clés: Biologie des mauvaises herbes, gaillet grateron, gaillet bâtard, *Galium aparine*, *Galium spurium*

1. Names
I. *Galium aparine* L.—**cleavers** (Alex et al. 1980); bedstraw, catchweed (Weed Science Society of America 1984); gaillet grateron (Alex et al. 1980).
II. *Galium spurium* L.—**false cleavers**; gaillet bâtard (Alex et al. 1980). Rubiaceae, madder family, Rubiacées.

2. Description and Account of Variation
Both species are annual, broadleaved plants that reproduce by seed. Under certain environmental conditions, they may exhibit a biennial habit. The following description of

G. *aparine* is based on those by Moore (1975), Holm et al. (1977), Korsmo et al. (1981) and Hanf (1983). The description of G. *spurium* is based on personal observations by the authors.

(a) I. *Galium aparine* is a slender, annual herb with branched roots (Fig. 1). Cotyledons are petioled, ovate, usually notched at the apex, slightly rough above, 8–15 mm long and 6–9 mm broad. Stems are green, soft, freely branched and numerous, weak, straggly, semiprostrate or climbing-ascending, adhering to or lying on adjacent vegetation, up to 120 cm long, quadrangular in cross section, with prominent ribs densely set with recurved thornlike spines, jointed, branched at the first node. Nodes are usually densely tomentose, but sometimes only slightly so. Leaves are sessile in whorls of four to eight at the nodes, simple, narrow, oval-lanceolate, mucronate, single-veined, 30–60 mm long, 3–8 mm broad, usually dark green, thin and lax, mucronate. Leaf margins weakly retrosely scabrous, upper surface hairy, lower surface with a row of spines along the midrib, forward-directed spines. Flowers are 2 mm in diameter on peduncles in the axils of the leaf whorls, two to five flowers per peduncle (five to six bracts), in cymes. The corolla has four acute lobes, white. Flowers are bisexual, with four stamens and one pistil with two styles. Pollen grains are oval in equatorial view and the polar diameter (width) of the hexaploid plant ranges from 25 to 31 μm. The fruit is a schizocarp with two carpels per flower forming two globose mericarps. Fruits are grey, greyish-brown or dark brown, oval in outline, reniform seen from the side, 2–4 mm long excluding spines with the scar somewhat oblong, weighing 0.3–0.6 g per hundred. Fruit surfaces are covered with hooked bristles, about 0.8 mm long, on tuberculate bases that are dilated and usually arise from a small tubercle formed by an elevation of the surface layer of the fruit. Fruits are sometimes sparsely spiny and very rarely smooth or tuberculate.

Chromosome numbers range from $2n=22$ to 88, but 64 and 66 are most common. The base number is $X=11$, the most common number found in the genus *Galium* and in the family Rubiaceae. Four levels of ploidy have been found. Deviations by two to four chromosomes such as $6X-2=64$ or $6X-3=63$ have been reported (Kliphuis 1962; Gadella and Kliphuis 1963; Kramer et al. 1972). Metaphase plates from the root tip of the same plant have been found with 61 to 66 chromosomes (Kliphuis 1980). Microscopic examination of 221 species from 89 localities, mainly in Europe, showed them all to be hexaploids. Most plants had 64 chromosomes but a few with 66 were also found. The hexaploid number 66 has been observed from sources as far apart as Afghanistan (Podlech and Dieterle 1969), Maltese Islands (Kramer et al. 1972), Austria (Kliphuis 1962) and Iceland (Love and Love 1956). In North America, the hexaploid number 66 was found in three specimens from Ontario (Moore 1975), one specimen from B. C. (Taylor and Mulligan 1968), two specimens from Illinois, and three specimens from Oklahoma (Moore 1975). Plants with 44 chromosomes have been reported from Texas (Lewis 1962) and, with some uncertainty, from a Canadian source (Kliphuis 1962). Plants with 22, 44 and 66 chromosomes have been reported from France (De Poucques 1949). The source of plants with 86 and 88 chromosomes is probably Sweden (Fagerlind 1934, cited by Moore 1975).

II. *Galium spurium* is similar to G. *aparine* except for the following characteristics. Cotyledons are smaller, 5–10 mm long and 2–4 mm broad (Fig. 2a). Leaves are linear, 12–62 mm long and 2.5–6 mm wide, always notched at the apex, a lighter green, stiff and more "sticky" than leaves of G. *aparine*. The number of leaves gradually increases from four at the first node to eight, and occasionally nine or ten, at upper nodes (Fig. 2b). Stems reach up to 200 cm, and are stiffer, rougher, and more branched than those of G. *aparine*. Stem thickness increases from

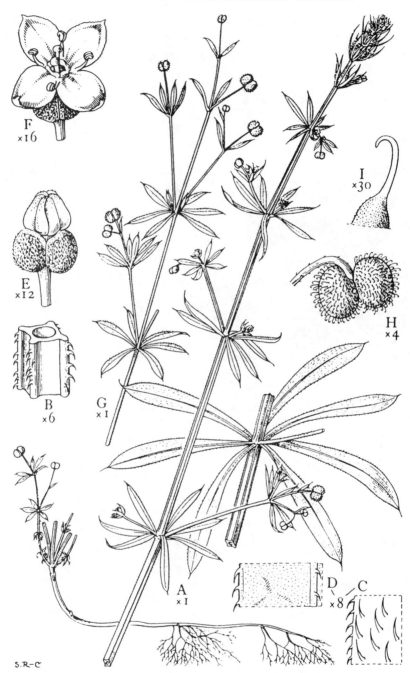

Fig. 1. *G. aparine*. (A) lower, middle, and upper parts; (B) part of stem; (C) part of leaf, upper surface; (D) part of leaf, lower surface; (E) flower-bud; (F) flower; (G) fruiting stem; (H) fruit; (I) tubercled bristle from fruit. Reproduced with permission from Drawings of British Plants by S. Ross-Craig. G. Bell and Sons Ltd. London, U.K. 1960–1963.

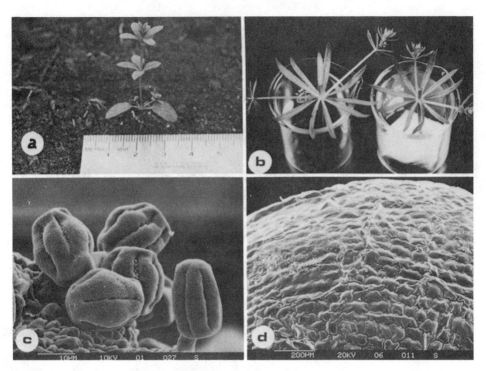

Fig. 2. *G. spurium* from Alberta. (a) seedling; (b) maximum number of leaves per whorl reaches 10; (c) pollen grains, ×1070; (d) surface of smooth fruit, ×58.

1–2 mm at the base to as much as 4 mm in upper plant parts. Flowers are 1–1.5 mm in diameter, with pale yellow to yellowish-green corolla. The pollen grains measure 20 μm in polar diameter (Moore 1975). Pollen grains from Alberta plants measured 20 μm (Fig. 2c). Fruits consist of two hemispherical mericarps, smooth or with hooked spines, stomated, mean size 1.5×2.5 mm, mean weight 2.8 mg.

The base number of chromosomes is $X=10$. The diploid number 20 has been reported from sources as far apart as Afghanistan (Podlech and Dieterle 1969), Bulgaria (Ancev 1974, cited by Moore 1975), Sweden (Fagerlind 1934, cited by Moore 1975) and Alberta (Malik and Vanden Born

1984). Unlike *G. aparine*, no polyploidy has been observed.

(b) Two forms of *G. aparine* have been recognized (Moore 1975):
1. *Galium aparine* forma *aparine*, the most common form. Fruits spiny. Fruits of the variety *subglabrum* are sparsely hairy.
2. *Galium aparine* forma *intermedium* (Bonnet) R. J. Moore stat. nov. Fruits smooth or tuberculate and without spiny hairs. This form is rare.

Two forms of *G. spurium* have been recognized in Canada:
1. *Galium spurium* forma *spurium*, fruits smooth (Fig. 2d). Moore (1975) listed seven

synonyms for this form.

2. *Galium spurium* forma *vaillanttii* R. J. Moore stat. nov., fruits spiny. Moore (1975) listed 10 synonyms for this form which is often confused with *G. aparine*. The herbarium specimens of Biosystematics Research Centre which were annotated by Moore as *G. spurium* variety *echinospermum* (Wallr.) Hayek in 1972–1973, had initially been identified as *G. aparine* by the earlier collectors.

A variant which is intermediate between the above forms was identified by the authors in Alberta and Saskatchewan. The fruits of this variant are sparsely hairy.

The spines of *G. spurium* are about 0.2 mm in length and are supported by a group of eight or nine cells that rise above the plane of the seed surface (Fig. 3a). The spines consist of several water-permeable layers and are hollow inside. The spines become transparent when seeds are imbibed. Cytological examination of the spiny, smooth, and sparsely hairy forms of *G. spurium* collected from Alberta cropland showed that they all had 20 chromosomes.

Identification of the two *Galium* species on the basis of fruit size and flower size is not infallible because of the degree of overlap in these characters. Chromosomes of the two species are not different morphologically, and the best diagnostic character is a chromosome count.

In North America, *G. spurium* is generally not identified as a distinct species by farmers, extension personnel, and most weed scientists. The smaller-fruited *G. spurium* is considered to be a variety of *G. aparine*. Examination of about 100 specimens in the United States by Moore (1975) showed that most were *G. aparine*. Only in California is a species distinction made. The large-fruited and small-fruited species are referred to as *G. aparine* and *G. spurium* var. *echinospermum* Wallr., respectively. Several authors cited by Moore (1975) mention the name *G. aparine* (var. *vaillanttii* (DC) Koch) for the small-fruited variety in the southern states.

(c) Differences in growth rate among four accessions of *G. aparine* from Ontario, Illinois, Oklahoma and California grown under standard greenhouse conditions were observed 6 wk after emergence (Moore 1975). Plants from Oklahoma were most advanced in growth (height 1 m), followed by those from Ontario and California. The Illinois seedlings were the smallest (20 cm), with obovate and unusually small leaves. Flowering was observed first on Oklahoma seedlings followed by Illinois plants. The Ontario plants did not flower until 5 mo after emergence, and continued to flower sparsely over the next 3 mo. The plants that flowered earliest also produced the most flowers. The flowering stems of the Illinois plants died but dwarf green shoots continued to grow from the base of the old flowering stems. A few

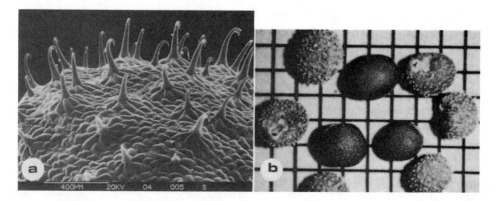

Fig. 3. (a) Surface of spiny fruit of *G. spurium*, ×47; (b) *G. spurium* and rapeseed, grid = 1 mm.

of the new shoots also developed flowers. The *G. spurium* plants from Saskatchewan studied by Moore (1975), however, died immediately after fruit ripening.

Experimental polyploids of the two species were produced by Moore (1975) through colchicine treatments, in order to investigate possible relationships between fruit size and ploidy level. He concluded that chromosome doubling which produced larger fruits in *G. spurium* but not in *G. aparine* may be due to an interaction of the genetic content and the natural ploidy levels of the two species.

3. Economic Importance

(a) *Detrimental—Galium aparine* has been reported to compete effectively with cereals, rapeseed and sugarbeet. In cereals, it causes lodging, interferes with combine operations, and reduces potential yields by 30–60% (Rola 1969). Reductions in yields of sugarbeet and corn have been reported from Europe (Rottele 1980). In England, it is one of the predominant weeds of winter cereals (Anonymous 1968). In Poland, it is the predominant weed in spring barley and winter wheat (Pawlowski and Wszolek 1978). In Japan, it is a serious weed of drained winter paddy (Noda et al. 1965).

Localized, heavy infestations of *G. spurium* are found in many fields of wheat, barley, rapeseed, flax, field peas, and forage legume seed crops in Alberta and Saskatchewan. Plants of *G. spurium* that emerge at the same time as rapeseed or up to a week after the crop, compete successfully with the crop (Malik and Vanden Born 1987a). Early establishment can result in 30–70 cleavers seeds per gram of harvested rapeseed and 13–28% reduction in rapeseed yield. *Galium spurium* cannot be separated from rapeseed mechanically with present methods because of similarity in size and shape (Fig. 3b), resulting in a reduction in the quality of oil extracted from rapeseed.

In addition to reduction in potential crop yields, *G. aparine* has been reported to have several other noxious characteristics. Its water-soluble extracts contain substances with allelopathic effects which suppress the growth of oak seedlings (*Quercus robur*) (Mateev and Timoteev 1965). *Galium* spp. contain anthraquinones which have low systemic toxicity to mammals and may cause skin irritation (Batra 1984). *Galium aparine* causes internal inflammation when ingested by livestock and has a diuretic effect (Long 1960). *Galium aparine* serves as a host to the oat race of stem eelworm (*Ditylenchus dispaci* Kühn), stem and bulb eelworm (*Anguillulina dispaci* Kühn) and leaf eelworm [*Aphelenchoides fragariae* (Ritzma Bos, 1890) Christie, 1932] (Johnson 1940; Bendixen et al. 1979). A survey of aphids on sugar beets in England revealed that the potato aphid, *Macrosiphum solanifolii* (Ashmead) = *M. euphorbiae* (Thomas), overwintered on *G. aparine* (Heathcote et al. 1965). *G. aparine* also harbors *Macrosiphum miscanthi* Takahashi which infests cereal crops in New Zealand (Lowe 1969).

(b) *Beneficial—*The fruits of *G. aparine* form one of the best substitutes for coffee and are used for this purpose in Sweden (Long 1960). The whole plant can be used as a substitute for tea or chopped up and used as poultry feed. The flowers serve as an important food source for adult nonphytophagous beneficial insects (Batra 1984). *Galium* spp. have secondary plant substances with fungistatic effects and may be used as food or wine flavoring (Batra 1984).

(c) *Legislation—*The Canada Seeds Act (Anonymous 1986) lists *G. aparine* and *G. spurium*, referred to as bedstraw (cleavers), under class 2 weed seeds, "primary noxious weed seeds". Hence, the tolerance limit for the presence of the two *Galium* species is zero in all grades of pedigreed seed for cereals, oilseeds and forage crops. The Alberta Weed Control Act (Anonymous 1979) and the Noxious Weeds Act of Saskatchewan (Anonymous 1984) list only *G. aparine* as a noxious weed. An amendment to these provincial Acts is urgently needed to include *G. spurium* in the class of noxious weeds.

4. Geographical Distribution

Galium aparine is found in temperate zones throughout the world and at higher altitudes in the tropics (Holm et al. 1977). In North America, it extends from the Aleutian Islands and southern Alaska (*c.* 61°N) to B.C., across the prairie provinces, Ontario (north to James Bay *c.* 52°N), Quebec (north to James Bay, Anticosti Island and Gaspe Peninsula), Newfoundland, New Brunswick, and Nova Scotia (Fig. 4), south to California, Texas and Florida (Scoggan 1979).

Galium spurium is found throughout Europe except the north and western Asia (Hanf 1983). In Canada (Fig. 5), *G. spurium* is found on the southern tip of Vancouver Island, across the prairie provinces, and in southwest Ontario and southwest Quebec (Moore 1975). In Manitoba the infestations are light (Thomas and Wise 1982), except in the Gilbert Plains where infestations are on the increase (pers. commun., Wayne Coukell). In western and east-central parts of Saskatchewan the infestations are light (Thomas and Wise 1983; Thomas and Wise 1986). In the northeastern parkbelt of Saskatchewan, light to moderate infestations of the spiny, intermediate, and smooth-fruited forms were observed by the authors during the summers of 1985–1987. In Alberta, field surveys conducted by the authors during the summers of 1982 and 1983 showed that moderate to severe but localized infestation are present in the northern and eastern parts of the Peace River region and the central part of the province.

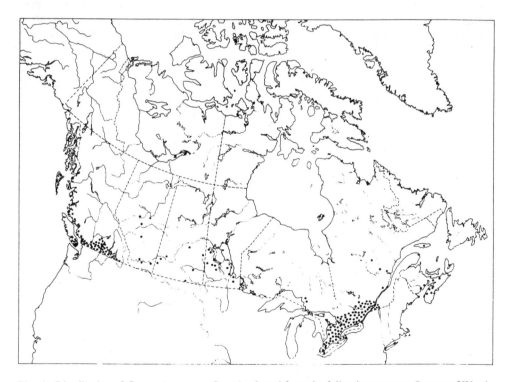

Fig. 4. Distribution of *G. aparine* across Canada plotted from the following sources: Survey of Weeds in Alberta (Dew 1982), Moore (1975), Scoggan (1979), Taylor and Mulligan (1968), Thomas and Wise (1982, 1983, 1986), Canada Weed Survey (Groh and Frankton 1946, 1948), herbaria of Biosystematic Research Center and University of Alberta.

5. Habitat

(a) *Climatic requirements*—A temperate species, *G. aparine* thrives in moist habitats (Holm et al. 1977). *Galium spurium*, however, thrives in relatively dry and sunny habitats and is intolerant of shade (Moore 1975; Malik and Vanden Born 1984). Occurrence of *G. spurium*, however, is rare in very dry plains where summer rainfall is scant.

(b) *Substratum*—Both *G. aparine* and *G. spurium* prefer nutrient-rich soils. In a survey of 8500 fields in cereal crops in England, dense infestations of *G. aparine* were found on heavy organic soils (Anonymous 1968). In a survey of 121 sites in West Germany, Behrendt (1973) concluded that *G. aparine* was more prevalent in winter rape in the south than in the north and that the frequency of its occurrence was influenced by soil type. In a survey of sugarbeet fields in West Germany, *G. aparine* was found most frequently on loess soils (Wiesner and Haberland 1980). If excessive moisture is not a problem, *G. aparine* grows well on both loam and sandy loam (Holm et al. 1977). In Alberta, *G. spurium* is found on black, dark brown, and dark grey wooded soils. In Saskatchewan, *G. spurium* is most common on black, gray-black, and gray wooden soils.

(c) *Communities in which the species occur*—In Canada, *G. aparine* is found on arable land, particularly in grainfields, and in native habitats such as deciduous woods, thickets and rockly coastal bluffs (Moore 1975). It is also found in waste ground, fence rows, barnyards and pastures. *Galium spurium* is found in drier and open sunnier habitats such as cultivated fields, coastal areas, roadsides, borders of fields, dry open woods, gardens and waste grounds. In Alberta and Saskatchewan, *G. spurium* is found in association with wheat, barley, oat, rapeseed, flax, field peas, forage seed crops, as well as in association with other troublesome weeds such as Canada

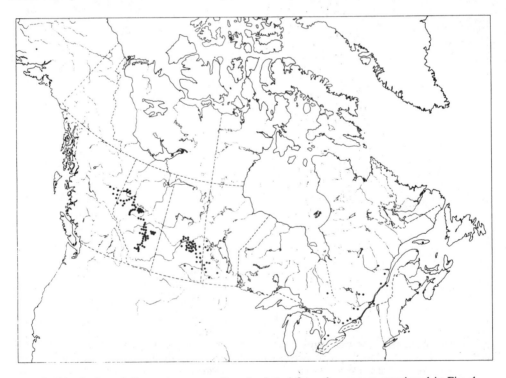

Fig. 5. Distribution of *G. spurium* across Canada plotted from the sources mentioned in Fig. 4.

thistle, perennial sow thistle, quackgrass and wild oats along the border of fields.

6. History

According to Holm et al. (1977) and Moore (1975), who examined specimens from many herbaria across North America, *G. aparine* is native in coastal and moist wooded habitats but introduced in grainfields by early settlers who imported contaminated seed from Eurasia. The earliest collections of *G. aparine* in Canada date from 1870 to 1880 and were all spiny-fruited forms. Collections made from waste grounds, fence rows, barnyards and pastures could have been weedy introductions or they may have spread from native habitats. Collections from such habitats as deciduous woods, thickets and rocky coastal bluffs are unlikely to be introductions. *Galium aparine* plants observed along the shores of the Aleutian Islands, in southern Alaska, and along the Atlantic coast must be regarded as native (Hulten 1968; Welsh 1974).

Galium spurium is believed to be solely an European introduction. The earliest collections are from Belleville, Ontario in 1878, and Ottawa, Ontario in 1884. The earliest collection from the prairies was from Alberta in 1935 (Dew 1982). With the exception of two specimens from Melfort, Saskatchewan, and Glenevis, Alberta, which were of the smooth-fruited type, all other specimens collected during 1935–1973 and examined by Moore (1975) were of the spiny-fruited type. Our observations in Alberta and northeastern Saskatchewan croplands in the summers of 1982 to 1987 indicate that spiny, smooth, as well as intermediate forms of *G. spurium* are found. The presence of more than one form in a given field is common.

7. Growth and Development

(a) *Morphology*—Both species have recurved spines (Fig. 6a, b) on stems and leaves that enable them to become attached to other weeds or crop plants and to penetrate the crop canopy. The hooked bristles on the spiny- and sparsely-haired-fruited forms are adapted to animal dispersal. Our observations indicate that the fruits have a hollow space near the point of attachment between the two "halves" of the fruit that enables them to float on water. The spines may also protect the seeds from smaller birds. Seeds do not germinate unless they are covered with soil, which helps insure the survival of seedlings.

(b) *Perennation—Galium aparine* has been reported to be one of the most winterhardy weeds of fall-sown rape, wheat, barley and rye in West Germany (Rademacher 1963). Winter survival of *G. spurium* was studied in Edmonton, Alberta during the winter of 1983–1984 when air temperatures occasionally dropped below −25°C (Malik and Vanden Born 1987b). Survival was related to the stage of development of the plants at the onset of winter. Plants that were in the flowering stage in October when the first frost was recorded did not survive the winter but those that were still in the vegetative state, including seedling plants, did survive. When observed in April, plants were prostrate in growth habit and had shorter internodes, shorter leaves, and more numerous branches than plants grown from spring-germinated seeds.

(c) *Physiological data—Galium* spp. are reported to have anthraquinones, mollugin, coumarins, and the iridoid glucosides asperuloside, arbutin and secogalioside (Batra 1984). Some of these substances have allelopathic, fungistatic or repellent effects.

(d) *Phenology*—Information from herbarium specimens from across Canada indicates that *G. aparine* begins to flower in late May and that flowering is completed by mid-June (Moore 1975). Mature fruits are found from late June to mid-July. After ripening, the plant foliage dies. A few flowering plants were collected as late as August and September. In temperate Japan, *G. aparine* emerges from mid-November to February (Noda et al. 1965). Peak germination usually occurs in mid- to late December, about 40 d after initial germination. Occasionally, a second flush

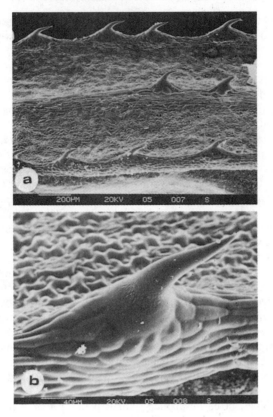

Fig. 6. (a) Lower surface of *G. spurium* leaf showing a row of spines along the midrib and margins, ×44; (b) close-up of a spine along the leaf margin, ×250.

of germination is observed in February or in March.

The effect of sowing date (14 May–8 Sept.) on growth and development of *G. spurium* was investigated under field conditions in Edmonton, Alberta (Malik and Vanden Born 1987b). Seedlings emerged 12–14 d after sowing in mid-May. Flowering began in early July when the plants were at the 8- to 10-leaf-whorl-stage, and continued until late August. Fruit development started in mid-July with mature fruit by early August and continued until early September. Fruit development proceeded from the base of plants upward and was accompanied by a general loss of green color of the foliage. When seeds were sown in June through August, emergence occurred in 5–7 d. Seedlings that emerged in mid-July remained in a vegetative state until early October when the first frost was recorded, and developed very few seeds. Plants that emerged in the beginning of August developed numerous short branches (20–30 cm) that were all erect and had shorter internodes than did early-emerging plants. After the onset of senescence in September when plant foliage was mostly brown, new growth was observed on some early-emerging plants. Dwarf leaf whorls, flowers, and fruits appeared. In greenhouse experiments, this phenomenon of "rejuvenation" was observed to a greater extent. There was no significant difference in germination between the early- and late-development seeds. The appearance of such new growth on *G. aparine* (Moore 1975) and *G. spurium* under certain environmental conditions suggests that these species may not be strictly annuals. The phenomenon recalls Ehrendorfer's (1971) hypothesis that three racial stocks including a perennial (*G. pseudoasprellum*) entered into the evolution of *G. aparine*.

Moore (1975) noted distinct differences in growth habit and flowering behavior between the two species. *Galium spurium* produced a few long stems that development numerous flowers. There was no pause between the early vegetative stage and the flowering stage. *Galium aparine* plants, however, developed a large number of short branches and entered a vegetative phase that differed in length for different accessions.

Noda et al. (1965) studied the growth and development of *G. aparine* in Japan and observed that seminal roots grew to a length of 3 cm before the aerial portion of the plant broke the soil surface. By the time the first leaves appeared, the roots were 5–6 cm in length. The roots elongated faster than the shoots and this was suggested as one of the reasons why it is difficult to kill even small *G. aparine* seedlings with herbicides. The root system spreads extensively through the entire plow layer and utilizes the available water and nutrients from a large area. In addition to the main roots, plants that emerge from the deeper layers develop supplementary adventitious roots on the hypocotyl (Hanf 1941).

(e) *Mycorrhiza*—Data not available.

8. Reproduction

(a) *Floral biology*—Flowers are self-pollinated and self-compatible (Moore 1975). Each flower gives rise to two seeds. The masses of small, shallow, flagrant flowers are visited by many Lepidoptera, beetles, flies, ants, wasps, and short or long-tongued bees (Batra 1984).

(b) *Seed production and seed dispersal*—Fruit is a schizocarp with two carpels forming two seeds, born on slender branches in cymes. Both species develop up to 18 seeds per cyme. The average number of seeds per plant for *G. aparine* is about 300–400 (Hanf 1983). In Alberta, seed production of *G. spurium* was greatest after early emergence and declined drastically when emergence was delayed until July (Malik and Vanden Born 1987b). Plants established on 14 May, 28 May and 11 June developed 600, 1520 and 670 seeds/plant, respectively. Seed weight also decreased with later emergence. In the greenhouse, the number of seeds produced decreased from 3500 to 175 per plant as density increased from 1 to 16 plants/pot.

In the prairie provinces, the planting of contaminated rapeseed appears to be the principal mode of dissemination. Both species can also spread when contaminated straw, mixed with manure or used for animal bedding, is scattered on the fields. Movement of harvesting equipment along farm roads can also aid in transport and dissemination of the seeds. Seeds are also adapted to both water and animal dispersal as described in Section 7a.

(c) *Viability of seeds and germination*—Freshly-harvested seeds of *G. aparine* have been reported to germinate readily in Sweden (Sjostedt 1959) and West Germany (Lauer 1953). Natural dormancy of *G. aparine* in the soil is usually less than 2 yr as indicated by long-term experiments in England by Brenchley and Warington (1930). Viability in the soils is limited to 2–3 yr in Germany (Holm et al. 1977). Seeds do not lose viability when ingested by animals and the germination percentage of *G. aparine* actually increases. Viable seeds have been recovered from the droppings of horses, cattle, pigs, goats and birds (Holm et al. 1977). Seed dormancy of *G. aparine* has received considerable attention in Japan (Noda et al. 1965; Ueki and Shimizu 1967). Seeds that were harvested and then dried for 1 mo were completely dormant for 1 yr or more, although dormancy gradually decreased with long-term dry storage. Also, keeping the seeds first at 30°C for about a month while the seeds were still moist, and then at 10°C, enhanced germination of dormant seeds. Gibberellic acid (GA) at 1000 ppm significantly increased the breaking of dormancy where high temperature treatment had failed. Large seeds appeared to have deeper dormancy. Chadoeuf et al. (1980) reported that soil storage resulted in a steady increase in germination of *G. aparine* with a broader optimum temperature range for germination and loss of photosensitivity. Lonchamp and Gora (1980) found that the effects of light and temperature became less important as the seeds aged.

Germination of *G. spurium* was studied under controlled and field conditions by the authors. About 30% of the seeds germinated immediately after harvest. Germination increased with further dry storage at room temperature. Optimum temperature for germination was a constant 22°C or alternating 10–20°C, 15–20°C, or 14–24°C. Only 5% of the seeds germinated at 4°C after 3 wk. The optimum temperature ranges reported for germination of *G. aparine* from European sources are quite variable and are generally lower than the requirement observed by us for *G. spurium*. Lauer (1953) reported an optimum range of 7–13°C, with a minimum and maximum at 2–5 and 20°C, respectively. Optimum temperature ranges of 12–15°C (Sjostedt 1959), 10–20°C (Arai et al. 1961) and even 0.5–12°C (Kurth 1967) have also been reported.

Germination of *G. aparine* was optimal at 40–60% of soil water-holding capacity and declined at 80% (Hirinda 1959). We found that optimum soil moisture for germination of *G. spurium* in a clay loam was 50–80% of its water-holding capacity. Moisture tension experiments with polyethylene glycol indicated a reduction in germination percentage below −2.5 bars; no germination occurred below −7.5 bars.

Soil pH in the range normally encountered in agricultural soils does not have a significant effect on germination of the two species. Hirinda (1959) reported 40–60% germination of *G. aparine* between pH 4.2 and 7 and only a 10% reduction above pH 7. We found that germination of *G. spurium* was not influenced greatly by pH of diluted buffer solutions or soil extracts in the range of 3–7. Moderate to severe necrosis of the seedlings occurred at pH 3, 4, 8 and 9 when diluted buffer solutions were used as the germination medium. Concentrations of KC1, NaCl, MgCl$_2$ and CaCl$_2$ above 0.05 M reduced germination of *G. spurium*.

Soil and soil extracts were better germination media than distilled water for *G. aparine* (Sjostedt 1959) and *G. spurium* (Malik and Vanden Born 1987c). Germination of *G. spurium* was stimulated by solutions of KNO$_3$, NaNO$_3$, Ca(NO$_3$)$_2$ and Mg(NO$_3$)$_2$ at concentrations as low as 2.5 μ M. The type of cations associated with nitrates did not affect germination. Kinetin at 0.2–10 ppm and GA$_3$ at 1–100 ppm were not as effective as nitrates in stimulating germination.

Observations on optimum depth of planting for emergence of *G. aparine* range from 2 to 5 cm (Hirinda 1959; Tsuruuchi 1971). Seed distribution in the soil was irregular, both in the horizontal and vertical planes (Rottele 1980). An average of 93% of emerged seedlings originated from the 0- to 5-cm soil depth. Maximum depth of planting has been variously reported at 4–20 cm (Hirinda 1959; Kurth 1967; Tsuruuchi 1971). The optimum depth of planting for emergence of *G. spurium* under greenhouse conditions was 0.5 cm (Malik and Vanden Born 1987c). Under field conditions in Alberta, earliest emergence occurred from a planting depth of 3–6 cm in a clay loam soil. Germination, growth and development were delayed when seeds were sown 7–10 cm deep. Lack of adequate soil moisture in the top 3 cm of soil resulted in delayed emergence from the 1- to 1.5–cm and 2- to 3-cm depths.

For *G. aparine*, oxygen levels had to be at least 6–8% for germination to occur at all, and 12–16% to reach 75% germination

(Mullverstedt 1963). Very low levels of oxygen induced secondary dormancy after a long duration, and the absence of oxygen killed the seeds.

Germination of both species is inhibited in the presence of light. Sjostedt (1959) reported that germination of freshly-harvested *G. aparine* occurred most readily in darkness. A light intensity of about 20% of full daylight retarded germination of both freshly harvested seeds and 1–yr-old seeds. Hirinda (1959) reported 50–76% germination of *G. aparine* in the dark, 0–4% in the light, and 39–50% under "intermediate" conditions. We found that germination of *G. spurium* was inhibited by light and that the degree of this inhibition was related to the intensity and duration of exposure to light (Malik and Vanden Born 1987c). Subsequent dry storage and reincubation in the dark did not fully restore the germination potential of the seeds to that of untreated seeds, indicating that a secondary dormancy was induced by continuous exposure to light. Germination was completely inhibited with intermittent 1–h exposures of light every 3, 7 and 11 h for 8 d. Red, far-red and blue light inhibited germination and the degree of inhibition was related to the duration of exposure. Far-red light was more inhibitory than red or blue light. Nitrate salts in the medium during light exposure did not prevent the onset of light-induced dormancy. In subsequent dark incubation, light-induced dormancy was overcome by the addition of nitrates and, to a lesser extent, by kinetin and GA_3.

(d) *Vegetative reproduction*—No vegetative reproduction has been reported to occur in nature, but we have observed regeneration from shoot cuttings of *G. spurium*, left on a moist soil surface after thinning seedlings grown in pots, under greenhouse conditions.

9. Hybrids
Moore (1975) identified one *G. spurium* plant, grown from colchicine-treated seeds, with 41 chromosomes that differed morphologically from other plants from the same *G. spurium* source and from *G. aparine*. The odd plant had a stiffer stem with thicker, subcoriaceous and apiculate leaves. Flowers showed lower fertility and fruits were 3 mm long, larger than those of *G. spurium*. The progeny of this plant had 40–41 chromosomes. Moore speculated that the unusual morphology and lower fertility may have resulted from a cross with a hexaploid such as *G. boreale*, the only common native species found in rapeseed fields. Another possibility is that the strange plant may have been a tetraploid *G. spurium* induced by the use of a herbicide. The strange plant did not differ from the colchicine-induced tetraploids of *G. spurium*. Both had stiffer stems and lower fertility than the diploid.

There is no other evidence for hybrids for either of the two species.

10. Population Dynamics
In a study of population dynamics of *G. aparine* in West Germany, seed counts were higher on sites that had been cropped with sugarbeet than on sites under grain production (Rottele 1980). Seed production was lowest in spring barley (9 seeds/plant) and highest in sugarbeet (2170 seeds/plant). Mullverstedt (1975) conducted a 3–yr investigation of the competitive effect of *G. aparine* on winter wheat on loess loam soils in the Mainz area of West Germany, and reported that *G. aparine* plants had suppressed ear formation. No relationship was found between weed stand and crop yield. In another competition study in West Germany (Anonymous 1977), *G. aparine* did not become competitive until after emergence of the winter cereals. Weeds left untreated beyond the point when phenoxy compounds were effective were increasingly competitive, though late-germinating *G. aparine* failed to develop strongly.

The effect of intraspecific competition on growth and development of *G. spurium* was studied under field and greenhouse conditions by the authors. Plant height, number of nodes on stem, total shoot dry matter m^{-2}, and number of seeds m^{-2} did not differ significantly as the number of plants increased from 4 to 50 m^{-2}. Individual plants developed fewer branches, leaf whorls and seeds as plant density increased to 100 m^{-2}. The effect of population density (1, 2, 4, 8, 16 plants/pot) on growth of *G. spurium* was apparent as early as 23 d after emergence (Malik and Vanden Born 1987b). By the 33rd day, the number of branches at the first node was 14 at the lowest density and 6 at the highest density. Development of flowers occurred first on plants grown in groups of 16 plants/pot, 38 d after emergence. Seed production per plot did not change significantly as plant density increased from 1 to 8. The number of seeds per plant decreased by 50% as plant density per pot was doubled. At comparable densities, plants with mechanical support produced significantly more seeds than plants without such support.

Normally, one generation of *G. aparine* and *G. spurium* per season is possible in Canada. Growth of a second generation of *G. spurium* from mature seeds shed in late August has been observed by us under field conditions in Alberta and Saskatchewan. However, the development of such seedlings is interrupted by the onset of winter. These late-emerging seedlings can reach the four- to five-leaf-whorl stage and then resume growth in the following spring. The mean life of individual *G. spurium* plants is about 100 days in cultivated fields under prairie conditions.

11. Response to Herbicides

Both species are resistant to phenoxyacetic herbicides. Continuous use of these herbicides in cereal crops, before the advent of sulfonylurea herbicides, has led to an increase in population of *G. aparine* in many European countries. Rola (1969) reported that herbicides used for broadleaf weed control in cereals in Poland led to the spread of *G. aparine*. Surveys of sugarbeet fields over a 15–yr period in West Germany showed that infestations of *G. aparine* increased (Bachthaler and Dancau 1970). In western Canada, MCPA and 2,4–D, still the most commonly used herbicides for broadleaf weed control in cereals,

do not provide effective control of *Galium* species (O'Sullivan 1983). Other herbicides and herbicide mixtures available in Canada for broadleaf weed control in cereals such as mecoprop, bromoxynil + MCPA, propanil + MCPA, dicamba + 2,4–D amine, dicamba + mecoprop + MCPA, and dicamba + mecoprop + 2,4–D, cyanazine, cyanazine + MCPA provide satisfactory control of the two species at the one- to four-leaf-whorl stage. Chlorsulfuron applied at 20 g ha^{-1} provides season-long control. We observed satisfactory control of *G. spurium* with Dowco 433 (fluoroxypyr), BAS 479 (metazachlor) and buthidazole.

Complete control of *G. spurium* in rapeseed is not achieved with the herbicides currently used by producers in the prairie provinces. Herbicides registered for control of broadleaf weeds in rapeseed include trifluralin, ethalfluralin, benazolin and clopyralid. Clopyralid is not very effective against *G. spurium*, and results with trifluralin have been erratic. In field experiments conducted in Alberta, visual control ratings indicated that trifluralin (1.2 kg ha^{-1}), ethalfluralin (1.2 kg ha^{-1}) or trifluralin + ethalfluralin (0.6+0.6 kg ha^{-1}) provided 80–90% control of *G. spurium* (Malik and Vanden Born 1987a). However, the few seedlings that escaped control, managed to establish themselves and competed successfully with the crop. Production of *G. spurium* seeds ranged from 0.6 to 2.3 g m^{-2}, and crop seed contamination was unacceptably high at 1.2–4.8 seeds g^{-1} rapeseed. Satisfactory control of *G. spurium* was achieved with postemergence application of benazolin ethyl ester at 0.25 kg ha^{-1} and benazolin dimethylamine at 0.5 kg ha^{-1}. Moderate crop injury in the form of stunting was observed after application of the ester formulation. O'Sullivan (1983) reported that a wettable powder formulation was safer on rapeseed than the liquid ester and dimethylamine formulations and that there were no differences in degree of control when the latter formulation was applied at the one-, three- or five-leaf-whorl stage of *G. spurium*. Although a registered product, benazolin is seldom used by rapeseed producers because of its prohibitive cost.

Since a greater number of herbicides can be used selectively in cereal crops for broad-leaf weed control, it is recommended that a cereal crop be planted for 2 consecutive years in fields that have *G. aparine* or *G. spurium* infestations.

12. Response to Other Human Manipulation

Monocultures of rye, oats, clover and flax led to increased infestations of *G. aparine* and other weeds (200–600 m^{-2}) in the Kalinin region of the Soviet Union (Dospekhov 1967). Fertilizers increased infestations in monocultures but not in rotated crops. Continuous bare plowing for 6 yr completely controlled *G. aparine*. Unusually high rainfall and a high level of available N provided good growing conditions for *G. aparine* in East Germany (Buhr et al. 1977). Infestations spread rapidly in cereals that were prone to lodging. Intensification of crop production has led to a reduction in *G. aparine* population in Poland (Rola and Kuzniewski 1979).

Pre-emergence application of 80 kg ha^{-1} of N in cereals delayed the emergence of *G. aparine* under greenhouse conditions (Nieman 1977), while harrowing enhanced germination because it increased aeration (Merz 1975). In paddy and upland fields in Japan, where *G. aparine* is a major problem, Ueki (1965) recommended certain preventive measures that included flooding, deep plowing, use of straw mulch at germination and crop rotation.

13. Response to Parasites

(a) *Insects and other nondomestic animals*— Parasitism of *G. spurium* by aphids and white flies was observed by authors in the greenhouse. Aphids were also observed to feed on *G. spurium* under field conditions. A sphinx caterpillar (*Hyles galii* Rottemberg) was observed to feed selectively on *G. spurium* shoots and green fruits in a rapeseed field. The caterpillars were brought to the laboratory and placed in separate boxes containing

G. spurium foliage, rape foliage and mixed *G. spurium* and rape foliage. The caterpillars fed only on *G. spurium* shoots with a preference for young succulent shoots and immature fruits.

A survery of phytophages and pollinators of *Galium* spp. in Eurasia and North America was conducted by Batra (1984) to identify potential biocontrol agents. *Geocrypta galii* (H. Lw.), a gall-forming Eurasian Cecidomyiidae, has the greatest potential for use in biological control. The phytophagous arthropod forms spheroidal galls that resulted in stem necrosis and breakage on *G. aparine* (Klein and Meyer 1963). *Schizomyia galiorum* Keiffer galls the flower buds of *Galium* spp. and prevents fruit development. In Europe, *G. aparine* is also galled by *Dasyneura aparines* Keiffer (Buhr 1964, cited by Batra 1984). Other Eurasian organisms that are relatively host-specific and have some potential for biocontrol include the leaf-rolling mite, *Cecidophyes galii* Karpelles, and the stem-galling mite, *Aceria galiobia* Can. (Batra 1984).

Five species of sawflies feed on *Galium* spp. (Batra 1984). Larvae of *Halidamia affinis* Fallen were observed on *G. aparine* in North America (Arthur and Cummins 1962).

The gall-forming aphids specific to *Galium* spp. are *Aphis galiiscabri* Schrank and *Galiobium langei* Borner (Batra 1984).

Galium spp. are also parasitised by several nematodes of economic importance mentioned in Section 3a.

Galium spp. have secondary plant substances with repellent effects which may determine the composition and survival of natural enemy populations (Batra 1984).

(b) *Microorganisms and viruses*—Pathogenic rust fungi specific to *Galium* spp. in North America are *Puccinia punctata* Lk., *P. punctata* var. *troglodytes*, *P. rubefaciens* Johans (Batra 1984). *P. punctata* Lk. has been observed on *G. spurium* across Canada.

Powdery mildew caused by *Erysiphe cichoracearum* DC. has been observed on both *G. aparine* and *G. spurium* (Anonymous

1960; Conners 1967) while *E. polygoni* DC. has been observed on *G. aparine* (Anonymous 1960).

Leaf spot caused by *Cercospora galii* Ell. & Holow., *Melasmia galii* Ell. & Ev.; leaf and stem spots caused by *Psuedopeziza repanda* (Fr.) Karst., *Septoria aparine* Ell. & Kell; stem spots caused by *Rhabdospora galiorum* have been observed on *G. aparine* (Anonymous 1960).

Downy mildew caused by *Pernospora caleotheca* d By., also distinguished as *P. aparines* has been observed on *G. aparine* (Anonymous 1960).

(c) *Higher plant parasites*. *G. aparine* is parasitised by dodder (*Cuscuta europea* L.) (Batra 1984).

ACKNOWLEDGMENT

Financial support was provided by the Alberta Agricultural Research Trust, Farming for the Future and Agriculture Canada. The advice of J. P. Tewari, University of Alberta, on specimen preparation for S.E.M. is gratefully acknowledged. We thank M. D. Devine, University of Alberta, for valuable discussions during the course of this study; A. McClay, Alberta Environmental Centre, for information on natural enemies of *Galium* spp.; S. Allyson-Morello, Biosystematics Research Center, for insect identification; S.I. Warwick, B.R.C., for valuable critical review of the manuscript; L. Adams and S. Wittig, Melfort Research Station, for preparation of the manuscript. We appreciate the loan of specimens from B.R.C.

Alex, J. F., Cayouette, R. and Mulligan, G. A. 1980. Common and botanical names of weeds in Canada. Agriculture Canada, Ottawa, Ont. Publ. 1397, 132 pp.

Ancev, M. E. 1974. *In* IOPB chromosome number reports. XLIV. Taxon. **23**: 373–380.

Anonymous. 1960. Index of plant diseases in the United States. Agriculture Handbook No. 165. Crops Research Division, ARS-USDA, Washington, D. C. 416 pp.

Anonymous. 1968. Broad-leaved weed infestations in cereals. Fisons Agric. Tech, Inf., 1968 (Spring), 21–28. *In* Weed Abstr. 1968, **17(4)**: 1806.

Anonymous. 1977. Biologische Bundesanstalt fur Land und Forstwirtschaft [Annual Report 1977.]

Jahresbericht 1977. (1978) 147 pp. *In* Weed Abstr. 1979, **28(10)**: 3214.

Anonymous. 1979. The Weed Control Act 1979. Alberta Regulation 138/80. Queen's Printer, Edmonton, Alta.

Anonymous. 1984. Noxious Weeds Act (Saskatchewan). 1984. Queen's Printer. Regina, Sask.

Anonymous. 1986. Seeds Act, Canada Gazette Part II, Vol. 120, No. 18. Queen's Printer for Canada, Ottawa, Ont.

Arai, M., Chisaka, H. and Ueki, K. 1961. Comparisons in ecological characteristics of noxious weeds in winter cropping. Proc. Crop Sci. Soc. Japan **30**: 39–42. *In* Weed Abstr. 1963, **12(3)**: 482.

Arthur, J. C. and Cummins, G. B. 1962. Manual of the rusts in the United States and Canada. Hafner, New York.

Bachthaler, G. and Dancau, B. 1970. [Influence of production technique on the weed flora in sugarbeet, with particular regard to chemical weed control.] Proc. 2nd Int. Meeting Selective Weed Cont. Beetcrops, Rotterdam, 1970, 1, 221–233. *In* Weed Abstr. 1971, **20(2)**: 826.

Batra, W. T. S. 1984. Phytophages and Pollinators of *Galium* (Rubiaceae) in Eurasia and North America. Environ. Entomol. **13**: 1113–1124.

Behrendt, S. 1973. [The most important weeds of winter rape in the German Federal Republic]. Z. Pflanzenkr. Planzenschutz (1973) **80(7)**: 385–394. Landw. Versuchsstn. der BASF Ag. *In* Weed Abstr. 1974, **23(9)**: 1909.

Bendixen, L. E., Reynolds, D. A. and Riedel, R. M. 1979. An annotated bibliography of weeds as reservoirs for organisms affecting crops. I. Nematodes. Ohio Agric. Res. and Dev. Centre U.S. 250 and Ohio 83 South. Wooster, Ohio. 64 pp.

Brenchley, W. and Warington, K. 1930. The weed seed population of arable soil. 1. Numerical estimation of viable seeds and observations on their natural dormancy. J. Ecol. **18**: 235–272.

Buhr, H. 1964. Bestimmungstabellen der Gallen (Zoound Phytocecidien) an Pflanzen Mittel- und Nordeuropas, Bd. 1. Fisher, Jena.

Buhr, L., Feyerabend, G., Pallutt, B. and Becker, H. G. 1977. [Position regarding the occurrence of beetgrass (*Apera spica-venti* (L.) P. B.) and cleavers (*Galium aparine* L.) as well as possibilities of their control.] Nachr. Pflanzenschutz DDR (1977) **31(12)**: 237–240. Inst. PflSchutzforsch Akad. LandwWiss. DDR, Kleinmachnow, E. Germany. In Weed Abstr. 1978, **27(10)**: 3385.

Chadoeuf, R., Magriere, J. P., Lonchamp, J. P. and Barralis, G. 1980. [Comparative evolution of the germination capacity of weed seeds when buried or dry-stored.] *In* Proc. 6th Intern. Colloquium Weed Ecol., Biol. and Systematics, Montpelier, 1980. Vol. I, 103–112. *In* Weed Abstr. 1981, **30(10)**; 3549.

Conners, I. L. 1967. An Annotated index of plant diseases in Canada. Research Branch, Canada Department of Agriculture, Ottawa, Ont. Publ. 1251, pp. 121–122.

De Poucques, M. L. 1949. Recherches caryologiques sur les Rubiales. Rev. Gen. Bot. **56**: 5–27, 74–96, 172–188.

Dew, D. A. 1982. Survey of weeds in Alberta. Weed Control Branch, Alberta Agric., Edmonton, Alta. pp. 36–37.

Dospekhov, B. A. 1967. [The effect of long term fertilizer application and crop rotation on the infestation of fields by weeds.] Izv. timiryazev sel'khoz. Akad., 1967 (3): 51–64. *In* Weed Abstr. 1968, **17(2)**: 807.

Ehrendorfer, F. 1971. Evolution and ecogeographical differentiation in some Southwest Asiatic Rubiaceae. Pages 195–215 *in* P. H. Davis, P. C. Harper, I. C. Hedge, eds. Plant life of Southwest Asia. Botanical Society of Edinburgh, University Press, Aberdeen, U.K.

Fagerlind, F. 1934. Beitrage zur Kenntniss der Zytologie der Rubiaceen. Hereditas **19**: 223–232.

Gadella, T. W. J. and Kliphuis, E. 1963. Chromosome numbers of flowering plants in the Netherlands. Acta Bot. Neerl. **12**: 195–230.

Groh, H. and Frankton, C. 1946. Canadian Weed Survey. Fifth Report. Agriculture Canada, Ottawa, Ont. 86 pp.

Groh, H. and Francton, C. 1948. Canadian Weed Survey. Seventh Report. Agriculture Canada, Ottawa, Ont. 144 pp.

Hanf, M. 1941. Keimung and Entwicklung des Klettenlab Krautes (*Galium aparine*) in verscheidener Aussaattiefe. Angew. Bot. **23**: 152–163.

Hanf, M. 1983. The arable weeds of Europe. BASF, U.K. 494 pp.

Heathcote, G. D., Dunning, R. A. and Wolfe, M. D. 1965. Aphids on sugar beets and some weeds in England and notes on weeds as a source. Plant Patol. **14**: 1–10. Bibl. 24.

Hirinda, F. 1959. [The biology and control of cleavers (*G. aparine* L.)]. Z. Acker and PflBau. **109**: 173–194, (G). *In* Weed Abstr. 1960, **9(1)**: 79.

Holm, L. G., Plucknett, D. L., Pancho, J. V. and Herberger, J. P. 1977. The world's worst weeds. University Press of Hawaii, Honolulu, Hawaii pp. 285–290.

Hulten, E. 1968. Flora of Alaska and neighboring territories. Stanford University Press, Stanford, Calif. 836 pp.

Johnson, L. R. 1940. On the stem and bulb eelworm (*Anguillulina dispaci* Kühn) with special reference to its occurrence on weeds of arable land. Ann. Appl. Biol. **27**: 248–251.

Klein, C. and Meyer, J. 1963. Etude du développement de la galle de *Perrisia galii* J. Lw. sur *Galium mollugo* L. Marcellia **31**: 77–94.

Kliphuis, E. 1962. Cytotaxonomical studies on the genus Galium. A preliminary report. Proc. Kon. Ned. Akad. Wet., Ser. Biol. Med. Sci. C. **65**: 279–285.

Kliphuis, E. 1980. Cytotaxonomic studies on *Galium aparine*. Proc. Kon. Ned. Akad. Wet. Ser. Biol. Med. Sci. C. **83**: 53–64.

Korsmo, E., Vindme, T. and Fykse, H. 1981. Korsmos Ugras Plansjer. Norsk Landbruk/Landbruksforlaget, Oslo, Norway. pp. 278–279.

Kramer, K. V., Westra, L. Y. T., Kliphuis, E. and Gadella, T. W. J. 1972. Floristic and cytotaxonomic notes on the flora of the Maltese Islands. Acta Bot. Neerl. **21**: 54–66.

Kurth, H. 1967. [The germination behavior of weeds] SYS Reptr (3), 6–11, [D; PflSchutz Abt., VEB Synthesewerk Schwarzheide, 7817 Schwarzheide, Democratic Republic of Germany]. *In* Weed Abstr. 1968, **17(4)**: 1783.

Lauer, E. 1953. Uber die Keimtemperatur von Ackerunkrautern und deren Einfluss auf die Zusammensetzung von Unkrautgesellschaften. Flora Allg. Bot. Zeit. **140**: 551–595.

Lewis, W. H. 1962. Chromosome numbers in North American Rubiaceae. Brittonia **14**: 285–290.

Lonchamp, J. P. and Gora, M. 1980. [Evolution of the germinative capacity of weed seeds during dry storage.] I.N.R.A. Lab. Malherbologie, Dijon, France. *In* Weed Abstr. 1981, **30(3)**: 973.

Long, H. C. 1960. Weeds of arable land. Bull. 108, Ministry of Agriculture and Fisheries, London, U.K.

Love, A. and Love, D. 1956. Cytotaxonomical conspectus of Icelandic flora. Acta Hortic. Gotob. **20**: 65–290.

Lowe, A. D. 1969. A preliminary account of *Macrosiphum miscanthi* Takahashi on grasses and cereals in New Zealand. Entomologist **4**: 33–35.

Malik, N. and Vanden Born, W. H. 1984. False cleavers thrives on the prairies. Weeds Today **15(4)**: 12–14.

Malik, N. and Vanden Born, W. H. 1987a. False cleavers competition and control in rapeseed. Can. J. Plant Sci. **67**: 839–844.

Malik, N. and Vanden Born, W. H. 1987b. Growth and development of false cleavers (*Galium spurium* L.). Weed Sci., **35**: 490–495.

Malik N. and Vanden Born, W. H. 1987c. Germination response of *Galium spurium* L. to light. Weed Res. **27**: 251–258.

Mateev, M. M. and Timoteev, P. O. 1965. [Effect of water-soluble exudates of certain forest and forest-weed species on one-year oak seedlings.] Ukr. Bot. Zh., 1965, **22(4)**: 28–32. *In* Weed Abstr. 1966, **15(4)**: 1225.

Merz, R. 1975. [Type and signficance of weed competition in carrots with particular regard to carrot crops in Baden-Wurttenberg.] Dissertation, University of Hohenheim. (1975) 117 pp. *In* Weed Abstr. 1977, **26(4)**: 1043.

Moore, R. J. 1975. The *Galium aparine* complex in Canada. Can. J. Bot. **53**: 877–893.

Mullverstedt, R. 1963. Investigations on the germination of weed seeds as influenced by oxygen partial pressure. Weed Res. **3**: 154–163.

Mullverstedt, R. 1975. [The importance of plant density of *Galium aparine* and time of its control on the yield of winter wheat.] Ergebnisse der 10. Deutschen Arbeitsbesprechung über Fragen der Unkrautbiologie und Bekampfung, 1975, Stuttgart-Hohenheim. Z. Pflanzenkr. Pflanzenschutz Sonderheft **7**: 31–33. *In* Weed Abstr. 1975, **24(8)**: 1692.

Nieman, P. Von. 1977. Konkurrenz zwischen Kletten-Labkraut (*Galium aprine* L.) and Wintergetreide im Jugendstadium. Ergebnisse der 11. Duetschen Arbeitsbesprechung über Fragen der Unkrautbiologie und Bekampfung, 1977, Stuttgart-Hohenheim, Federal Republic of Germany.

Noda, K., Ibaraki, D., Eguchi, W. and Ozawa, K. 1965. Studies on ecological characteristics of the annual weed cleaver and its chemical control on drained paddy fields for wheat plants in temperate Japan. Bull. Kushu Agric. Exp. Sta. **11**: 345–374.

O'Sullivan, P. A. 1983. Selective control of false cleavers in rapeseed with benazolin. Can. J. Plant Sci. **63**: 497–501.

Pawlowski, F. and Wszolek, M. 1978. [Weediness of the summer barley and winter wheat grain on loess and chernozem soils in the Hrubieszow region.] Roczniki Nauk Rolniczych, A (1978) **103(2)** 131–145. Instytut Uprawy Roli i ruslin Akad. Roln. W. Lublinie, Ul. Akademica 15, Lublin, Poland. *In* Weed Abstr. 1979, **28(11)**: 3603.

Podlech, D. and Dieterle, A. 1969. Chromosomenstudien an afghanischen Pflanzen. Candollea **24**: 185–243.

Rademacher, B. 1963. [Effects of the severe frost of the winter 1961/62 on the stand of the previous year's surviving weeds and their control in wintersown crops.] Deutsche Arbeitsbesprechung über Fragen der Unkrautbiologie und Bekampfung. Hohenheim, 1963, pp. 9. [Inst. f. PflSchutz, Landw. Hochschule, Stuttgart-Hohenheim, W. Germany.] *In* Weed Abstr. 1963, **12(3)**: 630.

Rola, J. 1969. [Causes and effects of weed compensation in crops.] Biul. Inst. Ochr. Roslin, **44**: 409–424. *In* Weed Abst. 1971, **20(6)**: 2730.

Rola, J. and Kuzniewski, E. 1979. [Weed control in plant production on an industrial scale. **1**: General principles. Effect of intensification and specification of plant production on weediness.] Wissenschaftliche Beitrage Martin-Luther University (1979), **7**: 22–28. *In* Weed Abstr. 1979, **28(12)**: 4142.

Rottele, M. A. 1980. [Population dynamics of cleavers (*Galium aparine* L.).] Dissertation, University of Hohenheim (1980) 133 pp. *In* Weed Abstr. 1981, **30(6)**: 2129.

Scoggan, H. S. 1979. The flora of Canada. National Museum of Canada, Ottawa, Ont. pp. 1408–1413.

Sjostedt, S. 1959. Germination biology of cleavers (*Galium aparine* L.). Publ. Dep. Plant Husbandry, Roy. School Agric., Uppsala, Sweden, No. 10, pp. 87–105.

Taylor, R. L. and Mulligan, G. A. 1968. Flora of the Queen Charlotte Islands. Part 2. Cytological aspects of the vascular plants. Canada Department of Agriculture, Ottawa, Ont. Monogr. No. 4 (Part 2).

Thomas, A. G. and Wise, R. 1982. 1981 Weed survey of cultivated land in Manitoba. Research Station, Agriculture Canada, Regina, Sask. 124 pp.

Thomas, A. G. and Wise, R. F. 1983. Weed survey of Saskatchewan Cereal and Oilseed Crops from 1976 to 1979. Research Station, Agriculture Canada, Regina, Sask. 260 pp.

Thomas, A. G. and Wise, R. F. 1986. Weed survey of Saskatchewan cereal and oilseed crops. Research Station, Agriculture Canada, Regina, Sask. 251 pp.

Tsuruuchi, T. 1971. [Studies on weeds in wheat and barley fields in Nagasaki Prefecture. 2. Some ecological characteristics and chemical control of ivy-leaved speedwell (*Veronica hederifolia* L.) Weed Res. (Japan), 1971, **12**; 32–36. *In* Weed Abstr. 1973, **22(11)**: 2584.

Ueki, K. 1965. Physiological and ecological

studies on cleavers (*G. aparine*) control. Ph.D. Thesis. Kyoto University, Kyoto, Japan.

Ueki, K. and Shimizu, N. 1967. Studies on the termination of dormancy in cleaver seeds. 2. The effect of some chemicals on the breaking of dormancy. Weed Res. (Japan) **6**: 23–26.

Weed Science Society of America. 1980. Composite list of weeds. Weed Sci. **32**, Suppl. 2. WSSA, 309 West Clark St., Champaign, Ill.

Welsh, S. L. 1974. Anderson's flora of Alaska and adjacent parts of Canada, Brigham University Press, Provo, Utah. pp. 398–399.

Wiesner, K. and Haberland, R. 1980. [Population density and species spectrum of surviving weeds in sugarbeet crops.] Archiv Phytopath. Pflanzenschutz (1980) **16(3)**: 217–226. Inst. Rubenforsch. den AdL der DDR., Klein Wanzleben, German Democratic Republic. *In* Weed Abstr. 1981, **39(5)**: 1863.

THE BIOLOGY OF CANADIAN WEEDS. 87.
Cynoglossum officinale L.

MAHESH K. UPADHYAYA, HEIDY R. TILSNER[1], and MICHAEL D. PITT

Department of Plant Science, University of British Columbia, Vancouver, British Columbia, Canada V6T 2A2. Received 27 July 1987, accepted 10 Jan. 1988.

UPADHYAYA, M. K., TILSNER, H. R. AND PITT, M. D. 1988. The biology of Canadian weeds. 87. *Cynoglossum officinale* L. Can. J. Plant Sci. **68**: 763–774.

Cynoglossum officinale L. is a biennial or short-lived perennial weed which reproduces by seed. It has been introduced to North America from Eurasia. Although usually not a weed of cultivated fields, *C. officinale* may become a serious rangeland weed. High seed production, seed dormancy, dissemination by attaching seeds to animal hair, wool and fur, plus the ability to withstand environmental stress are important in the success of *C. officinale* as a weed. Because *C. officinale* foliage is toxic to both cattle and horses, it is a particular problem in areas where grazing occurs. This paper reviews the biology and control of *C. officinale*.

Key words: Weed biology, *Cynoglossum officinale* L., hound's tongue

[La biologie des mauvaises herbes canadiennes. 87. *Cynoglossum officinale* L.]
Titre abrégé: *Cynoglossum officinale* L.
Cynoglossum officinale L. est une mauvaise herbe bisannuelle ou vivace qui se reproduit par graines. C'est une espèce naturalisée de l'Eurasie. Même si elle n'est habituellement pas considérée comme une mauvaise herbe des champs cultivés, *C. officinale* peut devenir une grave nuisance dans les parcours. La production d'un grand nombre de graines, la possibilité des graines d'entrer en période de dormance, leur aptitude à se répandre en s'accrochant à la fourrure des animaux et l'aptitude de la plante à résister au stress environnemental expliquent les succès de cette espèce. Comme le feuillage de *C. officinale* est toxique pour les bovins et les chevaux, elle présente un problème particulier dans les aires de pâturage. Dans le présent document, nous faisons un tour d'horizon de la biologie de *C. officinale* et des méthodes de lutte contre cette mauvaise herbe.

Mots clés: Biologie des mauvaises herbes, *Cynoglossum officinale* L., langue-de-chien

1. Name

Cynoglossum officinale L. — **hound's tongue** (Alex et al. 1980); *Cynoglosse officinale* — **herbe d'antal**, langue-de-chien (Ferron and Cayouette 1970; Scoggan 1978). Boraginaceae, Borage family, Boraginacées. Other names are beggar's lice (Scoggan 1978), dog's tongue (Greatorex 1966), sheep bur (Macoun 1884), dog bur, sheep lice (Muenscher 1980), common bur (Clark and Fletcher 1909), glovewort (Cockayne 1961) and woolmat (Kummer 1951; Muenscher 1980).

2. Description and Account of Variation

(a) The following description of *C. officinale* is based on Gains and Swan (1972), Alex and Switzer (1976), Taylor and MacBryde (1977), Scoggan (1978), Muenscher (1980), Boorman and Fuller (1984) and Van Breemen (1984). *Cynoglossum officinale* is an herbaceous biennial or short-lived perennial reproducing by

[1]Present address (H.R.T.): Alberta Environmental Centre, Bag 4000, Vegreville, Alberta, Canada T0B 4L0.

Can. J. Plant Sci. 68: 763–774 (July 1988)

seed only. *Cynoglossum officinale* forms a rosette in the first year; leaves softly pubescent, 10–30 cm long, 2–5 cm wide, shaped like a hound's tongue; tap root thick, black, branching, extending to depths > 100 cm. Flower stems are produced in the second year, 30–120 cm high; upper part of stem branching; stem leaves sessile or clasping, pubescent, entire, alternate, lanceolate — generally broadest near the base and narrowing towards the tip. Inflorescence a raceme, axillary to leaves (Fig. 1b) or on

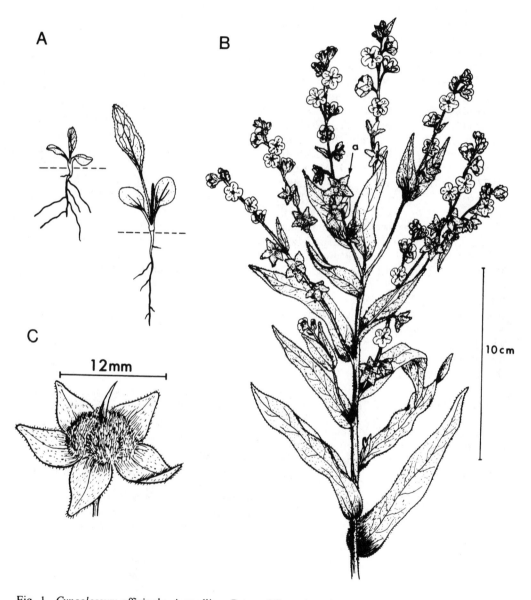

A

B

C

12mm

10cm

Fig. 1. *Cynoglossum officinale*, A seedling; B top of flowering plant; and C fruit of four nutlets. A is from Kummer (1951) and B and C from Alex and Switzer (1976).

terminating short branches; pedicels ca. 1 cm long, stout; flower a dull reddish purple, 1 cm across, regular, perfect; 5 sepals with triangular lobes fused to form a star-shaped calyx; 5 petals, fused, forming a cup (funnelform). Anthers, 5, borne on corolla throat. Pistil with a deeply lobed ovary and a simple style. Indehiscent fruit consists of 4 nutlets, nutlet brown or greyish-brown, roundedtriangular with dorsal surface flattened, whole surface covered with short, barbed prickles (Fig. 1c). Line diagrams of the mature plant appear in Muenscher (1980), Hegi (1927) and Alex and Switzer (1976). A photograph and a colored line diagram of *C. officinale* "seeds" appear in Gains and Swan (1972) and Clark and Fletcher (1909), respectively. Its seedling morphology (Fig. 1a) has been described by Kummer (1951). Taylor and MacBryde (1977) reported a chromosome base number of $x=6$ for *C. officinale*. Mulligan (1957) found counts of $2n=24$ for Ontario material. This $2n$ value has also been reported in plants from Belgium (Britton 1951), Iceland (Love and Love 1956) and Poland (Skalinska et al. 1959). Britton (1951) also reported $n=12$ for plants from Denmark and U.S.A.

(b) *Cynoglossum officinale* has large pubescent leaves, and distinctive flowers and fruits. As a rosette *C. officinale* may be confused with *Echium vulgare* L. (blueweed), which has narrow, more harshly-hairy rosette leaves (Frankton and Mulligan 1970). The conspicuous blue flowers of *E. vulgare* contrast sharply with the reddish-purple flowers of *C. officinale*. Rosette leaves of *Verbascum thapsus* L. (common mullein) resemble those of *C. officinale*, but have much denser pubescence and are not as conspicuously veined.

The pollen morphology of *C. officinale*, which is very distinctive from most other Northwest European genera, is described in Clarke (1977).

(c) No subspecies of *C. officinale* has been reported.

3. Economic Importance

(a) *Detrimental* — *Cynoglossum officinale* rarely causes problems in cultivated fields. Populations of *C. officinale* may, however, become established on rangelands (Cranston and Pethybridg 1986) and hinder the reestablishment of valuable range species, thereby decreasing forage availability for grazing.

The barbed seeds of *C. officinale* readily cling to hair, wool and fur (Gains and Swan 1972), which reduces the value of sheep, and causes irritation and behavioral problems in cattle. Attachment of burred seeds to livestock reduces their sale price (Cranston and Pethybridge 1986). Removal of burs from the skin is expensive and stresses the animal. Moreover, ranchers in *C. officinale*-infested areas incur extra veterinary costs as irritation to eyes often results from the attachment of the burred seeds (Cranston and Pethybridge 1986). *Cynoglossum officinale* has been reported to cause dermatitis (Muenscher 1939; Taylor and MacBryde 1977).

The most detrimental aspect of *C. officinale* is its poisonous nature (Greatorex 1966; Mandryka 1979; Bartik and Piskac 1981; Knight et al. 1984). The toxic constituents of *C. officinale* are pyrrolizidine alkaloids including echinatine (Knight et al. 1984), heliosupine (McGaw and Woolley 1979; Knight et al. 1984) and acetylheliosupine (Resch and Meinwald 1982). The concentration of toxic pyrrolizidine alkaloids is highest in the rosette leaves (2.1% of dry weight compared to 0.6% in mature plants; Knight et al. 1984). Poisoning usually occurs when dry plants, mixed with hay, are fed to animals (Knight et al. 1984). Mandryka (1979) reported poisoning of cattle feeding on chopped sainfoin contaminated with *C. officinale*. Diarrhoea and nervous symptoms commencing 12–24 h after feeding (6–12 h in calves) were observed. Other reported symptoms include dizziness, cardiac disorders and respiratory failure (Sikula 1981). Greatorex (1966) reported death of four cows within 36 h after grazing land infested with *C. officinale* and leafy spurge. Poisoning symptoms included varying degrees of tymphany, accelerated respiration, dyspnoea, diarrhoea with dark greenish feces, incoordination, increased thirst and decline in milk yields. Poisoning symptoms in horses have been reported by Knight et al. (1984).

(b) *Beneficial* — Extracts of Boraginaceous roots have been used for centuries as "folk" remedies for a variety of disorders such as eczema, keratodermia, acne vulgaris, corn callus, dermatophytosis, burns and hemorrhoids (Papageorgiou 1980). Cockayne (1961) reported that root extracts of hound's-tongue cured tertian fever and "oppression of the chest". Altschul (1973) also mentioned the use of *Cynoglossum* root as a fever remedy. Lipophilic red pigments (alkannins) associated with the outer surface of the roots of many members of the Boraginaceae, including the genus *Cynoglossum*, are antibacterial, antitumorogenic and possess wound-healing activity (Papageorgiou 1980). Alkannin pigments have also been used as food and wine colorants in at least 12 European countries (Papageorgiou 1980).

Roots and leaves of *C. officinale* have been used as "folk" pesticides. Bocs (1983) reported the use of *C. officinale* herbage to repel moles in gardens and to protect stored fruits and vegetables from rodents.

(c) *Legislation* — *Cynoglossum officinale* is classified as a noxious weed in the North Okanagan, Columbia-Shuswap, Thompson-Nicola, Cariboo and Kootenay-Boundary regional districts of British Columbia under its Weed Control Regulation (Cranston and Pethybridge 1986). It is not included on the noxious weed lists of Alberta, Saskatchewan, Manitoba, Ontario, Quebec and Nova Scotia.

4. Geographical Distribution

Cynoglossum officinale occurs in all provinces of Canada, except Prince Edward Island and Newfoundland (Fig. 2; Breitung 1957a,b;

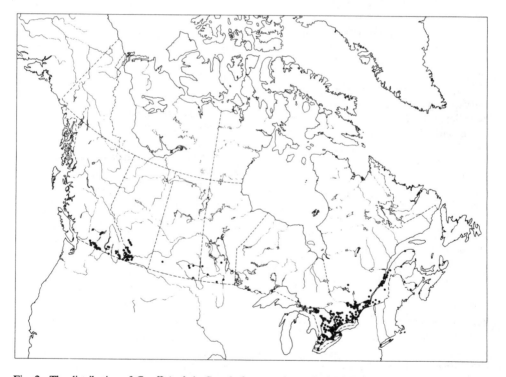

Fig. 2. The distribution of *C. officinale* in Canada from specimens in the following herbaria: ACK, ALTA, CAN, FQH, LKHD, LRS, MMMN, NASC, NBM, OAC, OLDS, PMAE, QFA, QK, QUE, SASK, SCS, SLU, TRT, TRTE, UAC, ULF, UNB, UVIC, UWO, UWPG, V, WIN AND WLU (herbarium abbreviations as in Holmgren et al. 1981).

Boivin 1966; Scoggan 1978). It appears to be most abundant in southern British Columbia and Ontario (Fig. 2). *Cynoglossum officinale* occurs in Russia (Fedoreev et al. 1980), throughout Europe (Tutin et al. 1972) and in the United States (Cochrane 1975; Dickerson and Fay 1982; Knight et al. 1984).

5. Habitat

(a) *Climatic requirements — Cynoglossum officinale* is a weed of temperate regions. In British Columbia it occurs predominately in the Interior Douglas-fir (*Pseudotsuga menziesii* Mirb. Franco) and ponderosa pine (*Pinus ponderosa* Laws)-bunchgrass biogeoclimatic zones (Taylor and MacBryde 1977). Both zones are characterized by hot, dry summers and cold winters. The Interior Douglas-fir zone has average annual precipitation of 44.8 cm, and mean January and July temperatures of approximately –5 and 21°C, respectively; the ponderosa pine-bunchgrass zone annual precipitation averages approximately 26.8 cm, and mean January and July temperatures are approximately –7 and 22°C, respectively (Watts 1983).

Cynoglossum officinale-infested regions of Ontario (Fig. 2) have annual precipitation and mean January and July temperature variations in the range of 77–102 cm, 3.9–10.9°C and 19.2–22.2°C, respectively (based on values for 10 reporting stations in the region; Anonymous 1982).

(b) *Substratum — Cynoglossum officinale* occurs mostly on gravelly, somewhat limey soils in eastern North America (Muenscher 1980). Cockayne (1961) reported that *C. officinale* grows "in sandy lands" in England, U.K. Similarly, Boorman (1982) reported that *C. officinale* is associated with old dune-grasslands, in the U.K., which have sandy soils with low moisture status. In the Netherlands, *C. officinale* has been reported on calcareous coastal dunes, especially where high soil nitrogen levels prevail; the species is absent from acid coastal dunes and from acid sandy soils, and does not occur on peat or clay soils (Freijsen et al. 1980). It occurs in the British Isles in grassy places and borders of woods on rather dry soils, on sand, gravel,

chalk or limestone, particularly near the sea (Clapham et al. 1962). In eastern Canada, *C. officinale* occurs on rocky pastures in limestone regions (Frankton and Mulligan 1970). In B.C., *C. officinale* is found on Eutric and Dystric Brunisolic, Brown and Dark Brown Chernozemic and Luvisolic soils (Cranston and Pethybridge 1986). The region of Alberta where *C. officinale* occurs (Fig. 2) is associated with soils of the Brunisolic, Chernozemic, and Luvisolic orders (Lodge et al. 1971).

(c) *Communities in which the species occurs — Cynoglossum officinale* is found on rangeland, pastures, abandoned croplands, roadsides and waste places (Alex and Switzer 1976; Scoggan 1978; Dickerson and Fay 1982). Boorman and Fuller (1984) found *C. officinale* to be most abundant in areas with more than 10% bare ground.

In British Columbia, hound's-tongue occurs on disturbed sites of the Interior Douglas-fir and ponderosa pine-bunchgrass biogeoclimatic zones. Dense infestations are known from a number of clear-cut logged areas in B.C. (Cranston and Pethybridge 1986).

6. History

Cynoglossum officinale is believed to be native to Eurasia (Scoggan 1978) or Asia (Dickerson and Fay 1982). Introduction to North America likely occurred as a seed contaminant in cereals (Knight et al. 1984). Macoun (1884) noted it as common around Montreal and as a pest in Ontario. Herbarium specimens of *C. officinale* were collected in Ontario as early as 1859 and in the western provinces between 1922 and 1934. Clarke and Fletcher (1909) mentioned *C. officinale* as a troublesome weed of Canada, as its burs entangle in the wool of sheep.

7. Growth and Morphology

(a) *Morphology* — Several features of *C. officinale* morphology contribute to its success as a weed. The prostrate rosette of the first year resists mowing and grazing. Rosettes also withstand drought stress, enabling the plant to survive water deficits and to delay flowering until conditions are favorable. *Cynoglossum officinale* produces a thick, deep tap-root (Gains and Swan 1972; Alex and Switzer 1976) that exploits lower soil strata for water and nutrients. A line diagram of *C. officinale* roots appears in Salisbury (1952). Nutrient reserves of the tap-root acquired during the first year are sufficient for normal seed production the following year, even if the plants are completely defoliated early in the spring (Boorman and Fuller 1984). The large nutrient reserves in seeds of *C. officinale* allow rapid seedling root growth so that plants are well established before drier weather begins (Van Breemen 1984). Barbs on the seeds promote long-distance dispersal by becoming entangled in the hair of passing animals (Dickerson and Fay 1982; Boorman and Fuller 1984; Knight et al. 1984).

(b) *Perennation* — *Cynoglossum officinale* overwinters as a hemicryptophyte with a robust tap root in the first year (Boorman 1982). Extensive root reserves may help the plant avoid winter-kill. Second-year plants produce seeds which overwinter predominantly in the top 1 cm of soil (Van Breemen 1984). Some seeds may remain attached to the parent plant throughout the winter (Lhotska 1982; Van Breemen 1984).

(c) *Physiological data* — Boorman (1982) reported relatively low root and shoot growth rates of first-year *C. officinale* plants compared to several other associated sand dune species, including four winter annuals and the biennial *Lactuca virosa* L.. Although the relative growth rate of *C. officinale* (0.16 d^{-1}) was lower than that of *L. virosa* (0.30 d^{-1}), the larger seed size of *C. officinale* resulted in higher mean plant weight for the first 27 d of the study.

Freijsen (1975, 1976, 1977) studied accumulation of Ca^{2+}, and its effect on the growth of *C. officinale* (a calcicolous plant). In laboratory experiments, *C. officinale* showed a strong tendency to accumulate Ca^{2+} from liquid culture medium. Rosettes of *C. officinale* accumulated greater amounts of Ca^{2+} on a dry weight basis than the rosettes and shoots of two noncalcicoles,

Melandrium rubrum (Weig.) Garcke and *Hypericum perforatum* L., respectively (Freijsen 1977). *Cynoglossum officinale* biomass increased with increasing Ca^{2+} concentraton (0.05–2 meq Ca^{2+} L^{-1}) in the liquid culture medium (Freijsen 1977).

(d) *Phenology* — *Cynoglossum officinale* forms a rosette in the first year, and flowering usually occurs in the second year. In B.C., *C. officinale* flowers from May to July (Taylor and MacBryde 1977). In the U.K., *C. officinale* seedlings emerge in the spring; emergence is synchronous, occurring almost entirely (>90%) in March and April (Roberts and Boddrell 1984). In a glasshouse and field study in the U.K., Boorman and Fuller (1984) reported the main period of *C. officinale* flowering to be ca. 55 d, with seed ripening requiring an additional 70 d. In the wild, development required 3–4 wk longer than in the glasshouse (Boorman and Fuller 1984). Most ripened seeds fall to the ground within 4 mo (Van Breemen 1984). In an exposed environment, Van Breemen (1984) found that 6% of seeds remained on the infructescence in the first December after fruit formation, compared to 38% of seeds on plants in sheltered scrub.

Although frequently classified as biennial, *C. officinale* can behave as a short-lived perennial. Under adverse environmental conditions, flowering can be delayed until the third year of the plant's life-cycle (Boorman and Fuller 1984). This delay could indicate a minimum rosette size requirement for bolting and flowering; however, since even large rosettes failed to flower in their first year, vernalization may also play a role in regulation of bolting (Boorman and Fuller 1984). Boorman and Fuller (1984) also found that while the majority of plants died after flowering, of 55 plants studied, seven flowered again in both the second and third years and two in their third and fourth years. *Cynoglossum officinale* is not, therefore, strictly monocarpic.

8. Reproduction

(a) *Floral biology* — *C. officinale* flowers are perfect (Taylor and MacBryde 1977) and seed production occurs via autogamy. No insect pollinators are required. No reports of outcrossing or vivipary were found in the literature.

(b) *Seed production and dispersal* — Although the fruit of *C. officinale* usually consists of 4 nutlets, Boorman and Fuller (1984) reported an average of 2.75 seeds per flower. While most *C. officinale* plants have one or two stems, Boorman and Fuller (1984) found up to 8 stems per plant; a single stem could produce up to 300 seeds. Estimates of total seed number per plant range from 50 to 800 (Van Leeuwen and Van Breemen 1980) to more than 2000 (Boorman and Fuller 1984). Dickerson and Fay (1982) found seed production per plant to vary between 314 and 674. Boorman and Fuller (1984) found that half the seed collected from wild *C. officinale* plants weighed between 21 and 35 mg compared to 31–40 mg for seed from cultivated plants. Van Leeuwen and Van Breemen (1980) reported seed weight of wild plants to be 20 mg. Fruits collected from the interior of B.C. averaged 27 mg; seed (without fruit coat) weight averaged 15.3 mg (Authors, unpubl. obs.). Embryo and endosperm development in *C. officinale* and related species are described in Tokc (1976).

Cynoglossum officinale seeds are dispersed slowly over time by attaching to animal wool, hair and fur (Van Leeuwen and Van Breeman 1980; Lhotska 1982). Boorman and Fuller (1984) found that more than 75% of seeds fell within a 0.12-m radius of the mother plant; the greatest recorded dispersal distance was 1.4 m. Similarly, Van Leeuwen and Van Breemen (1980) found dispersal distances of *C. officinale* seeds to be less than 5 m. Long-distance dispersal of *C. officinale* occurs when seeds attach to animals. Lhotska (1982) suggested that the specific gravity of *C. officinale* seeds is too high for long distance dispersal by floating on water. Dispersal via streams and irrigation ditches is, therefore, likely to be insignificant.

(c) *Viability of seeds and germination* — The viability of freshly-harvested *C. officinale* seeds exceeds 90% (Boorman and Fuller

1984). In the Netherlands, viable seeds were found to occur almost entirely within the first 1 cm of soil; viable seeds did not occur deeper than 5 cm (Van Breemen 1984). Lhotska (1982) reported that, in Czechoslovakia, *C. officinale* seeds retain germinative capacity for 2–3 yr. Excised embryos from 3- to 6-yr-old seeds exhibited abnormal seed-lobe enlargement, and seldom produced a secondary radicle.

Newly ripened seeds of *C. officinale* exhibit innate dormancy (Lhotska 1982; Boorman and Fuller 1984; Roberts and Boddrell 1984; Van Breemen 1984). Based upon seedling emergence, Roberts and Boddrell (1984) suggested that *C. officinale* seeds remain ungerminated throughout the fall and winter and germinate uniformly in the spring. In the field, dormancy release presumably requires vernalization. Under laboratory conditions, moist stratification released seed dormancy; 6–12 wk of moist chilling at 0–10°C was the most effective dormancy-releasing treatment (Van Breemen 1984). Seed burial depth, ambient temperature and moisture, soil fertility and light have been shown to affect seed germination in *C. officinale*. Maximum percentage germination, approximately 48% at 53 d after sowing, occurs at 1-cm soil depth; seeds buried 5 cm deep germinate but do not emerge. Seeds on the soil surface desiccate and do not germinate (Van Breemen 1984). Low (0–10°C, 12% soil moisture; Van Breemen 1984) and alternating (8.5/2.5°C; Freijsen et al. 1980) temperatures stimulate *C. officinale* seed germination. The germination of seeds from some populations of *C. officinale* is somewhat inhibited by light, which may prevent surface seeds from germinating (Van Breemen 1984). Freijsen et al. (1980) reported stimulation of *C. officinale* seed germination by addition of KNO_3, $Ca(NO_3)_2$ and $NaNO_3$ to calcicolous dune sand and acid dune sand.

Cynoglossum officinale does not produce a large, persistent bank of buried seeds (Van Leeuwen and Van Breemen 1980; Boorman and Fuller 1984; Van Breemen 1984). When *C. officinale* seeds were buried in soil, none survived 1 year after burial (Van Leeuwen and Van Breemen 1980). A persistent seed bank, however, may result from seeds overwintering either on the infructescences or on the soil surface (Van Breemen and Van Leeuwen 1983). While *C. officinale* seeds germinate synchronously after winter, some temporal distribution of germination may be possible, given the continuous dissemination of seeds over time. Seeds remaining on the parent plant throughout the winter can not undergo chilling in a moist state and thus dormancy must be overcome the following year (Lhotska 1982). The depth of dormancy may, however, diminish while seeds persist on the parent plant (Lhotska 1982).

The dormancy mechanism(s) of *C. officinale* is not known. Lhotska (1982) suggested that *C. officinale* dormancy is maintained by the testa which impedes the leaching of germination inhibitors from the embryo. Under laboratory conditions, peak germination percentage was achieved when seeds with damaged testa were placed on a germination bed with the ruptured side facing down — suggesting movement of germination inhibitors out of the seed (Lhotska 1982). Conclusive evidence supporting this hypothesis has not been presented. Dickerson and Fay (1982) showed that removal of the pericarp tip and complete pericarp increased seed germination by 37 and 84%, respectively. One hour of soaking in concentrated H_2SO_4 followed by 24 h in 500 ppm GA_3 also stimulated the germination (18%) of dormant seeds (Boorman and Fuller 1984).

(d) VEGETATIVE REPRODUCTION — No vegetative reproduction has been reported for *C. officinale*.

9. Hybrids
No hybrids are reported in the literature. The autogamous nature of reproduction of *C. officinale* makes hybridization unlikely.

10. Population Dynamics
Although *C. officinale* often occurs in dense stands, Boorman and Fuller (1984) found that in the dune grasslands of England, *C. officinale* formed a low but regular proportion of the flora. The gradual increase of *C. officinale* incidence over the dune was attributed to the loss of permanent grassland, resulting in bare ground, which favors *C. officinale* establishment. Similarly, Svensson and Wigren (1982) suggested that vanishing open habitats were responsible for the decline of *C. officinale* on Swedish farmlands.

Van Breemen and Van Leeuwen (1983) monitored populations of *Cirsium vulgare* (Savi) Ten, *Echium vulgare* and *C. officinale*. After 4 yr, *C. vulgare* and *E. vulgare* populations had declined, but *C. officinale* populations remained stable. Boorman and Fuller (1984) estimated that less than 1% of shed *C. officinale* seeds survive to produce more seed. They estimated *C. officinale* mortality to be 75% from seed to seedling, 77% from seedling to vegetative rosettes and 94% from rosettes to flowering. The high seedling mortality was attributed to water deficit in the early summer months, before the development of a deep and extensive root system.

11. Response to Herbicides
Picloram, dicamba, chlorsulfuron at 0.56–1.68, 1.12 and 0.04 kg ha^{-1}, respectively (Cranston and Pethybridge 1986; Cranston and Woods 1986; in B.C.), and 2,4-D amine at 1.12 kg ha^{-1} (Dickerson and Fay 1982; in Montana, U.S.A.) control *C. officinale*. Picloram and chlorsulfuron, applied either in spring or fall, provide excellent control of this weed in B.C. (Cranston and Ralph 1983; Cranston et al. 1983). The initial early spring control with dicamba, however, disappears by midsummer as evidenced by heavy weed seedling establishment (Cranston and Ralph 1983). Although picloram has been suggested as the herbicide of choice for *C. officinale* control in B.C., its cost and strong public opposition to its use preclude its widespread application (Cranston and Pethybridge 1986). Dickerson and Fay (1982) found that seed production of second-year *C. officinale* plants, in Montana, U.S.A., was most sensitive to 2,4-D applied when the bolted plants were 28 cm tall. Chlorsulfuron gave complete control when applied any time beginning with the rosette stage until the bolted

plants had attained 28 cm height (Dickerson and Fay 1982).

12. Response to other Human Manipulations

Muenscher (1980) suggested control of *C. officinale* by cutting young rosettes below the crown with a spud or hoe in autumn or early spring, by mowing flowering stems close to ground before seeds are formed, and by plowing followed by a clean cultivated crop for 1 yr in the case of badly infected fields.

Clipping second-year *C. officinale* plants during flowering dramatically reduces seed production (Dickerson and Fay 1982). Sixty percent of plants cut 0–7 cm aboveground failed to regrow. Seed production of the plants which resumed growth (16.5 cm average height compared to 75 cm for the unclipped plants) declined to approximately 25 seeds plant^{-1} compared to 364 seeds plant^{-1} in the unclipped controls. Boorman and Fuller (1984) reported that removal of leaves from second-year *C. officinale* plants had little effect on seed production, affecting neither seed number nor seed weight.

Fertilization significantly increases *C. officinale* growth (Svensson and Wigren 1982). Four kilograms per hectare of 20:6:6 (N:P:K) fertilizer increased dry weight of first-year rosettes and second-year flowering plants growing without grass cover by over 100 and 50%, respectively. Flowers per plant increased from 3323 to 4570 with fertilization (Svensson and Wigren 1982). Nitrate addition increased germination of *C. officinale* seeds by 36–81% (Freijsen et al. 1980).

At high N levels, Verkaar et al (1986) found higher net assimilation rate in defoliated *C. officinale* plants compared to control plants. Defoliation also significantly increased the leaf weight ratio at high N level but had no significant effect at low N level. There was no effect of defoliation on specific leaf area and the leaf N content.

Interspecific competition severely reduces dry weight of first-and second-year *C. officinale* plants (Svensson and Wigren 1982).

Seeding with 1.5 kg grass seeds per 100 m^2 reduced dry weight of *C. officinale* by almost 100%. Surviving plants produced only 77 flowers per plant compared to 3323 flowers per plant in monoculture. Fertilization did not significantly increase *C. officinale* dry weight in the presence of grass competition (Svensson and Wigren 1982).

13. Response to Parasites

(a) *Insects and other nondomestic animals* — Green plants of *C. officinale* produce a distinctive odor (Gains and Swan 1972) which acts as a grazing deterrent (Knight et al. 1984). Rabbits do not graze *C. officinale*; consequently this species maintains a competitive advantage wherever rabbit grazing is heavy (Boorman and Fuller 1984). Similarily, Bocs (1983) reported that *C. officinale* leaves repel moles in gardens.

Ceutorhynchus trisignatus Gylh. (Coleopteran) feeds exclusively on *C. officinale* in Germany (Kallweit 1977). Larvae are initially present in swelling of the epidermis on the stalks. Larvae later penetrate the stalks and feed on plant pith. Eventually the larvae move through the roots and pupate in the soil. The total period spent in the host plant averages approximately 35 d. Larvae of the Curculinoid *Ceuthorrynchus crucifer* have also been reported to infest *C. officinale* in the Rhein valley of Germany (Schroder 1976).

(b) *Microorganisms and viruses* — *Botrytis cinerea* Pers. is reported to occur on *Cynoglossum* species; *Erysiphe cichoracearum* D.C. ex Merat has been recorded to infect *C. officinale* (Shaw 1973).

(c) *Higher plant parasites* — None are reported to infect *C. officinale*.

ACKNOWLEDGMENTS

The authors are grateful to curators of the herbaria listed in Section 4 for providing information on hound's-tongue distribution in Canada and to Ms. Angela Kummer for preparing the weed distribution map. This work was supported by the Jean Bostoc Memorial Grant (to MKU and MDP) and an NSERC of Canada Operating Grant (to MKU).

Alex, J. F., Cayouette, R. and Mulligan, G. A. 1980. Common and botanical names of weeds in Canada. Agriculture Canada, Ottawa, Ont. Publ. 1397. 132 pp.

Alex, J. F. and Switzer, C. M. 1976. Ontario weeds. Ont. Min. Agric. and Food, Toronto, Ont. Publ. 505. 200 pp.

Altschul, S. 1973. Drugs and foods from little-known plants. Harvard University Press, Cambridge, Mass. 366 pp.

Anomymous. 1982. Canadian climate normals, temperature and precipitation, Ontario (1951–1980). Environment Canada, Atmospheric Environment Service, Govt. of Canada. 254 pp.

Bartic, M. and Piskac, A. 1981. Veterinary toxicology, M. Bartik and A. Piskac eds., Elsevier Scientific Publ. Co., Amsterdam. 346 pp.

Bocs, A. 1983. *Cynoglossum officinale* against moles and rodents. Kerteszet es Szoleszet. **32**: 13.

Boivin, B. 1966. Enumeration des plantes du Canada. IV. Herbidées, 2 partie: Connatae Nat. Can. **93**: 989–1063.

Boorman, L. A. 1982. Some plant growth patterns in relation to the sand dune habitat. J. Ecol. **70**: 607–614.

Boorman, L. A. and Fuller, R. M. 1984. The comparative ecology of two sand dune biennials: *Lactuca virosa* L. and *Cynoglossum officinale* L. New Phytol. **96**: 609–629.

Breitung, A. J. 1957a. Plants of Waterton Lakes National Park, Alberta. Can. Field-Nat. **71**: 39–71.

Breitung, A. J. 1957b. Annonated catalogue of the vascular flora of Saskatchewan. Am. Midl. Nat. **58**: 1–72.

Britton, D. M. 1951. Cytogenetic studies on the Boraginaceae. Brittonia 7: 233–266.

Clapham, A. R., Tutin, T. G. and Warburg, E. F. 1962. Flora of the British Isles, Cambridge University Press, Cambridge, U.K. 1269 pp.

Clarke, G. C. S. 1977. The northwest European pollen flora. Part 10. Boraginaceae. Review of Palaeobotany and Palynology. **24**: 59–101.

Clark, G. H. and Fletcher, J. 1909. Farm weeds of Canada. Agriculture Canada, Ottawa, Ont. 192 pp.

Cochrane, T. S. 1975. Notes on the flora of Wisconsin — I. New and corrected distribution records of Boraginaceae. Mich. Bot. **14**: 115–123.

Cockayne, T. O. 1961. Leechdoms, wortcunning, and starcraft of early England. Vol. 1. The Holland Press, London, 405 pp.

Cranston, R. S. and Pethybridge, J. L. 1986. Report on houndstongue (*Cynoglossum officinale*) in British Columbia, B.C.M.A. & F., Internal Rept. 8 pp.

Cranston, R. S. and Ralph, D. E. 1983. Evaluation of fall applied herbicides for houndstongue (*Cynoglossum*) control on rangeland. Expert Comm. on Weeds (Western Sect.), Res. Rept. **3**: 126–127.

Cranston, R. S., Ralph, D. E. and Falsetta, P. 1983. Evaluation of spring applied herbicides for houndstongue (*Cynoglossum*) control on rangeland. Expert Comm. on Weeds (Western Section), Res. Rept. **3**: 126.

Cranston, R. S. and Woods, J. A. 1986. Picloram rates for houndstongue control. Expert Comm. on Weeds (Western Section), Res. Rept. **3**: 68–69.

Dickerson, J. R. and Fay, P. K. 1982. Biology and control of houndstongue (*Cynoglossum officinale*). Proc. Western Soc. Weed Sci. **35**: 83–85.

Fedoreev, S. A., Krivoshchekova, O. E., Denisenko, V. A., Gorovoi, P. G. and Maksimov, O. B. 1980. Quinoid pigments of far-eastern representatives of the family Boraginaceae. Chem. Nat. Comp. **15**: 546–550.

Ferron, M. and Cayouette, R. 1970. Nom des mauvaises herbes du Québec. Ministère de l'Agriculture et de la Colonisation du Québec. Publ. 288–71. 113 pp.

Frankton, C. and Mulligan, G. A. 1970. Weeds of Canada. Can. Dept. Agric., Ottawa, Ont. Publ. 948. 217 pp.

Freijsen, A. H. J. 1975. Some experiments on the calcicolous plant *Cynoglossum officinale* L. Verh. Kon. Ned. Akad. Wetensch., afd. Natuurk., II, **66**: 97–99.

Freijsen, A. H. J. 1976. Germination and culture experiments with calcicolous and acidic dune-sand substrates on the calcicolous *Cynoglossum officinale* L. Verh. Kon. Ned. Akad. Wetensch., afd. Natuurk., II, **67**: 138–140.

Freijsen, A. H. J. 1977. A comparison of the growth and calcium accumulation of *Cynoglossum officinale*, *Melandrium rubrum*, and *Hypericum perforatum* in water culture. Verh. Kon. Ned. Akad. Wetensch., afd. Natuurk., II, **69**: 134–137.

Freijsen, A. H. J., Troelstra, S. R. and Van kats, M. J. 1980. The effect of soil nitrate on the germination of *Cynoglossum officinale* and its ecological significance. Oecologica Plantarum **1**: 71–79.

Gains, X. M. and Swan, D. G. 1972. Weeds of eastern Washington and adjacent areas. Camp-Na-Bor-Lee Assoc., Inc. Publ. Davenport, Wash. 349 pp.

Greatorex, J. C. 1966. Some unusual cases of plant poisoning in animals. Vet. Rec. **78**: 725–727.

Hegi, G. 1927. Illustriert Flora von Mittel-Europa. Volume 3, J. F. Lehmanns Verlag, Munchen, Federal Republic of Germany. 607 pp.

Holmgren, P. K., Keuken, W. and Schofield, E. K. 1981. Index herbariorum. Part I. Bohn, Scheltema and Holkema, Utrecht, The Netherlands. 452 pp.

Kallweit, U. 1977. Observations on the biology of Ceutorhynchus trisignatus gyllenhal (Col. Curculionidae). Entomologische Nachrichten 21: 72-73.

Knight, A. P., Kimberling, C. V., Stermitz, F. R. and Roby, M. R. 1984. Cynoglossum officinale (Hound's-tongue) - A cause of pyrrolizidine alkaloid poisoning in horses. J. Am. Vet. Med. Assoc. 184: 647-650.

Kummer, A. P. 1951. Weed seedlings. The University of Chicago Press, Chicago, Ill. 450 pp.

Lhotska, M. 1982. Germination ecology and diasporology of the Czechoslovak representatives of the genus Cynoglossum. Folia Geobotanica et Phytotaxonomica 17: 269-293.

Lodge, W. R., Campbell, J. B., Smoliak, S. and Johnston, A. 1971. Management of the western range. Can. Dept. Agric. Publ. 1425. 34 pp.

Love, A. and Love, D. 1956. Cytotaxonomical conspectus of the Icelandic flora. Acta Hortic. Gotoburgensis 20: 65-290.

Macoun, J. 1884. Catalogue of Canadian plants. Part II - Gamopetalae. Dawson Brothers, Montreal, Que. pp. 194-394.

Mandryka, I. I. 1979. Cynoglossum officinale (Hound's tongue) as a poisonous plant. Veterinarya 9: 69-70.

McGaw, B. A. and Wooley, J. G. 1979. The biosynthesis of angelic-acid in Cynoglossum officinale. Phytochemistry 18: 1647-1649.

Muenscher, W. C. 1939. Poisonous plants of the United States. The Macmillan Co., New York. 266 pp.

Muenscher, W. C. 1980. Weeds. Cornell University Press, Ithaca, N.Y. and London, U.K. 586 pp.

Mulligan, G. A. 1957. Chromosome numbers of Canadian weeds. Can. J. Bot. 35: 779-789.

Papageorgiou, V. P. 1980. Naturally occurring isohexenylnaphthazarin pigments: a new class of drugs. Planta Medica 38: 193-203.

Resch, J. F. and Meinwald, J. 1982. A revised structure for acetylheliosupine. Phytochemistry 21: 2430-2431.

Roberts, H. A. and Boddrell, J. E. 1984. Seed survival and seasonal emergence of seedlings of some ruderal plants. J. Appl. Ecol. 21: 617-628.

Salisbury, E. 1952. Downs & Dunes. G. Bell & Sons Ltd., London, U.K. 328 pp.

Schroder, D. 1976. Investigations on the natural enemies of some Canadian weeds. Commonwealth Institute of Biological Control. Report of work carried out during 1975. pp. 36-38.

Scoggan, H. J. 1978. The flora of Canada. Part 4. Dicotyledonae (Loasaceae to Compositae). National Museum of Natural Sciences, National Museums of Canada, Ottawa, Ont. pp. 1282-1283.

Shaw, C. G. 1973. Host fungus index for the Pacific Northwest. 1. Hosts. Washington State Agric. Exp. Station Bull. 765. 121 pp.

Sikula, J. 1981. Poisonous plants. Pages 201-336 in M. Bartik and A. Piskac, eds. Veterinary toxicology. Elsevier Scientific Publ. Co., Amsterdam, Oxford, New York.

Skalinska, M., Czapik, R. and Piotrowicz, M., et al. 1959. Further studies in chromosome numbers of Polish angiosperms (Dicotyledons). Acta Soc. Bot. Poloniae 28: 487-529.

Svensson, R. and Wigren, M. 1982. Competition and nutrient experiments illustrating the decline of some village weeds. Svensk Botanisk Tidskrift. 76: 51-65.

Taylor, R. L. and MacBryde, B. 1977. Vascular plants of British Columbia: A descriptive resource inventory. Tech. Bull. No. 4. The Botanical Garden, University of British Columbia Press, Vancouver, B.C. 745 pp.

Tokc, E. 1976. Endosperm and embryo development in Cynoglossum officinale L. Acta Biologica Cracoviensia 19: 47-58.

Tutin, T. G., Heiwood, V. H., Burges, N. A., Moore, D. M., Valentine, D. H., Walters, A. M. and Webb, D. A. 1972. Flora Europaea, Volume 3: Diapensiaceae to Myoporaceae. Cambridge University Press, Cambridge, U. K. pp. 119-120.

Van Breemen, A. M. M. 1984. Comparative germination ecology of three short-lived monocarpic Boraginaceae. Acta Bot. Neerl. 33: 283-306.

Van Breemen, A. M. M. and Van Leeuwen, B. H. 1983. The seed bank of three short-lived monocarpic species, Cirsium vulgare (Compositae), Echium vulgare and Cynoglossum officinale (Boraginaceae). Acta Bot. Neerl. 32: 245-246.

Van Leeuwen, B. H. and Van Breemen, A. M. M. 1980. Similarities and differences in some biennials. Acta Bot. Neerl. 29: 209-210.

Verkaar, H. J., van der Meijden, E. and

Breebaart, L. 1986. The responses of *Cynoglossum officinale* L. and *Verbascum thapsus* L. to defoliation in relation to nitrogen supply. New Phytol. **104**: 121–129.

Watts, S. B. (ed.) 1983. Forestry handbook of British Columbia, 4th ed., For. Undergrad. Soc., Fac. For., Univ. of B.C., Vancouver, D. W. Friesen & Sons Ltd., Cloverdale, B.C. 611 pp.

THE BIOLOGY OF CANADIAN WEEDS. 88.
Elodea canadensis Michx.

K. W. SPICER and P. M. CATLING

Biosystematics Research Centre, Agriculture Canada, Ottawa, Ontario, Canada K1A 0C6. Received 15 Jan. 1987, accepted 20 Apr. 1988.

SPICER, K. W. AND CATLING P. M. 1988. The biology of Canadian weeds. 88. *Elodea canadensis* Michx. Can. J. Plant Sci. **68**: 1035–1051.

A review is provided of information on the biology of elodea (*Elodea canadensis* Michx.). This submersed aquatic develops dense beds that impede water traffic and restrict water-based recreation in the southern portions of Quebec, Ontario, in British Columbia and Alberta. In some regions the dense beds decrease the efficiency of irrigated agriculture. Native to North America, elodea has recently spread to other parts of the world including Europe, Asia, South Africa, Australia and New Zealand. Elodea is beneficial in providing food and cover for insects and other small aquatic organisms, and consequently it increases food availability for fish and ducks. It also has some potential as a source of food and forage because of its relatively high nutritional content. Elodea is most frequent in clear, nutrient-rich, alkaline water. Phosphorus levels in the plant have been utilized as an indication of trends in the nutrient enrichment of water bodies. Limiting nutrients include bicarbonate and iron. Although seed formation is rare, dispersal of overwintering dormant apices and stem fragments by water and by waterfowl can result in rapid spread. Mechanical controls, including boats equipped with cutters, are the preferred methods of managing elodea, but adequate harvesting of cut material is necessary because every fragment with an axillary or terminal bud may develop into a new plant. Biological control using nonreproductive plant-eating fish is a promising area of research.

Key words: *Elodea canadensis*, weed biology, aquatic, Canada, distribution

[La biologie des mauvaises herbes canadiennes. 88. *Elodea canadensis* Michx.]
Titre abrégé: Elodea canadensis Michx.
Cette étude monographique porte sur l'élodée du Canada (*Elodea canadensis* Michx.). Cette plante aquatique submergée forme des tapis végétaux denses qui entravent la navigation et restreignent les loisirs aquatiques dans le sud du Québec et de l'Ontario, ainsi qu'en Colombie-Britannique et en Alberta. Dans certaines régions, ces tapis denses réduisent l'efficience de l'agriculture irriguée. Originaire d'Amérique du Nord, l'élodée s'est récemment répandue dans d'autres parties du monde, notamment l'Europe, l'Asie, l'Afrique du Sud, l'Australie et la Nouvelle-Zélande. L'élodée est utile pour fournir nourriture et couvert aux insectes et à d'autres petits organismes aquatiques, et augmente du fait même la disponibilité d'aliments pour les poissons et les canards. Elle montre également certaines possibilités comme source d'aliments et de fourrage à cause de sa valeur nutritive relativement élevée. L'élodée abonde dans les eaux claires alcalines et riches en substances nutritives. Les teneurs en phosphore de la plante servent d'indicateur des tendances à l'enrichissement des plans d'eau en éléments nutritifs. Les substances nutritives restrictives comprennent le bicarbonate et le fer. Même si la grenaison est rare, la dispersion des apex dormants et des fragments de tiges par l'eau et la sauvagine peut entraîner une dissémination rapide. Les moyens de lutte mécaniques, notamment des bateaux-faucheurs, sont les méthodes préférées de

Can. J. Plant Sci. 68: 1035–1051 (Oct. 1988)

gestion de l'élodée, mais il faut bien récupérer le matériel fauché car chaque fragment muni d'un bourgeon auxiliaire ou terminal peut reformer une nouvelle plante. La lutte biologique à l'aide de poissons phytophages stériles constitue une avenue de recherche prometteuse.

Mots clés: *Elodea canadensis*, biologie des mauvaises herbes, aquatique, Canada, distribution

1. Name

Elodea canadensis Michx. (= *Anacharis canadensis* (Michx.) Planch., *Elodea planchonii* Casp.) — **elodea** (Alex et al. 1980), Canada waterweed (Marie-Victorin 1964; Brayshaw 1985), Broad waterweed (Seymour 1969); Canadian pondweed (Bursche 1968; Haslam 1978); **élodée du Canada** (Alex et al. 1980). Many texts do not give specific common names, referring to all members of the genus *Elodea* as elodea, waterweed or ditchmoss (e.g. Fernald 1950; Gleason and Cronquist 1963; Scoggan 1978). Hydrocharitaceae, frog's-bit Family, Hydrocharitacées.

2. Descripton and Account of Variation

The following description is based upon the recent monograph of the genus in Canada by Catling and Wojtas (1986). Various aspects of gross morphology are illustrated in Fig. 1.

Perennial, dioecious, submersed aquatic herbs with dichotomously branching elongate leafy shoots, mostly 2–10 dm long; roots slender, unbranched, from nodes along the stem; stems glabrous, becoming leafless toward the base, fragile and easily fragmenting; leaves of middle and upper stem branches whorled in groups of three, 6–17 mm long, 1–5 mm wide, ovate-oblong, ovate-lanceolate to linear-lanceolate, light green, thin and subflaccid to firm and dark green, finely serrulate; leaves on basal parts of stem and basal parts of lateral branches opposite in pairs or in whorls of three, more or less ovate and relatively short; leaf whorls up to 2 cm apart on lower stems, but crowded toward the growing apices and often overlapping and shingle-like; dormant overwintering apices with densely crowded and strongly cuticularized leaves developing in late summer. These dormant apices are sometimes called turions but are generally considered insufficiently differentiated for the latter terminology (e.g., Sculthorpe 1967, p. 346). Staminate spathes borne in the upper axils, 7–15 mm long, lower portion narrowed into a peduncle-like base, upper portion inflated, 6–8 mm long, 4 mm wide, with two divergent lobes at the tip; staminate flowers terminating the slender, thread-like, elongated base of the hypanthium which is 3–20 cm long; sepals three (3.0) 3.5–5.0 mm long, 2.0–2.5 mm wide, elliptic; petals three, 3.5–5.0 mm long, 0.3–0.7 mm wide, white, linear-lanceolate with a short claw; stamens (7–) 9 (–18); anthers 2.0–3.5 mm long, with the three inner filaments basally connate so that the inner anthers are raised on a stalk 1.0–1.3 mm long; pollen in tetrads 180–200 μm in diameter, irregularly reticulate with cylindrical, disc-tipped spines at the junctions of the reticulate walls; pistillate spathes (9) 10–20 (25) mm long, cylindric, somewhat enlarged at the bifid tip; pistillate flowers terminating the slender, thread-like elongated hypanthium 2–28 cm long; pistillate flowers with three sepals (1.4) 1.8–2.7 (3) mm long, approximately 1.1 mm wide, oblong-elliptic; petals three, 2.4–2.8 mm long, 1.3–1.7 mm wide, broadly elliptic-spatulate; staminodia three, approximately 0.7 mm long; style equalling the hypanthium; stigmas three, recurved, pinkish-purple or white, to 4 mm long, 2-cleft at the apex; fruit 5–6 mm long, 2–3.2 mm wide, narrowly ovoid with a 5–6 mm long beak; seeds 4–5.7 mm long, approximately 1 mm wide, narrowly cylindric, glabrous, short beaked at the apex.

Fig. 1. *Elodea canadensis* Michx. A, portion of flowering stem of staminate plant; B, portion of flowering stem of pistillate plant; C, portion of stem showing staminate spathe; D, portion of stem showing pistillate spathe; E, staminate flower; F, pistillate flower; G, portion of stem showing fruit in median leaf axil; H, seed. Drawn by Marcel Jomphe from fresh material from Westmeath and Long Point, Ontario, and Gatineau Park, Quebec. Reproduced with the permission of the National Research Council of Canada.

Elodea canadensis is best distinguished from its much rarer relatives (*E. nuttallii* (Planch.) St. John and *E. longivaginata* St. John) by its relatively wide leaves (1–5 mm wide) in whorls of three, pistillate sepals at least 1.8 mm long, and long-stalked, non—detaching staminate flowers (Catling and Wojtas 1986). *Hydrilla verticillata* (L. f.) Casp. resembles *Elodea canadensis* but differs in having conspicuously toothed leaves. *Egeria densa* Planch. is also similar but has leaves in whorls of four to five instead of three.

The reported chromosome numbers based on counts made in both North America and Europe are $2n = 24$, 48 and 96 (Winge 1923; Rohweder 1937; Darlington and Janaki-Ammal 1945; Delay 1947; Harada 1956; Löve and Löve 1961; St. John 1965; Skalinska et al. 1971; Uhríková and Feráková 1980). Cook and Urmi-König (1985) suggest a base number of $X = 8$ contrary to Löve and Löve (1961) who suggested a base number of $X = 12$.

3. Economic Importance

(a) *Detrimental* — Elodea usually develops dense submersed beds. In southern parts of Quebec, southern Ontario and British Columbia, it is a frequent contributor to the major aquatic weed problems that prevent or limit recreational use of lakes and reservoirs (Warrington, pers. commun. 1983; pers. obs.). In Alberta it has become a major weed problem associated with the early stages of thermal effluent (Beak Consultants Ltd. 1980). It has also contributed to similar aquatic weed problems in the United States and particularly in areas outside North America where it has been introduced, including Europe (Unni 1977), Australia and New Zealand (Robson 1967, 1976, 1981; Bowmer et al. 1979, 1984; Cook and Urmi-König 1985; St. John 1920; Horn 1872; Sculthorpe 1967; Simpson 1984). Although it has not yet become a major problem in Canadian irrigation systems, Elodea may impede flow of water thereby decreasing the efficiency of irrigated agriculture (Bowner et

al. 1979, 1984; Robson 1981). Since it was first observed in the Murray River in Aus—tralia in 1957—1958, it spread rapidly and has become particularily troublesome in larger supply and drainage canals (Bowmer et al. 1979). Effects on water quality have also been documented. Rørslett et al. (1985) noted that during invasion stages elodea caused a decline in water transparency, increase in pH, and major variations in total phosphorus. They predicted, however, that these effects would subside as elodea biomass declined in the postinvasion stage. More serious changes in water quality may result from careless attempts to control elodea.

(b) *Beneficial* — Important and often a codominant in aquatic ecosystems, elodea provides food and cover for aquatic insects (Krecker 1939; Berg 1941-1942; McGaha 1952; Krull 1970; Kuflikowski 1974; Soszka 1975), small fish and fish fry (Holland and Huston 1984; Prejs and Jackowska 1978). Consequently it increases food availability for gamefish and ducks. Although it has little direct value as a waterfowl foodplant (e.g. McAtee 1939; Martin and Uhler 1939; Krull 1970; Fassett 1969), and it was ranked 37th on a list of 41 species in terms of potential duck food, it was nevertheless ranked second and fourth (of 12) with respect to diversity and abundance of organisms it supported (Krull 1970). Angerilli and Beirne (1980) reported a significantly higher number of egg rafts and mosquito larvae in artificial ponds lacking aquatic plants than others where elodea and other vegetation grew.

Elodea has been used as subject material in the teaching of plant physiology and has proved to be valuable in experimental biology (Catling and Wojtas 1986). It is often used as an aquarium plant to considerable advantage due to oxygen generation. Because of its high nutritional content with crude protein levels of ca. 27%, elodea has potential value as a source of food and forage (Boyd 1968; Nelson and Palmer 1938). Wick and Sand-strom (1939) reported that oven-dried elodea contains about 4% nitrogen as compared to legume hays which contain 1.9–3.6% (Morrison 1936). Elodea has been used as an indicator of trends in nutrient enrichment (Ministry of Environment 1976) and heavy metal pollution (Mortimer 1985).

4. Geographical Distribution

Elodea canadensis is the most common and widespread native species of *Elodea* in North America. It is found in neutral and alkaline waters across most of southern Canada from Nova Scotia to British Columbia but it is rare in Saskatchewan and Alberta (Fig. 2); in the United States it extends south to Alabama and California. It is especially abundant in the Great Lakes area of Canada and the United States. *Elodea canadensis* has been introduced and is now well established in Europe (Dandy 1980; Simpson

1986), Australia and New Zealand (Cook and Urmi—König 1985; Simpson 1984; Aston 1973), southern Africa, and central and east Asia (Cook 1985).

5. Habitat

(a) *Climatic requirements* — Elodea prefers relatively cool conditions with an optimum water temperature of 10 – 25°C (Cook and Urmi-König 1985). Stuckey et al. (1978) reported the plant overwintering as a whole intact leafy plant in water temperatures ranging from 1 to 4°C with a snow cover of 12.5 cm over the ice. During the winter of this study the ambient air temperatures remained below freezing continuously from 28 Dec. to 2 Feb. and below 10°C until 22 Feb. Light intensity directly beneath the ice varied from 29 to 120 foot candles.

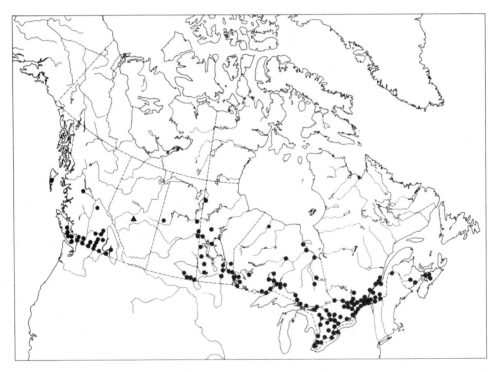

Fig. 2. Distribution of Elodea (*Elodea canadensis*) in Canada based on specimens at ACAD, ALTA, CAN, DAO, GH, MT, NY, OAC, QFA, SASK, SCS, TRT, UBC, UWO, UNB, V, WAT, and WIN (acronyms from Holmgren et al. 1981) and in the collection of the Water Management Branch, British Columbia Ministry of the Environment. The solid triangle represents a literature report from Wabamun Lake, Alberta (Beak Consultants 1980).

(b) *Substratum* — Elodea is a submersed aquatic, commonly found in water depths between 1 and 8 m (Wilson 1941; Crum and Bachmann 1973; Chapman et al. 1974; Schmid 1965) but has been recorded in water to 12 m deep in North America (Cook and Urmi-König 1985). Slow-moving rivers, lakes and ponds are preferred (Bilby 1977) with fine sediments and organic matter ranging from 10 to 25% (Misra 1938; Pearsall 1920; Chapman et al. 1974; Reed 1977; British Columbia Ministry of Environment 1981; Nichols and Mori 1971; Madsen 1982). Although tolerant of a varied water chemistry, it is most frequent in hard, nutrient-rich, alkaline waters (Moyle 1945; Seddon 1972; Spence 1967; St. John 1965; Hellquist 1972; Crow and Hellquist 1982; Reed 1977). A natural pH range of 6.5–10 has been reported. Elodea flourished in relatively clear and hard water in southern Ontario impoundments where specific conductance ranged from 224 to 300 μmhos, and Secchi disc readings ranged from 2.7 to 5.8 m (McCombie and Wile 1971). In British Columbia lakes where elodea occurs, specific conductance ranges from 22 to 472 μmhos, and Secchi disc readings ranged from 0.5 to 9.0 m (P. D. Warrington, British Columbia Ministry of Environment and Parks, pers. commun.). Some comparative studies have suggested that elodea is sometimes restricted by light (see under "10. Population Dynamics"), so that water clarity is probably an important environmental factor. Availability of nutrients including bicarbonate as a carbon source (Steemann Nielsen 1944; Allen and Spence 1981; Maberly and Spence 1983) and a supply of iron in the reduced form (Olsen 1954) are required (Bowmer et al. 1979).

Based on studies in Ohio, Stuckey (1974) suggested *Elodea canadensis* Michx. as "a probable indicator of good water quality". Davis and Brinson (1980) described it as tolerant of the changes leading to eutrophication and increased turbidity, hence it is often a component of more eutrophic systems. With increasing levels of nutrient enrichment, significant increases in phosphorus levels in elodea have been reported (Adams et al. 1971) so that the phosphorus level in the plant can and has been utilized as an indicator of trends in nutrient enrichment of water bodies (e.g. Ministry of Environment 1976). Lind and Cottam (1969) and Hellquist (1972) consider eutrophic conditions suitable for elodea and Forest (1977) considers it an indicator of eutrophic conditions. Elodea has survived in high fertility ponds with nutrient levels of 75 mg N L^{-1} and 7.5 mg P L^{-1} (Mulligan et al. 1976). In 55 British Columbia lakes where elodea occurred, total phosphorus ranged from 0.003 to 0.059 mg L^{-1} (P. D. Warrington, pers. commun.).

(c) *Communities in which the species occurs* — Elodea occurs in submersed aquatic plant communities, often dominant or co-dominating with *Ceratophyllum demersum*, *Myriophyllum spicatum*, *Myriophyllum exalbescens*, *Utricularia vulgaris* and various pondweeds (*Potamogeton* spp.). Other associated species are listed in Table 1.

6. History

Elodea canadensis Michx. is native to North America. It was first discovered in Northern Ireland in 1836 and 6 yr later it was found in Scotland (Cook and Urmi-König 1985). By 1847 it had begun spreading rapidly throughout the travelled waterways of Britain, frequently resulting in major weed problems (Robson 1967, 1976; St. John 1920; Simpson 1986). Elodea was naturalized in Europe in 1859, after having been introduced as an aquarium and pool plant in botanic gardens (Dandy 1980; Cook and Urmi-König 1985). It quickly spread over much of Europe (Dandy 1980; Dring 1981). In 1916 the first collection was made in New Zealand where it eventually became a widespread and troublesome pest (Healy and Edgar 1980). Elodea was first recorded in Australia in 1931 (Aston 1973), where it rapidly became a serious problem (Bowmer et al. 1984).

7. Growth and Development

(a) *Morphology* — Seed formation is very rare (Lawrence 1976) and is not a primary means

Table 1. Common vascular plant associates of elodea (*Elodea canadensis*) in Canada based on field work (X), other recorded associates from herbarium specimen labels (–), and literature reports (*) including Pearsall (1920), Forest (1977), Moyle (1945), Curtis (1959) and Wilson (1937, 1941).

*	*Callitriche intermedia* Hoffmann
* X	*Ceratophyllum demersum* L.
*	*Chara* sp.
–X	*Elodea nuttallii* (Planch.) St. John
* X	*Heteranthera dubia* (Jacq.) MacM.
*	*Isoetes lacustris* L.
*	*Myriophyllum alterniflorum* DC.
* X	*Myriophyllum exalbescens* Fern.
*–X	*Myriophyllum spicatum* L.
*	*Myriophyllum verticillatum* L.
* X	*Najas flexilis* (Willd.) Rostk. and Schmidt
*	*Nitella flexilis* (L.) Agardh.
–	*Nuphar* sp.
–	*Podostemon ceratophyllum* Michx.
* X	*Potamogeton amplifolius* Tuckerm.
* X	*Potamogeton crispus* L.
–	*Potamogeton filiformis* Pers.
X	*Potamogeton gramineus* L.
* X	*Potamogeton nodosus* Poir.
*	*Potamogeton obtusifolius* Mert. and Koch.
X	*Potamogeton pectinatus* L.
*–X	*Potamogeton perfoliatus* L.
*	*Potamogeton praelongus* Wulfen
*–X	*Potamogeton pusillus* L.
* X	*Potamogeton richardsonii* (Benn.) Rydb.
*	*Potamogeton robbinsii* Oakes
*	*Potamogeton strictifolius* Bennett
*	*Potamogeton zosteriformis* Fern.
–	*Potamogeton* sp.
–	*Ranunculus aquatilis* L.
*	*Ranunculus longirostis* Godron
–	*Sparganium* sp.
X	*Utricularia vulgaris* L.
*–X	*Vallisneria americana* Michx.

of reproduction. Flowering plants are rare in North American collections and males are rarer than females (Catling and Wojtas 1986). It is unusual to find both male and female plants growing together in quantity in a given population. Female plants dominated in New Zealand from an early collection date of 1916, until male plants were found in the mid 1960s (Mason 1960; Cook and Urmi-König 1985); the males are now becoming more widespread than the females. In Australia only male plants have been found in New South Wales and Victoria while elsewhere only females are reported (Cook and Urmi-König 1985). Male

plants have rarely been collected in Europe (St. John 1962, 1965; Sculthorpe 1967) other than the documented collection (Douglas 1880; Kinnear 1883) from a pond near Edinburgh, Scotland, where they persisted until 1903 (Cook and Urmi-König 1985). When both sexes are in close proximity seed production occurs, but no detailed information on early development was found. The study by Wylie (1904) of floral development and fertilization apparently refers to *Elodea nuttallii* rather than *Elodea canadensis*, because he describes male flowers detaching. Other developmental studies have involved effects of the environment on established plants (e.g. Dale 1957; Lawrence 1976).

Because of a low fiber content, elodea decomposes rapidly when it dies back. Ninety-five percent decomposes in 47–57 d, this being the fastest rate of decomposition reported for submersed vascular plants (Stephenson et al. 1980).

(b) *Perennation* — Some elodea plants survive throughout the winter in ice-covered ponds (Evermann and Clark 1920; Soszka 1975; Allen 1973; Dale 1956; Stuckey et al. 1978; Marchand 1985). Leafy intact plants have been observed on the bottom of Shawnigan Lake, British Columbia, in February when the surface water temperature was 0°C (P. D. Warrington, pers. commun.). Overwinter survival may be the rule rather than the exception. New growth develops from winter-dormant apices in the spring. These dormant apices are axillary terminal buds with dense clusters of leaves which have a relatively high starch content and are more cuticularized than the normal foliage leaves (Sculthorpe 1967). Dormant apices (Catling and Wojtas 1986, Fig. 12) are produced in large numbers in the autumn with the approach of cold weather. Up to 5000 have been recovered from 1 m^2 of sediment (Bowmer et al. 1984). They remain dormant on the bottom sediment during the winter (Sculthorpe 1967; Nichols and Shaw 1986; Haag and Gorham 1979).

(c) *Physiological data* — A prolonged period of higher temperatures is not necessary before germination of winter buds can be induced (Dale 1957; Sculthorpe 1967; Allen 1973); 3 d at 18°C has resulted in germination and growth (Allen 1973; Dale 1956; Sculthorpe 1967). The buds sink when growth begins. These phenomena are indicative of reduced photosynthesis (Dale 1956; Sculthorpe 1967).

Elodea evidently acts as a nutrient sink, obtaining a large proportion of its elements from the sediment (Wetzel 1975). Supporting this, Rawlence and Whitton (1977) and Chittendon et al. (1976) found that levels of iron and manganese are significantly higher in weed-free areas than beneath beds of aquatic macrophytes and Boyd (1971) indicated that these are the most abundant micronutrients within the plant. Mayes et al. (1977) showed that *E. canadensis* and other vascular hydrophytes play a role in the recycling of phosphorus and trace metals. These substances are moved from the sediment into the plants, and into the water when the plants decay, where they can become part of the aquatic food web (Nichols and Shaw 1986). Although some researchers conclude that there is a significant release of phosphorus from live plants into the water (DeMarte and Hartman 1974; Schults and Malueg 1971), others deny it (Barko and Smart 1980; Welsh and Denny 1979). Carpenter and Gasith (1978) reported that even when plants are injured by harvesting, little phosphorus or nitrogen escapes into the water. Rørslett et al. (1985) found little evidence for phosphorus excretion from young elodea stands, but they reported significant release of phosphorus from 3- to 4-yr-old stands. After elodea was well established in Lake Steinsfjord, Norway, the internal phosphorus loading due to elodea tissue-phosphorus release was 45% of the annual external loading.

Production and consumption of oxygen by elodea may have a substantial effect on the environment. A concentration of 8 ppm O_2 above a 1-m-tall plant bed increased to 9 ppm in the upper parts but was reduced to 0.4 ppm within 5 cm of the substrate, while outside the bed the oxygen was 5 ppm (Buscemi 1958). Preference may be for lower light intensities and cool temperatures (Sheldon and Boylen 1977; Peverly 1979) but relatively high levels of light are tolerated. The optimum is about 16 000 lx, and the net photosynthesis reaches light saturation between 18 000 and 38 000 lx (ca. 15–30% full sunlight) (Cook and Urmi-König 1985). Buscemi (1958) and Kunii (1982) reported that elodea concentrates photosynthetic tissue near the water surface and Hough (1979) and DeGroote and Kennedy (1977) indicate that light saturation occurred between 15% and full sunlight.

Plants of elodea that survive the winter (see under "(b) perennation") under ice and snow cover probably continue to photosynthesize based on measurements of oxygen uptake and release (Marchand 1985).

(d) *Phenology* — Actual flowering time is possibly related to photoperiod and age of the plant (Sculthorpe 1967). Light intensity may influence the abundance of flowers produced (Levitt 1969).

Temperature affects the rate of maturity; populations subjected to warmer temperatures reach maturity earlier (Sculthorpe 1967; Allen 1973). In Canada, flowering generally occurs from the middle of June through to the end of September (based on available herbarium data).

8. Reproduction

(a) *Floral biology* — Both pistillate and staminate flowers are lifted to the surface of the water by elongating hypanthia originating from axils of leaves, sometimes many maturing intermittently from a single plant. In pistillate flowers the hypanthium rises above the water before the weight of the flower causes it to fall on its side on the surface. The three bifid stigmas protrude heavily beyond the perianth creating a depression on the surface film (St. John 1920). When staminate flowers are similarly raised by the hypanthium the dehiscence of anthers results in the scattering of pollen grains over the surface of the water. The pollen grains are covered with small cylindrical spines tipped with a disc. Air trapped by the spines allows them to float freely, eventually to slip into the depression about a stigma where pollination takes place (St. John 1920). When wave action submerges pistillate flowers in the presence of floating pollen grains, an air bubble is formed around the flowers, and when they resurface the pollen may be observed clinging to the stigmas.

(b) *Seed production and dispersal* — Seed production appears to be relatively unimportant in the regenerative process and is indeed rare. Seeds are transported by action of wind and wave (St. John 1965).

(c) *Viability of seeds and germination* — No information is available.

(d) *Vegetative reproduction* — Overwintering buds and brittle slender branches with stems rarely greater than a few millimetres in diameter and various lengths are easily detached by wave action, currents, animals and water traffic and are swept away to assist in the establishment of new colonies (Adams et al. 1971). New roots appear at nodes of the drifting fragmented plants and growth commences readily, thus conferring a competitive advantage over annual aquatics (Bowmer et al. 1984). Stem fragments are also dispersed by waterfowl, accidentally, or when the birds gather nesting material. The rapid spread of male elodea in England, prior to the advent of female plants, has been attributed to effective dispersal by birds (Ridley 1930). It has been shown that plants can remain alive out of water for at least 23 h. A duck flying at 40 m.p.h. could readily disperse a plant 920 miles (Ridley 1930). Dispersal overland by small recreational boats as a consequence of plants catching in propellors or on ropes (pers. obs.) is an important dispersal mechanism. This is well documented by the British Columbia Ministry of Environment in 1979–1981 boater "quarantine" checks on British Columbia highways. "Rafts" of drifting *Elodea canadensis* can settle over

rooted aquatics, the elodea plants extending roots through the mat of rooted vegetation into the substrate (Haag and Gorham 1977), resulting in a light deficiency for the plants below.

9. Hybrids

In their revision of the genus *Elodea*, Cook and Urmi-König (1985) state their lack of success in crossing *Elodea* with *Egeria*, *Hydrilla* and *Lagarosiphon*. They refer to Ernst-Schwarzenbach (1945) attempting crossing experiments between *E. canadensis* × *Lagarosiphon muscoides* Harvey (*sub L. capensis*), *E. canadensis* × *Hydrilla verticillata* (female parent cited first). These attempts were also unsuccessful.

Ernst-Schwarzenbach (1951, 1953) published results of other investigations in which the cross between *E. callitrichoides* and *E. canadensis* proved to be unviable after 29 attempts. She obtained viable seed, however, from intraspecific crosses and crosses between *E. canadensis* and *E. nuttallii*. The latter cross was also accomplished by Cook and Urmi-König (1988) but the ripe seed was lost before harvesting. It is their opinion that *E. canadensis* and *E. nuttallii* crosses occur naturally.

Ernst-Schwarzenbach (1953) reported that the progeny of *E. canadensis* × *E. nuttallii* and the reciprocal cross were fertile. Backcrosses were also executed. Unfortunately, voucher material has not been found and little is known of the morphology of these hybrids. The chromosome number $2n = 48$ was reported which she considered the normal diploid number.

10. Population Dynamics

Elodea canadensis has a much discussed history of spectacular population explosion and often a just as remarkable sudden decline. Many theories have been projected as to possible causes of rapid growth and virtual disappearance. Brown et al. (1974) stated that in New Zealand it displaced native species in the Rotorua Lakes but in turn was displaced by *Lagarosiphon* as the dominant species. The suggested cause for the decline was reduction in water transparency which might well be related to photosynthetic capacity. They showed that under laboratory conditions *Elodea* is a relatively light-demanding species compared with *Lagarosiphon* (see also under "5. Habitat").

Bowmer et al. (1984) refer to the light-demanding factor quoting other supporting reports (Haslam 1978; Brown et al. 1974; Brown 1975), and suggesting that self-shading by dense macrophyte beds must be restrictive to growth in many situations. They further suggested that photosynthesis may be limited by changes in the carbonate-bicarbonate balance and by carbon dioxide availability.

Sculthorpe (1967) refutes claims that the exclusive vegetative mode of reproduction and consequent lack of genetic variability lead to dramatic decline of populations. Rather, the facts support a specific relationship between *Elodea canadensis* and the concentrations of relative proportions of certain nutrients. Sculthorpe (1967) postulates: "Perhaps in each habitat, as the supply of some limiting nutrient(s) was steadily depleted, the weed declined until an equilibrium was reached between the nutrient demand of a finite population frequency and the total amount or constituent proportions of the nutrient supply made continuously available by leaching or silt deposition." The studies of Chapman et al. (1974), Boyd (1971), Chittenden et al. (1976) and Schelske (1962) concluded that iron is the most important micronutrient limiting *Elodea* growth. In a study of Wabamun Lake in Alberta, Beak Consultants Ltd.'s "postulated pattern of *Elodea* colonization" showed that new colonies are initiated in areas where sediment is abundant in iron. Here it thrives reaching nuisance proportions, lasting from 1 yr to as much as 9 yr depending on iron reserves and replenishment. Haag (1979) estimated the growing season net productivity to be between 160–203 g m^{-2} at this location which he considered to be at the northern edge of its range. Rapid decline occurs when sediment iron availability falls below a critical level. Populations may be decimated or merely reduced in proportion to the iron yet available (Chittenden et al. 1976; Bowmer et al. 1979). In the Wabamun Lake study the iron source was apparently related to a thermal discharge from a generating station.

11. Response to chemicals

Cooke et al. (1986) have pointed out that there is abundant evidence that herbicidal chemicals have been associated with major adverse impacts on lake systems, and the use of herbicides cannot be considered "restorative". Among the problems are sudden nutrient release due to decomposition of the killed aquatic weeds, depletion of dissolved oxygen due to plant decay, death of other aquatic organisms, rapid regrowth or replacement of weeds following treatment due to nutrient release resulting from treatment, and finally unresolved issues pertaining to possible mutagenic and carcinogenic effects on humans. Although many of the aquatic weed problems in lakes may be addressed with other procedures (see under "12. Response to other manipulations"), in certain situations the use of herbicides may be regarded as appropriate. Robson (1981) suggests that localized chemical control to combat the explosive spread of an invading weed which has no natural enemies or other factors limiting its growth may be the only option available.

In most Canadian provinces a license or permit is required by anyone proposing to control aquatic weeds with herbicides.

The organic divalent cationic salts of herbicides such as paraquat and diquat readily dissolve in water controlling submergent and free-floating aquatic plants while contributing a low level of toxicity to aquatic fauna (Ashton and Crafts 1973; Calderbank 1968; Dodge 1971). Paraquat is most effective during the late spring and summer growth phase (Best and Wittenboer 1978). Simazine is also contained in some of the registered herbicides. Most of the brands available in Canada do not contain 2, 4–D, and indications are that elodea can be controlled adequately without it. In Ontario, the province where most of the weed problems involving elodea occur, none of the 10 products registered for control of "Canada Waterweed" contains 2, 4–D. Lower temperatures slow the action of herbicides and thus require a longer period to achieve control (Mackenzie 1971). The herbicides are non-toxic to fish at concentrations well above those necessary for elodea control. Invertebrates (dragonfly and mayfly nymphs, caddisfly larvae and others) are reported not to suffer excessively from poisoning by these chemicals (Mackenzie 1971). A field application to control elodea reduced habitat and caused migration of organisms to shoreline vegetation resulting in a decline in numbers of four genera of snails and one amphipod (Hilsenhoff 1966).

Utilization of aquatic herbicides may be relatively safe when precautions are taken, and ecological effects are well documented (Cassie 1966; Newman and Way 1966; Newman 1968; Wilson and Bond 1969; Walsh et al. 1971; Way et al. 1971), but even specific herbicides such as dalapon are capable of causing drastic ecological changes within a drainage area if used extensively (Brooker and Edwards 1975; Newbold 1975). Control and local eradication of elodea in Australian irrigation systems has been achieved with the soil-residual herbicides chlorfenac and dichlobenil (Bowmer et al. 1979). Several other herbicides have also been used and a variety of techniques have been employed such as slow-release formulations and flushing of concentrated chemicals through the ditches. The herbicides dalapon, diquat and cyanatryn were used to control aquatic growth in only 13 km of British waterways in 1976 (Murphy and Eaton 1980), whereas mechanical control measures were favored and employed very extensively.

Unanticipated problems with herbicides may include replacement of elodea by an equally troublesome herbicide-resistant species, as occurred in Australia and New Zealand where lagarosiphon or nitella became a problem following the control of elodea (Bowmer et al. 1979).

Mortimer (1985) noted that elodea plants absorb mercury and other metals through the leaves and stems, transporting them to the roots where they are added to the sediment concentration when the roots die. Therefore disturbance of sediments below elodea in mercury-enriched waters may have undesirable consequences.

12. Response to Other Manipulations

It is important to realize that an aquatic weed problem is not just a matter of getting rid of the weeds; rather it may sometimes be advantageously approached with the idea of eliminating the cause of the excess weed growth. Restoration and management of aquatic systems is a branch of science that has grown very rapidly over the past 20 yr. A useful and detailed summary is provided by Cooke et al. (1986). Manipulations used to control aquatic weeds include water-level drawdown, sediment covers, mechanical harvesting and biological control (the latter discussed under "13. Response to parasites".).

The success of elodea in propagating vegetatively from fragmented plants, in fact the principal method of regeneration, may result in mechanical control being less effective than control by chemical herbicides. However, environmental safety concerns have increased pressure directed toward use of mechanical methods for submerged aquatic weed control (Johnson 1977; Mossier 1968; Murphy and Eaton 1980). Since every fragment of elodea stem which has an axillary bud (ca. every 10 cm) may develop into a new plant (Adams et al. 1971), it is imperative that adequate harvesting of cut material is part of mechanical control procedures. In some provinces, failure to remove cut vegetation from the water can result in prosecution (e.g. Ontario Water Resources Act). In some cases the cut plants may be dumped directly on the adjacent shore where they decay over a period of weeds and months while the nutrients run back into the system creating new water quality problems.

Mechanical harvesting techniques have been applied effectively in various parts of Ontario where elodea is one of the species contributing to the weed problems (pers.

obs.). Extensive information on mechanical harvesting is available in Cooke et al. (1986).

Since the reproductive parts of elodea are above the sediment, drying out as a consequence of water-level drawdown can also be effective. Irrigation channels in Australia are drained and the plants are exposed to either high summer temperatures or winter frosts (Bowmer et al. 1979, 1984).

Other potentially effective manipulations include sediment covers (see Cooke et al. 1986) and plant competition. With regard to the latter, current work in Holland involves testing the use of plants with floating leaves which will reduce growth of submerged weeds without impeding water flow (Robson 1981). Effectiveness of control by shading by trees is also under study in England (Dawson 1978).

13. Response to Parasites

The fungi *Chytridium elodeae* Dangeard and *Varicosporium elodeae* Kegel have been reported on elodea (Cook and Urmi-König 1985). Zettler and Freeman (1972) refer to elodea as being remarkably free of disease, an important factor relating to its persistance.

Destruction of elodea by insects was observed in Mikotajskie Lake, Masurian Lake district, Poland (Urban 1975). Mining or tunneling insects such as *Glyptotendipes gripekoveni* Kieff. actively bored out tunnels in stems while others such as *Cricotopus sylvestris* F. and *Endochironomus tendens* F. used the ready-made burrows. *Endochironomus dispar* Meig. also used hollows in the plant stems to hide and construct fixed cases (i.e. retreats). A total of 10 insect taxa were present in stems but none in leaves. Loss in stem tissue due to tunneling was 1.2% of net weight of stems. In the Masurian Lakeland of Poland, the common freshwater snails (*Gastropoda, Bithynia tentaculata* and *Valvata piscinalis* f. *antiqua*) were frequently observed feeding on the leaves of elodea (Soszka 1975). Most of these organisms (if not all) live on a variety of aquatic plants and no organisms have been identified as potentially useful biocontrol agents with the exception of fish.

When total weed control is the objective of management, as may be the case in irrigation systems, then biological control using a plant-eating fish, the grass carp (*Ctenopharyngodon idella* Val.), may be an attractive alternative (Anonymous 1987; Fowler and Robson 1978). Introduction of grass carp into the United States produced considerable controversy (Cassani 1981) but this fish has nevertheless proved to be effective in the control of aquatic weeds and has now been employed in many countries. Uneasiness regarding potential reproduction and ecological consequences of grass carp introduction lead to consideration of an alternative sterile triploid grass carp and a sterile triploid intergeneric hybrid (female grass carp crossed with a male bighead carp (*Hypophalmichthys nobilis* Rich.)). Various studies have indicated that elodea is a preferred food of triploid grass carp (Alabaster and Stott 1967; Cross 1969; Fowler and Robson 1978). The fish have proved to be especially effective in control of elodea because they consume the parts that regenerate, the stem fragments and the dormant overwintering apices (Fowler and Robson 1978). They are less effective in controlling certain other macrophyte species that regenerate from tubers buried in the sediment. The use of grass carp may result in the replacement of elodea by an unpalatable aquatic weed such as *Myriophyllum spicatum* L., especially if the fish are understocked (Fowler and Robson 1978). A more detailed account of the advantages and problems of macrophyte control with grass carp is provided by Cooke et al. (1986).

ACKNOWLEDGMENTS

Dr. P. D. Warrington of the Water Management Branch, British Columbia Ministry of Environment, provided ecological information on *Elodea canadensis* in British Columbia, and permitted us to examine the very extensive collections made by the Water Management Branch. These contributed substantially to the morphological and phytogeographic parts of this study. Curators of 18 Canadian herbaria (see Fig. 2 caption) made specimens available. Dr. J. Waddington of the Agriculture

Canada Research Station at Swift Current drew our attention to occurrences of *Elodea canadensis* in Saskatchewan. Mr. Mark Barlow of Agriculture Canada Pesticides Directorate provided information on herbicides. Mr. Marcel Jomphe of the Biosystematics Research Centre of Agriculture Canada kindly prepared the illustration and permission for the use of this illustration was granted by the National Research Council of Canada.

Adams, F. S., MacKenzie, D. R., Cole, H., Jr. and Price, M. W. 1971. The influence of nutrient pollution levels upon element constitution and morphology of *Elodea canadensis*. Enviro. Poll. **1**: 285–298.

Alabaster, J. S. and Stott, B. 1967. Grass Carp (*Ctenopharyngodon idella* Val.) for aquatic weed control. Europ. Weed Res. Council Symposium papers. pp. 123–126.

Alex, J. F., Cayouette, R. and Mulligan, G. A. 1980. Common and botanical names of weeds in Canada. Agriculture Canada, Ottawa, Ont. Publ. 1397, 132 pp.

Allen, E. D. 1973. An ecophysiological study of the effects of thermal discharges on the submerged macrophytes of Wabamun Lake, M.Sc. Thesis, University of Alberta, Edmonton, Alta. 88 pp.

Allen, E. D. and Spence, D. H. N. 1981. The differential ability of aquatic plants to utilize the inorganic carbon supply in fresh water. New Phytol. **87**: 269–284.

Angerilli, N. and Beirne, B. 1980. Influences of aquatic plants on colonization of artificial ponds by mosquitos and their insect preditors. Can. Entomol. **112**: 793–796.

Anonymous 1987. Triploid grass carp, a new weapon in the aquatic weed battle. Water Hauler's Bull. **27**: 1–2.

Ashton, F. M. and Crafts, A. S. 1973. Mode of action of herbicides. John Wiley and Sons, London, U.K.

Aston, H. I. 1973. Aquatic plants of Australia. Melbourne University Press, Melbourne, Australia. pp. 216–217.

Barko, J. W. and Smart, R. M. 1980. Mobilization of sediment phosphorus by submergent freshwater macrophytes. Freshw. Biol. **10**: 229–239.

Beak Consultants Ltd. 1980. The effects of thermal discharges on the aquatic plants and other biota of Wabaman Lake, Alberta. Prepared for Calgary Power, Vol. 1, pp. 1–380, vol. 2, figures and maps.

Berg, K. 1941–1942. Contributions to the biology of the aquatic moth *Acentropus niveus* (Oliv.) Videnskabelige Meddelelser, pp. 60–139.

Best, P. H. and Wittenboer, J. P. v. d. 1978. Effects of paraquat on growth and photosynthesis of *Ceratophyllum demersum* and *Elodea canadensis*. Proc. EWRS 5th Symposium on Aquatic Weeds. pp. 157–162.

Bilby, R. 1977. Effects of a spate on the macrophyte vegetation of a stream pool. Hydrobiologia vol. 56, 2, pp. 109–112.

Bowmer, K. H., Sainty, G. R., Smith, G. and Shaw, K. 1979. Management of *Elodea* in Australian Irrigation Systems. J. Aquat. Plant Man. **17**: 4–12.

Bowmer, K. H., Mitchell, D. S. and Short, D. L. 1984. Biology of *Elodea canadensis* Michx. and its management in Australian irrigation systems. Aquat. Bot. **18**(1984): 231–238.

Boyd, C. E. 1968. Fresh-water plants: a potential source of protein. Econ. Bot. **22**: 359—368.

Boyd, C. E. 1971. Vascular aquatic plants for mineral nutrient removal from polluted waters. Econ. Bot. **24**(1): 95–103.

Brayshaw, T. C. 1985. Pondweeds and Bur-reeds, and their relatives, of British Columbia. British Columbia Provincial Museum Occasional Paper No. 26.

British Columbia Ministry of the Environment 1981. A summary of biological research on Eurasian Milfoil in British Columbia. 11 Inf. Bull. XI, Aquat. Pl. Manage. Prog. Victoria, B.C. 18 pp.

Brooker, M. A. and Edwards, R. W. 1975. Aquatic herbicides and the control of water weeds. Water Res. **9**: 1–16.

Brown, J. M. A. 1975. Ecology of macrophytes. Pages 244–262 *in* V. H. Jolly and J. M. A. Brown, eds., New Zealand Lakes. Aukland University Press, Aukland, New Zealand.

Brown, J. M. A., Dromgoole, F. I., Towsey, M. W. and Browse, J. 1974. Photosynthesis and photorespiration in aquatic macrophytes. Bull. R. Soc. N.Z. **12**: 243–249.

Bursche, E. M. 1968. A handbook of water plants. [English translation by H. Czech, 1981.] Frederick Warne and Co., London, U.K.

Buscemi, P. A. 1958. Littoral oxygen depletion produced by a cover of *Elodea canadensis*. Oikos **9**(2): 239–245.

Calderbank, A. 1968. The bipyridylium herbicides. Adv. Pest Contr. Res. **8**: 127–235.

Carpenter, S. R. and Gasith, A. 1978. Mechanical cutting of submerged macrophytes: immediate effects on littoral water chemistry and metabolism. Wat. Res. **12**: 55–57.

Cassini, J. R. 1981. Feeding behaviour of underyearling hybrids of the grass carp, *Ctenopharyngodon idella* female and the bighead, *Hypophthalmicthys nobilis* male on selected species of aquatic plants. J. Fish Biol. **18**: 127–133.

Cassie, V. 1966. Effects of spraying phytoplankton in Lake Rotorua. Proceedings Rotorua Seminar on water weeds sponsored by University Ext. Serv. University Aukland, Aukland, New Zealand, 15 Oct. pp. 31–40.

Catling, P. M. and Wojtas, W. 1986. The water-weeds (*Elodea* and *Egeria*, Hydrocharitaceae) in Canada. Can. J. Bot. **64**: 1525–1541.

Chapman, V. J., Brown, J. M. A., Hill, C. F. and Carr, J. L. 1974. Biology of excessive weed growth in the hydro-electric lakes of the Waikato River, New Zealand. Hydrobiology **44**(4): 349–363.

Chittenden, E. T., Childs, C. W., and Smidt, R. E. 1976. Sediments of Lake Rotoroa, South Island, New Zealand. N.Z. J. Mar. Freshw. Res. **10**(1): 61–76.

Cooke, G. D., Welch, E. B., Peterson, S. A. and Newroth, P. R. 1986. Lake and reservoir restoration. Butterworths, Boston, Mass.

Cook, C. D. K. 1985. Range extensions of aquatic vascular plant species. Aquat. Plant Man. **23**: 1–6.

Cook, C. D. K. and Urmi-König, K. 1985. A revision of the genus *Elodea* (Hydrocharitaceae). Aquatic Bot. **21**: 111–156.

Cross, D. G. 1969. Aquatic weed control using Grass Carp. J. Fish Biol. **1**: 27–30.

Crow, G.E. and Hellquist, C.B. 1982. Aquatic vascular plants of New England: Part 4. Juncaginaceae, Scheuchzeriaceae, Butomaceae, Hydrocharitaceal. New Hampshire Agricultural Experiment Station Bull. **520**: 1–20.

Crum, G. H. and Bachmann, R. W. 1973. Submersed aquatic macrophytes of the Iowa Great Lakes Region. Iowa St. J. Res. **48**: 147–173.

Curtis, J. T. 1959. The vegetation of Wisconsin. University of Wisconsin Press, Madison, Wisc. 657 pp.

Dale, H. M. 1956. 11. Morphological effects of various temperatures, light intensities and photoperiods in experimental studies on the morphological development of *Elodea canadensis* Michx. Ph.D. Thesis, University of Toronto, Toronto, Ont.

Dale, H. M. 1957. Developmental studies of *Elodea canadensis* Michx. Experimental studies on morphological effects of darkness. Can. J. Bot. **35**: 51–64.

Dandy, J. E. 1980. *Elodea* Michx. Pages 4–5 *in* T. G. Tutin et al. eds. Flora Europea 5. Cambridge University Press, Cambridge, U.K. 452 pp.

Darlington, C. D. and Janaki-Ammal, E. K. 1945. Chromosome atlas of cultivated plants. G. Allen and Unwin. London, U.K.

Davis, G. J. and Brinson, M. M. 1980. Responses of submersed vascular plant communities to environmental changes. U.S. Dep. of the Interior, FWS/OBS -79/33: 1–70.

Dawson, F. H. 1978. Aquatic plant management in semi-natural streams; The role of marginal vegetation. J. Environ Man. **6**: 213–221.

Delay, C. 1947. Recherches sur la structure des noyaux quiescents chez les Phanérogames. Rev. Cytol. Cytophysiol. Veg. **9**(1–4): 169–222: **10**(1–4): 103–229.

DeGroote, D. and Kennedy, R. A. 1977. Phytosynthesis in *Elodea canadensis* 4 carbon acid synthesis. Pl. Physiol. **59**: 1133–1135.

DeMarte, J. A. and Hartman, R. T. 1974. Studies on absorption of 32P, 50Fe and 45Ca by watermilfoil (*Myriophyllum exalbescens*). Ecology **55**: 188–194.

Dodge, A. D. 1971. The mode of action of the bipyridylium herbicides, paraquat and diquat. Endeavour 30(110): 130–135.

Douglas, D. 1880. Notes on the water thyme (*Anacharis alsinastrum*). Bab. Sci. Gossip **16**: 227–229.

Dring, P. 1981. Live submerged aquatic vegetation in nest construction by tree swallows. Inland Bird Banding, Vol. 53, No. 2, Summer 1981.

Ernst-Schwarzenbach, M. 1945. Kreuzungsversuche an Hydrocharitaceen. Archiv Julius Klaus-Stiftung Vererbungsforschung, sozialanthropologie. Rassenhygiene (Zurich), erganzungsband zu Band, **20**: 22–41.

Ernst-Schwarzenbach, M. 1951. Die Ursachen der verminderten Fertilitat von *Elodea* Arten. Planta **39**: 542–569.

Ernst-Schwarzenbach, M. 1953. Zur Kompatibilitat von Art-und Gattungs-Bastardierung bei Hydrocharitaceen Oesterr. Bot. Z. **100**: 403–423.

Evermann, B. W. and Clark, H. W. 1920. Lake Maxinkuckee: A physical and biological survey. Vol. 11. The Dep. of Conservation. Indianapolis, Ind. 512 pp.

Fassett, N. 1969. A manual of aquatic plants. University of Wisconsin Press, Madison, Wisc. 405pp.

Fernald, M. L. 1950. Gray's manual of botany. American Book Company, New York. 1632 pp.

Forest, H. S. 1977. Study of submersed aquatic vascular plants in northern glacial lakes, New York state, U.S.A. Folia Geobot. Phytotax. **12**: 329–341.

Fowler, M. C. and Robson, T. O. 1978. The effects of the food preferences and stocking rates of Grass Carp (*Ctenopharyngodon idella* Val.) on mixed plant communities. Aquatic Bot. **5**: 261–276.

Gleason, H. A. and Cronquist, A. 1963. Manual of the vascular plants of northeastern United States and adjacent Canada. D. Van Nostrand Co., Princeton, New Jersey. 810 pp.

Haag, R. W. 1979. The ecological significance of dormancy in some rooted aquatic plants. J. Ecol. **67**: 727–738.

Haag, R. W. and Gorham, P. R. 1977. Effects of thermal effluent on standing crop and net production of *Elodea canadensis* and other submerged macrophytes in Lake Wabamun, Alberta. J. Appl. Ecol. **14**: 835–851.

Haag, R. W. and Gorham, P. R. 1979. Community dynamics of submerged macrophytes in Lake Wabamun, Alberta. Summary report to Alberta Environment.

Harada, P. 1956. Cytological studies in Helobiac. 1. Cytologia **21**: 306–328.

Haslam, S. M. 1978. River plants: the macrophyte vegetation of water courses. Cambridge University Press, Cambridge, U.K. 396 pp.

Healy, A. J. and Edgar, E. 1980. Flora of New Zealand. 111. Adventive cyperaceous, petalous and spatheceous monocotyledons. Hasselberg, Wellington, New Zealand. pp. 25–29.

Hellquist, C. B. 1972. Range extension of vascular plants in New England. Rhodora **74**: 131–141.

Hilsenhoff, W. 1966. Effect of diquat on aquatic insects and related animals. J. Econ. Entomol. **59**: 1520.

Holland, L. E. and Huston, M. L. 1984. Relationship of young-of-the-year northern pike to aquatic vegetation types in backwaters of the upper Mississippi River. N. A. J. Fish Manage. **4**: 514–522.

Holmgren, P. K., Keuken, W. and Schofield, E. K. 1981. Index herbariorum. W. Junk, Boston, Mass.

Horn, P. 1872. Veber die sogenannte "Wasserpest" (*Elodea canadensis* Casp.). Arch. Pharmac. **199** (2 Reihe 149): Ser 3 Bot. pp. 51–68.

Hough, R. A. 1979. Photosynthesis, respiration and organic carbon release in *Elodea canadensis*. Aquatic. Bot. **7**: 1–12.

Johnson, R. E. 1977. Effects of mechanical cutting on submerged vegetation in a Louisiana Lake. State of Louisiana Dep. of Wildlife and Fisheries. 33 pp.

Kinnear, W. T. 1883. Note on the continued flowering of male flowers. Natl. Field Club, Edinburgh **1**: 81.

Krecker, F. H. 1939. A comparative study of the animal populations of certain submerged aquatic plants. Ecology **20**: 553–562.

Krull, J. N. 1970. Aquatic plant macroinvertibrate associations and waterfowl. J. Wildl. Man. **34**: 707–718.

Kuflikowski, T. 1974. The phytophilous fauna of the dam reservoir at Goczalkowice, Poland. Acta Hydrobiol. **16**: 189–207.

Kunii, H. 1982. Life cycle and growth of *Potamogeton crispus* L. in shallow pond. Ojageike. Bot. Mag. (Tokyo) **95**: 109–124.

Lawrence, D. K. 1976. Morphological variation of Elodea in western Massachusetts: field and laboratory studies. Rhodora **78**: 739–749.

Levitt, J. 1969. Introduction to plant physiology. C. V. Mosby Co., St. Louis, Mo. 304 pp.

Lind, C. T. and Cottam, G. 1969. The submersed aquatics of University Bay: a study in eutrophication. Am. Midl. Nat. **81**: 353–369.

Löve, A. and Löve, D. 1961. Chromosome numbers of central and northwest European plant species. Opera Bot. **5**: 1–581.

Maberly, S. C. and Spence, D. H. H. 1983. Photosynthetic inorganic carbon use by freshwater plants. J. Ecol. **71**: 705–724.

Mackenzie, J. W. 1971. Chemical control of *Elodea densa* Planch. and other submerged aquatic plants as influenced by several environmental factors. Ph.D. Thesis. Oregon State University Corvallis, Oreg. 79 pp.

Madsen, J. D. 1982. The aquatic macrophyte communities of two trout streams in Wisconsin. M. Sci. Thesis, University Wisconsin, Madison, Wisc. 108 pp.

Marchand, P. J. 1985. Oxygen evolution by *Elodea canadensis* under ice and snow cover: A case for winter photosynthesis in subnivean vascular plants. Aquilo Ser. Bot. **23**: 57–61.

Marie-Victorin, F. 1964. Flore Laurentienne. Les presses de l'université de Montréal, Montréal, Qué. 924 pp.

Martin, A. C. and Uhler, F. M. 1939. Food of game ducks in the United States and Canada, U.S.D.A. Tech. Bull. **634**: 1–156.

Mason, R. 1960. Three water weeds of the family Hydrocharitaceae in New Zealand. N.Z. J. Sci. **3**: 382–395.

Mayes, R. A., McIntosh, A. W. and Anderson, V. L. 1977. Uptake of cadmium and lead by a rooted aquatic macrophyte (*Elodea canadensis*). Ecology **58**: 1176–1180.

McAtee, W. L. 1939. Wildfowl food plants, their value, propagation and management. Collegiate Press Inc., Ames, Iowa. 141 pp.

McCombie, A. M. and Wile, I. 1971. Ecology of aquatic vascular plants in southern Ontario impoundments. Weed Sci. **19**: 225–228.

McGaha, Y. J. 1952. The limnological relations of insects to certain aquatic flowering plants. Trans. Am. Microsc. Soc. **71**: 355–381.

Ministry of the Environment 1976. The Kawartha Lakes water management study — water quality assessment (1972–1976). Ontario Ministry of Natural Resources, Toronto, Ont. 185 pp.

Misra, R. D. 1938. The distribution of aquatic plants in the English lakes. J. Ecol. **26**: 411–452.

Morrison, F. B. 1936. Feeds and feeding. 20th ed. Morrison Publ. Co., Ithaca, New York.

Mortimer, D. C. 1985. Freshwater aquatic macrophytes as heavy metal monitors — the Ottawa River experience. Environ. Monitoring Assess. 5(1985): 311–323.

Mossier, J. N. 1968. Response of submerged macrophytes to harvesting. M. Sc. Thesis. University of Wisconsin, Madison, Wisc. 71 pp.

Moyle, J. B. 1945. Some chemical factors influencing the distribution of aquatic plants in Minnesota. Am. Midl. Nat. **34**: 402–421.

Mulligan, H. F., Baranowski, A. and Johnson, R. 1976. Nitrogen and phosphorus fertilization of aquatic vascular plants and algae in replicated ponds. 1. Initial response to fertilization. Hydrobiologia **48**: 109–116.

Murphy, K. J. and Eaton, J. W. 1980. A survey of aquatic weed growth and control in the canals and river navigations of the British Waterways Board. Proc. 1980. British Crop Protection Conf. British Crop Protection Council Croydon, Surrey, U.K. pp. 707–713.

Nelson, W. J. and Palmer, L. S. 1938. Nutritive value and general chemical composition of *Elodea, Myriophyllum, Vallisneria,* and other aquatic plants. Minn. Agric. Exp. Sta. Tech. Bull. **136**: 1–34.

Newbold, C. 1975. Herbicides in aquatic systems. Biol. Conserv. **7**: 97–118.

Newman, J. F. 1968. The ecological effects of paraquat and diquat when used to control aquatic weeds. Weed Abstr. **17**: 361(2211).

Newman, J. F. and Way, J. M. 1966. Some ecological observations in the use of paraquat and diquat as aquatic herbicides. Proceedings British Weed Control Conference. pp. 582–585.

Nichols, S. A. and Mori, S. 1971. The littoral macrophyte vegetation of Lake Wingra. Trans. Wisc. Acad. Sci. **59**: 107–119.

Nichols, S. A. and Shaw, B. H. 1986. Ecological life histories of the three aquatic nuisance

plants, *Myriophyllum spicatum, Potomogeton crispus* and *Elodea canadensis.* Hydrobiology **131**: 3–21.

Olsen, C. 1954. Hvilke botingelser ma vaere opfyldte, for at *Helodea canadensis* kan opna den optimale udvikling, der er arsay til dens massevise optraeden i naturen. Bot. Tidsskr. **51**: 272–273.

Pearsall, W. H. 1920. The aquatic vegetation of English lakes. J. Ecol. **8**: 163–199.

Peverly, J. H. 1979. Elemental distribution and macrophyte growth downstream from an organic soil. Aquatic Bot. **7**: 319–338.

Prejs, A. and Jackowska, H. 1978. Lake macrophytes as a food of Roach (*Rutilus rutilus* L.) and Rudd (*Scardinius erythrophthalmus* L.) 1. Species composition and dominance relations in the lake and food. Ekol. Polska 26(3): 429–438.

Rawlence, D. J. and Whitton, J. S. 1977. Elements in aquatic macrophytes, water, plankton and sediments surveyed in three North Island lakes. N.Z. J. Marine Freshw. Res. **11**(1): 73–93.

Reed, C. F. 1977. History and distribution of Eurasian water milfoil in the United States and Canada. Phytologia **36**: 416–436.

Ridley, H. N. 1930. The dispersal of plants throughout the world. L. Reeve & Co. Ashford, Kent, U.K. 744 pp.

Robson, T. A. 1967. A survey of the problem of aquatic weed control in England and Wales. Agricultural Research Council (Britain), Weed Res. Org. Tech. Rep. **5**: 1–27.

Robson, T. A. 1976. Aquatic plants in Britain — their occurence and significance as weeds. British Crop Protection Council. Monograph **1**: 1–6.

Robson, T. A. 1981. Aquatic weed research in Britain. J. Aquatic Plant Man. **19**: 47–48.

Rohweder, H. 1937. Oersuch zur Erfassung der mengenmassigen Bedeckung der Rarss and Zingst mit polyploiden Pflanzen. Ein Beitrag zur Bedeutung der Polyploidie bei der Eroberung Ineuer Lebensraume. Planta 27(4): 501–549.

Rørslett, B., Berge, D. and Johnson, S. W. 1985. Mass invasion of *Elodea canadensis* in a mesotrophic, south Norwegian Lake — impact on water quality. Verh. Internat. Verein. Limnol. **22**: 2920–2926.

Schelske, C. L. 1962. Iron organic matter and other factors limiting primary productivity in a marl lake. Science **136**: 45–46.

Schmid, W. P. 1965. Distribution of aquatic vegetation as measured by line intercept with SCUBA. Ecology **46**: 816–823.

Schults, D. W. and Malueg, K. W. 1971. Uptake of radiophosphorus by rooted aquatic plants. In

Proc. 3rd Nat. Symp. Radio-ecol. Oak Ridge, Tenn. pp. 417–424.

Scoggan, H. J. 1978. The flora of Canada. Part 2. Pteridophyta, Gymnospermae, Monocotyledoneae. National Museum of Natural Sciences, publications in botany **7**(2): 93–545.

Sculthorpe, C. D. 1967. The biology of aquatic vascular plants. Edward Arnold, London, U.K. pp. 1–610.

Seddon, B. 1972. Aquatic macrophytes as limnological indicators. Freshw. Biol. **2**: 107–130.

Seymour, F. C. 1969. The flora of New England. Charles E. Tuttle Co., Rutland, Vermont. 596 pp.

Sheldon, R. B. and Boylen, C. W. 1977. Maximum depth inhabited by aquatic vascular plants. Am. Midl. Nat. **97**: 248–254.

Simpson, D. A. 1984. A short history of the introduction and spread of *Elodea* Michx. in the British Isles. Watsonia **15**: 1–9.

Simpson, D. A. 1986. Taxonomy of *Elodea* Michx. in the British Isles. Watsonia **16**: 1–14.

Skalinska, M., Jankun, A. and Wislo, H. 1971. Studies in chromosome numbers of Polish angiosperms. 8th contrib. Acta Biol. Cracov. Ser. Bot. **14**: 55–102.

Soszka, G. J. 1975. The invertebrates on submerged macrophytes in three Masurian lakes. Ekol. Polska.

Spence, D. H. N. 1967. Factors controlling the distribution of freshwater macrophytes with particular reference to the lochs of Scotland. J. Ecol. **55**: 147–170.

Steeman Nielsen, E. 1944. Dependence of freshwater plants on quantity of carbon dioxide and hydrogen ion concentration. Illustrated through experimental investigations. Dan. Bot. Ark. **11**: 1–25.

Stephenson, M., Turner, G., Pope, P., Colt, J., Knight, A. and Tchobanglous, G. 1980. The use and potential of aquatic species for waste-water treatment. Appendix A: The environmental requirements of aquatic plants. California State Water Resources Control Board, Sacramento, Calif. Publ. 65, pp. 1–654.

Stuckey, R. L. 1974. Submersed aquatic vascular plants as indicators of environmental quality. Ohio Biological Survey, Information Circular No. 8, pp. 27–30.

Stuckey, R. L., Wehrmeister, J. R. and Bartolotta, R. J. 1978. Submersed aquatic vascular plants in ice-covered ponds of central Ohio. Rhodora **80**: 575–579.

St. John, H. 1920. The genus *Elodea* in New England. Rhodora **22**(254): 17–29.

St. John, H. 1962. Monograph of the genus *Elodea*: Part 1, Western N.A. Research Studies, Washington State University, Pullman, Wash. Vol. 30, No. 2.

St. John, H. 1965. Monograph of the genus *Elodea*: Part 4, Species of Eastern and Central N.A. and summary. Rhodora **67**: 1–180.

Unni, K. S. 1977. The distribution and production of macrophytes in Lunz Mittersee and Lunz Untersee. Hydrobiology **56**(1): 89–94.

Urban, E. 1975. The mining fauna in four macrophyte species in Mikotajskie Lake. Ekologia Polska.

Uhríková, A. and Feráková, V. 1980. *In* A. Löve, ed. Chromosome number reports LXIX. Taxon **29**: 727.

Walsh, G. E., Miller, C. W. and Heitmuller, P. L. 1971. Uptake and effects of dichlobenil in a small pond. Bull. Environ. Contam. Toxicol. **6**: 279–288.

Way, J. M., Newman, J. F., Moore, N. W. and Knaggs, F. W. 1971. Some ecological effects of the use of paraquat for the control of weeds in small lakes. J. Appl. Ecol. **8**: 509–532.

Welsh, R. P. H. and Denny, P. 1979. The translocation of phosphorus-32 in 2 submerged aquatic angiosperm species. New Phytol. **82**: 645–656.

Wetzel, R. G. 1975. Limnology. W. B. Saunders Co., Toronto, Ont. 743 pp.

Wick, A. N. and Sandstrom, W. M. 1939. 11. The nitrogen distribution of *Elodea canadensis*. *In* Nutritive value and chemical composition of certain fresh-water plants of Minnesota. University of Minnesota Agric. Exp. Sta. Tech. Bull. **136**: 35–42.

Wilson, D. C. and Bond, C. E. 1969. The effects of the herbicides diquat and dichlobenil on pond invertebrates. 1. Acute toxicity. Trans. Am. Fish Soc. **98**: 438–442.

Wilson, L. R. 1937. A quantitative and ecological study of the larger plants of Sweeney Lake, Oneida County, Wisconsin. Bull. Torrey Bot. Club **64**: 199–208.

Wilson, L. R. 1941. The larger vegetation of Trout Lake, Vilas County, Wisconsin. Trans. Wis. Acad. Sci. **33**: 135–146.

Winge, O. 1923. On sex chromosomes, sex determination and preponderance of females in some dioecious plants. C. R. Trav. Lab. Carlsberg. **15**(5): 1–25.

Wylie, R. 1904. The morphology of *Elodea canadensis*. Bot. Gaz. (Chicago) **37**: 1–22.

Zettler, F. W. and Freeman, T. E. 1972. Plant pathogens as biocontrols of aquatic weeds. Ann. Rev. Phytopathol. **10**: 455–470.

THE BIOLOGY OF CANADIAN WEEDS. 89.
Carduus nutans L. and *Carduus acanthoides* L.

A. M. DESROCHERS[1,3], J. F. BAIN[1], and S. I. WARWICK[2]

[1]*Department of Plant Sciences, Macdonald College, Ste. Anne de Bellevue, Quebec, Canada H9X 1C0; and* [2]*Biosystematics Research Centre, Agriculture Canada, Ottawa, Ontario, Canada K1A 0C6. Received 22 Dec. 1987, accepted 26 Apr. 1988.*

DESROCHERS, A. M., BAIN, J. F. AND WARWICK, S. I. 1988. The Biology of Canadian weeds. 89. *Carduus nutans* L. and *Carduus acanthoides* L. Can. J. Plant Sci. **68**: 1053–1068.

Carduus nutans L. and *C. acanthoides* L. are introduced weeds, primarily of roadsides, fields and pasturelands. Both species occur in eastern and western Canada with *C. nutans* more common than *C. acanthoides* in western Canada. High seed production and germination rate on open soil contribute to the success of the species as weeds, as do the spiny leaves and stems which deter grazing by animals. Mowing or the application of hormone-like herbicides are both effective means of control. Biological control methods have also been used for both species, but have been most successful in the control of *C. nutans*.

Key words: Musk thistle, nodding thistle, plumeless thistle, *Carduus* spp.

[La biologie des mauvaises herbes canadiennes. 89. *Carduus nutans* L. et *Carduus acanthoides* L.]
Titre abrégé: *Carduus nutans* L. et *Carduus acanthoides* L.
Carduus nutans L. et *C. acanthoides* L. sont des mauvaises herbes introduites qui colonisent principalement les bords des routes, les champs et les pâturages. Les deux espèces s'observent dans l'Est et dans l'Ouest du Canada, *C. nutans* étant plus commune que *C. acanthoides* dans l'Ouest. Une production élevée de semences et un taux élevé de germination sur sol découvert contribuent au succès de ces espèces, ainsi d'ailleurs que les feuilles et les tiges épineuses qui les protègent des animaux brouteurs. La tonte et l'épandage d'herbicides de type hormonal sont deux moyens efficaces de lutte contre cette mauvaise herbe. Des méthodes de lutte biologique ont également été employées contre les deux espèces mais elles se sont surtout avérées efficaces pour la lutte contre *C. nutans*.

Mots clés: Chardon penché, chardon épineux, *Carduus* spp.

1. Name
I. *Carduus nutans* L. — **nodding thistle**, musk thistle, **chardon penché** (Ferron and Cayouette 1964; Alex et al. 1980).
II. *Carduus acanthoides* L. — **plumeless thistle, chardon épineux** (Ferron and Cayouette 1964; Alex et al. 1980). Compositae, Asteraceae, composite family, composées.

2. Description and Account of Variation
I. *Carduus nutans* is an herbaceous biennial or occasionally winter annual, or annual, 20–200 cm tall, with a long fleshy taproot. Stem erect, single or up to seven, usually much branched, with spiny wings. Basal rosette well developed, leaves elliptic to lanceolate, 15–30 cm long, glabrous to densely

---

[3]Present address (A.M.D.): Department of Botany, University of British Columbia, Vancouver, British Columbia, Canada V6T 2B1.

Can. J. Plant Sci. 68: 1053–1068 (Oct. 1988)

pubescent, pinnately lobed, each lobe ending in a spine. Cauline leaves are similar but smaller, simple, alternate, decurrent. Heads few, terminal, solitary on branches or branchlets. Peduncle naked or with a few bracts 1.5–5(7) cm below the head, or those bearing later maturing flower heads often leafy below. Head 1.5–4.5(7) cm in diameter, usually nodding; phyllaries numerous, glabrous to densely pubescent, imbricate, 9–27 mm long, reflexed or spreading, tapering to a spine (1)2–4(15) mm long, middle row phyllaries with a constriction at or slightly below the mid-point, portion above constriction wider than or equal to the lower portion. Flower perfect, tubular, pink to purple or occasionally white; corolla tube 10–14 mm long, 1.4 mm wide. Anthers 5–8 mm, filaments woolly. Achenes 3.5–4 mm long, brown at maturity, outer achenes curved.

Chromosome number $2n = 16$ has been reported from Canadian material (Mulligan and Frankton 1954; Warwick and Bain 1987; Desrochers et al. 1988) and from European material (Bolkhovskikh et al. 1969).

II. *Carduus acanthoides* is an annual, winter annual or biennial, 20–150 cm tall, glabrate or with scattered hairs on stems and leaves. Stem is branched above with spiny wings extending to the flower heads. Basal rosette well developed, leaves narrowly elliptic or oblong, deeply pinnatifid, the lobes 1–3 pointed, each point ending in a spine. Flower heads terminal, solitary or clustered on young branches, 1.2–1.6 cm in diameter, erect; phyllaries numerous, erect to spreading or reflexed, tapering to a spine 1.5–2 mm long, inner phyllaries unarmed. Flower perfect, tubular, usually purple but some white or cream-colored; tube 7–9 mm long, 1–1.2 mm wide. Anthers 5–7 mm long, filaments woolly. Achenes 2.5–3 mm long, light brown at maturity.

Chromosome number $2n = 22$ from both European material (Bolkhovskikh et al. 1969) and Canadian material (review in Moore and Frankton 1974; Warwick and Bain 1987).

Figure 1 illustrates typical flowering plants of both *C. nutans* and *C. acanthoides*.

Carduus species can be easily distinguished from species of *Cirsium* by their filamentous rather than feathery pappus and, to a lesser degree, by their winged stems (Frankton and Mulligan 1970). *Carduus nutans, C. acanthoides* and *C. crispus* L. (the third *Carduus* species found in Canada) can be distinguished from one another using the characters listed in Table 1.

Two subspecies of *C. nutans* occur in Canada: ssp. *nutans* and ssp. *leiophyllus* (Petr.) Stoj. and Stef. *Carduus nutans* ssp. *nutans* is distinguished from ssp. *leiophyllus* by its moderate to dense pubescence on leaves and phyllaries, by its generally smaller head diameter (1.5–3.5 cm in ssp. *nutans* and 1.8–4.5(7) in ssp. *leiophyllus*) and by the shape of its phyllary. In ssp. *nutans* the lower portion of the phyllary is more or less equal to the upper portion while in ssp. *leiophyllus* the lower portion is distinctly narrower than the upper portion. The two subspecies can also be separated chemically. *Carduus nutans* ssp. *nutans* is characterized by the presence of luteolin 7-0-rutinoside and ssp. *leiophyllus* by apigenin 7-0-glucoside and luteolin 7-0-diglucoside. Genetically the two subspecies are closely related with a mean genetic identity of 0.93 based on allozyme studies of nine enzyme systems (Desrochers et al. 1988). A third taxon within *C. nutans s.l.*, *C. nutans* ssp. *macrocephalus* (Desf.) Nyman (*sensu* McGregor 1986) or *C. macrocephalus* Desf. (*sensu* McCarty 1978) has been reported from the United States but not from Canada. This taxon differs from ssp. *nutans* in having a wider head diameter and phyllaries and differs from ssp. *leiophyllus* by being pubescent on leaves and phyllaries and by having phyllaries with the lower portion more or less equal to the upper portion. Finally, McCarty (1985) and McGregor (pers. commun.) report a population from Alexis Creek, British Columbia, whose individuals are not referable to any of the taxa mentioned above. Further study may reveal that these individuals are indeed members of a distinct taxon.

Fig. 1. *Carduus nutans* and *Carduus acanthoides* A–C. *Carduus nutans*. A. Habit. B. Achene. C. Head (of ssp. *leiophyllus*). D–E. *Carduus acanthoides*. D. Habit. E. Head.

Table 1. Distinguishing characters for the three *Carduus* species in Canada†

Character	C. nutans	C. acanthoides	C. crispus
Heads	Solitary	Solitary on mature branches; clustered on young branches	Usually clustered
Head diameter	2–7 cm	1–3 cm	1–3 cm
Head height	2–4 cm	1.8–2.5 cm	1.5–1.8 cm
Phyllaries	Reflexed or spreading	Erect to spreading	Spreading to ascending
Phyllary width	2–8 mm	1–1.5 mm	1 mm
Phyllary constriction	Sub-median	None	None
Peduncle	Naked	Spiny-winged	Sometimes naked for 1–2 cm below head
Leaf vesture	Pubescent or glabrous	Pubescent to tomentose on lower surface	Densely tomentose on underside
Leaf margin	Deeply pinnatifid	Deeply pinnatifid	Sub-entire to shallowly pinnatifid
Chromosome no.	$n = 8$	$n = 11$	$n = 8$

†Based on data from Mulligan and Moore (1961); Moore and Frankton (1974); and those of the authors.

In Europe, several more taxa (both specific and infraspecific) have been described in the large-headed thistle group (= the *nutans* group) (Kazmi 1964; Franco 1976).

3. Economic Importance

(a) *Detrimental* — Infestations of both species may reduce productivity of pastureland and rangeland, by suppressing growth of desirable vegetation and preventing livestock from eating plants growing in the vicinity of the thistle. *Carduus nutans* is most widespread in Saskatchewan, Quebec (the area of Lac St-Jean) and in southern Ontario, while *C. acanthoides* is only widespread in the latter region. In 1970, prior to the establishment of the biological control program, densities up to 150 000 plants per hectare of *C. nutans* were reported from pastureland in Saskatchewan (Harris 1984). Harris (unpubl.) reported that in 1974, *C. nutans* covered an area of 30 000 km^2 in Saskatchewan. In Quebec, Letendre et al. (1976) reported infestations covering 325 km^2 in the Lac St-Jean area. *Carduus acanthoides* stands of 90 000 plants per hectare were observed in permanent pasture in southern Ontario and parts of Quebec (Harris 1984).

Since the introduction of *C. nutans* in the United States, the species has spread within the northeastern states as well as to the midwestern and western states. Dunn (1976) reported that more than one county in 10 across the United States is infested by the weed, and that infestations are increasing in size and severity. In the United States *C. acanthoides* is a problem in Virginia, and parts of the midwest (McCarty 1985).

(b) *Beneficial* — Neither species is particularly beneficial. Moore and Frankton (1974) reported that the pappus of *C. nutans* has been used to make paper. The inflorescence of *C. nutans* is showy and attractive but it is apparently seldom grown for its esthetic value.

(c) *Legislation* — Nodding thistle (*Carduus nutans*) is classified as a noxious weed in Ontario under the Weed Control Act, in

Quebec under the Agricultural Abuses Act, in B.C. (Cariboo and Kootenay Boundary regions) under the Weed Control Act (1983), in Saskatchewan under the 1984 Weed Control Act, and as restricted under the 1979 Weed Control Act of Alberta. Both nodding thistle (*C. nutans*) and plumeless thistle (*C. acanthoides*) are listed on the 1970 Noxious Weeds Act of Manitoba.

4. Geographical Distribution

I. *Carduus nutans* — With respect to its Canadian distribution, *C. nutans* occurs in all provinces, except in Prince Edward Island (Fig. 2). *Carduus nutans* ssp. *nutans* reaches its greatest abundance in southern Ontario and occurs in isolated populations in the provinces east of Ontario. *Carduus nutans* ssp. *leiophyllus* is more common in the provinces west of Ontario, especially in Saskatchewan between Regina and Saskatoon. Populations of ssp. *leiophyllus* occur occasionally in Quebec and Ontario. According to Dunn (1976) *C. nutans* is distributed across the United States. Although the distributions of the subspecies were not presented in the latter paper, McGregor (1986) reported that, in the area covered by the Flora of the Great Plains, only ssp. *leiophyllus* and ssp. *macrocephalus* are present. Presumably, the distribution of ssp. *nutans* in the United States is similar to its distribution in Canada where it is mainly distributed in the eastern part of the country. The native distribution of *C. nutans* covers Europe, western Siberia, Asia Minor, and North Africa (Moore and Frankton 1974). The species has also been introduced to Argentina (Mulligan and Frankton 1954), Australia and New Zealand (Doing et al. 1969; Medd 1981).

II. *Carduus acanthoides* — *C. acanthoides* is found in British Columbia, Ontario, Quebec and Nova Scotia (Fig. 3). It is most common in Ontario where it reaches its greatest abundance in Bruce and Grey counties. In British Columbia, Quebec, and Nova Scotia the species occurs in only a few localities. Economically important infestations of *C. acanthoides* are more extensive in the United States than in Canada, especially in the northeastern states (Hensley 1973; Johnson 1974; Batra 1978). The native distribution of the species covers Europe and Asia (Moore and Frankton 1974).

5. Habitat

(a) *Climatic requirements* — Both species occur in temperate regions. The wide geographical range covered by *C. nutans* and *C. acanthoides* in North America suggests that both taxa do not have specific climatic requirements. Both are frequently found on grasslands in many parts of North America (Moore and Frankton 1974; Harris 1984). Harris (1984) reported that in the Canadian prairies these two taxa grow most commonly in places that are covered by snow drifts in winter such as gullies, fence lines, brush patches, and the lee side of stone piles. *Carduus nutans* may grow at altitudes from sea level to 2438 m and produce viable seeds with as little as 25 cm of annual rainfall (Hull and Evans 1973).

(b) *Substratum* — Batra (1978) reported that in the northeastern United States the economic infestations of *C. nutans* and *C. acanthoides* were associated with fertile soils formed over limestone. Conversely, on poorer mica-shist derived soils, the two species did not form any serious infestation. Similarly, in Ohio, Stuckey and Forsyth (1971) found that populations of *C. nutans* generally occurred where limestone or dolomite bedrock is less than 2 m below the surface. In the Canadian prairies, Harris (unpubl.) observed that neither calcium and magnesium levels nor pH influenced the distribution of nodding thistles. He reported mean percentages of 1.91 and 0.96 for calcium and magnesium, respectively. The pH values ranged between 6.0 and 8.9 and included most soil types in the southern part of the Canadian prairies. Most of the stands examined were on soils with high sand content. One stand was on heavy clay soil and the occurrence of *C. nutans* was attributed to lower interspecific competition. In Australia

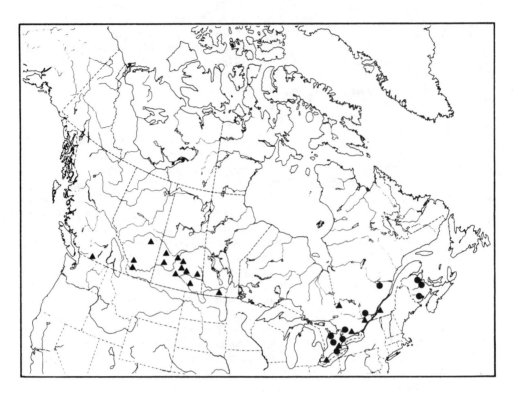

Fig. 2. Distribution of *Carduus nutans* L. in Canada. ▲ , *Carduus nutans* ssp. *nutans*. ● , *C. nutans* ssp. *leiophyllus* (based on data from herbarium specimens from ACAD, ALTA, CAN, DAO, DAS, MIN, MTMG, QFA, QK, QUE, RMS, SASK, SFS, TRT, TRTE, UAC, UBC, UNB, USAS, WIN; abbreviations follow Holmgren et al. (1981).

the distribution of *C. nutans* is restricted mainly by its low tolerance of extremes in soil water content, nutrient deficient or acid soils, and competition from other plant species (Doing et al. 1969). Specific information for *C. acanthoides* is lacking, but since *C. nutans* and *C. acanthoides* are often present in the same populations, the conditions described for *C. nutans* probably apply for *C. acanthoides* as well. However, Moore and Mulligan (1956) did note, in the Grey County region of Ontario, *C. acanthoides* tended to occupy drier, better-drained sites than did *C. nutans* within the same pasture.

(c) *Communities in which the species occur* — Both *C. nutans* and *C. acanthoides* occur in well-drained pastures, along roadsides, in waste places, and frequently in the vicinity of gravel pits (Mulligan and Frankton 1954; Harris 1984). On the Canadian prairies, *C. nutans* and *C. acanthoides* generally occur in the mid-grass prairie vegetation zone (Harris 1984). In Saskatchewan, *C. nutans* is frequently found in the Spear Grass-Wheat Grass zone (*Stipa spartea* Trn.–*Agropyron dasytachyum* (Hook.) Scrb.) and in Alberta it is mostly found in the Fescue Grass zone (*Festuca scabrella* Torr.) and occasionally in the Spear Grass-Wheat Grass zone (Strong and Leggat 1981). Some of the plant species commonly associated with *C. nutans* and *C. acanthoides* in Canada are listed in Table 2. The density of *C. nutans* varies from dense to sparse depending on the level of interspecific competition. Both *C. nutans* and *C.*

Table 2. A list of the plant species frequently found with *Carduus nutans* and *C. acanthoides* in Canada†

Achillea millefolium L.
Agrostis stolonifera L.
Agropyron repens (L.) Beauv.
A. cristatum (L.) Gaertn.
Ambrosia artemisiifolia L.
Artemisia absinthium L.
A. biennis Willd.
Axyris amaranthoides L.
Bromus inermis L.
Chrysanthemum leucanthemum L.
Cichorium intybus L.
Cirsium arvense (L.) Scop.
C. vulgare (Savi) Tenore
Cynoglossum officinale L.
Dactylis glomerata L.
Daucus carota L.
Echium vulgare L.
Elaeagnus commutata Bernh.
Erigeron strigosus Muhl.
Grindelia squarrosa (Pursh) Dunal
Hieracium florentinum All.
Hypericum perforatum L.
Lactuca pulchella (Pursh) DC.
Linaria vulgaris Hill
Melilotus alba Desr.
M. officinalis (L.) Desr.
Panicum capillare L.
Phleum pratense L.
Poa compressa L.
Polygonum convolvulus L.
Potentilla recta L.
P. argentea L.
Rudbeckia hirta L.
Rumex acetosella L.
R. crispus L.
Salvia sylvestris L.
Silene cucubalus Wibel.
Stipa comata Trin. & Rupr.
Taraxacum officinale Weber
Thlaspi arvense L.
Tragopogon pratensis L.
T. dubius Scop.
Trifolium pratense L.
T. agrarium L.
Verbascum thapsus L.

†Data from Harris (1984), Moore and Mulligan (1956, 1964), Mulligan and Frankton (1954), and observations of the authors.

acanthoides do not tolerate competition and are mainly found in open areas (see Section 10).

6. History

Carduus nutans — The earliest known localities of *C. nutans* in North America are from the east. The introductions are thought to result from seed brought to North America in ships' ballasts. The species was first collected at Harrisburg, Pennsylvania in 1853 and in Canada at Chatham, New Brunswick in 1871. Studies of the earliest known collections of *C. nutans* in North America indicate several independent introductions (Stuckey and Forsyth 1971). The first herbarium records of *C. nutans* in the Canadian provinces were: Que.–1903; Ont.–1920; Sask.–1941; BC–1944; Nfld.–1949; Man.–1950; Alta.–1976. Following its introduction at Renown, Saskatchewan, *C. nutans* was collected between Regina and Saskatoon along the railway line which, according to Mulligan and Frankton (1954), provided a dispersal route. They suggest *C. nutans* was introduced into Saskatchewan in rape seed of Argentine origin. However, Harris (unpubl.) speculated that the introduction of the species in the provinces of Alberta, Saskatchewan, and Manitoba was probably as a contaminant of farm seed or hay originating from the United States.

Carduus acanthoides — Based on data from herbarium specimens, it appears that *C. acanthoides* was also first introduced on the east coast of North America. The earliest collection was from the United States, at Camden, N.J. in 1879. The first record of the species in Canada is from Peel Co., Ont. in 1907 (Rousseau and Raymond (1945) as cited by Moore and Frankton (1974)). By 1950, the species had been collected in seven counties in Ont.: Berks, Russell, Centre, Hasting, Lanark, Bruce, and Grey. In Ontario, *C. acanthoides* is now most abundant in Grey and Bruce Counties (Moore and Frankton 1974). The species also occurs in Nova Scotia (Yarmouth) and in Huntingdon and Missisquoi Counties, Quebec (Moore and Frankton 1974).

7. Growth and Development.

(a) *Morphology* — *Carduus nutans* and *C. acanthoides* both colonize pastures and waste areas through seed dispersal rather than by

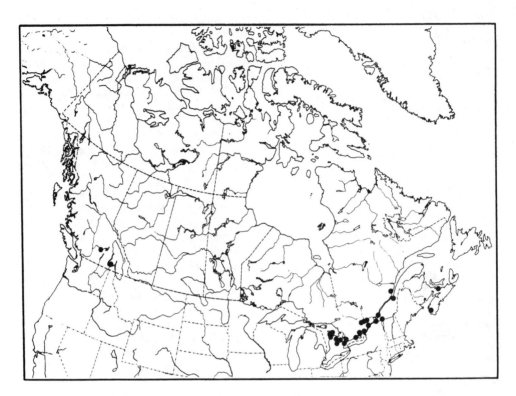

Fig. 3. Distribution of *Carduus acanthoides* L. in Canada. (based on data from herbarium specimens from ACAD, DAO, GH, MTMG, QFA, QK, QUE, SASK, SFS, TRT, TRTE, UBC; abbreviations follow Holmgren et al. (1981).

vegetative means. Both species produce a large number of seeds per individual which contributes to their success as weeds. Spines on the leaves deter grazing. Doing et al. (1969) mention that sheep often eat seed heads of *C. nutans* and thus may facilitate seed dispersal.

(b) *Perennation — Carduus nutans* and *C. acanthoides* overwinter either as seeds or rosettes.

(c) *Physiological data* — Haderlie and McCarty (1980) reported that *C. nutans* rosettes have a vernalization requirement of at least 40 d below 10°C. Time required for the initiation of bolting decreased if the vernalization time was increased to 60 d. They found that gibberellic acid did not substitute

for vernalization. Exposure to short days prior to vernalization reduced vernalization time (Medd and Lovett 1978a).

(d) *Phenology* — Germination of *C. nutans* seed occurs in the spring and fall approximately 14–21 d after the seed is shed (Lee and Hamrick 1983). Although reports of seed dormancy conflict (see Section 8c.), seeds have no light requirement for germination, but are affected by temperature. Higher germination rates occur at temperatures between 20 and 28°C (Lee and Hamrick 1983). Development from seedling to rosette stages occurs rapidly and individuals overwinter as rosettes. McCarty and Scifres (1969) found that a few individuals germinating in the spring may behave as annuals, flowering and setting seed in the same season. Lee and Hamrick (1983) found plants with a rosette diameter of at least 14 inches (36 cm) at the end of the growing season had a high probability of flowering the following season regardless of germination time. Rosette size was determined at least partially both by plant density and cohort membership, with earlier germinating cohorts achieving larger diameters. Flowering occurs in late May or early June in the midwestern United States (Meed and Smith 1978; Lee and Hamrick 1983); somewhat later (June-July) in Canada (pers. obs. and Harris 1984). Flowering time of *C. nutans* in Canada is relatively short (3–4 wk in southern Ontario), while the many heads in *C. acanthoides* enable it to flower more continuously; from June until October in southern Ontario (Harris 1984). Seed maturation and dispersal occurs very shortly after flowering (1–3 wk).

(e) *Mycorrhiza* — Vesicular-arbuscular mycorrhizal associations have been described for *C. acanthoides* from Europe (Frydman (1957) as cited in Harley and Harley (1987)). No reports of mycorrhizal associations have been found for *C. nutans*.

8. Reproduction

(a) *Floral biology* — *Carduus nutans* and *C. acanthoides* are primarily outcrossing species, but show greater selfing rates in northern populations (McCarty et al. 1980; Smyth and Hamrick 1984, 1987; Warwick 1987). Smyth and Hamrick (1984) reported significant heterogeneity in outcrossing rates among individuals in two Kansas populations of *C. nutans*. They reported low seed set in isolated greehouse plants. In contrast, Warwick and Thompson (in prep.) report considerable variation in degree of selfing among individuals in Ontario populations of both species grown in the greenhouse. Mean seed set averaged 32 and 68 seeds per bagged head for *C. acanthoides* and *C. nutans*, respectively. This corresponded to *c.* 30% selfed seed set in both species, with mean individual values ranging from 8 to 80%.

In Nebraska and Kansas, *Carduus nutans* is predominantly pollinated by *Apis* and *Bombus* ssp. and Lepidoptera (McCarty et al. 1980; Smyth and Hamrick 1984, 1987). Personal observations of the authors confirm *Apis* and *Bombus* spp. on plants in Canada. Various species of wasps, anthoporids, halictids, and megachilids have been observed visiting flowers (Smyth and Hamrick 1987). Mean pollinator flight distance increased with increased plant density while flight directionality decreased (Smyth and Hamrick 1987). These results support a trend toward greater gene flow with increased plant density, considered partly attributable to the insects' behavior.

(b) *Seed production and dispersal* — In field studies of *C. nutans* in Nebraska, McCarty (1964) reported that 10 000 – 11 000 achenes per individual may be produced. In a later study McCarty (1982) observed that the first flower heads to bloom (i.e., the terminal heads) averaged 1200 – 1500 seeds per head, while the last ones to bloom produced 25 seeds per head or fewer. On the other hand, seed production in Ontario is lower, ranging from mean values of 165 – 256 seeds per head (sample size = 36–41) for *C. nutans* and 56 – 83 seeds per head (sample size = 33–41) for *C. acanthoides* (Warwick and Thompson, in prep.). Achenes are mainly dispersed by wind and fall near the parent plant (within 50 m) with less than 1% being carried further than 100m (Smith and Kok 1984).

(c) *Viability of seeds and germination* — In Nebraska, little or no loss of viability occurred when achenes were stored in a dry state, at low temperature (0 or 5°C) for at least 160 d (McCarty and Scifres 1969). Any damage to the achene coat reduced viability. Seed viability remains high over several years (Kok 1978; Roberts and Chancellor 1979). Burnside et al. (1981) obtained little loss of viability after a 10-yr burial of *C. nutans* seeds. In a greenhouse experiment, fresh seed of *C. nutans* showed innate dormancy (Medd and Lovett 1978b). In contrast, laboratory tests indicated a period of dormancy of about 8 wk (Lacefield and Gray 1970). McCarty and Scifres (1969) reported that no dormancy mechanism is operative in *C. nutans*. Similarly, Dorph-Petersen (cited in Anderson 1968), in Denmark, reported that seeds germinate soon after harvest. In New Zealand, a germination rate of 63% occurred within 12 d (Delahunty 1962).

In the field, germination of *C. nutans* can occur at any time during the growing season (McCarty et al. 1984), usually within 14 – 21 d of shedding (Lee and Hamrick 1983), with germination potential varying between 93 and 95% (McCarty 1964; Furrer and McCarty 1966). Germination is initiated under moist conditions if light is sufficient (Doing et al. 1969; McCarty et al. 1969; Lee and Hamrick 1983). Hamrick and Lee (1987) reported that optimum levels of germination occurred in microhabitats with reduced evaporation. Cracked and irregular soil surface topographies provided the best conditions.

In laboratory studies, a temperature effect has been demonstrated. McCarty and Scifres (1969) found that germination occurred between 15 and 28°C, with a greater germination rate at higher temperatures. Medd and Lovett (1978b) found highest germination rates between 20 and 30°C in darkness and 15 and 20°C in the light. They also demonstrated a stimulatory, far-red reversible effect of white and red light on germination. Addition of either potassium nitrate (2×10^{-2} M) or gibberellic acid (at rates between 6.2 and 100 mg L^{-1}) substituted, to some degree, for the stimulatory light effect. Seed coat scarification significantly improved germination in the dark but depressed germination in light, possibly because of treatment damage. Decay of the seed coat, due to saprophytes or weathering, likely affects germination in the field.

(d) *Vegetative reproduction* — No vegetative reproduction has been reported to occur in either *C. nutans* or *C. acanthoides*.

9. Hybrids

Hybridization between *C. nutans* and *C. acanthoides* has been reported (the hybrid is referred to as *C. × orthocephalus* Wallr. by Moore and Frankton (1974) and extensively studied in Grey Co. Ontario by Moore and Mulligan (1956), Mulligan and Moore (1961) and Moore and Mulligan (1964). They reported the existence of numerous hybrid swarms and suggested that *acanthoides* type intermediates were more common than *nutans* types due to a selective advantage. Hybrid swarms were as vigorous and widespread within individual fields as parental populations, so detrimental effects similar to the parent species are to be expected. Introgression between the two species was hypothesized. Recent follow-up studies (Warwick and Bain 1987, in prep.) support this hypothesis but suggest that introgression is very localized. Moreover, morphologically intermediate individuals often have a lower seed set than parental types. Kazmi (1964) described hybrids from Europe between *C. nutans* and four other *Carduus* species (in addition to *C. acanthoides*) and between *C. acanthoides* and 17 other *Carduus* species (besides *C. nutans*).

10. Population Dynamics

In Canada, both *C. nutans* and *C. acanthoides* are capable of forming dense stands — 150 000 ha^{-1} for *C. nutans* and 90 000 ha^{-1} for *C. acanthoides* (Harris 1984). Population sizes vary in response to climatic conditions. Harris (1984) reported populations of *C. nutans* from Findlater, Saskatchewan as fluctuating from dense, following a moist fall and/or spring, to sparse when these seasons were dry. For both species, dense stands are usually formed on disturbed sites where competition is low (i.e. gravel pits), but may also occur in overgrazed or disturbed pastureland.

The plants usually function as biennials and therefore complete a generation every second year. Most plants die before flowering (Popay and Thompson 1979). Germination occurs mainly in the spring and fall with resulting plants acting either as winter annuals or as spring or fall biennials (Lee and Hamrick 1983). Germination in early autumn in populations of *C. nutans* in Nebraska generally favored high survivorship and early flowering. These individuals were usually larger and produced more seeds than those germinating later in the fall or spring. However, germination in early fall, followed by a period of drought, may result in high seedling mortality (Hamrick and Lee 1987).

Established stands of the species are thought to be self-perpetuating. At high stand densities the seed bed is devoid of competing vegetation. In addition, the dead flowering stalks trap winter snow which provides moisture for spring seed germination (Harris 1984).

Increases in interspecific competition cause *Carduus* populations to decline. In Nebraska pastures, competition reduces plant size and flower number and increases mortality (McCarty and Scrifes 1969). In Australia, *C. nutans* is more productive in communities where levels of inter- and intraspecific competition are low (Austin et al. 1985).

11. Response to Herbicides and Other Chemicals

Carduus nutans and *C. acanthoides* are most susceptible to hormone-like herbicides applied during periods of active growth of the seedlings or rosettes, i.e., during the spring or fall. Feldman et al. (1968), in Nebraska, applied different herbicides at different rates and dates during the spring and fall and determined that picloram was the most effective herbicide. Because of the great potential seed production of *C. nutans*, a second year application of herbicide was considered to be necessary. After 1 yr, in most treatment plots, a 75 – 80% reduction in density of rosettes or new seedlings was obtained. Harris (1984) reported that *C. nutans* and *C. acanthoides* can both be controlled with 2,4–D applied at a rate of 1 kg ha^{-1}.

Herbicide application has been shown to reduce seed production most effectively just prior to flowering and when all parts of the plants were exposed (McCarty and Hatting 1975). Production of viable seed was reduced with the application of 2,4–D ester at 4.48 kg ha^{-1}, dicamba at 0.56 kg ha^{-1} and dicamba

at 0.56 kg ha^{-1} plus 2,4–D amine at 1.12 kg ha^{-1}. Control of *C. nutans* using herbicides has also been documented from New Zealand (McKellar 1955; Delahunty 1961, 1962; Leonard 1964). In all the latter cases the most effective control of *C. natans* was obtained by spraying hormone-like herbicides in the spring or fall, when both seedlings or actively growing rosettes are most frequent in populations.

Reece and Wilson (1983) applied combinations of herbicides (3,6–dichloropicolinic acid + 2,4–D; picloram + 2,4–D; dicamba + 2,4–D; dicamba + IT 3456) and nitrogen on several plots of *C. nutans* in Nebraska during the spring over a 3-yr period. All treatments provided excellent control and annual treatments controlled the few plants that emerged after the first application. On the unfertilized herbicide treated plots, perennial grass production increased considerably over 3 yr suggesting that the application of ammonium nitrate favored the competitive ability of the thistles over the grasses.

12. Response to Other Human Manipulations

Mowing of *C. nutans* as a means of control is most effective when applied to flowering plants (McCarty and Hatting 1975). Plants mowed within 2 d of anthesis did not produce viable seeds while those mowed 6 d after produced a significant quantity of viable seeds and those mowed after 11 d produced an amount of viable seed similar to unmowed plants. More than a single mowing per season was required for effective control because of the large differences in plant maturity in natural populations. When plants were mowed before anthesis, regrowth occurred and viable seeds were produced.

Harris (1984) observed that, in Canada, neither *C. nutans* nor *C. acanthoides* tolerated regular cultivation. Similarly, Doing et al. (1969) in Australia, and Hull and Evans (1973) in the United States, reported that pasture improvement (cultivation and herbicide application) can be an effective control of *C. nutans*.

Reece and Wilson (1983) reported that the addition of fertilizer enhances the competitive ability of *C. nutans*. In a greenhouse experiment, Austin et al. (1985) determined that in both monoculture and mixtures, yield of *C. nutans* increased in response to increasing nutrient concentration (Hoagland no. 2 nutrient solution), although when compared with six other thistles species, *C. nutans* seemed to have the lowest competitive ability.

13. Responses to Parasites

(a) *Insects and other nondomestic animals —* Several insects have been reported to feed on *C. nutans* and *C. acanthoides* (see review by Batra et al. (1981)). Approximately 182 different insect species were recorded on *C. nutans* and *C. acanthoides*, 39 of which were found on both species, and 17 on *C. acanthoides* only. The frequency of the insects on the thistles varies from rare to abundant. Table 3 presents the insects recorded on *C. nutans* and *C. acanthoides* in Canada. Some have been tested for biological control in North America but very few have been released as yet. Two of these, *Rhinocyllus conicus* (Froelich) and *Trichosirocalus horridus* (Panzer) (Coleoptera: Curculionidae), both of European origin, have been extensively studied and used for controlling the two thistles in North America.

The main host of *Rhinocyllus conicus* is *C. nutans*, but it has been found on other species of *Carduus, Cirsium, Silybum* and *Onopordum* (Harris 1984). This insect has been released in populations of *C. nutans* and *C. acanthoides*, in four provinces (Saskatchewan, Ontario, Manitoba, and Quebec) and 23 states (Virginia, West Virginia, Nebraska, Missouri, Montana, California, Iowa, Minnesota, North Dakota, South Dakota, Utah, Idaho, Washington, Wyoming, Kentucky, Louisiana, Oklahoma, Kansas, Colorado, Maryland, New Jersey, Pennsylvania and Nevada) (Harris and Zwolfer 1971; Hawkes et al. 1972; Surles et al. 1974; Goeden and Ricker 1974; Kok 1974, 1977; Rees 1977, 1978). Numerous studies have reported that density levels (number of weevils per head)

Table 3. A list of insects recorded on *Carduus nutans* and *C. acanthoides* in Canada (data from Batra et al. 1981)

COLEOPTERA
Mordellidae
Epicauta atrata (F.)
E. ferruginea (Say)
Nemgnatha lutea LeConte
Chrysomelidae
Cassida ruginosa Mueller
Curculionidae
Ceutorhynchus litura (F.)
Cleonus piger Scopoli
Rhinocyllus conicus (Froelich)
Trichosirocalus horridus (Panzer)
LEPIDOPTERA
Nymphalidae
Cynthia cardui (L.)
Pyralidae
Homoeosoma electellum (Hulst)
DIPTERA
Tephritidae
Urophora cardui (L.)
U. stylata (F.)

increase steadily from the time of release and level off at between three and six weevils per head within a few years (Harris 1984; Laing and Heels 1978; Letendre et al. 1976). In the spring the insects feed on the leaves and oviposit on the involucral bracts of the flower bud. The larva feeds by mining the receptacle and peduncle. The callus tissue which fills the mined receptacle serves as another food source (Harris 1984). The net result of the larval feeding is reduction in seed production.

Flower heads with eggs of *Rhinocyllus conicus* were observed in populations of *C. acanthoides*, although only a minor reduction in seed production has been reported (Surles and Kok 1977). In Europe, *R. conicus* is not adapted to *C. acanthoides* (Zwolfer and Harris 1984).

Trichosirocalus horridus has established itself on both species under field conditions in Virginia, although it has a preference for *C. nutans* (Kok 1986). Larvae attack the rosette causing necrosis of the crowns, destroying apical dominance and altering subsequent growth. Both *C. nutans* and *C. acanthoides* usually produce more stems and a larger crown when attacked by *T. horridus* (Cartwright and Kok 1985). Response to weevil attack depends upon the size and growing conditions of the thistles. Based on observations in Saskatchewan, Harris (1984) believes the effect of *T. horridus* is very small. He observed large rosettes attacked in the spring survived to produce seeds. In Virginia, when healthy and vigorous rosettes were infested, many recovered and reached maturity (Kok 1986; Sieburth et al. 1983). However, when smaller rosettes of *C. nutans* and *C. acanthoides* were attacked, a reduction in the number of heads and seeds per plant resulted. Release of *T. horridus* should result in a decrease in thistle populations (Kok 1986). *Trichosirocalus horridus* has been released in Canada as well as in the eastern and midwestern regions of the United States.

(b) *Microorganisms and viruses* — Batra et al. (1981) list four fungi (*Puccinia carduorum* Jacky, *P. galatica* Sydow (= *P carduipycnocephali* Syd.) (Uredinales), *Ustilago cardui* F. Waldheim and *U. violacea* (Pers.) Roussel (Ustilaginales)) capable of infecting musk and/or plumeless thistles. Of these only *P. carduorum* has been introduced in North America. The authors also presented a list of 35 nonspecific fungi recorded on unspecified *Carduus* species, as well as an unidentified phloem necrosis virus found to infect *C. nutans* at Beltsville, Md. In addition, *Albugo tragopogonis* (DC.) S. F. Gray was also found on *C. acanthoides* in the Ukraine (Burdyukova and Dudka 1982). No information on fungi and viruses associated with *Carduus* in Canada is available.

Puccinia carduorum Jacky has been studied for its use as a biological control agent. Politis et al. (1984) and Politis and Bruckart (1986) determined that the host specificity of *P. carduorum* is restricted to the subtribe Carduinae in the tribe Cardueae. It was very aggressive on most collections of *C. nutans* in North America and virulent on six *Carduus* spp., eight *Cirsium* spp. and two *Cynara* spp. *Carduus acanthoides* was not susceptible to the fungus. Rosettes of *C. nutans* seedlings inoculated with *P. carduorum* were susceptible during the first 10 wk of growth. Plants inoculated 2 wk after planting were the most susceptible and susceptibility of the rosette declined with age. Infection occurred between 8 and 27°C at 4 – 16 h of dew period. The optimal dew period was 12 h regardless of the temperature and the optimal temperature ranged between 17 and 24°C regardless of the dew period. Inoculation of *C. nutans* resulted in a reduction of rosette and root dry weight. Politis and Bruckart (1986) believe that *P. carduorum* may stress plants without interfering with activity of insects introduced for biological control.

ACKNOWLEDGMENTS

Appreciation is expressed to the herbarium curators of ACAD, ALTA, CAN, DAO, DAS, GFND, GH, KANU, MIN, MONTU, MTMG, NFLD, QFA, QK, QUE, RMS, SASK, SFS, TRT, TRTE, UAC, UBC, UNB, US, USAS, WIN (abbreviations follow Holmgren et al. 1981) for providing loans of specimens used in this study. Helpful advice was provided by P. Harris. Financial support from Agriculture Canada and The Natural Sciences and Engineering Research Council of Canada is gratefully acknowledged.

Alex, J. F. Cayouette, R. and Mulligan, G. A. 1980. Common and botanical names of weeds in Canada. Agriculture Canada, Ottawa, Ont. Publ. 1397, 132 pp.

Anderson, R. N. 1968. Germination and establishment of weeds for experimental purposes. W. F. Humphrey Press. Geneva, N.Y. 236 pp.

Austin, M. P., Groves, R. H., Fresco, L. M. F. and Kaye, P. E. 1985. Relative growth of six thistle species along a nutrient gradient with multispecies competition. J. Ecol. **73**: 667–684.

Batra, S. W. T. 1978. *Carduus* thistle distribution and biological control in the northeastern states. *In* K. E. Frick ed. Biological control of thistles in the genus *Carduus* in the United States. U.S. Department of Agriculture, New Orleans, La. 50 pp.

Batra, S. W. T., Coulson, J. R., Dunn, P. H. and Boldt, P. E. 1981. Insects and fungi associated with *Carduus* thistles (Compositae). USDA Tech. Bull. 1616, Washington, D.C. 100 pp.

Bolkhovskikh, Z., Grif, U. and Matavejeva, T. 1969. Chromosome numbers of flowering plants. Academy of Sciences of the USSR, V. L. Komarev Botanical Institute. Leningrad, USSR.

Burdyukova, L. I. and Dudka, I. A. 1982.

Albugo spp. on new and rare host plants in the Ukrainian-SSR, USSR. Mikol. Fitopatol. **16**: 289–294.

Burnside, O. C., Fenster, C. R., Evetts, L. L. and Mumm, R. F. 1981. Germination of exhumed weed seed in Nebraska USA. Weed Sci. **29**: 577–586.

Cartwright, B. and Kok, L. T. 1985. Growth responses of musk and plumeless thistles (*Carduus nutans* and *Carduus acanthoides*) to damage by *Trichsirocalus horridus* (Coleoptera: Curculionidae). Weed Sci. **33**: 57–62.

Delahunty, E. 1961. Nodding thistle control with chemicals. N.Z. J. Agric. **103**: 23–25.

Delahunty, E. 1962. Nodding thistle. New Zealand Weed Control Conf. Proc. **15**: 24–28.

Desrochers, A. M., Bain, J. F., Warwick, S. I. 1988. A biosystematic study of the *Carduus nutans* L. complex in Canada. Can. J. Bot. **66**: 1621–1631.

Doing, H., Biddiscombe, E. F., and Knedlhans, S. 1969. Ecology and distribution of the *Carduus nutans* group, nodding thistles, in Australia. Vegetatio **17**: 313–351.

Dunn, P. H. 1976. Distribution of *Carduus nutans, C. acanthoides, C. pycnocephalus,* and *C. crispus,* in the United States. Weed Sci. **24**: 518–524.

Feldman, I., McCarty, M. K. and Scrifes, C. J. 1968. Ecological and control studies of musk thistle. Weed Sci. **16**: 1–4.

Ferron, M. and Cayouette, R. 1964. Noms des mauvaises herbes du Québec. Min. Agr. Colonisation, Québec, P. Q. 68 pp.

Franco. J. Do Amaral. 1976. *Carduus. In* T. G. Tutin, V. H. Heywood, N. A. Burges, D. M. Moore, D. H. Valentine, S. M. Walters, and D. A. Webb, eds. Flora Europaea. Vol 4. Cambridge University Press, Cambridge, U.K.

Frankton, C. and Mulligan, G. A. 1970. Weeds of Canada. Canada Department of Agriculture Ottawa, Ont. Publ. no. 948. 217 pp.

Furrer, J. D. and McCarty, M. K. 1966. Musk thistle — its appearance, spread and control. Nebr. Agric. Exp. Sta. Res. Bull. **EC66–160**: 1–6.

Goeden, R. D. and Ricker, D. W. 1974. Imported seed weevils attack Italian and milk thistles in southern California. Calif. Agric. **28**: 8–9.

Haderlie, L. C. and McCarty, M. K. 1980. Musk thistle flowering induction. Proc. N. Cent. Weed Control Conf. **34**: 100–101.

Hamrick, J. L. and Lee, J. M. 1987. Effect of soil surface topography and litter cover on the germination, survival, and growth of musk thistle

(*Carduus nutans*). Am. J. Bot. **74**: 451–457.

Harley, J. L. and Harley, E. L. 1987. A checklist of mycorrhiza in the British flora. New Phytol. **105**: 1–102.

Harris, P. 1984. *Carduus nutans* L., nodding thistle and *C. acanthoides* L., plumeless thistle (Compositae). Pages 115–126 *in* J. S. Kelleher and M. A. Hulme, eds. Biological control programmes against insects and weeds in Canada, 1969–1980.

Harris, P. and Zwolfer, H. 1971. *Carduus acanthoides* L. (welted thistle) and *Carduus nutans* L. (nodding thistle). *In* Biological control programs against insects and weeds in Canada, 1959–1968. Commonwealth Instit. Biol. Control Tech., Farnham Royal, U.K. Commun. 4, pp. 76–79.

Hawkes, R. B., Andres, L. A. and Dunn, P. H. 1972. Seed weevil released to control milk thistle. Calif. Agric. **26**: 14.

Hensley, M. S. 1973. Taxonomy and distribution of *Cirsium* thistles in Rockingham county Virginia. Va. J. Sci. **24**: 140.

Holmgren, P. K., Keuken, W. and Schofield, E. 1981. Index herbariorum. Part 1. The herbaria of the world. 7th ed. (Regnum Veg. 106) Oosthock, Schetema and Holkema, Utrecht, The Netherlands. 452 pp.

Hull, A. C. and Evans, J. O. 1973. Musk thistle (*Carduus nutans*): an undesirable range plant. J. Range Manage. **26**: 383–385.

Johnson, M. F. 1974. Cynareae (Asteraceae) in Virginia: *Cirsium, Carduus, Onopordum.* Va. J. Sci. **25**: 152–160.

Kazmi, S. M. A. 1964. Revision der Gattung *Carduus* (Compositae). Teil II. Mitt. Bot. Munchen **5**: 279–550.

Kok, L. T. 1974. Efficacy of spring releases in colonization of *Rhinocyllus conicus* for the biocontrol of thistles. Environ. Entom. **3**: 429–430.

Kok, L. T. 1977. Biological control of *Carduus* thistles in northeastern U.S.A. Proc. IVth Int. Symp. Biological control of weeds. pp. 101–107.

Kok, L. T. 1978. Status of biological control of musk thistle in Virginia. *In* K. E. Frick, ed. Biological control of thistles in the Genus *Carduus* in the United States. U.S. Department of Agriculture, New Orleans, La. 50 pp.

Kok, L. T. 1986. Impact of *Trichosirocalus horridus* (Coleoptera: Curculionidae) on *Carduus* thistles in pastures. Crop Prot. **5**: 214–217.

Lacefield, G. D. and Gray, E. 1970. The life cycle of nodding thistle (*Carduus nutans* L.) in Kentucky. Proc. N. Cent. Weed Control Conf. **25**: 105–107.

Laing, J. E. and Heels, P. R. 1978. Establishment of an introduced weevil *Rhinocyllus conicus* (Coleoptera: Curculionidae) for the biological control of nodding thistle (Compositae) in southern Ontario. Proc. Entomol. Soc. Ont. **109**: 3–8.

Lee, J. M. and Hamrick, J. L. 1983. Demography of two natural populations of musk thistle (*Carduus nutans*). J. Ecol. **71**: 923–936.

Leonard, W. F. 1964. Weed identification and control. N.Z. J. Agric. **109**: 293.

Letendre, M., Ritchot, C., Guibord, O. C. and Leduc, C. 1976. Essai d'éradication du chardon penché, *Carduus nutans* L. à l'aide du charancon, *Rhinocyllus conicus* Froel. Phytoprotection **57**: 47–55.

McCarty, M. K. 1964. New and problem weeds: Musk thistle. Proc. N. Cent. Weed Control Conf. **20**: 62–63.

McCarty, M. K. 1978. The genus *Carduus* in the United States. *In* K. E. Frick, ed. Biological control of thistles in the Genus *Carduus* in the United States. U.S. Department of Agriculture, New Orleans, La. 50 pp.

McCarty, M. K. 1982. Musk thistle (*Carduus thoermeri*) seed production. Weed Sci. **30**: 441–445.

McCarty, M. K. 1985. A nursery study of large-flowered taxa of *Carduus*. Weed Sci. **33**: 664–668.

McCarty, M. K. and Hatting, J. L. 1975. Effects of herbicides or mowing on musk thistle seed production. Weed Res. **15**: 363–367.

McCarty, M. K. and Scifres, C. J. 1969. Life cycle studies with musk thistle. Nebr. Agric. Exp. Sta. Res. Bull. 230. 15 pp.

McCarty, M. K., Scifres, C. J., Smith, A. L. and Horst, G. L. 1969. Germination and early development of musk (*Carduus nutans* L.) and plumeless (*Carduus acanthoides* L.) thistles. Nebr. Agric. Exp. Sta. Res. Bull. 229. 29 pp.

McCarty, M. K., Gorz, H. J. and Haskins, F. A. 1980. Inheritance of flower color in musk thistle (*Carduus thoermeri*). Weed Sci. **28**: 347–352.

McCarty, M. K., Scifres, C. J. and Robinson, L. R. 1984. A descriptive guide for major Nebraska thistles. Neb. Univ. Agric. Exp. Sta. Publ. SB 493. 24 pp.

McGregor, R. L. 1986. *Carduus. In* Great Plains Flora Association, Flora of the Great Plains. University Press of Kansas, Lawrence, Kansas. pp. 895–897.

McKellar, W. A. 1955. Hormone control of nodding thistle. N.Z. J. Agric. **90**: 515–516.

Medd, R. W. 1981. Taxonomy of *Carduus nutans* in northeastern New South Wales, Australia. Proc. 8th Asian-Pacific Weed Sci. Soc. Conf., Sydney, Australia. pp. 171–173.

Medd, R. W. and Lovett, J. V. 1978a. Biological studies of *Carduus nutans* ssp. *nutans*. Part 2. Vernalization and phenological development. Weed Res. **18**: 369–372.

Medd, R. W. and Lovett, J. V. 1978b. Biological studies of *Carduus nutans* ssp. *nutans*. Part 1. Germination and light requirement of seedlings. Weed Res. **18**: 363–368.

Meed, R. W. and Smith, R. C. G. 1978. Prediction of the potential distribution of *Carduus nutans* ssp. *nutans*, nodding thistle, in Australia. J. Appl. Ecol. **15**: 603–612.

Moore, R. J. and Frankton, C. 1974. The thistles of Canada. Research Branch, Canada Department of Agriculture. Monograph no. 10. pp. 54–61.

Moore, R. J. and Mulligan, G. A. 1956. Hybridization between *Carduus acanthoides* and *Carduus nutans* in Ontario. Can. J. Bot. **34**: 71–85.

Moore, R. J. and Mulligan, G. A. 1964. Further studies on natural selection among hybrids of *Carduus acanthoides* and *Carduus nutans*. Can. J. Bot. **42**: 1605–1613.

Mulligan, G. A. and Frankton, C. 1954. The plumeless thistles (*Carduus* spp.) in Canada. Can. Field Nat. **68**: 31–36.

Mulligan, G. A. and Moore, R. J. 1961. Natural selection among hybrids between *Carduus acanthoides* and *C. nutans* in Ontario. Can. J. Bot. **39**: 21–33.

Politis, D. J., Watson, A. K. and Bruckart, W. L. 1984. Susceptibility of musk thistle and related composites to *Puccinia carduorum*. Phytopathology **74**: 687–691.

Politis, D. J. and Bruckart, W. L. 1986. Infection of musk thistle *Carduus nutans* by *Puccinia carduorum* influenced by conditions of dew and plant age. Plant Dis. **70**: 288–290.

Popay, A. I. and Thompson, A. 1979. Some aspects of the biology of *Carduus nutans* in New Zealand pastures. Proc. 7th Asian-Pacific Weed Sci. Soc. Conf., Sydney, Australia. pp. 343–346.

Reece, P. E. and Wilson, R. G. 1983. Effect of Canada thistle (*Cirsium arvense*) and musk thistle (*Carduus nutans*) control on grass herbage. Weed Sci. **31**: 488–492.

Rees, P. E. 1977. Impact of *Rhinocyllus conicus* on thistles in southwestern Montana. Environ. Entomol. **6**: 839–842.

Rees, P. E. 1978. Interactions of *Rhinocyllus conicus* and thistles in the Gallatin Valley. *In* K. E. Frick, ed. Biological control of thistles in the genus *Carduus* in the United States. U.S. Department of Agriculture, New Orleans, La. 50 pp.

Roberts, H. A. and Chancellor, R. J. 1979. Periodicity of seedling emergence and achene survival in some species of *Carduus, Cirsium*, and *Onopordum*. J. Appl. Ecol. **16**: 641–648.

Sieburth, P. J., Kok, L. T. and Lentner, M. 1983. Factors influencing the effectiveness of *Trichosirocalus horridus* (Panzer) in the control of *Carduus* thistles. Crop Prot. **2**: 143–151.

Smith, L. M. and Kok, L. T. 1984. Dispersal of musk thistle (*Carduus nutans*) seeds. Weed Sci. **32**: 120–125.

Smyth, A. and Hamrick, J. L. 1984. Variation in estimates of outcrossing in musk thistle populations. J. Hered. **75**: 303–307.

Smyth, A. and Hamrick, J. L. 1987. Realized gene flow via pollen in artificial populations of musk thistle, *Carduus nutans* L. Evolution **41**: 613–619.

Strong, W. L. and Leggat, K. R. 1981. Ecoregions of Alberta. Alberta Energy and Natural Resources Tech. Rep. No. T/4, 64 pp.

Stuckey, R. L. and Forsyth, J. L. 1971. Distribution of naturalized *Carduus nutans* (Compositae) mapped in relation to geology in northwestern Ohio. Ohio J. Sci. **71**: 1–15.

Surles, W. W. and Kok, L. T. 1877. Ovipositional preferences and synchronization of *Rhinocyllus conicus* with *Carduus nutans* and *C. acanthoides*. Environ. Entomol. **6**: 222–224.

Surles, W. W., Kok, L. T. and Pienkowski, R. L. 1974. Rhinocyllus conicus establishment for biocontrol of thistles in Virginia. Weed Sci. **22**: 1–3.

Warwick, S. I. 1987. Estimates of outcrossing rates in pure populations and hybrid swarms of *Carduus nutans* and *C. acanthoides*. Am. J. Bot. **74**: 763. (Abstr.)

Warwick, S. I. and Bain, J. F. 1987. Hybridization and introgression in *Carduus nutans* L. and *C. acanthoides* L. Am. J. Bot. **74**: 764. (Abstr.)

Zwolfer, H. and Harris, P. 1984. Biology and host specificity of *Rhinocyllus conicus* (Froel.) (Coleoptera: Curculionidae), a successful agent for biocontrol of the thistle, *Carduus nutans* L. Z. Angew. Entomol. **97**: 36–62.

THE BIOLOGY OF CANADIAN WEEDS. 90.
Abutilon theophrasti

S. I. WARWICK and L. D. BLACK

Biosystematics Research Centre, Agriculture Canada, K.W. Neatby Bldg., Central Experimental Farm, Ottawa, Ontario Canada K1A 0C6. Received 29 Feb. 1988, accepted 1 June 1988.

WARWICK, S. I. AND BLACK, L. D. 1988. The biology of Canadian Weeds. 90. *Abutilon theophrasti*. Can. J. Plant Sci. **68**: 1069–1085.

Abutilon theophrasti Medic. (velvetleaf) forms extensive weed infestations in all major maize and soybean growing areas of Ontario and Quebec. A review of the literature on the biology of the species is presented. Velvetleaf causes crop losses through competition, allelopathic effects and by hosting insect pests and pathogens of crops. Velvetleaf has a number of features which contribute to its success as a weed, including: the production of a large number of seeds that have high viability with prolonged dormancy and sporadic, continuous germination patterns; robust seedling vigor; and the ability to produce seed under competition. Because of sporadic germination patterns, control is difficult. Effective control measures include the application of pre-emergence and/or postemergence herbicides followed by cultivation and additional herbicide applications to control escapes and later flushes of germination. A triazine-resistant biotype of velvetleaf has recently been reported from the northeastern United States.

Key words: Velvetleaf, *Abutilon theophrasti*, weed biology

[La biologie des mauvaises herbes canadiennes. 90. *Abutilon theophrasti*.]
Titre abrégé: *Abutilon theophrasti*.
Abutilon theophrasti Medic. (abutilon) est une mauvaise herbe envahissante dans toutes les principales régions de culture du maïs et du soja de l'Ontario et du Québec. Les auteurs présentent une étude bibliographique sur la biologie de l'espèce. L'abutilon cause des pertes de récolte par la concurrence qu'il exerce, ses effets allélopathiques et le fait qu'il héberge des insectes parasites et des agents pathogènes des cultures. Il possède un certain nombre de caractéristiques qui contribuent à son efficacité comme mauvaise herbe, notamment la production de beaucoup de graines d'une grande viabilité, à dormance prolongée et à germination continue, mais sporadique. Il est difficile à combattre à cause de sa germination sporadique. Les moyens de lutte efficaces comprennent l'application d'herbicides de pré- ou de post-levée, suivie par le travail du sol et d'autres traitements herbicides pour détruire les plants qui ont échappé au traitement et combattre les poussées de germination subséquentes. On a récemment signalé la présence d'un biotype d'abutilon résistant à la triazine dans le nord-est des États-Unis.

Mots clés: Abutilon, *Abutilon theophrasti*, biologie des mauvaises herbes

1. Name

Abutilon theophrasti Medic. — **velvetleaf**, abutilon, butterprint, elephant ears, Indian mallow, piemarker (Alex and Switzer 1970; Alex et al. 1980), buttonweed (United States Department of Agriculture 1970), cottonweed (Roeth 1987), China jute, abutilon hemp, Manchurian jute, American jute (Spencer

1984), **abutilon** (Alex et al. 1980), Malvaceae, mallow family, Malvacées.

2. Description and Account of Variation

The following description is based on Alex and Switzer (1970), Shaw et al. (1974) and personal observations of the authors.

Annual herb, reproducing only by seed. Taproot slender with many smaller branches. Stems erect, 1–2.5 m tall, much branched in

Can. J. Plant Sci. **68**: 1069–1085 (Oct. 1988)

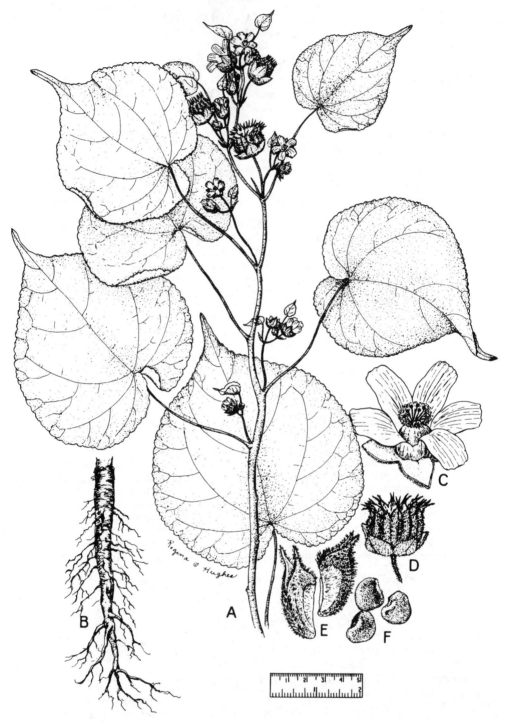

the upper part, smooth with short velvety hairs. Leaves alternate, long-petiolated, blade broadly heart-shaped, round to cordate at the base, 7–20 cm wide, taper-pointed at apex, shallowly round-toothed, velvety, hairy surface. Flowers single or in small clusters from the leaf axils, peduncles shorter than the petioles, five sepals, five yellow to yellow-orange petals slightly notched apically, 1.3–2.5 cm wide when open. Anther filaments united to form a central column. Fruit or capsule, cup-shaped, circular cluster of 12–15 carpels (seedpods), 1.3–2.5 cm long and 2.5 cm wide, hairy, beaked, each carpel opening with a vertical slit along outer edge and containing from one to three seeds. Seeds purplish-brown, kidney-shaped, notched, flattened, 1 mm thick and 2–3 mm long. Velvetleaf is a hexaploid species with $2n = 6x = 42$ chromosomes (Bolkhovskikh et al. 1969; Warwick and Black 1986).

Velvetleaf (Fig. 1) is easily distinguished by its erect tall habit of growth, its large, alternate, heart-shaped leaves which are soft and velvety to the touch, small yellow to yellow-orange flowers, distinct black capsules, and in the late autumn by the distinct appearance of its erect, branched, brownish to blackish stem with numerous seed capsules.

Life history and allozyme variation were examined in 39 populations of velvetleaf collected from southern Ohio (39°N) to central Ontario (45°N) (Warwick and Black 1986). Representing a climatic gradient at the northern extreme of its North American distribution, plants from each of the populations were grown in a standard garden trial. Among population differences were evident for 33 of 51 growth, germination and morphological characters measured. Many of these population differences were correlated with latitude and climate. Results from 16 enzyme systems provided evidence for very low levels of allozyme variation. Only two enzymes were variable and only four multilocus electrophoretic

genotypes were evident among the 39 populations, although high levels of enzyme multiplicity were evident within an individual as a result of polyploidy.

Studies by Andersen et al. (1985) on 14 accessions of velvetleaf originating between Mississippi (33°N) and Minnesota (44°N) indicated that although all accessions began to flower within a few days of one another, higher levels of floral abortion occurred in the southern accessions resulting in a greater delay in the onset of seed capsule development. As a result, cumulative seed capsule production during the first months of seed production was greater for the northern accessions. Since seed production continued for longer in southern accessions, cumulative seed capsule production over the entire season was not different between northern and southern accessions.

3. Economic Importance

(a) *Detrimental* — In North America, velvetleaf is a troublesome weed of cultivated land, causing severe crop losses particularly in fields of maize, sorghum, soybean, and cotton (United States Department of Agriculture 1970; Spencer 1984). During 1982, costs for velvetleaf control in the United States in the above crops were estimated at $343 million (Spencer 1984). In a 1985 survey of the North Central States, velvetleaf was ranked as the major troublesome weed in soybeans by 9 of 14 states (Roeth 1987). In Canada, velvetleaf forms extensive weed infestations in most major maize and soybean growing areas of Ontario and Quebec and in a limited region of the Annapolis Valley, Nova Scotia (Doyon et al. 1986; Warwick and Black 1986).

Numerous studies in the United States have shown decreases in soybean yield due to competition from velvetleaf (Staniforth 1965; Eaton et al. 1976; Oliver 1979; Colton and Einhellig 1980; Hagood et al. 1980; Higgins et al. 1984a). Estimates of soybean losses

---

Fig. 1. A-F. A. Flowering specimen of *Abutilon theophrasti* × 0.5. B. Rootstock × 0.5. C. Flower × 2.25. D. Capsule × 1. E. Carpels × 1.5. F. Seeds × 4.5. Taken from United States Department of Agriculture (1970).

include: 31% crop loss at velvetleaf densities of three plants per 30 cm row in the Midwest (Staniforth 1965); 66% crop loss at velvetleaf densities of 130-240 plants m^2 in Kansas (Eaton et al. 1976); 13-27% crop loss at velvetleaf densities of 1.6-3.3 plants m^2 in Arkansas (Oliver 1979); 25% and 56% crop losses at velvetleaf densities of 5 and 40 plants m^2, respectively in Indiana (Hagood et al. 1980); 40-50% reduction in soybean yields at velvetleaf densities of 4-25 plants m^2 in Michigan (Dekker and Meggitt 1983); 12-31% reduction in soybean yields at velvetleaf densities of 0.7-2.5 plants m^2 in Illinois (Stoller and Woolley 1985); 37 and 72% crop loss at velvetleaf densities of 3 and 12 velvetleaf plants m^2 in Wisconsin (Sterling and Putnam 1987). Trials in South Dakota by Khedir (1981) indicated that velvetleaf delayed flowering and pod formation in soybean, reduced pod number/plant by 65%, and reduced pod weight by 35% and seed weight by 23%. Interference was greatest when velvetleaf emerged at the same time as the crop and when the height differential of the weed above the crop increased.

Studies by Campbell and Hartwig (1982) in Pennsylvania indicated up to 70% reduction in maize yields after 6 wk growth in velvetleaf infested fields. Studies by Sterling and Putnam (1987) in Wisconsin indicated that depending on planting date, growth of maize plants were inhibited from 51 to 91% by a plant of velvetleaf 5 cm away. In Kentucky, DeFelice et al. (1984) found that maize grain yield, number of grains per ear and soil moisture content were significantly lower on plots with full season velvetleaf competition. Studies by Schweizer and Bridge (1982) in Colorado reported reduction in sugarbeet root yields from 14 to 30% and recoverable sucrose levels of 14-31% with velvetleaf densities of 6-24 plants per 30-m row. Chandler (1977) reported in Mississippi that 8, 16, and 64 plants of velvetleaf per 12-m crop row competing for the full season caused 25, 50 and 98% reduction in cotton yield, respectively.

Velvetleaf has allelopathic effects on seed germination and seedling root elongation of other plants. In laboratory studies aqueous extracts from seeds and leaves depressed the germination and growth of alfalfa, maize, radish, soybean, and turnip seedlings (Gressel and Holm 1964; Colton and Einhellig 1980; Elmore 1980; Bhowmik and Doll 1982; Sterling et al. 1987). Interference by velvetleaf in soybean seedling water relations appeared to be the cause of inhibited seedling growth (Colton and Einhellig 1980). Studies by Sterling et al. (1987) also indicated potential autoinhibitory effects of the exudates from velvetleaf glandular trichomes. In field trials, velvetleaf residues decreased the yield of both maize and soybean (Bhowmik and Doll 1982). Many studies indicate that there is a high probability that allelopathic interactions play a significant role in the interference by velvetleaf in a variety of crop systems (Gressel and Holm 1964; Retig et al. 1972; Raynal and Bazzaz 1973). In field and greenhouse studies Sterling and Putnam (1987), attempting to separate allelopathic influences of velvetleaf from other mechanisms of interference, found that velvetleaf trichome exudates did not increase interference by velvetleaf. Microorganisms appear to rapidly detoxify the velvetleaf toxins and may reduce or eliminate their impact in the field.

Velvetleaf serves as the host for a number of crop pests, including fungal pathogens, insect pests and nematodes (see Section 13 for details).

(b) *Beneficial* — Velvetleaf is grown in China for its bast fiber, which is used to make rope, cordage, bags, coarse cloth, fishing nets, paper, etc. (Spencer 1984). The origin of velvetleaf in North America probably relates to its introduction as a potential fiber producer (Spencer 1984). Seeds contain 15-30% lipids and are suitable for use as food; apparently the seeds of velvetleaf are eaten in China and in Kashmir (Spencer 1984). Plants of velvetleaf contained 23% crude protein on a dry weight basis (Brown 1985).

(c) *Legislation* — Velvetleaf is not listed on any provincial weed or seed act.

4. Geographical Distribution

Introduced from Asia, velvetleaf occurs throughout the United States as a major agricultural weed between 32° and 45°N latitude (Spencer 1984). In Canada, velvetleaf occurs throughout the maize and soybean growing areas of Ontario and Quebec and in a limited region of the Annapolis Valley, Nova Scotia (Doyon et al. 1986; Warwick and Black 1986) (Fig. 2). Velvetleaf has also been reported as a weed in a waste area in York County, New Brunswick (Hinds 1986). Single herbarium specimens of velvetleaf from non-cultivated habitats have been collected from Alberta, Saskatchewan, Manitoba and Prince Edward Island; however, there is no indication that these introductions have persisted.

Velvetleaf has been introduced into Europe where it occurs as a weed of cultivated land and waste places, particularly in southeastern Europe and the Mediterranean region (Tutin et al. 1968). Velvetleaf is listed as one of the weed species of Finland that has immigrated with North American grain (Suominen 1979) and as a contaminant of bird seed into Britain (Hanson and Mason 1985). Velvetleaf continues to spread in Europe as seen, for example, by its first report in the Netherlands in 1981 (Rotteveel 1981).

5. Habitat

(a) *Climatic requirements* — Except for *Abutilon theophrasti* which occurs in temperate climates, the genus *Abutilon* occurs in tropical and subtropical climates (Stegink and Spencer 1988). In North America, velvetleaf is absent from the prairies where the dry climate and high evaporation stresses restrict growth (Lindsay 1953). Velvetleaf is continuing to expand northward into Canada with climates of progressively shorter growing seasons. Studies by Andersen et al. (1985) indicated that velvetleaf did not reproduce in Alaska with only 88 frost-free days.

(b) *Substratum* — Velvetleaf occurs on a range of soil types, including Gray-Brown Podzols (Lindsay 1953), alluvial flood plains (Oliver 1979) and sandy to clay loams with a pH of 6.1 to 7.8 (Dekker and Meggitt 1986). Weaver and Hamill (1985) compared the growth of velvetleaf at Harrow, Ontario on a sandy loam soil at three pH's and found the aboveground weight of velvetleaf significantly lower and S, Zn and Mn levels in leaf tissue higher at pH 4.8 compared with pHs 6.0 and 7.3.

(c) *Communities in which the species occurs* — Velvetleaf is found in waste places, vacant lots, gardens and cultivated fields, especially maize and soybean fields and along fence rows (United States Department of Agriculture 1970; Shaw et al. 1974). In the midwestern United States and southwestern Ontario, velvetleaf commonly occurs together with jimsonweed in the early successional annual community that develops on cultivated fields and field margins (Benner and Bazzaz 1987; Garbutt and Bazzaz 1987).

6. History

Conflicting reports as to the native origin of velvetleaf exist, including both India (United States Department of Agriculture 1970; Shaw et al. 1974; Flint et al. 1983) and China (Spencer 1984). In an unsuccessful attempt to determine the parental species of velvetleaf and hence the center of origin of the species, isozyme studies by Stegink and Spencer (1988) indicated that the progenitors of velvetleaf were not among the 11 tropical or subtropical *Abutilon* species surveyed. The above results, as well as the fact that velvetleaf is the only known *Abutilon* species that grows in temperate climates, it is absent from South or Central America and the inability to find biological control agents for this species in tropical and subtropical areas, have led Stegink and Spencer (1988) to suggest that the center of origin of velvetleaf was not in a tropical or subtropical region.

Velvetleaf was originally introduced into North America as a potential fiber crop in the mid-1700s (Spencer 1984). Commercial fiber production of velvetleaf was attempted by U.S. farmers for more than a century. These early experimental plantings were apparently

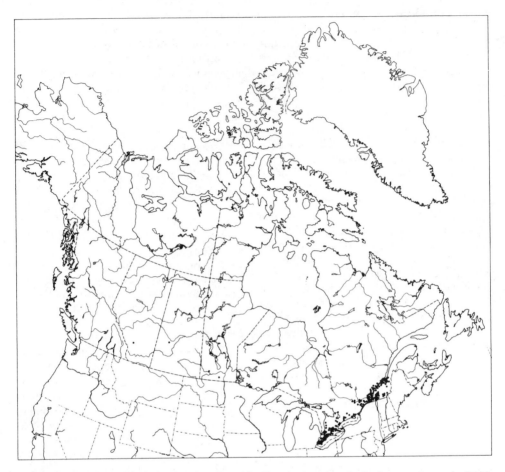

Fig. 2. Distribution map of *Abutilon theophrasti* in Canada, based on herbarium specimens in CAN, DAO, GUE, and TRT and data from Warwick and Black (1986) and Doyon et al. (1986). Velvetleaf has also been reported from York County, New Brunswick (Hinds 1986).

the source of velvetleaf as a weed in row crops. It is now a major weed throughout most of the United States (Spencer 1984) and eastern Canada (Doyon et al. 1986; Warwick and Black 1986). The history of invasion into eastern Canada has been summarized by Warwick and Black (1986) and into Quebec by Doyon et al. (1986). Herbarium records from the 1860s to ca. 1950 show that velvetleaf colonies were small and restricted to waste places and garden habitats. Large populations of velvetleaf were not found in cultivated fields in southwestern Ontario until the 1950s. It was thought at the time that the Canadian

climate would prove too severe for velvetleaf to expand to more northerly locations in Ontario and Quebec (Lindsay 1953; Rousseau 1968). However in a 35-yr period to 1984, velvetleaf extended its range as a weed of cultivated land to all but three counties in Ontario (Brown 1985; Warwick and Black 1986), 72 localities in Quebec (Doyon et al. 1986), and at least one location near Wilmo (Annapolis Valley), Nova Scotia (Warwick and Black 1986). Much of the spread of velvetleaf in eastern Canada would appear to be due to movement of seed in feed grain, mainly maize and soybeans, and on tillage and harvesting equipment (Brown 1985). Hinds (1986) has suggested that recent collections of velvetleaf from waste ground in York County, New Brunswick were probably introduced in grain.

7. Growth and Development

(a) *Morphology* — The hard seed coat of velvetleaf protects the seed from damage from ingestion by poultry and most livestock, and from storage in manure (Brown 1985; Authors' pers. obs.).

(b) *Perennation* — Velvetleaf is an annual, overwintering as seed.

(c) *Physiological data* — The adaptive effects of leaf thickness on photosynthesis and transpiration were studied in velvetleaf grown under high (600 μmol m^{-2} s^{-1}) and low (200 μmol m^{-2} s^{-2}) levels of photosynthetically active radiation (Yun and Taylor 1986). Plants grown under high light levels had thicker leaves and showed higher net photosynthetic rates, but little difference in transpiration rates compared to plants grown under low light levels.

Dry matter production in velvetleaf, a C_3 plant, was increased significantly by higher CO_2 concentrations. Controlled environment studies by Patterson (1979) showed that increasing CO_2 concentration over 350 ppm (vol/vol) to 600 and 1000 ppm increased the net assimilation rate. A comparison of photosynthetic, assimilation and transpiration rates, photosynthesis: transpiration ratios and water use efficiencies of soybean and velvetleaf are given in Patterson and Flint (1983). In studies by Hesketh et al. (1984), field-grown plants of velvetleaf subjected to additional light (1300 μmol m^{-2} s^{-2}) and to 1000 cm^3 m^{-3} of CO_2 responded to added CO_2 four times as much as to an added increment of irradiance. Garbutt and Bazzaz (1984) found that varying the concentration of CO_2 from 300 to 900 μL L^{-1} did not significantly affect time of flowering or number of fruit abortions of velvetleaf, but that flower, capsule and seed number all significantly decreased and individual seed weight

increased with increasing CO_2 concentrations.

Greenhouse studies by Patterson and Flint (1979) and Flint et al. (1983) showed that cool temperatures inhibited the growth of velvetleaf. Plants grown under cooler regimes (17/13°C and 26/17°C) showed decreased height, dry weight and leaf area compared to plants grown at higher temperatures (26/21°C and 32/23°C, respectively). Decreased growth was caused by decreases in net assimilation rate, photosynthetic rate and stomatal conductance. Goeschl et al. (1980) studied the effect of temperature on translocation and productivity of velvetleaf and found that a 10°C cold collar restricted the transport system and decreased photosynthesis compared to the control.

Studies by Munger et al. (1987a,b) indicated that as leaf water potential decreased in plants of velvetleaf, stomatal conductance, photosynthetic rate and transpiration rate all decreased. Photosynthetic rate increased as stomatal conductance increased up to 1.5 cm s^{-1} but not beyond, indicating no stomatal limitations to photosynthesis. Bunce (1986) examined response to humidity of net photosynthesis and leaf conductance of single attached leaves of velvetleaf and found a nearly linear response of net photosynthesis to substomatal CO_2 pressure, and that sensitivity of both photosynthesis and conductance to high vapor pressure increased progressively with increasing diurnal temperature fluctuations and air saturation deficit during growth.

The leaves of velvetleaf undergo a circadian rhythm in the orientation of the leaf from horizontal during the day to a near vertical position at night because of movement of the blade as a result of changes in diffusive resistance (Fuhrman and Koukkari 1981, 1982).

(d) *Phenology* — Emerging seedlings of velvetleaf immediately produce a tap root followed by development of lateral roots 1 or 2 d after emergence. Studies by Chandler and Dale (1974) in Mississippi showed that under noncompetitive field conditions maximum height and ground cover occurred 10 wk after emergence with peak capsule production at 13 wk. In eastern Canada, velvetleaf starts to flower in late August to September, setting seed from September to October, and continuing to produce flowers on axillary branches until the first frost. Flowering occurred 12–13 wk from sowing in 39 northeastern North American accessions of velvetleaf grown in a field plot in Ottawa, Ontario (Warwick and Black 1986). Oliver (1979) suggested that velvetleaf was highly photoperiodic (short-day) and that its competitive ability could be influenced by daylength. However, the northern range expansion of the species suggests a lack of strong photoperiodic control (Andersen et al. 1985).

(e) *Mycorrhiza* — No mycorrhizae have been reported for velvetleaf.

8. Reproduction

(a) *Floral biology* — Velvetleaf is a self-compatible, autogamous species (Winter 1960; Garbutt and Bazzaz 1984; authors' per. obs.). Flowers produced early in the season are prone to abortion, abscising 1–2 d after opening (Winter 1960). New flowers appear every 2 d. The flower is usually fertilized the day it opens and seeds mature 17–22 days after pollination (Winter 1960).

(b) *Seed production and dispersal* — Average number of seeds ranges from 35 to 45 per capsule, with 70–199 mature capsules per plant and seed production per plant ranges from 700 to 17 000 seeds (Winter 1960; Chandler and Dale 1974; Shaw et al. 1974; Hartgerink and Bazzaz 1984; Anderson et al. 1985; Brown 1985; Warwick and Black 1986). Individual seed weights have been reported to range from 4–6 mg seed^{-1} (Warwick and Black 1986) to 6–10 mg seed^{-1} (Hartgerink and Bazzaz 1984). Mean seed production varies among accessions, e.g., seed from Minnesota and Mississippi grown in Texas produced 74 and 118 mature seed capsules per plant, respectively (Andersen et al. 1985). Studies by Brown (1985) in Ridgetown, Ontario indicated that when grown in a monoculture in 45-cm rows, velvetleaf grew 3 m tall and produced c. 4032 kg seed ha^{-1}.

(c) *Viability of seeds and germination* — Velvetleaf seeds are known to remain viable for up to 50 yr when stored dry or in the soil. Estimates of percent germination after burial in the soil ranged from 58% after 2.5 yr in Mississippi (Egley and Chandler 1978), 70% after 3 yr in Illinois (Stoller and Wax 1974), 37% after 4 yr in Minnesota (Lueschen and Andersen 1980), 36% after 5.5 yr in Mississippi (Egley and Chandler 1983) to 43% after 39 yr of burial in the soil in Virginia (Toole and Brown 1946). Depth of burial from 8 to 38 cm had little effect on seed longevity (Egley and Chandler 1978). Velvetleaf persists in cultivated fields as a result of the ability of seeds to remain dormant and presumably resist microbial attack in the soil (Kremer et al. 1984). Factors influencing the latter include a physical barrier in the form of a dense palisade layer in the seed coat, tannin-like compounds localized within the seed coat that are inhibitory to certain microorganisms external to the seed, and antagonistic nonpathogenic bacteria located within the seed. Studies by Kremer (1986a) showed that seeds of velvetleaf released phenolic compounds which inhibited the growth of 117 to 202 bacteria and all of the fungi tested.

Velvetleaf characteristically shows a type of primary dormancy known as "hardseededness" which is caused by an impermeability of the seed coat to water (Egley and Chandler 1978; Lueschen and Andersen 1980; Horowitz and Taylorson 1984; Warwick and Black 1986). Most newly harvested velvetleaf seeds show hard seed dormancy. After 1 yr dry storage, seeds had lost their dormancy and became permeable, and seeds stored under high relative humidities became permeable more rapidly (Steinbauer and Grigsby 1959). Under field conditions, termination of this type of dormancy would result from naturally occurring fractures in the seed coat produced by alternate freezing-thawing, wetting-drying, etc. (LaCroix and Staniforth 1964). Studies by Egley and Chandler (1978), Lueschen and Andersen (1980) and Warwick and Black (1986) provided evidence of a second type of primary dormancy (embryo dormancy) in velvetleaf. Seeds exhibiting embryo dormancy do not germinate immediately after the seed coat is broken, but rather show sporadic germination patterns (Warwick and Black 1986). Studies by Warwick and Black (1986) on 39 northeastern North American populations of velvetleaf indicated differences in proportions of hard seed or seedcoat dormancy both among populations and among individuals within populations. Evidence was also provided for small proportions (up to 8% of the seeds) of embryo dormancy in 31 of the 39 populations studied (Warwick and Black 1986). The ability of a small percentage of the seeds to remain viable but dormant even after the seed coat has been broken contributes to the extreme difficulty of eradicating velvetleaf from the soil.

Various chemical and physical treatments can effectively break primary dormancy. The most effective method is the immersion of seed in water at 60–70°C for 5–10 min (Mulliken and Kust 1970; Khedir and Roeth 1981; Warwick and Black 1986). Other treatments include sulphuric acid and mechanical scarification (Steinbauer and Grigsby 1959; Khedir and Roeth 1978, 1981; Horowitz and Taylorson 1985). Exposure of seeds to gamma radiation did not affect hard seed coat dormancy but damaged the embryo (Horowitz and Taylorson 1985). Wolf (1986) found that 5 mM p-methoxycinnamaldehyde isolated from *Illicium verum* Hook. reduced the germination of velvetleaf seed to 1% of the untreated controls.

Studies have been conducted by Thompson et al. (1984a,b) on the maternal regulation of weed seed dormancy in velvetleaf, particularly maternal nutrition and environment using ovule cultures. Their studies indicated that abscisic acid at 1×10^{-7} M combined with 6% sucrose in the medium increased the development of embryo cultures and prevented precocious germination. Higher concentrations of abscisic acid inhibited embryo development.

In studies of six maize fields in Nebraska, Khedir and Roeth (1981) estimated an average of 51 million velvetleaf seeds ha^{-1} in the top 20 cm of soil, with 70% of these seeds found in the top 10 cm. Burnside et al. (1981) found that seed accessions from Nebraska buried in sandy loam and clay loam soils to a depth of 23 cm showed 43% germination in the first year and an average of 7–10% per yr over a 10-yr period. Similarly, estimates of 5–15% germination of the seeds in the soil per year were provided by Roeth (1987) in Nebraska.

Studies on seed depth in Ohio (Herr and Stroube 1970) indicated that as seed depth increased from 3 to 15 cm, with each successive 3 cm the number of established plants was reduced by 40–50% compared to the previous 3 cm. Studies by Chandler and Dale (1974) in Mississippi indicated greatest seedling emergence from a depth of 1.9 cm with good emergence at depths of 7.6 cm. Studies by Brown (1985) in Ontario indicated that most velvetleaf seeds germinated in the top 2.5 cm of soil, only one-third as many germinated from the 5.0-cm depth and very few seeds germinated from depths lower than this. Dekker and Meggitt (1986) found in field studies in Michigan that velvetleaf seedlings emerged from successively shallower depths in the soil as the growing season progressed, with the mean depth of emergence ranging from 1 to 4 cm below the soil surface.

Excessive exposure to heat impairs germination (Steinbauer and Grigsby 1959; La Croix and Staniforth 1964; Horowitz and Taylorson 1983). Laboratory studies by Horowitz and Taylorson (1984) indicated that germination of permeable seeds was optimal at 24–30°C and declined above 35°C. In Mississippi, Egley (1983) studied the field effect of soil solarization on velvetleaf germination using transparent mulch sheets and found that heat stress decreased the number of viable seeds buried in the soil.

Raynal and Bazzaz (1973) found that velvetleaf germinated over a range of water potentials from −1 to −9 bars, but that germination decreased rapidly with decreasing potential from 0 bars. Similarly, Becker (1979) found that increased moisture stress delayed initial germination and slowed root and shoot elongation of seedlings. Studies by Horowitz and Taylorson (1983) indicated that the rate of water uptake by seeds increased with the temperature of imbibition. Pareja and Staniforth (1985) examined the effect of soil structure on seed germination of velvetleaf and found that finer seedbeds provided better conditions for germination and better seed/soil contact improving the capacity of the seed to take up H_2O and reduce evaporative H_2O losses. Holm (1972) found that velvetleaf germination was inhibited by decreased O_2 levels. Parrish and Bazzaz (1982) found that seeds of velvetleaf germinated over a range of nutrient concentrations, with the highest total germination at moderate nutrient concentrations and decreased germination at the highest concentrations.

(d) *Vegetative reproduction* — Velvetleaf does not reproduce vegetatively.

9. Hybrids
Hybridization between *A. theophrasti* and other species has not been reported.

10. Population Dynamics
Seedling emergence in the field can be quite synchronous, producing densities of up to 400 seedlings m^{-2} (Hartgerink and Bazzaz 1984). Studies by Lee and Bazzaz (1980) showed that plants grown in the greenhouse at high densities (100 plants m^{-2}) suffered 75% defoliation and a 50% decrease in seed production as compared with low densities (16 plants m^{-2}). Willson et al. (1987) studied sibling competition in velvetleaf. In a greenhouse experiment, seeds obtained from greenhouse-grown plants were grown under different densities and in competition with sibs and nonsibs. At the end of the experiment, height and dry weight of high-density plants were significantly smaller than those of single plants. Single seeds germinated less success-

fully than grouped seeds. Sibs of velvetleaf survived significantly better than nonsibs, but plant biomass was similar for both. Thus positive sib effects were seen with respect to survival but there was no evidence that competition for limited resources was more intense among sibs than among nonsibs.

Velvetleaf is an excellent competitor due to its rapid root growth compared to other weed species, and its ability to produce sugars at a relatively efficient rate in low sunlight allowing growth under partially shaded crop canopies (Roeth 1987). Investigators have attributed the interference of velvetleaf with crop growth to allelopathy (see Section 3a) and to competition for water (Hagood et al. 1980; Dekker and Meggitt 1983), light (Stoller and Woolley 1985), and nutrients (Oliver 1979).

Pacala and Silander (1987) studied spatially local interference among individuals of pigweed and velvetleaf. They found that although survivorship was density-independent for both species, individual fecundities were affected by the local population density of velvetleaf and pigweed near each plant. Forcella (1987) compared the competitiveness of two lines of tall fescue (*Festuca arundinacea* Schreb.) with velvetleaf and found that the fescue line with the greatest leaf area could suppress velvetleaf growth by 14–24%. Jordan (1979) compared the growth of velvetleaf with and without competition from maize in Iowa. Weed height increased by 13% in competition with maize, the number of branches was reduced by 99%, fresh weight by 96%, and number of inflorescences by 90%. Studies were conducted by Oliver (1979) in Arkansas to determine the influence of early and late soybean planting dates on the competitiveness of velvetleaf. Velvetleaf at densities of one plant per 30 and 60 cm of crop row emerging with soybeans in mid-May were twice as competitive as those emerging with soybeans planted in late June due to the shortday-photoperiodic response of velvetleaf. Full season competition with soybeans reduced the leaf area index of velvetleaf 73–76%. Similar studies by Higgins et al. (1984b) in Iowa showed that plants of velvetleaf growing without competition had nine times the dry matter compared with plants intercropped with soybean.

Parrish and Bazzaz (1982, 1985) compared velvetleaf growth under five nutrient levels, ranging from no additional fertilizer in a greenhouse soil mixture up to 0.15 g of N:P:K (3:20:30) per 100 g of soil. They found that seedling survival was reduced under higher nutrient concentrations and that both seedlings and older plants grew fastest at intermediate nutrient concentrations. Plant tissue concentrations of N, K, Ca, Mg and P increased with increased soil nutrient concentrations and did not decline at higher soil nutrient concentrations. Seed output (seed number and size) increased as plant size increased, but there was no change in percent allocation of plant weight to seed production at higher soil and plant nutrient concentrations. In two competition experiments designed to eliminate the effects of genotype, seed size and germination, Parrish and Bazzaz (1985) found that plants from seeds produced under higher nutrient conditions showed greater competitive ability compared to those produced at lower soil nutrient levels.

The species has been shown to have a broad response to several resource gradients (Zangerl and Bazzaz 1984). Garbutt and Bazzaz (1987) surveyed 20 maternal families of velvetleaf from a field in Illinois for response to light and nutrient gradients. The structure of the population niche for both biomass and reproductive output was found to be quite different on the two gradients. On the light gradient there was a greater diversity of responses among the families, while on the nutrient gradient the families responded in a similar manner. On both gradients the plants showed a significant genotype/environmental interaction.

11. Response to Herbicides and other Chemicals

Because velvetleaf germinates throughout the season, diverse practices are needed to sustain effective control of velvetleaf infestations, including crop rotation, multiple herbicide applications and cultivation. Once established in a field it is very difficult to eradicate velvetleaf so that preventive practices to reduce the chances of its introduction into an uninfested field should receive high priority (Roeth 1987). Herbicides containing metribuzin are preferred for pre-emergence velvetleaf control (Brown 1985; Roeth 1987). Postemergence herbicides that are effective on velvetleaf include the following chemicals either singly or in combination: atrazine, 2,4-D, bentazon, bromoxynil, cyanazine, dicamba, metribuzin, linuron (Brown 1985; Roeth 1987; Ontario Ministry of Agriculture and Food 1988). Atrazine applied at less than 2 kg ha^{-1} to the soil is often not adequate for velvetleaf control. Successful postemergence control depends on application to velvetleaf at the two- to four-leaf stage. According to Roeth (1987), the spread of velvetleaf is in part due to the trend of increased use of maize herbicide combinations with lower rates of atrazine, decreased postemergence use of 2,4-D in maize, and less intensive tillage, cultivation and roguing.

Recent reports indicate the presence of triazine-resistant velvetleaf in Maryland (Ritter 1986). The population was found in a maize field that had been 5 yr in a continuous maize, no tillage system. Andersen and Gronwald (1987) crossed the resistant biotype with a susceptible biotype and found that atrazine tolerance was not cytoplasmically inherited like most known triazine-resistant weeds, but that it was controlled by a single partially dominant gene which enhanced atrazine metabolism in the tolerant biotype (Gronwald et al. 1987).

12. Response to other Human Manipulations

Benner and Bazzaz (1985) examined the effects of timing of nutrient availability on both seed quantity and seed quality of velvetleaf. The species showed an opportunistic response, being able to use nutrients supplied at different times for reproduction; for example when nutrient availability was delayed, plants were able to extend the fruiting period. However, plants were not able to completely use a pulse of nutrients that became available after fruit maturation had begun. Benner and Bazzaz (1987) studied the effects of early and late nutrient addition on competition within pure and mixed pairs of *A. theophrasti* and *Datura stramonium*, varying relative emergence times of the two species. As expected, the addition of nutrients resulted in higher seed production than in control plants, although plant age and developmental stage affected the degree of response to nutrient addition. Timing of the nutrient additions did not affect the competitive relationships of the two species. Studies by Chandler and Wauchope (1979) showed that nitrogen fertilization up to 220 kg N ha^{-1} generally did not affect dry matter production or nutrient removal by velvetleaf.

Lueschen and Andersen (1980) compared the effect of a variety of cultural practices on longevity of seed in the soil. Tilling was particularly effective in hastening declines in the seed population, e.g., after 4 yr in a fallowed field subjected to intensive tillage only 10% of the seed remained.

13. Response to Parasites

(a) *Insects and other nondomestic organisms* — Nymphs of *Niesthrea louisianica* Sailer (Hemiptera: Rhophalidae), the scentless plant bug, can cause extensive reductions in the reproductive ability of velvetleaf in Mississippi and is potentially an agent for biological control (Jones et al. 1985; Spencer 1987). Large populations of the insect were found on populations of velvetleaf in cotton and soybean fields in Mississippi. Laboratory studies indicated 98–99% reduction in viable seed production in biotypes of velvetleaf from Mississippi and Minnesota in comparison with insect-free control plants (Patterson et al. 1987).

In the Mississippi delta, velvetleaf is a potentially important early season host for larval generations of both *Heliothis virescens* (F.), tobacco budworm, and *H. zea* (Boddic), bollworm (Stadelbacher 1981). Both species

were found feeding in the plant terminal, on young leaves and on immature fruits.

In Iowa, Jacques and Peters (1971) found that velvetleaf serves as an alternative host for the flea beetle, *Systena frontalis* (F.) which is a pest of maize.

(b) *Microorganisms and viruses* — The pathogens, *Verticillium dahliae* Kleb. and *V. nigrescens* Pethybr. caused symptoms of wilt on velvetleaf in Ontario (McKeen and Thorpe 1973, cf. Ginns 1986) and in Wisconsin (Sickinger et al. 1987). *Verticillium dahliae* has been suggested as a biocontrol agent of velvetleaf (Green and Wiley 1987); however, soybean inoculated with *V. dahliae* also suffered rapid and severe wilting in the greenhouse (Epstein and Tacibana 1982). The United States Department of Agriculture (1960) lists a number of fungi on velvetleaf in the United States: *Alternaria abutilonis* (Pass.) Schwarze, leaf spot; *Cercospora abutilonis* Tehon & Daniels, leaf spot; *C. althaeina* Sacc.; *Cladosporium herbarum* (Pers.) Link: Fr., secondary leaf spot; *Colletotrichum malvarum* (A. Braun & Casp.), leaf spot; *Macrophomina phaseoli* (Maubl.) Ashby, stem rot; *Phyllosticta althaeina* Sacc., leaf spot; *Phymatotrichum omnivorum* (Shear) Duggar, root rot; *Puccinia heterospora* Berk. & Curtis, rust. Velvetleaf serves as the host of three soybean pathogens, *Phomopsis sojae*, *Colletotrichum dematium* (Pers.:Fr.) Grove and *C. gloeosporioides* (Penz.) Penz. & Sacc. in Illinois (Hepperley et al. 1980).

The use of *Fusarium lateritium* Nees, a natural pathogen of velvetleaf (Walker 1981), has received considerable attention as a mycoherbicide in biological control of the species (Boyette and Walker 1985, 1986). In greenhouse studies, *F. lateritium* effectively suppressed velvetleaf when sprays containing conidia of the fungus or fungus-infested granules were applied. A number of factors influence biocontrol of velvetleaf with *F. lateritium*, including seedling size, postinoculative air temperature, and an adequate dew period. Satisfactory control (80%) was achieved if the plants had fewer than seven leaves, air temperature was 25°C with a dew period of 16 h. In a 2-yr field trial, postemergence foliar applications of the fungus controlled velvetleaf by 27–40%, while pre-emergence applications of the fungus formulated as granules gave 35–46% control of velvetleaf.

A foliar pathogen of velvetleaf, *Colletotrichum coccodes* (Wallr.) Hughes (Gotlieb et al. 1987; Raid and Pennypacker 1987), is another potential mycoherbicide for velvetleaf control (Wymore and Watson 1986; Wymore et al. 1987). Applied as a spore suspension, *C. coccodes* causes severe anthracnose on inoculated leaves, premature abscission of the diseased leaves, and if conditions are optimum, death of the plant. Weed control can be substantially improved if the bioherbicide is combined with the plant growth regulator thidiazuron (Wymore et al. 1987).

Studies of the microbial populations of two velvetleaf sites in Missouri were made by Kremer et al. (1984) and Kremer (1986b). A total of 22 fungi were isolated from the root zone of velvetleaf, the most abundant being *Fusarium* spp., *Gliocladium roseum*, *Peniccillium frequentans*, *Trichoderma viride* and *Verticillium* spp. They also found an association of sporulating fungi comprising *Alternaria alternata* (Fr.) Keissel., *Cladosporium cladosporioides* (Fres.) de Vries, *Epicoccum purpurascens* Ehrenb. ex Schlecht, and *Fusarium* spp. on the surface of velvetleaf seeds. About 80% of the bacteria isolated from within seeds of velvetleaf were antagonistic to fungi borne on the seed surface. These seedborne microorganisms, therefore, appear to act as a barrier against potential seed pathogens. Earlier studies by Kirkpatrick and Bazzaz (1979) on velvetleaf also provided evidence for both internally and numerous (three to four fungal spp. per seed) externally seed borne fungi. Root extracts of velvetleaf inhibited the growth of these fungi.

(c) *Other parasites* — The United States Department of Agriculture (1960) lists *Heterodera marioni* (Cornu) Goodey and *Meloidogyne* sp., root knot nematodes, as associated with velvetleaf. In the greenhouse, velvetleaf was parasitized by *Meloidogyne incognita* (Kofoid and White, 1919) Chitwood, 1949 (Gaskin 1958) and *Meloidogyne hapla* Chitwood, the northern root-knot nematode (Edwards and Jones 1984).

ACKNOWLEDGMENTS

We wish to thank J. Cayouette and C. Crompton, Biosystematics Research Center for their comments on the manuscript.

Alex, J. F. and Switzer, C. M. 1970. Ontario Weeds. Ontario Ministry of Agriculture and Food. Publication 505. Ontario Agricultural College, Guelph, Ont. 200 pp.

Alex, J. F., Cayouette, R. and Mulligan, G. A. 1980. Common and botanical names of weeds in Canada. Agriculture Canada, Ottawa, Ontario. Publ. 1397 132 pp.

Andersen, R. N. and Gronwald, J. W. 1987. Noncytoplasmic inheritance of atrazine tolerance in velvetleaf (*Abutilon theophrasti*). Weed Sci. 35: 496–498.

Andersen, R. N., Menges, R. M. and Conn, J. S. 1985. Variability in velvetleaf (*Abutilon theophrasti*) and reproduction beyond its current range in North America. Weed Sci. 33: 507–512.

Becker, R. L. 1979. Weed seedling emergence under osmotic stress. [Abstract]. Proc. North Cent. Weed Control Conf., 34: 45.

Benner, B. L. and Bazzaz, F. A. 1985. Response of the annual *Abutilon theophrasti* Medic. (Malvaceae) to timing of nutrient availability. Am. J. Bot. 72: 320–323.

Benner, B. L. and Bazzaz, F. A. 1987. Effects of timing of nutrient addition on competition within and between two annual plant species. J. Ecol. 75: 229–245.

Bhowmik, P. C. and Doll, J. D. 1982. Corn and soybean response to allelopathic effects of weed and crop residues. Agron. J. 74: 601–606.

Bolkhovskikh, Z., Grif, V. and Matvejeva, T. 1969. Chromosome numbers of flowering plants. Acad. Sci. USSR, V. L. Komarov Botanical Institute.

Boyette, C. D. and Walker, H. L. 1985. Factors influencing biocontrol of velvetleaf (*Abutilon theophrasti*) and prickly sida (*Sida spinosa*) with *Fusarium lateritium*. Weed Sci. 33: 209–211.

Boyette, C. D. and Walker, H. L. 1986. Evaluation of *Fusarium lateritium* as a biological herbicide for controlling velvetleaf (*Abutilon theophrasti*) and prickly sida (*Sida spinosa*). Weed Sci. 34: 106–1

Brown, R. H. 1985. Velvetleaf (*Abutilon theophrasti* Medic.) Factsheet Advisory Information. Ontario Ministry of Agriculture and Food. Agdex No. 642V. 3 pp.

Bunce, J. A. 1986. Responses of gas exchange to humidity in populations of three herbs from environments differing in atmospheric water. Oecologia (Berlin). **71**: 117–120.

Burnside, O. C., Fenster, C. R., Evetts, L. L. and Muvom, R. F. 1981. Germination of exhumed weed seed in Nebraska. Weed Sci. **29**: 577–586.

Campbell, R. T. and Hartwig, N. L. 1982. Competition between corn, velvetleaf and yellow nutsedge. Proc. Northeastern Weed Sci. Soc. **36**: 2–4.

Chandler, J. M. 1977. Competition of spurred anoda, velvetleaf, prickly sida, and venice mallow in cotton. Weed Sci. **25**: 151–158.

Chandler, J. M. and Dale, J. E. 1974. Comparative growth of four Malvaceae species. Proc. South Weed Sci. Soc. **27**: 116–117.

Chandler, J. M. and Wauchope, R. D. 1979. Relative utilization of nutrients by five broadleaf weed species. Ann. Meeting Weed Sci. Soc.: 85–86. (Abstr.)

Colton, C. E. and Einhellig, F. A. 1980. Allelopathic mechanisms of velvetleaf (*Abutilon theophrasti* Medic., Malvaceae) on soybean. Am. J. Bot. **67**: 1407–1413.

DeFelice, M. S., Witt, W. W. and Slack, C. H. 1984. Velvetleaf competition with conventional and no-tillage corn. Proc. North Cent. Weed Cont. Conf., Winnipeg, Manitoba, Canada **39**: 45–46. (Abstr.)

Dekker, J. and Meggitt, W. F. 1983. Interference between velvetleaf (*Abutilon theophrasti* Medic.) and soybean (*Glycine max* (L.) Merr.) I. Growth. Weed Res. **23**: 91–101.

Dekker, J. and Meggitt, W. F. 1986. Field emergence of velvetleaf *Abutilon theophrasti* in relation to time and burial depth. Iowa State J. Res. **61**: 65–80.

Doyon, D., Bouchard, C. J. and Néron, R. 1986. Répartition géographique et importance dans les cultures de quatre adventices du Québec: *Abutilon theophrasti, Amaranthus powellii, Acalypha rhomboidea* et *Panicum dichotomiflorum*. Nat. Can. **113**: 115–123.

Eaton, B. J., Russ, O. G. and Feltner, K. C. 1976. Competition of velvetleaf, prickly sida, and venice mallow in soybeans. Weed Sci. **24**: 224–228.

Edwards, W. H. and Jones, R. K. 1984. Additions to the weed host range of *Meliodogyne hapla*.

Plant Dis. **68**: 811–812.

Egley, G. H. 1983. Weed seed and seedling reductions by soil solarization with transparent polyethylene sheets. Weed Sci. **31**: 404–409.

Egley, G. H. and Chandler, J. M. 1978. Germination and viability of weed seeds after 2.5 years in a 50-year buried seed study. Weed Sci. **26**: 230–239.

Egley, G. H. and Chandler, J. M. 1983. Longevity of weed seeds after 5.5 years in the Stoneville 50-year buried-seed study. Weed Sci. **31**: 264–270.

Elmore, C. D. 1980. Inhibition of turnip (*Brassica rapa*) seed germination by velvetleaf (*Abutilon theophrasti*) seed. Weed Sci. **28**: 658–660.

Epstein, A. H. and Tacibana, H. 1982. Verticillum wilt in soybeans. Proc. Iowa Acad. Sci. **89**: 2.

Flint, E. P., Patterson, D. T. and Beyers, J. L. 1983. Interference and temperature effects on growth of cotton (*Gossypium hirsutum*), spurred anoda (*Anoda cristata*), and velvetleaf (*Abutilon theophrasti*). Weed Sci. **31**: 892–898.

Forcella, F. 1987. Tolerance of weed competition associated with high leaf-area expansion rate in tall fescue. Crop. Sci. **27**: 146–147.

Fuhrman, M. H. and Koukkari, W. L. 1981. Anatomical and physiological characteristics of the petiole of *Abutilon theophrasti* in relation to circadian leaf movements. Physiol. Plant. **51**: 309–313.

Fuhrman, M. H. and Koukkari, W. L. 1982. Characteristics of the circadian rhythm in diffusive resistance of *Abutilon theophrasti* leaves in humid and dry environments. Chronobiologia **9**: 21–32.

Garbutt, K. and Bazzaz, F. A. 1984. The effects of elevated CO_2 on plants III. Flower, fruit and seed production and abortion. New Phytol. **98**: 433–446.

Garbutt, K. and Bazzaz, F. A. 1987. Population niche structure-differential response of *Abutilon theophrasti* progeny to resource gradients. Oecologia (Berlin) **72**: 291–296.

Gaskin, T. A. 1958. Weed hosts of *Meloidogyne incognita* in Indiana. Plant Dis. Rep. **42**: 802–803.

Ginns, J. H. 1986. Compendium of plant disease and decay fungi in Canada 1960–1980. Agric. Canada Res. Branch Publ. 1813. 416 pp.

Goeschl, J. D., Fares, Y., Magnuson, C. E., Strain, B. R. and Nelson, C. E. 1980. Role of translocation in productivity of velvetleaf *Abutilon theophrasti* biotypes as determined by continuous carbon-11 tracer. Plant Physiol. **65** (6 Suppl.): 150.

Gotlieb, A. R., Watson, A. K. and Poirier, C. 1987. First report of *Colletotrichum coccodes* on velvetleaf. Plant Dist. **71**: 281.

Green, R. J. and Wiley, G. L. 1987. *Verticillium dahliae* as a biocontrol agent of velvetleaf, *Abutilon theophrasti*. Can. J. Pl. Pathol. **9**: 81.

Gressel, J. G. and Holm, L. G. 1964. Chemical inhibition of crop germination by weed seeds and the nature of inhibition by *Abutilon theophrasti*. Weed Res. **4**: 44–53.

Gronwald, J. W., Andersen, R. N. and Yec, C. 1987. Enhanced atrazine metabolism in an atrazine-tolerant velvetleaf (*Abutilon theophrasti* Medic.) biotype. Plant Physiol. **83**: 135. (Abstr.)

Hagood, E. S., Jr., Bauman, T. T., Williams, T. L., Jr. and Schreiber, M. M. 1980. Growth analysis of soybeans (*Glycine max*) in competition with velvetleaf (*Abutilon theophrasti*). Weed Sci. **28**: 729–734.

Hanson, C. G. and Mason, J. L. 1985. Bird seed aliens in Britain. Watsonia **15**: 237–252.

Hartgerink, A. P. and Bazzaz, F. A. 1984. Seedling-scale environmental heterogeneity influences individual fitness and population structure. Ecology **65**: 198–206.

Hepperly, P. R., Kirkpatrick, B. L. and Sinclair, J. B. 1980. *Abutilon theophrasti*; wild host for three fungal parasites of soybean. Phytopathology **70**: 307–310.

Herr, D. E. and Stroube, E.W. 1970. Velvetleaf control as influenced by herbicide placement and seed depth. Weed Sci. **18**: 459–461.

Hesketh, J. D., Woolley, J. T. and Peters, D. B. 1984. Leaf photosynthetic CO_2 exchange rates in light and CO_2 enriched environments. Photosynthetica **18**: 536–540.

Higgins, R. A., Pedigo, L. P. and Staniforth, D. W. 1984a. Effect of velvetleaf competition and defoliation simulating a green cloverworm (Lepidoptera: Noctuidae) outbreak in Iowa on indeterminate soybean yield, yield components and economic decision levels. Environ. Entomol. **13**: 917–925.

Higgins, R. A., Staniforth, D. W. and Pedigo, L. P. 1984b. Effects of weed density and defoliated or undefoliated soybeans (*Glycine max*) on velvetleaf (*Abutilon theophrasti*) development. Weed Sci. **32**: 511–519.

Hinds, H. R. 1986. Flora of New Brunswick. Primrose Press, Fredericton, New Brunswick.

Holm, R. E. 1972. Volatile metabolites controlling germination in buried weed seeds. Plant Physiol. **50**: 293–297.

Horowitz, M. and Taylorson, R. B. 1983. Effect of high temperatures on imbibition, germination, and thermal death of velvetleaf (*Abutilon theophrasti*) seeds. Can. J. Bot. **61**: 2269–2276.

Horowitz, M. and Taylorson, R. B. 1984. Hard-seededness and germinability of velvetleaf (*Abutilon theophrasti*) as affected by temperature and moisture. Weed Sci. **32**: 111–115.

Horowitz, M. and Taylorson, R. B. 1985. Behaviour of hard and permeable seeds of *Abutilon theophrasti* Medic. (velvetleaf). Weed Res. **25**: 363–372.

Jacques, R. L., Jr. and Peters, D. C. 1971. Biology of *Systema frontalis*, with special reference to corn. J. Econ. Entomol. **64**: 135–138.

Jones, W. A., Jr., Walker, H. E., Quinuby, P. C. and Ouzts, J. D. 1985. Biology of *Niestbrea louisianica* (Hemiptera: Rhopalidae) on selected plants, and its potential for biocontrol of velvetleaf, *Abutilon theophrasti* (Malvaceae). Ann. Entomol. Soc. Am. **78**: 326–330.

Jordan, J. L. 1979. The growth habit of Pennsylvania smartweed and velvetleaf. Proc. North Cent. Weed Cont. Conf. **34**: 48. (Abstr.)

Khedir, K. D. 1981. Velvetleaf (*Abutilon theophrasti*; Medic.) competition with soybean (*Glycine max*). Proc. North Cent. Weed Cont. Conf. **36**: 23. (Abstr.)

Khedir, K. D. and Roeth, F. W. 1978. Velvetleaf seed population and control in central Nebraska. Proc. North Cent. Weed Cont. Conf. **33**: 44–45. (Abstr.)

Khedir, K. D. and Roeth, F. W. 1981. Velvetleaf (*Abutilon theophrasti*) seed populations in six continuous-corn (*Zea mays*) fields. Weed Sci. **29**: 485–490.

Kirkpatrick, B. L. and Bazzaz, F. A. 1979. Influence of certain fungi on seed germination and seedling survival of four colonizing annuals. J. Appl. Ecol. **16**: 515–527.

Kremer, R. J. 1986a. Antimicrobial activity of velvetleaf (*Abutilon theophrasti*) seeds. Weed Sci. **34**: 617–622.

Kremer, R. J. 1986b. Microorganisms associated with velvetleaf (*Abutilon theophrasti*) seeds on the soil surface. Weed Sci. **34**: 233–236.

Kremer, R. J., Hughes, Jr., L. B. and Aldrich, R. J. 1984. Examination of microorganisms and deterioration resistance mechanisms associated with velvetleaf seed. Agron. J. **76**: 745–749.

LaCroix, L. J. and Staniforth, D. W. 1964. Seed dormancy in velvetleaf. Weeds **12**: 171–174.

Lee, T. D. and Bazzaz, F. A. 1980. Effects of defoliation and competition on growth and reproduction in the annual plant *Abutilon* *theophrasti*. J. Ecol. **68**: 813–821.

Lindsay, D. R. 1953. Climate as a factor influencing the mass ranges of weeds. Ecology **34**: 308–321.

Lueschen, W. E. and Andersen, R. N. 1980. Longevity of velvetleaf (*Abutilon theophrasti*) seeds in soil under agricultural practices. Weed Sci. **28**: 341–346.

Mulliken, J. A. and Kust, C. A. 1970. Germination of velvetleaf. Weed Sci. **18**: 561–564.

Munger, P. H., Chandler, J. M. and Cothren, J. T. 1987a. Effect of water stress of photosynthetic parameters of soybean (*Glycine max*) and velvetleaf (*Abutilon theophrasti*). Weed Sci. **35**: 15–21.

Munger, P. H., Chandler, J. M., Cothren, J. T. and Hons, F. M. 1987b. Soybean (*Glycine max*) velvetleaf (*Abutilon theophrasti*) interspecific competition. Weed Sci. **35**: 647–653.

Oliver, L. R. 1979. Influence of soybean planting date on velvetleaf competition. Weed Sci. **27**: 183–188.

Ontario Ministry of Agriculture and Food. 1988. Guide to weed control. OMAF, Toronto, Ont. Publ. 75. 200 pp.

Pacala, S. W. and Silander, Jr., J. A. 1987. Neighbourhood interference among velvetleaf, *Abutilon theophrasti* and pigweed, *Amaranthus retroflexus*. Oikos **48**: 217–224.

Pareja, M. R. and Staniforth, D. W. 1985. Seed-soil microsite characteristics in relation to weed seed germination. Weed Sci. **33**: 190–195.

Parrish, J. A. D. and Bazzaz, F. A. 1982. Responses to plants from three successional communities to a nutrient gradient. J. Ecol. **70**: 233–248.

Parrish, J. A. D. and Bazzaz, F. A. 1985. Nutrient content of *Abutilon theophrasti* seeds and the competitive ability of the resulting plants. Oecologia (Berl.) **65**: 247–251.

Patterson, D. T. 1979. The effects of CO_2 concentration on the growth of C_3 and C_4 weed and crop species. Agron. 92. (Abstr.)

Patterson, D. T. and Flint, E. P. 1979. Effects of chilling on cotton (*Gossypium hirsutum*), velvetleaf (*Abutilon theophrasti*) and spurred anoda (*Anoda cristata*). Weed Sci. **27**: 473–479.

Patterson, D. T. and Flint, E. P. 1983. Comparative water relations, photosynthesis and growth of soybean (*Glycine max*) and seven associated weeds. Weed Sci. **31**: 318–323.

Patterson, D. T., Coffin, R. D. and Spencer, N. R. 1987. Effects of temperature on damage to velvetleaf (*Abutilon theophrasti*) by the scentless plant bug *Niesthrea louisianica*. Weed Sci. **35**: 324–327.

Raid, R. N. and Pennypacker, S. 1987. Weeds as hosts for *Colletotrichum coccodes*. Pl. Dis. **71**: 643–646.

Raynal, D. J. and Bazzaz, F. A. 1973. Establishment of early successional plant populations on forest and prairie soil. Ecol. **54**: 1335–1341.

Retig, B., Holm, L. G. and Struckmeyer, B. E. 1972. Effects of weeds on the anatomy of roots of cabbage and tomato. Weed Sci. **20**: 33–36.

Ritter, R. L. 1986. Triazine resistant velvetleaf and giant foxtail control in no-tillage corn. Proc. Northeast. Weed. Sci. Soc. **40**: 50–52.

Roeth, F. W. 1987. Velvetleaf-coming on strong. Crops Soils Mag. **39**: 10–11.

Rotteveel, A. J. W. 1981. Alien weeds, a menace to the Netherlands. Ann. Rep. Neth. Plantenziektenkundige Dienst. pp. 145–149.

Rousseau, C. 1968. Histoire, habitat et distribution de 220 plantes introduite au Québec. Nat. Can. (Que.), **95**: 49–169.

Schweizer, E. E. and Bridge, L. D. 1982. Sunflower (*Helianthus annuus*) and velvetleaf (*Abutilon theophrasti*) interference in sugarbeets (*Beta vulgaris*). Weed Sci. **30**: 514–519.

Shaw, J. E., Pitblado, R. E. and Brown, R. H. 1974. Velvetleaf. OMAF factsheet AGDEX 642. 4 pp.

Sickinger, S. M., Grau, C. R. and Harvey, R. G. 1987. *Verticillium* wilt of velvetleaf, *Abutilon theophrasti*. Plant Dis. **71**: 415–418.

Spencer, N. R. 1984. Velvetleaf, *Abutilon theophrasti* (Malvaceae), history and economic impact in the United States. Econ. Bot. **38**: 407–416.

Spencer, N. R. 1987. *Niesthrea louisianica* (Hemiptera, Rhopalidae) reduces velvetleaf *Abutilon theophrasti* (Malvaceae) and viability. Environ. Entomol. **16**: 963–966.

Stadelbacher, E. A. 1981. Role of early-season wild and naturalized host plants in the build-up of the F_1 generation of *Heliothis zea* and *H. virescens* in the delta of Mississippi. Environ. Entomol. **10**: 766–770.

Staniforth, D. W. 1965. Competitive effects of three foxtail species on soybeans. Weeds **13**: 191–193.

Stegink, S. J. and Spencer, N. R. 1988. Using protein electrophoresis to investigate the phylogeny of velvetleaf (*Abutilon theophrasti*). Weed Sci. **36**: 172–175.

Steinbauer, G. P. and Grigsby, B. 1959. Methods of obtaining field and laboratory germination of seeds of bindweeds, lady's thumb and velvetleaf. Weeds **7**: 41–46.

Sterling, T. M. and Putnam, A. R. 1987. Possible role of glandular trichome exudates in interference by velvetleaf (*Abutilon theophrasti*). Weed Sci. **35**: 308–314.

Sterling, T. M., Houtz, R. L. and Putnam, A. R. 1987. Phytotoxic exudates from velvetleaf (*Abutilon theophrasti*) glandular trichomes. Am. J. Bot. **74**: 543–550.

Stoller, E. W. and Wax, L. M. 1974. Dormancy changes and the fate of some annual weed seeds in the soil. Weed Sci. **22**: 151–155.

Stoller, E. W. and Woolley, J. T. 1985. Competition for light by broad leaf weeds in soybeans (*Glycine max*). Weed Sci. **33**: 199–202.

Suominen, J. 1979. The grain immigrant flora of Finland. Acta. Bot. Fennica **111**: 1–108.

Thompson, L. K., Leather, G. R. and Hale, M. G. 1984a. The in-vitro culture of exised ovules from velvetleaf (*Abutilon theophrasti*). Weed Sci. **32**: 792–797.

Thompson, L. K., Leather, G. R. and Hale, M. G. 1984b. Abscisic acid and sucrose control of velvetleaf (*Abutilon theophrasti*) ovule development in vitro. Weed Sci. **32**: 798–801.

Toole, E. H. and Brown, E. 1946. Final results of the buried seed experiment. J. Agric. Res. **72**: 201–210.

Tutin, T. G., Heywood, V. H., Burges, N. A., Moore, D. M., Valentine, D. H., Walter, S. M. and Webb, D. A. (eds.). 1968. Flora Europaea. Vol. 2. Cambridge University Press, Cambridge, U.K.

United States Department of Agriculture. 1960. Index of plant diseases in the United States Agric. Res. Serv. Agric. Handbook 165. 531 pp.

United States Department of Agriculture. 1970. Selected weeds of the United States. Agric. Res. Serv. Agric. Handbook 366. 463 pp.

Walker, H. L. 1981. *Fusarium lateritium*: a pathogen of spurred anoda (*Anoda cristata*), prickly sida (*Sida spinosa*) and velvetleaf (*Abutilon theophrasti*). Weed Sci. **29**: 629–631.

Warwick, S. I. and Black, L. D. 1986. Genecological variation in recently established populations of *Abutilon theophrasti* (velvetleaf). Can. J. Bot. **64**: 1632–1643.

Weaver, S. E. and Hamill, A. S. 1985. Effects of soil pH on competitive ability and leaf nutrient content of corn (*Zea mays* L.) and three weed species. Weed Sci. **33**: 447–451.

Willson, M. F., Thomas, P. A., Hoppes, W. G., Katusic-Malmborg, P. L., Goldman, D. A. and Bothwell, J. L. 1987. Sibling competition in plants: an experimental study. Am. Nat. **129**: 304–311.

Winter, D. M. 1960. The development of the seed of *Abutilon theophrasti*. I. Ovule and embryo. Am. J. Bot. **47**: 8–14.

Wolf, R. B. 1986. Effects of p-methoxycinnamaldehyde from star anise and related cinnamic acid derivatives on velvetleaf germination. J. Nat. Prod. (LLOYDIA) **49**: 156–158.

Wymore, L. A. and Watson, A. K. 1986. An adjuvant increases survival and efficacy of *Colletotrichum coccodes*, a mycoherbicide for velvetleaf (*Abutilon theophrasti*). Phytopathology **76**: 1115–1116.

Wymore, L. A., Watson, A. K. and Gotlieb, A. R. 1987. Interaction between *Colletotrichum coccodes* and thidiazuron for control of velvetleaf. Weed Sci. **35**: 377–383.

Yun, J. I. and Taylor, S. E. 1986. Adaptive implications of leaf thickness for sun-and shade-grown *Abutilon theophrasti*. Ecology **67**: 1314–1318.

Zangerl, A. R. and Bazzaz, F. A. 1984. Effects of short term selection along environmental gradients on variation in populations of *Amaranthus retroflexus* and *Abutilon theophrasti*. Ecology **65**: 207–217.

THE BIOLOGY OF CANADIAN WEEDS. 91.
Malva pusilla Sm. (= *M. rotundifolia* L.)

ROBERTE M. D. MAKOWSKI[1] and IAN N. MORRISON[2]

[1]*Research Station, Agriculture Canada, 5000 Wascana Parkway, P.O. Box 440, Regina, Saskatchewan, Canada S4P 3A2; and* [2]*Department of Plant Science, University of Manitoba, Winnipeg, Manitoba, Canada R3T 2N2. Received 3 Feb. 1988, accepted 20 Dec. 1988.*

MAKOWSKI, R. M. D. AND MORRISON, I. N. 1989. The biology of Canadian weeds. 91. *Malva pusilla* Sm. (= *M. rotundifolia* L.) Can. J. Plant Sci. **69**: 861–879.

This account provides information on the biology of round-leaved mallow, *Malva pusilla* Sm. (= *M. rotundifolia* L.). Primarily a weed of gardens and waste places, it has recently become troublesome in field crops causing yield losses of up to 90% in flax and lentil and up to 30% in wheat. Introduced from Eurasia, it is common mainly in the prairie provinces. Although often confused with two other weedy mallows, *M. neglecta* Wallr. and *M. parviflora* L., it has a different geographical distribution and can easily be distinguished by its short petals with bearded claws. *Malva pusilla* propagates by seed which are impermeable to water, exhibiting low germination unless scarified, and therefore capable of remaining dormant for long periods. Plant growth form varies greatly with competition. Round-leaved mallow is difficult to control chemically, but it can be effectively controlled with a fungus which is being developed as a commercial bioherbicide.

Key words: *Malva neglecta*, *Malva parviflora*, Round-leaved mallow, weed biology

[La biologie des mauvaises herbes canadiennes. 91. *Malva pusilla* Sm. (= *M. rotundifolia* L.)]
Titre abrégé: *Malva pusilla* Sm.
L'auteur fournit une documentation biologique sur la mauve à feuilles rondes, *Malva pusilla* Sm. (= *M. rotundifolia* L.), principalement une mauvaise herbe de potagers et de terres désaffectées, mais récemment envahissante dans les terres cultivées pouvant causer des réductions de plus de 90% dans le lin et les lentilles et de plus de 30% dans les récoltes de blé. Introduite d'Eurasie, elle est commune surtout dans les Prairies. Elle est souvent confondue avec deux autres mauves, *M. neglecta* Wallr. et *M. parviflora* L., mais elle possède une distribution géographique différente et peut être séparée facilement avec ses pétales courtes et ciliées. Cette mauvaise herbe se propage par semences qui sont imperméables à l'eau et ont une faible germination sans traitement résultant en une dormance prolongée. Le port de cette mauve varie grandement avec différents niveaux de compétition. La mauve à feuilles rondes est difficile à contrôler avec des herbicides chimiques, mais peut être contrôlée efficacement à l'aide d'un champignon phytopathogène qui est en voie de développement comme bioherbicide.

Mots clés: *Malva neglecta*, *Malva parviflora*, mauve à feuilles rondes, biologie des mauvaise herbes

1. Name

Malva pusilla Sm. (= *Malva rotundifolia* L.) – Synonyms: *M. borealis* Wallm. (Baker 1890; Iljin 1922); **round-leaved mallow** (Fernald 1950; Looman and Best 1979; Alex et al. 1980; Frankton and Mulligan 1987), small mallow (Korsmo et al. 1981; Hanf 1983), dwarf mallow (Boivin 1967); **mauve à feuilles rondes** (Alex et al. 1980), petite mauve (Boivin 1967), fromagère (Scoggan 1978). Malvaceae, mallow family, Malvacées.

Can. J. Plant Sci. 69: 861–879 (July 1989)

Malva pusilla has been frequently confused in both name and identity with *M. neglecta* Wallr., common mallow (Frankton and Mulligan 1987), and occasionally with *M. parviflora* L., small-flowered mallow. This confusion has mainly arisen in North America, and there are many discrepancies between floras in which *M. rotundifolia* L. is used either for *M. pusilla* or *M. neglecta*, and *M. parviflora* is occasionally not even recognized (Rydberg 1932; Groh and Frankton 1949; Fernald 1950; Gleason 1952; Gleason and Cronquist 1963; Boivin 1967; Scoggan 1978). Looman and Best (1979) and Alex et al. (1980) used *M. pusilla*, *M. parviflora*, and *M. neglecta*, as do many European botanists who do not use *M. rotundifolia* (Shishkin 1949; Rasmussen 1954; Dalby 1968; Korsmo et al. 1981; Hanf 1983). Confusion has also arisen in biological studies published on mallow. The name *M. rotundifolia* was often used where, from the descriptions, it was obvious that *M. neglecta* was intended (Robertson 1893; Curts 1948). In others, *M. rotundifolia* was used without any descriptions and thus it is impossible to ascertain which species was intended (Anonymous 1870; Hoysradt 1875; Schneck 1890; Halsted 1892, 1893a,b; Bailey and Collins 1893; Drake and Harris 1931; Karling 1955; Makinen 1963; Dimetry 1971, 1972; Gaudreau 1972; Landis et al. 1972; Al-Saadi and Wiebe 1975; Thompson and Barker 1978; Kivilaan and Bandurski 1981; Shiber 1981; Carlson and Eberlein 1983; Spencer and Steyskal 1986).

Malva rotundifolia has been used for all three species on Canadian herbarium specimens. Of the 606 specimens examined, 45% were identified as *M. rotundifolia*. Of these more than half, 55%, referred to *M. neglecta*, 40% to *M. pusilla*, 3% to *M. parviflora*, and the remaining 2% to other *Malva* species. The identity of the type is presently being investigated by the authors and a proposal for rejection of the name "*Malva rotundifolia* L." is in preparation.

2. Description and Account of Variation

(a) The following descriptions are based on those in Shishkin (1949), Dalby (1968), Scoggan (1978), Hanf (1983) and on personal observations by the authors.

Annual (biennial occasionally reported), prostrate-decumbent or spreading with long taproot; stem with many branches which can extend to over 1 m in length, with sparse to dense, simple, 2-pronged, stellate hairs. Leaves alternate, reniform or round-cordate with shallow rounded lobes (5–7), doubly dentate to finely crenate, mostly glabrous above, underside of blade with mostly simple hairs on veins, occasionally covered throughout with simple, 2-pronged, and stellate hairs; petioles 2–24 cm long, densely pubescent along one line, glabrous or with scattered hairs elsewhere. Flowers in clusters of 2–5 (sometimes 20 or more) in leaf axils; pedicels usually over 10 mm long, mostly twice as long as calyx, reflexed in fruit; epicalyx bractlets 3, equaling calyx, narrowly linear, at least three times as long as wide. Flowers bisexual, with many stamens, filaments united into staminal column, surrounding a single pistil with approximately 10 stigmas. Calyx divided to two-thirds of its length into 5 ovate-triangular lobes, margin long-ciliated, barely enlarging in fruit. Petals whitish, oblong-lanceolate, truncate or shallowly emarginate, barely surpassing calyx by no more than a few mm, 1.4–5.2 mm (sometimes up to 12 mm) long, claws bearded. In the bud, corolla distinctly twisted (contorted) which persists even after flower opening (Davis 1964). Fruit multicarpellate, with 10–12 one-seeded mericarps with acute wingless angles. Mericarps arranged in a single whorl around concave apex of the receptacle. Margins of adjacent mericarps meeting in a wavy line, dorsal face reticulate-rugose, lateral faces thin especially in center, easily ruptured in fruit, radially wrinkled. Seeds changing from light brown to almost black with maturity, very finely textured, round to reniform in outline, laterally compressed and slightly concave, 1.2–2 mm wide, rounded edge broadest on dorsal side, tapering towards base with a depression, whitish at the hilum.

Figure 1 illustrates a mature flowering plant, a seedling, and a flower. Figure 2 illustrates the capsules of the three weedy mallow

Fig. 1. *Malva pusilla* Sm. (a) mature plant, (b) seedling with heart-shaped cotyledons, (c) flower. Bars represent 1 cm for (a) and (b), and 1 mm for (c).

Fig. 2. (a) *Malva pusilla* capsule, mericarps with reticulated dorsal face meeting in a wavy line and (b) seeds of different colors from light-brown to black with maturity; (c) *Malva parviflora* capsule with toothed and winged angles (w →) of the mericarps and with an enlarged calyx; (d) *Malva neglecta* capsule, mericarps with smooth dorsal face meeting in a straight line. Bars represent 1 mm.

species and the seeds of round-leaved mallow as they vary in color with maturity.

Novruzova and Velieva (1984) found that stomata were seldom present on the upper epidermis of *M. pusilla* leaves and that this was unlike other closely related *Malva* species, in which stomata are found on both the upper and lower epidermis (e.g. *M. neglecta*).

A chromosome number has not been reported for Canadian material. It was found to be $2n = 42$ in material from England (Davie 1934, under *M. rotundifolia*), Denmark (Skovsted 1941, under *M. borealis* Wallr.), and Poland (Pogan et al. 1985). It was reported as a true hexaploid derived from the basic number 7 characteristic of most *Malva* (Davie 1934; Ford 1938).

(b) Similar species and distinguishing characteristics — *Malva pusilla* is frequently confused with *M. neglecta* and occasionally with *M. parviflora*. A numerical taxonomic study of herbarium specimens of the three species was conducted using 65 morphological characters (Makowski 1987). The three species were morphologically distinct and could be separated by principal component analysis using only seven characters, namely leaf blade width, leaf lobe shape, petal length, petal length past calyx, petal claw pubescence, mericarp reticulation, and mericarp margins. From these characters and compilations from Shishkin (1949), Dalby (1968) and Scoggan (1978), the following key was constructed. For completeness and to avoid any possible confusion, *M. nicaeensis* All. [absent from Flora of Canada (Scoggan 1978)] is also included, as a few specimens were identified in Canadian herbarium collections. It resembles both *M. neglecta* (for its petals) and *M. pusilla* (for its mericarps).

Key to weedy species of *Malva* L. in Canada

Section Fasciculatae D.C. (De Candolle 1824)

Sub-section Planocentrae Kristoff. (Kristofferson 1926; Shishkin 1949)

Flowers clustered in leaf axils; leaves round-cordate or reniform; mericarps numerous, one-seeded.

  1. Petals at least twice as long as calyx; dorsal face of mericarps reticulate or not.

    2. Petals more than twice as long as calyx; carpels with rounded margins and not reticulate on densely short-hirsute backs (Fig. 2d); epicalyx bractlets linear, at least three times as long as wide .... *M. neglecta*

    2. Petals about twice as long as calyx; dorsal face of ripe mericarps distinctly reticulate; epicalyx bractlets ovate, not more than three times as long as wide ..... *M. nicaeensis*

  1. Petals barely surpassing the calyx by no more than a few millimeters; dorsal face of ripe mericarps distinctly reticulate, margins of adjacent ones meeting in a wavy line.

    3. Petal claws glabrous; leaves round-cordate or reniform, obtusely lobed;

carpels with winged and toothed angles; fruiting calyx greatly enlarged (Fig. 2c) .... *M. parviflora*

    3. Petal claws bearded; leaves round-cordate or reniform with rounded lobes; carpels with acute wingless angles; fruiting calyx barely enlarged (Fig. 2a) .... *M. pusilla*

(c) Intraspecific variation — *Malva pusilla* has been reported as very polymorphic with a large number of forms in Europe (Shishkin 1949). Variation of *M. pusilla* was examined from populations in Saskatchewan and Manitoba under controlled conditions using 69 morphological characters, as well as from natural populations from the field (Makowski 1987). In the uniform garden with four populations, plants from Manitoba were more similar than plants from Saskatchewan and plants from Strasbourg, Saskatchewan, were distinct from plants of the other sites. From the uniform garden, 17 characters were shown to be the minimum required for site variation by principal component analysis. Variation from natural populations from 35 different locations was determined using the characters identified in the uniform garden in canonical variates analysis as well as 19 environmental and soil variables in a stepwise multiple regression. Two main clustering groups were established with pubescence of both stem and leaf as the main differentiating character. The differences in pubescence exhibited in plants growing under natural conditions persisted under uniform garden conditions. In the field, a gradation in pubescent types was observed with the dense pubescent form in the western parts of Saskatchewan on drier, poorer soils and the less pubescent form towards the east and into Manitoba on richer soils with intermediate types in between (Makowski 1987).

3. Economic Importance

(a) *Detrimental* — Round-leaved mallow has long been considered a weed of yards, gardens, and waste places in Canada (Frankton and Mulligan 1987). Steffey (1980) reported mallow (species not specified) as one of the worst weeds of gardens in the United States. Recent weed surveys have also shown round-leaved mallow to occur as a weed of field crops including wheat, lentil, and flax on the Prairies (Douglas and Thomas 1986; Thomas 1978a,b; Thomas and Wise 1983, 1984, 1985, 1986, 1987, 1988) and of orchards in British Columbia [ECW (Western Section) Reports 1973–1986]. Provincial surveys for each of the Prairie Provinces indicate that the weed has become more common in cultivated land in the last decade. For example, in Manitoba, round-leaved mallow ranked 33rd in terms of relative abundance in 1978 (Thomas 1978b) compared to 24th in 1986 (Thomas and Wise 1988). In that province, round-leaved mallow occurred most frequently in the Central Region in the Altona and Carman districts where it was the 7th and 10th most abundant weedy species respectively, with densities ranging from 0.4 to 43 plants m^{-2}. In Saskatchewan, round-leaved mallow ranked 48th in relative abundance in 1978 (Thomas 1978a) compared to 37th in 1986 (Thomas and Wise 1987). From the Alberta Agriculture weed alert reporting system, *M. pusilla* has doubled in abundance on cultivated land from 1980 to 1985. In North Dakota in 1979, dwarf mallow (referred to as *M. rotundifolia*) and round-leaved mallow (referred to as *M. neglecta*) were identified as the 24th and 49th most abundant weeds in major field crops with a maximum density of 6.8 plants m^{-2} (Dexter et al. 1981).

In Saskatchewan in 1986, infestations of round-leaved mallow at mean densities of 115 plants m^{-2} reduced yields of lentil by over 60% at Indian Head, and at densities of 150 plants m^{-2} by over 85% at Regina. In wheat, yields were reduced by 30% at densities of 139 plants m^{-2} at Indian Head and by 85% at densities of 338 plants m^{-2} at Regina (Makowski 1987). In Manitoba, densities of 39 plants m^{-2} reduced the yield of flax by more than 90%. In contrast, wheat yields were reduced by just 20% in Manitoba at densities of round-leaved mallow ranging from 56 to 87 plants m^{-2} (Budzinsky 1987). In these experiments conducted in Saskatche-

wan and Manitoba, the weed emerged a few days before the crop. Subsequent experiments in Manitoba conducted by Friesen and Morrison (unpublished data) at Portage La Prairie indicated that 20 plants m^{-2} could reduce flax yields by 30%. In wheat, however, in other trials conducted in 1987 at Portage La Prairie and Morden, Manitoba (Nickel and Morrison, unpubl. data), round-leaved mallow densities of up to 100 plants m^{-2} had no significant effect on wheat yields. Furthermore, in 1985 at Indian Head, Saskatchewan, round-leaved mallow densities of 37 plants m^{-2} in lentil and 24 plants m^{-2} in wheat had no effect on either crop yield (Makowski 1987). In these trials, round-leaved mallow seedlings emerged with or slightly after the crop.

Round-leaved mallow plants remain green well into the fall and thus, can cause problems at harvest during combining operations by plugging both threshing and cleaning components. Round-leaved mallow will likely become a problem as a contaminant in crop seed as its occurrence increases. The Manitoba Seed Grain Survey (Manitoba 1982) reported mallow in seed from farmers' grain drills during seeding in 1981 but not in 1976.

(b) *Beneficial* — The Malvaceae have long been known for their food and medicinal value. Caius (1942) and Shishkin (1949) detailed the various uses of *M. pusilla* in popular medicine in Europe, India, and the U.S.S.R., due mainly to the high content of mucilage in the roots and foliage. In the United States, *Malva rotundifolia* has also been reported as possessing medicinal value (Cheney 1946; Curts 1948); however, these studies actually dealt with *M. neglecta*. Fruits of round-leaved mallow are edible and leaves and shoots can be used as a vegetable, raw or cooked, with a high protein and a satisfactory vitamin C content (Shishkin 1949). Other *Malva* species have also been reported as beneficial, for example, *Malva parviflora* has been used as feed for poultry in Egypt (Asar et al. 1972a,b). *Malva meluca* Graebn. or *M. verticilata* L. has been widely used as a fodder, fiber, and honey crop in the U.S.S.R. and Poland

(Shishkin 1949; Evgrafova et al. 1967; Kruglov 1967; Gavrilova 1984; Hanczakowski 1984).

(c) *Legislation* — Round-leaved mallow is listed as a noxious weed under the terms of the Noxious Weed Acts of Manitoba (Manitoba 1973) and Saskatchewan (Saskatchewan 1984).

4. Geographical Distribution
An introduction from Eurasia, *M. pusilla* occurs in every province except Newfoundland (Fig. 3). It is common in the prairie provinces, while *M. neglecta* is found mainly in Ontario, Quebec and British Columbia (Fig. 4). *Malva neglecta* has not been reported in Saskatchewan (Frankton and Mulligan 1987). However, two specimens were identified from a "Wild flower garden" where *M. neglecta* had been introduced 45 yr before (collected in 1974 at Parkbeg, Sask., DAO 356448, SASK 54227). *Malva parviflora* is sparsely distributed throughout Canada (Fig. 4). In Saskatchewan, *M. pusilla* is the most common introduced weedy mallow, occurring throughout the Grassland and Parkland regions (V. Harms, University of Saskatchewan, pers. commun.). It also extends south into the Great Plains region of the United States (Thompson and Barker 1978).

Malva pusilla is found in northern, eastern, and central Europe. It is a native of central and eastern Europe and was introduced into Britain, Finland, and France (Dalby 1968). In Scandinavia, it is most common in southern Sweden and Finland, and in Norway (Rasmussen 1954). It is found throughout the European U.S.S.R. except in the Arctic, in parts of Siberia, Caucasus, and central Asia to India (Shishkin 1949). It has also been reported along the Mediterranean coast of Lebanon as *M. rotundifolia* (Shiber 1981).

5. Habitat
(a) *Climatic requirements* — In Europe, *M. pusilla* has a more northerly distribution than *M. neglecta* (Kristofferson 1926; Shishkin 1949). In fields in Saskatchewan and Manitoba, round-leaved mallow seedlings emerge all summer and well into the fall. *Malva ne-glecta* was reported as exhibiting considerable tolerance to cold, retaining the capacity for photosynthesis and respiration after long periods of exposure to subfreezing temperatures (Anderson and Brotherson 1980). Cold tolerance was also observed in *M. rotundifolia* (Carlson and Eberlein 1983), which remained green even after several frosts in late fall. Major infestations were encountered mainly in the eastern parts of Saskatchewan and in Manitoba, where precipitation is considerably greater than in western regions of Saskatchewan (Makowski 1987). Pyasyatskene (1978) reported that air temperature and the amount of precipitation had marked effects on plant growth and the duration of phenological phases.

(b) *Substratum* — *Malva pusilla* has been reported as favoring nutrient-rich soils in Europe (Rasmussen 1954; Korsmo et al. 1981; Hanf 1983). Svensson and Wigren (1982) found the germination, growth, and flower number increased as nutrient levels increased. Saskatchewan and Manitoba weed surveys (Douglas and Thomas 1986; Makowski 1987; Thomas and Wise 1983, 1984, 1986, 1987, 1988) indicate that the weed occurs most frequently on the darker medium-textured soils (Dark Brown and Black Chernozemic soils). However, occurrences of *M. rotundifolia* on clay soils have been reported in the Clay Belt region of Quebec (Gaudreau 1972). Growth of round-leaved mallow on clay soils in Saskatchewan was less vigorous than on medium-textured dark soils (Makowski 1987). *Malva pusilla* has been reported as salt tolerant in Europe (Hanf 1983) and was also observed around saline sloughs in Saskatchewan.

(c) *Communities in which the species occurs* — Round-leaved mallow is now frequently found in cultivated fields, orchards, gardens, farmyards near manure piles, along roadsides, in towns and in waste places (Boivin 1967; Scoggan 1978; Looman and Best 1979; Douglas and Thomas 1986; Thomas 1978a,b; Thomas and Wise 1983, 1984, 1985, 1986, 1987; ECW (Western Section) Reports 1973–1987). There are no reports of occurrences in pasture or range land. In Europe, *M. pusilla* occurs in farmyards,

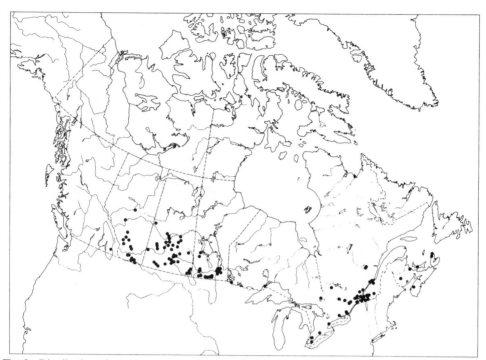

Fig. 3. Distribution of *M. pusilla* in Canada from specimens in the following herbaria: ACAD, ALTA, CAN, DAO, DAS, MMMN, MT, NSPM, QFA, QUE, SASK, SCCBC, SCS, UBC, UNB (abbreviations as in Holmgren et al. (1981)), and Vegreville Environmental Centre (Alberta).

gardens, and waste places with only sparse distribution (Shishkin 1949; Rasmussen 1954; Korsmo et al. 1981).

6. History

Early reports referred to round-leaved mallow mainly as *M. rotundifolia*. Taxonomic confusion of *M. rotundifolia*, *M. neglecta*, and *M. pusilla* have made a historical assessment difficult. *Malva rotundifolia* was introduced to North America relatively early as it was mentioned by Nuttall in 1818 (reported by Groh and Frankton (1949)). It was listed as common in the State of New York in the 1870s (Anonymous 1870; Hoysradt 1875) and in Rhode Island in 1892 (Bailey and Collins 1893), and already was considered a common weed, probably introduced with garden seed (Halsted 1892, 1893a). In Canada, *M. rotundifolia* was reported by Holmes in 1821 in Montreal, however, these specimens were later reidentified and found to be *M. neglecta* (Rousseau 1968). *Malva parviflora* was also

well established by the late 1800s in the United States (Anonymous 1876; Jepson 1891).

From the herbarium specimens examined, the first record of *M. pusilla* in Canada is from Grenville, Quebec in 1878. It was subsequently recorded from Egg Harbor, New Brunswick in 1891; Morden, Manitoba in 1896; Lethbridge, Alberta in 1929; Vona, Saskatchewan in 1933; Silver Islet, Ontario in 1936; and Red River, Nova Scotia in 1951. Only one specimen was recorded from British Columbia (Kimberley) in 1946 and from Prince Edward Island (Albany) in 1950. It was first introduced into Eastern Canada and may have spread to the West as a contaminant of garden seed during the colonization by the settlers or even grown for medicinal purposes, as it was a popular medicinal plant with Eastern Europeans (Shishkin 1949).

The first Canadian herbarium record of *M. neglecta* was earlier than for *M. pusilla*, in

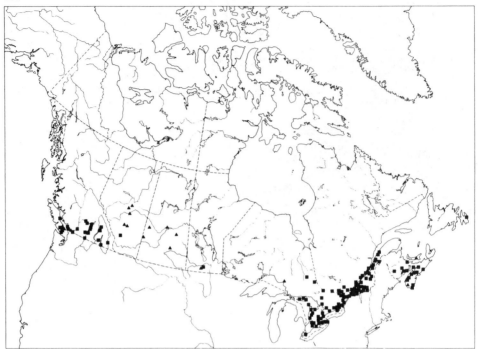

Fig. 4. Distribution of *M. neglecta* (squares) and *M. parviflora* (triangles) in Canada from specimens in herbaria listed in Fig. 3.

1844 from St. Mary's, New Brunswick. The first record of *M. parviflora* was in 1877 from Carleton, Nova Scotia.

7. Growth and Development

(a) *Morphology* — *Malva* species characteristically have dormant seed due to a hard seed coat which is impermeable to water (Vaiciuniene and Peseckiene 1978, 1981). *Malva pusilla* seed exhibits low germination if not scarified (Makowski 1987) and persists in the soil for a long time (Kivilaan and Bandurski 1981).

Malva rotundifolia has a stout often woody tap root (Halsted 1892). In Saskatchewan, after plant emergence, the tap root allowed round-leaved mallow to withstand extensive periods of drought. In a competitive situation, round-leaved mallow exhibited a more erect growth habit and grew to the height of the crop, but when alone, it had a spreading growth habit with branches over 1 m in length and was a very prolific seed producer (Makowski 1987).

(b) *Perennation* — *Malva pusilla* propagates exclusively by seed. *Malva rotundifolia* has been reported to be frost tolerant (Carlson and Eberlein 1983) and with a mild winter in Illinois survived until spring (Schneck 1890). Halsted (1892) reported that *M. rotundifolia* was a perennial. In Saskatchewan and Manitoba, *M. pusilla* plants were observed to tolerate frost but never to survive the winter.

(c) *Physiological data* — Most studies have referred to *M. rotundifolia* and have been included in this discussion as it is impossible to establish if *M. pusilla* or *M. neglecta* was intended. Of the various plant parts studied, stem tips and young stems of *M. rotundifolia* held more matric water than the leaf blades and held more than other species with woody stems (Al-Saadi and Wiebe 1975). Matric bound water is a measure of the water bound by cell colloids independent of solutes and is primarily a function of plant composition varying with plant part or maturity. Al-Saadi and Wiebe (1975) suggest that matric bound water may be correlated with cold hardening

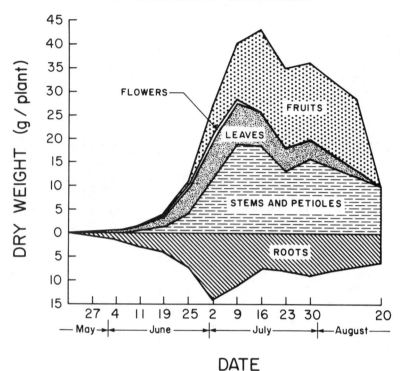

Fig. 5. Dry matter allocation of *M. pusilla* plants grown individually outdoors in 25-cm-diameter pots at the University of Manitoba, 1986. (Redrawn from Budzinsky (1987).)

which may relate to the frost tolerance observed in *M. rotundifolia*. *Malva rotundifolia* plants collected from the side of a busy highway within close proximity to the coast of Ras Beirut, Lebanon, generally had higher metal concentrations (Cu, Cd, Ni, Fe, Zn, and Cr) than the other species studied, *Tamarix pentandra* Pall., with the exception of Pb (Shiber 1981). Heliotropism or movement of the leaves following that of the sun was reported for *M. rotundifolia* (Halsted 1893b) and *M. neglecta* (Yin 1938).

Leaf weight ratios (LWR) and specific leaf areas (SLA) of *M. pusilla* grown outdoors in pots and within a wheat crop canopy were studied by Budzinsky (1987). The LWR of pot-grown plants declined from 0.75 at the beginning of the season to 0.21 g g^{-1} at the end of the season. Similarly, the decline in LWR of mallow in the wheat field as the season progressed was from 0.73 to 0.11 g g^{-1}. The SLA of mallow grown in pots in the absence of competition declined during the

first 3 wk of growth and then remained more or less constant for the duration of the experiment. However, marked differences in SLA occurred between plants grown in the two situations. Those grown in pots in the absence of competition had much higher SLAs than those growing in competition with wheat. For example, in the 7th week, the SLA of pot-grown plants was 208 cm^2 g^{-1} compared to 32 cm^2 g^{-1} for plants in the wheat field.

(d) *Phenology* — *Malva pusilla* emerges throughout the growing season beginning when temperatures are high enough to favor germination in the spring and continuing until the soil freezes. On cropland in western Canada and in the northern Great Plains of the United States, mallow seedlings frequently emerge after crop emergence (Carlson and Eberlein 1983). Growth of the weed is indeterminate. Flowering commences 4–5 wk after emergence and continues until late in the fall (Pyasyatskene 1978; Carlson and Eberlein

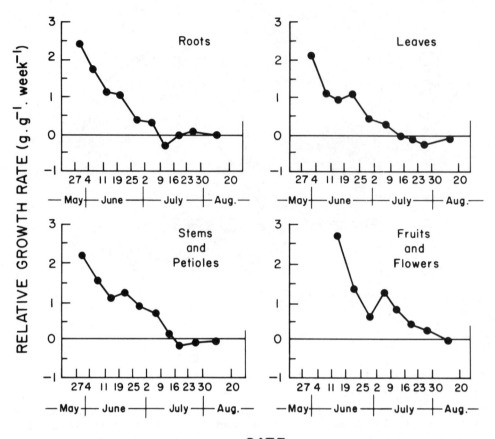

Fig. 6. Relative growth rates of organs of *M. pusilla* plants grown individually outdoors in 25-cm-diameter pots at the University of Manitoba, 1986. Plants were sampled on the dates indicated on the abscissas and the relative growth rates calculated for each of the preceding 7-d intervals. (Redrawn from Budzinsky (1987).)

1983; Budzinsky 1987). The pattern of resource allocation of mallow plants grown outdoors in 25-cm-diameter pots at the University of Manitoba in 1986 is shown in Fig. 5. Fruit production of these plants was initiated in early June and was maximal in July. In the U.S.S.R., Pyasyatskene (1978) reported that *M. pusilla* started to flower 42–54 d after germination and continued to flower for 80 d. Duration of plant growth from germination to autumn dying off occurred over a period of 125 d which was shorter than for several other *Malva* species included in the study.

Pyasyatskene (1978) reported that the "most intensive" growth of *M. pusilla* oc-

curred during July. In Budzinsky's study, the relative growth rates (RGRs) of all major organs was highest in the seedling stage in early June and declined during the remainder of the season (Fig. 6). In plants grown in pots, maximum leaf number and area (average of 167 and 1266 cm^2 plant^{-1}, respectively) was attained in mid- to late July. Budzinsky (1987) reported that in a natural infestation of *M. pusilla* growing in flax and wheat fields near Manitou, Manitoba in 1985, the average numbers of leaves per plant were 35 and 8, respectively. Approximate densities of the weed in the crops were 40 and 70 plants m^{-2}. In 1987, individual plants grown in the field in the absence of competition produced up to 2000 leaves with a maximum area of 3.3 m² in early August (Nickel and Morrison, unpubl. data).

Seed maturation occurred within 16 to 18 d after flowering (Abdullaeva 1966). Capsules on one plant do not mature in unison (Pyasyatskene 1978). Immature light-colored seed germinates readily and would emerge during the same growing season as when they were produced if shed (Makowski 1987). Mature dark-colored seed does not germinate unless scarified; however, seed coat permeability increases with age (Makowski 1987). Thus, mature seeds produced during one growing season will likely not germinate until the following year or later.

(e) *Mycorrhiza* — No mycorrhizal associations with *M. pusilla* have been reported.

8. Reproduction

(a) *Floral biology* — *Malva pusilla* is an inbreeding species. Meehan (1893) and Kristofferson (1926) found that the anthers open in the bud, and that pollination has already taken place when the flowers burst into blossom. Robertson (1893) reported many insects visiting *M. rotundifolia* flowers in Illinois. He compared his observations with findings in Europe which were completely opposite. Robertson was most likely referring to *M. neglecta* which has much larger flowers and occasionally may exhibit cross-pollination. Individual flowers are open for only 1–2 d (Abdullaeva 1966; Pyasyatskene 1978). No insects were observed on flowers of round-leaved mallow plants in Saskatchewan and Manitoba.

(b) *Seed production and dispersal* — Pyasyatskene (1978) reported that *M. pusilla* growing in the row spacings of a fruit orchard in the Lithuanian USSR had 10 – 11 seeds per capsule and an average of 512 capsules per plant (over 5000 seeds per plant). Carlson and Eberlein (1983) reported that *M. rotundifolia* produced 1647–5261 seeds per plant in pure stands and an average of 324 seeds per plant when in competition with wheat. The major source of spread of *M. pusilla* is encroachment into field edges from gardens, farmyards, and manure piles and further spread into fields from contaminated crop seed and with tillage equipment.

(c) *Viability of seeds and germination* — In Saskatchewan and Manitoba, *M. pusilla* emerges in the field throughout the entire growing season and produces seed from June to late fall. Mature *M. pusilla* seed characteristically exhibits a low percent germination due to the impermeability of the seed coat. Light, moisture, cold treatments and immersion in sulphuric acid or sodium hypochlorite had little effect on the germination of mature seed (Makowski 1987). Mechanical scarification with a scalpel was the only treatment which consistently increased total germination and the rate of germination significantly. Older seeds exhibited a greater total germination and rate of germination than newly harvested seed (Makowski 1987).

Malva pusilla seeds germinate over a wide range of temperatures. Seeds collected at Raymore, Saskatchewan, in 1983, at Regina, Saskatchewan, in 1983 and 1986 and at Manitou, Manitoba, in 1986 were tested in December 1986 on a thermogradient plate which provided 100 different constant and alternating temperature regimes with a 16-h photoperiod (McLaughlin et al. 1985). Seeds germinated at temperatures as low as 5°C, although they germinated optimally at temperatures between 15 and 30°C peaking around 20°C (Makowski 1987). Newly harvested seeds from Manitoba and Saskatchewan required higher temperatures than older seeds for germination (Makowski 1987).

The hard seed coat of *M. pusilla*, which breaks down over time, accounts for the persistence of seeds in the soil. In Beal's seed viability test in Michigan, seed of *M. rotundifolia* germinated and produced seedlings in the fifth year, the 20th year, and after 100 y (Kivilaan and Bandurski 1981). Thus, *M. rotundifolia* seed has the potential for surviving long periods and causing a persistent weed problem.

Malva seeds (unidentified species) were reported as remaining viable after passing through the intestinal tract of several birds (Proctor 1968).

(d) *Vegetative reproduction* — No means of vegetative reproduction exists in this annual species.

9. Hybrids

Dalby (1968) reported the existence of hybrids between *M. pusilla* and *M. neglecta* in Europe. Kristofferson (1926) reported that the occurrence of natural hybrids among *Malva* species was extremely rare even when species were growing side by side. Artificial hybrids among species belonging to the Planocentrae subsection, i.e., *M. pusilla*, *M. parviflora*, *M. neglecta*, and *M. sylvestris*, were slightly fertile, while crossings with species from other sections were not, as partial to complete sterility existed in many of the F_1 and F_2 generations (Kristofferson 1926). In Canadian collections, no evidence for hybridization was found.

10. Population dynamics

Seedlings of *M. pusilla* are often present in dense clusters of 6–10 plants, as the seeds from one fruit may germinate simultaneously. In waste places, roadsides, gardens, and farmyards, it usually has a sparse distribution (Makowski 1987). Where field infestations have been reported, densities were as high as 4000 plants m^{-2}. Sites of dense infestations occurred on dark nutrient-rich soils (Makowski 1987). Svensson and Wigren (1982) reported that generally *M. pusilla* could not compete under a grass cover unless high nutrient levels were present. The growth habit and rate of growth of *M. pusilla* is greatly affected by competition (Makowski 1987). In wheat (a good competitor), *M. pusilla* grows more erect and produces fewer branches, leaves, and fruits than it does when growing alone or in flax or lentil (poor competitors). Without competition, *M. pusilla* has a spreading growth habit with many branches which can extend to over 1 m in length, radiating from a short central stalk or stem.

11. Response to herbicides and other chemicals

Although numerous herbicides have been evaluated in field crops and other situations for control of round-leaved mallow, none have consistently provided a high level of control. Among the phenoxy herbicides, good results have been obtained with a commercial mixture of dichlorprop and 2,4-D ester at 1.1 kg ha^{-1} or with 2,4-D ester alone at 0.85 kg ha^{-1} (Donaghy and Sturko 1983a,b). Growth room experiments conducted by Hunter (1983a,b) indicate that mallow is more readily controlled by 2,4-D ester applied at the two- to four-leaf stage. Hunter (1983a,b) and Donaghy and Sturko (1983b) rated 2,4-D amine as being less effective than 2,4-D ester. By comparison, Maurice and Cole (1986) observed that 0.88 kg ha^{-1} of 2,4-D amine applied to mallow at the four-leaf stage in barley resulted in a 96% reduction in weed density, equivalent to that obtained with 1.0 kg ha^{-1} dichlorprop/2,4-D ester. The results of these trials (Donaghy and Sturko 1983b; Hunter 1983b; Maurice and Cole 1986) also indicate that MCPA is not as effective as 2,4-D in controlling the weed. The level of control of round-leaved mallow following applications of the commercial mixture of dichlorprop and 2,4-D ester (W.J. Green, May and Baker Canada Inc., pers. commun.) varied between different locations in Saskatchewan; this may be due to the two, i.e., hairy and less-hairy, forms of *M. pusilla* (Makowski 1987).

Control of round-leaved mallow with bromoxynil plus MCPA (1:1) was variable, from 3.5–7.8 on a visual rating scale of 0–9, where 0 indicates no effect on the weed and 9 indicates complete kill (Donaghy and Sturko 1983a; Hunter 1983b; Maurice and Cole 1986). Nickel and Morrison (1987, unpubl. data) recorded 25–33% mortality of round-leaved mallow seedlings sprayed with bromoxynil/MCPA at 0.56 kg ha^{-1} at the two- to four-leaf stage in wheat. The leaves of sprayed plants showed definite injury symptoms several days after treatment and some of the larger leaves became completely necrotic within 7–10 d. However, new growth initiated at the center of surviving plants within 1 wk of treatment appeared normal.

Other selective herbicides assessed in the field for control of round-leaved mallow include metribuzin, linuron, cyanazine, clopyralid, picloram, chlorsulfuron and met-sulfuron methyl, but none have provided a consistently high degree of control at the rates tested (Donaghy and Sturko 1983a,b; Maurice and Cole 1986, 1987; Hunter 1987). Among nonselective herbicides, glyphosate at 0.28 kg ha^{-1} and glufosinate-ammonium at 0.62–0.75 kg ha^{-1} have been reported to reduce the stand density of round-leaved mallow by 90% when plants were sprayed at an early growth stage (Wise et al. 1985, 1986). Assessments conducted 3 wk after treatment indicated that paraquat at 0.14 and 0.28 kg ha^{-1} did not affect stand density of the weed.

A mycoherbicide consisting of spores of a fungal pathogen, *Colletotrichum gloeosporioides* (Penz.) Sacc. f. sp. *malvae* (C.g.m.), gave excellent selective control of round-leaved mallow in wheat, lentil, and flax at a number of different locations in Saskatchewan and Manitoba (Anderson 1987a,b; Mortensen 1988; Mortensen and Makowski 1989). Details concerning the infection process, host specificity, optimum conditions for infection, etc., have been reported by Makowski (1987) and Mortensen (1988). Efficacy and requirements for infection under field conditions have been investigated for a number of years in Saskatchewan (Makowski and Mortensen 1989; Mortensen and Makowski 1989). In a field trial conducted in 1987 in Manitoba, the efficacy of the pathogen was reduced when it was applied in a tank-mixture with the post-emergence graminicide, sethoxydim (Friesen and Morrison 1987). Similarly, preliminary observations indicate that the activity of the mycoherbicide is also reduced in tank-mixtures containing bromoxynil/MCPA (L. F. Friesen, University of Manitoba, pers. commun.). A number of herbicides tested for their acute toxicity on C.g.m. spores did not inhibit or reduce spore germination or growth when mixed together on artificial media (K. Mortensen, Agriculture Canada, pers. commun.) In field trials conducted at Regina in 1988 with two of these herbicides, metribuzin and bromoxynil/MCPA at recommended rates, C.g.m. alone or applied 30 h before the herbicides gave the best control of round-

leaved mallow compared with tank-mixtures or C.g.m. applied after the herbicides.

12. Response to Other Human Manipulations

In experiments investigating the effect of fertilizer on the growth of several weeds, Svensson and Wigren (1982) reported that overall growth, the amount of branching, and the number of flowers produced by *M. pusilla* increased with increasing nutrient levels. Cultivation can kill mallow but only if the taproot of the mallow plant is severed below the crown, otherwise regrowth will occur. Mowing and grazing will delay growth for a short time; however, rapid recovery with increased branching below the injured area will result.

13. Response to Parasites

(a) *Insects* — In Saskatchewan, larvae of the *Vanessa cardui* (L.), Nymphalidae, were found feeding on leaves of *M. pusilla* (M. Maw, Agriculture Canada, Regina, pers. commun.). The potato aphid, *Macrosiphum euphorbiae* (Thos.), was found on *M. rotundifolia* in eastern Washington (Landis et al. 1972). In the United States, larvae of *Calycomyza malvae* (Burgess) were reported forming long narrow leaf mines in *M. rotundifolia* (Spencer and Steyskal 1986). The host range of this Agromyzid fly was similar to the fungal pathogen *Colletotrichum gloeosporioides* (Penz.) Sacc. f. sp. *malvae*. In Indiana, *Synchytrium australe* Speg. were reported as forming galls on *M. rotundifolia* under greenhouse conditions but none were observed in the field (Karling 1955). Adults of *Systena blanda* Melsh. were found feeding on *M. rotundifolia* in onion fields in Ohio (Drake and Harris 1931).

In France, adult weevils of *Baris timida* Rossi and *Apion* (*Aspidapion*) *radiolus* Kirby were reported feeding on the foliage of *M. rotundifolia* and larvae of the weevils of *Apion* (*Malvapion*) *malvae* F., *A.* (*Aspidapion*) *aeneum* F., *A.* (*Pseudapion*) *rufirostre* F. were recorded feeding and developing within its fruit (Hoffman 1950). In Egypt, plants of *M. rotundifolia* were found to support growth of the cotton seed bug, *Oxycarenus hyalinipennis* Costa, and the cotton leaf worm, *Spodoptera littoralis* Boisd. (Dimetry 1971, 1972). Many aphids from the world catalogue, *Acyrthosiphon gossypii* Mord., *Aphis gossypii* Glover, *A. helichrysi* Kalt., *A. laburni* Kalt., *A. malvae* Koch, *A. spiraecola* Patch, *A. urticae*. F., *Macrosiphin malvicola* Mats., *Myzus persicae* Sulzer, were reported as feeding on *M. rotundifolia* (Patch 1939).

(b) *Nematodes* — The nematode, *Ditylenchus dipsaci* (Kuhn) Filip., was found on *M. pusilla* in Italy (Greco 1976).

(c) *Fungi* — The following plant diseases were reported on *M. pusilla* in Canada and the United States: *Puccinia malvacearum* Bert. (United States Department of Agriculture (USDA) 1960; Arthur 1962; Conners 1967; Lambe 1973), *Cercospora althaeina* Sacc., *C. malvarum* Sacc., *Septoria heterochroa* Desm., *S. malvicola* Ell. and Martin, and *Colletotrichum* spp. (USDA 1960; Conners 1967).

Colletotrichum gloeosporioides (Penz.) Sacc. f. sp. *malvae*, isolated from *M. pusilla* at Regina (Mortensen 1988), is now being developed as a biological herbicide (see Section 11).

(d) *Viruses* — Aster yellows, beet curly top, malva yellow vein mosaic, tobacco streak, and tomato spotted wilt viruses were reported as occurring on *M. rotundifolia* in the United States (USDA 1966).

(e) *Higher plant parasites* — No higher plant parasites of *M. pusilla* have been reported.

ACKNOWLEDGMENTS

The loan of specimens from the herbaria listed in Fig. 3 is gratefully acknowledged. Appreciation is expressed to K. Nickel, L. Friesen and to Drs. A. G. Thomas and L. Hume for their critical review of the manuscript and to E. Prusinkiewicz for translating some of the literature and for her technical assistance in preparing the maps. We also wish to thank M. Budzinsky for permission to reproduce parts of her M.Sc. thesis and K. Nickel and L. Friesen for the use of some of their unpublished data.

Abdullaeva, M. 1966. Characteristics of the growth and development of some wild Malvaceae when they are cultivated. Uzb. Biol. Zh. **10:** 33–37.

Al-Saadi, H. A. and Wiebe, H. H. 1975. The influence of maturity, season and part of plant on matric bound water. Plant Soil **43:** 371–376.

Alex, J. F., Cayouette, R. and Mulligan, G. A. 1980. Common and botanical names of weeds in Canada. Agriculture Canada. Ottawa, Ont. Publ. 1397, 132 pp.

Anderson, J. 1987a. Control of round-leaved mallow in wheat with *Colletotrichum gloeosporioides*. Res. Rep. Expert Comm. on Weeds (West. Sect.). p. 620.

Anderson, J. 1987b. Control of round-leaved mallow with *Colletotrichum gloeosporioides* in wheat. Res. Rep. Expert Comm. on Weeds (West. Sect.). p. 621.

Anderson, W. R. and Brotherson, J. D. 1980. Ribulose diphosphate carboxylase activities in cold-resistant common mallow, *Malva neglecta*, and a cold-sensitive tomato, *Lycopersicon esculentum* cultivar ACE 55. Great Basin Nat. **40:** 121–126.

Anonymous. 1870. Flora of New York. Vol. 1. Bull. Torrey Bot. Club **1:** 16–17.

Anonymous. 1876. New localities. Bull. Torrey Bot. Club **6:** 100.

Arthur, J. C. 1962. Manual of rusts in the United States and Canada. Hafner Publ. Co. New York, N.Y. pp. 246–247.

Asar, M. A., Abou Akkada, A. R., Khalil, A. Z. and El-Naga, M. A. 1972a. Effect of feeding some weeds to growing chicks. Alexandria J. Agric. Res. **20:** 205–209.

Asar, M. A., Abou Akkada, A. R., Khalil, A. E. and El-Naga, M. A. 1972b. Effect of feeding some weeds on the performance of laying hens. Alexandria J. Agric. Res. **20:** 211–217.

Bailey, W. W. and Collins, J. F. 1893. A list of plants found on Block Island, R.I. in July and August. Bull. Torrey Bot. Club **20:** 231–239.

Baker, E. G. 1890. Synopsis of genera and species of Malveae. J. Bot. (British and Foreign) **28:** 15–18, 239–243, 339–343.

Boivin, B. 1967. Flora of the Prairie Provinces. Phytologia **15:** 329–446.

Budzinsky, M. F. 1987. The growth analysis of round-leaved mallow (*Malva pusilla* Sm.). M.Sc. Dissertation, University of Manitoba. Winnipeg, Man. 128 pp.

Caius, J. F. 1942. Medicinal and poisonous mallowworts, Part II. J. Bombay Nat. Hist. Soc. **43:** 494–505.

Carlson, K. D. and Eberlein, C. V. 1983. Growth and development of dwarf mallow. Proc. North Cent. Weed Control 38: 50.

Cheney, R. H. 1946. Medicinal herbaceous species in the north-eastern United States. Bull. Torrey Bot. Club 73: 60–72.

Conners, I. L. 1967. An annotated index of plant diseases in Canada and fungi recorded from plants in Alaska, Canada and Greenland. Agriculture Canada, Ottawa, Ont. Publ. 1251, pp. 168–169.

Curts, G. D. 1948. A phytochemical study of *Malva rotundifolia* L. and a proposed method of isolating plant constituents. Ph.D. Dissertation. Ohio State University. 51 pp.

Dalby, D. H. 1968. *Malva* L., Malvaceae. *In* T. G. Tutin, V. H. Heywood, N. A. Burges, D. M. Moore, D. H. Valentine, S. M. Walters, and D. A. Webb, eds. Flora Europaea. 2. Cambridge University Press, Cambridge, U.K. pp. 249–251.

Davie, J. H. 1934. Cytological studies in the Malvaceae and certain related families. J. Genet. 28: 33–67.

Davis, T. A. 1964. Aestivation in Malvaceae. Nature 201: 515–516.

De Candolle, A. P. 1824. Prodromus systematis naturalis regni vegetabilis. Malvaceae. 1. Treuttel and Wurtz. Paris, France pp. 429–474.

Dexter, A. G., Nalewaja, J. D., Rasmusson, D. D. and Buchli, J. 1981. Survey of wild oats and other weeds in North Dakota 1978 and 1979. N.D. Res. Report. 79: 80.

Dimetry, N. Z. 1971. Studies on the host preference of the cotton seed bug *Oxycarenus hyalinipennis* Costa (Lygaeidae: Hemiptera). Z. Angew. Entomol. 68: 63–67.

Dimetry, N. Z. 1972. Further studies on the host plant preference of *Spodoptera littoralis* Boisd. (Lepid., Noctuidae). Z. Angew. Entomol. 71: 350–355.

Donaghy, D. I. and Sturko, A. R. W. 1983a. Control of round-leaved mallow in wheat. Res. Rep. Expert Comm. on Weeds (West. Sect.). p. 642.

Donaghy, D. I. and Sturko, A. R. W. 1983b. Control of round-leaved mallow in wheat. Res. Rep. Expert Comm. on Weeds (West. Sect.). p. 642–643.

Douglas, D. W. and Thomas, A. G. 1986. Weed survey of Saskatchewan mustard, lentil, and dry pea crops 1985. Weed Survey Series. Agriculture Canada, Regina, Sask. Publ. 86–2, 157 pp.

Drake, C. J. and Harris, H. M. 1931. The pale-striped flea beetle, a pest of young seedling onions. J. Econ. Entomol. 24: 1132–1137.

Evgrafova, N. P., Korbut, L. S. and

Tambovtseva, L. V. 1967. The amino-acid composition of some fodder crops. Tr. Ural Nauch-Issled Inst. Sel'skogo Khoz. 7: 162–164.

Fernald, M. L. 1950. Gray's Manual of botany. 8th ed. American Book Co. New York, N.Y. pp. 1000–1002.

Ford, C. E. 1938. A contribution to a cytogenetical survey of the Malvaceae. Genetica 20: 431–452.

Frankton, C. and Mulligan, G. A. 1987. Weeds of Canada. Agriculture Canada, Ottawa, Ont. Publ. 948, pp. 120–121.

Friesen, L. F. and Morrison, I. N. 1987. Round-leaved mallow control in flax with *Colletotrichum gloeosporioides*. Res. Rep. Expert Comm. on Weeds (West. Sect.). p. 219.

Gaudreau, L. 1972. Extensions d'aire et additions à la flore de la zone d'argile, au Québec. Nat. Can. (Qué.) 99: 509–514.

Gavrilova, T. N. 1984. Mallow, a forage and honey crop (Moscow region). Pchelovodstvo Moskva: "Kolos" 7: 11–12.

Gleason. H. A. 1952. The new Britton and Brown illustrated flora of the Northeastern United States and adjacent Canada. 2. New York Botanical Gardens. New York, N.Y. pp. 525–527.

Gleason, H. A. and Cronquist, A. 1963. Manual of vascular plants of Northeastern United States and adjacent Canada. D. Van Nostrand Company, Inc. Princeton, N.J. pp. 461–463.

Greco, N. 1976. Weed host of *Ditylenchus dipsaci* in Puglia. Nematol. Mediterr. 4: 99–102.

Groh, H. and Frankton, C. 1949. Canadian weed survey sixth report 1947. Department of Agriculture, Ottawa, Ont. pp. 11–12.

Halsted, B. D. 1892. A century of American weeds. Their root systems tabulated. Bull. Torrey Bot. Club 19: 141–147.

Halsted, B. D. 1893a. A century of American weeds. Bull. Torrey Bot. Club 20: 51–55.

Halsted, B. D. 1893b. Heliotropism of the common mallow. Bull. Torrey Bot. Club 20: 489–490.

Hanczakowski, P. 1984. Preliminary results of investigations on the economic and fodder value of feeding mallow. Zesz. Probl. Post. Nauk Rolnic. 257: 249–256.

Hanf, M. 1983. The arable weeds of Europe with their seedlings and seeds. BASF, Federal Republic of Germany. pp. 375–377.

Hoffman, A. 1950. Faune de la France. Paul Lechevalier. Paris, France. pp. 1058–1059, 1503–1567.

Holmgren, P. K., Keuken, W. and Schofield, E. K. 1981. Index Herbariorum. Part I. The

Herbaria of the World. 7th ed. Dr. W. Junk B. V. Publ., The Hague, The Netherlands; Boston, Mass. 452 pp.

Hoysradt, L. H. 1875. Catalogue of the phaeogamous and acrogenous plants growing without cultivation within five miles of Pine Plains, Duchess Co., New York. Bull. Torrey Bot. Club **5**: 9–11.

Hunter, J. H. 1983a. Control of round-leaved mallow with 2,4-D ester at different leaf stages. Res. Rep. Expert Comm. on Weeds (West. Sect.). pp. 643.

Hunter, J. H. 1983b. Control of round-leaved mallow with herbicides registered on wheat. Res. Rep. Expert Comm. on Weeds (West. Sect.). pp. 643–644.

Hunter, J. H. 1987. Control of round-leaved mallow with herbicides registered on wheat. Res. Rep. Expert Comm. on Weeds (West. Sect.). pp. 621–622.

Iljin, M. M. 1922. Notes on a few species from the Malvaceae family. V. On the synonymy of two species of mallow. Izv. Glavn. Bot. Sada XXI **3**: 163–167.

Jepson, W. L. 1891. Botany of the Marysville Buttes. Bull. Torrey Bot. Club **18**: 315–327.

Karling, J. S. 1955. Hosts of *Synchytrium australe* Speg. Sydowia **9**: 441–447.

Kivilaan, A. and Bandurski, R. S. 1981. The one hundred-year period for Dr. Beal's seed viability experiment. Am. J. Bot. **68**: 1290–1292.

Korsmo, E., Vidme, T. and Fykse, H. 1981. Korsmos Ugras Plansjer. (*Malva pusilla* Sm.). Norsk Landbruk/Landbruksforlaget. Oslo, Norway. pp. 198–199.

Kristofferson, K. B. 1926. Species crossing in *Malva*. Hereditas **7**: 233–354.

Kruglov, T. L. 1967. Weed control in mallow sowings. [Translation from: Ref. Zh. Otd. Vyp. Rastenievod, 1968, No. 10.55.715]. Tr. Ural Nauch-Issled Inst. Sel'skogo Khoz. **7**: 155–161.

Lambe, R. C. 1973. Ornamental and flower diseases; hollyhock rust. Virginia Polytechnic Institute and State University. Ext. Div. Control Ser. No. 111. p. 1.

Landis, B. J., Powell, D. M. and Fox, L. 1972. Overwintering and winter dispersal of the potato aphid (*Macrosiphum euphorbiae*: Hem., Hom., Aphididae) in eastern Washington. Environ. Entomol. **1**: 68–71.

Looman, J. and Best, K. F. 1979. Budd's flora of the Canadian prairie provinces. Agriculture Canada, Ottawa, Ont. pp. 520–522.

Makinen, Y. 1963. On Finnish Micromycetes 2: *Puccinia malvacearum* Bert. in Finland. Karstenia **6–7**: 102–104.

Makowski, R. M. D. 1987. The evaluation of *Malva pusilla* Sm. as a weed and its pathogen *Colletotrichum gloeosporioides* (Penz.) Sacc. f. sp. *malvae* as a bioherbicide. Ph.D. Dissertation, University of Saskatchewan. Saskatoon, Sask. 225 pp.

Makowski, R. M. D. and Mortensen, K. 1989. *Colletotrichum gloeosporioides* f. sp. *malvae* as a bioherbicide for round-leaved mallow (*Malva pusilla*): Conditions for successful control in the field. Proc. VII Int. Symp. Biol. Cont. Weeds (In press).

Manitoba. 1973. Revised regulation N110-R1 of the Noxious Weeds Act 1971 being Chapter N110 of the Revised Statutes of Manitoba 1970. Queen's Printer of the Province of Manitoba, Winnipeg, Man. 3 pp.

Manitoba. 1982. Manitoba seed grain survey. Agdex 110. 4 pp.

Maurice, D. C. and Cole, D. E. 1986. Control of round-leaved mallow in barley. Res. Rep. Expert Comm. on Weeds (West. Sect.). pp. 561–562.

Maurice, D. C. and Cole, D. E. 1987. Round-leaved mallow control in wheat. Res. Rep. Expert Comm. on Weeds (West. Sect.). pp. 622–623.

McLaughin, N. B., Bowes, G. R., Thomas, A. G., Dyck, F. B., Lindsay, T. M. and Wise, R. F. 1985. A new design for a seed germinator with 100 independently temperature controlled cells. Weed Res. **25**: 161–173.

Meehan, T. 1893. Contributions to the life histories of plants, No. 9. Proc. Acad. Nat. Sci. Phila. pp. 289–309.

Mortensen, K. 1988. The potential of an endemic fungus, *Colletotrichum gloeosporioides*, for biological control of round-leaved mallow (*Malva pusilla*) and velvetleaf (*Abutilon theophrasti*). Weed Sci. **36**: 473–478.

Mortensen, K. and Makowski, R. M. D. 1989. Field efficacy at different concentrations of *Colletotrichum gloeosporioides* f. sp. *malvae* as a bioherbicide for round-leaved mallow (*Malva pusilla*). Proc. VII Int. Symp. Biol. Cont. Weeds (In press).

Novruzova, Z. A. and Velieva, H. A. 1984. A comparative anatomy of *Malva* L. species. Akad. Nauk Azerbaid. SSR **2**: 11–18.

Patch, E. 1939. Food-plant catalogue of the aphids of the world. Maine Agric. Exp. Sta. Bull. 393. pp. 176–178.

Pogan, E., Czapik, R. and Jankun, A. 1985. Further studies in chromosome numbers of Polish angiosperms Part XVIII. Acta Biol. Cracov. Ser. Bot. **27**: 57–74.

Proctor, V. W. 1968. Long-distance dispersal of

seeds by retention in digestive tract of birds. Science **160**: 321–322.

Pyasyatskene, A. A. 1978. Phenology and growth of plants of the Malvaceae family in the Lithuanian SSR. 1. Annual species of the mallows. Liet. TSR Mokslu Akad. Darb. Ser. C **4**: 21–32.

Rasmussen, S. M. 1954. The distribution of the Euphorbiaceae, Malvaceae and Violaceae within Denmark. Bot. Tidsskr. **50**: 239–278.

Robertson, C. 1893. Flowers and insects. XI. Bot. Gaz. **18**: 267–274.

Rousseau, C. 1968. Histoire, habitat et distribution de 220 plantes introduites au Québec. Nat. Can. (Qué.) **95**: 49–169.

Rydberg, P. R. 1932. Flora of the Prairies and Plains of central North America. New York Botanical Gardens, New York, N.Y. pp. 538–539.

Saskatchewan. 1984. Chapter N-9.1. An Act respecting Noxious Weeds. In Revised Statutes of Saskatchewan. Queen's Printer, Regina, Sask. pp. 3779–3792.

Schneck, J. 1890. Some effects of the mild winter. Bot. Gaz. **15**: 209–211.

Scoggan, H. J. 1978. The flora of Canada. Part 3 — Dicotyledoneae-Malvaceae. National Museum Natural Science. Publications in Botany, **7(3)**: 1087–1093.

Shiber, J. G. 1981. Trace metals in *Tamarix pentandra* and *Malva rotundifolia* from Beirut. Rev. Roum. Biol. Ser. Biol. Veg. **26**: 55–60.

Shishkin, B. K. 1949. Flora of the U.S.S.R. [Translated from Russian, Israel Program for Scientific Translations, Jerusalem, 1974]. Izdatel'stvo Akademii Nauk SSSR. pp. 44–50.

Skovsted, A. 1941. Chromosome numbers in the Malvaceae. II. Comptes-Rendus Laboratoire Carlsberg. Série Physiologique. **23**: 195–242.

Spencer, K. A. and Steyskal, G. C. 1986. Manual of the Agromyzidae (Diptera) of the United States. Agric. Handb. 638. Agric Res. Serv., U.S. Dep. Agric. Washington, D.C. pp. 140–149, 235.

Steffey, J. 1980. The mallow family (Malvaceae). Am. Hortic. **59**: 7–8.

Svensson, R. and Wigren, M. 1982. Competition and nutrient experiments illustrating the decline of some village weeds. Sven. Bot. Tidsskr. **76**: 51–65.

Thomas, A. G. 1978a. The 1978 weed survey of cultivated land in Saskatchewan. Weed Survey Series. Agriculture Canada, Regina, Sask. Publ. 78–2, 113 pp.

Thomas, A. G. 1978b. The 1978 weed survey of cultivated land in Manitoba. Weed Survey Series. Agriculture Canada-Manitoba Agriculture, Regina, Sask. Publ. 78–3. 109 pp.

Thomas, A. G. and Wise, R. F. 1983. Weed surveys of Saskatchewan cereal and oilseed crops from 1976 to 1979. Weed Survey Series. Agriculture Canada, Regina, Sask. Publ. 83–6, 260 pp.

Thomas, A. G. and Wise, R. F. 1984. Weed surveys of Manitoba cereal and oilseed crops from 1978, 1979 and 1981. Weed Survey Series. Agriculture Canada, Regina, Sask. Publ. 84–1, 230 pp.

Thomas, A. G. and Wise, R. F. 1985. Dew's Alberta Weed Survey 1973–1977. Weed Survey Series. Agriculture Canada, Regina, Sask. Publ. 85–3, 134 pp.

Thomas, A. G. and Wise, R. F. 1986. Weed survey of Saskatchewan winter wheat fields 1985. Weed Survey Series. Agriculture Canada, Regina, Sask. Publ. 86–3, 85 pp.

Thomas, A. G. and Wise, R. F. 1987. Weed survey of Saskatchewan cereal land oilseed crops 1986. Weed Survey Series. Agriculture Canada, Regina, Sask. Publ. 87–1, 251 pp.

Thomas. A. G. and Wise, R. F. 1988. Weed survey of Manitoba cereal and oilseed crops 1986. Weed Survey Series. Agriculture Canada, Sask. Publ. 88–1, 201 pp.

Thompson, J. C. and Barker, W. T. 1978. Malvaceae of the Great Plains, USA. Proc. N.D. Acad. Sci. **32**: 14.

United States Department of Agriculture. 1960. Index of plant diseases in the United States. Agric. Handb. 165. Crop Res. Div., Agric. Res. Serv., USDA, Washington, D.C. p. 302.

United States Department of Agriculture. 1966. Index of plant virus diseases in the United States. Agric. Handb. 307. Crop Res. Div., Agric. Res. Serv., USDA, Washington, D.C. p. 61.

Vaiciuniene, J. and Peseckiene, A. 1978. Biology of seeds of the Malvaceae family (1. Genus *Malva* L.). Darb. Liet. TSR Makslu Akad. Ser. C Trudy Akad. nauk Litovskoi SSR Ser. V **3**: 57–65.

Vaiciuniene, J. and Peseckiene, A. 1981. Biology of seeds of the Malvaceae family (4. Germination of seeds from species of the genera *Alcea*, *Althaea*, *Anoda*, *Hibiscus*, *Lavatera*, *Malope*, *Malva*, and *Sida*). Darb. Liet. TSR Makslu Akad. Ser. C Trudy

Akad. nauk Litovskoi SSR Ser. V **2**: 47–54.

Wise, I. L., Mader, K. J. and Makowski, E. J. 1985. Annual weed control in tilled fallow with Hoe 39866. Res. Rep. Expert Comm. on Weeds (West. Sect.). p. 627.

Wise, I. L., Feist, K. and Makowski, E. J. 1986. Annual weed control with Hoe 39866 in barley stubble. Res. Rep. Expert Comm. on Weeds (West. Sect.). p. 48.

Yin, H. C. 1938. Diaphototrophic movement of the leaves of *Malva neglecta*. Am. J. Bot. **25**: 1–6.

THE BIOLOGY OF CANADIAN WEEDS. 92.

Danthonia spicata (L.) BEAUV. IN ROEM. & SCHULT.

S. J. DARBYSHIRE and J. CAYOUETTE

Biosystematics Research Centre, Agriculture Canada, Research Branch, Central Experimental Farm, Ottawa, Ontario, Canada K1A 0C6. Received 28 Oct. 1988, accepted 15 May 1989.

DARBYSHIRE, S. J. AND CAYOUETTE, J. 1989. The Biology of Canadian weeds. 92. *Danthonia spicata* (L.) Beauv. in Roem. & Schult. Can. J. Plant Sci. **69**: 1217–1233.

Danthonia spicata, poverty-oat grass, is a native North American perennial grass of pioneer habitats. It invades agricultural lands in eastern Canada with dry soil and low fertility. Unpalatable to livestock, it is an increaser species in heavily grazed or nutrient depleted pasture. A polymorphic reproductive system incorporates chasmogamy, cleistogamy and heteromorphic diaspores (dispersal unit). Clavicipitaceous fungal parasites are often present and affect productivity, reproduction, competitive fitness and possibly predation of their hosts.

Key Words: *Danthonia spicata*, Poverty oat grass, weed biology

[La biologie des mauvaises herbes canadiennes. 00. *Danthonia spicata* (L.) Beauv. in Roem. & Schult.]
Titre abrégé: *Danthonia spicata* (L.) Beauv.
Danthonia spicata, la danthonie à épi, est une graminée vivace nord-américaine des habitats pionniers. Dans l'est du Canada, elle occupe les terres agricoles à substrat sec et peu fertile. Désagréable au goût, elle est délaissée par le bétail et envahit les pâturages fortement broutés et de faible valeur nutritive. Son système de reproduction polymorphe comprend la chasmogamie, la cleistogamie et produit des graines hétéro-morphes. Elle est fréquemment parasitée par un champignon endophyte qui affecte sa productivité, sa reproduction, sa compétition et sa prédation potentielle.

Mots clés: *Danthonia spicata*, herbe de pauvreté, danthonie à épi, biologie des adventices

1. Name

Danthonia spicata (L.) P. de Beauvois in Roemer & Schultes (*D. allenii* Austin, *D. canadensis* Baum & Findlay *pro parte*, *D. glumosa* (Michx.) Beauv., *D. pinetorum* (Piper) Piper in Piper & Beattie, *D. spicaeformis* Beauv., *D. thermale* Scribn. [*D. thermalis* Scribn.], *Merathrepta spicata* (L.) Raf., *Pentameris spicata* (L.) Nelson & Macbr.) — **poverty oat grass** (Alex et al. 1980), poverty grass (Fernald 1950), junegrass (Fernald 1950), common wild oat grass (Bingham 1987); **danthonie à épi** (Alex et al. 1980), herbe de pauvreté (Boivin 1981).

Poaceae (Gramineae, grass family, Graminées).

2. Description and Account of Variation

(a) *Description* — Perennial, fibrous roots, without rhizomes or stolons (Fig. 1A). Culms 10–100 cm high, erect or somewhat bent at lower nodes. Leaf blades curling with senescence, flat to involute, 0.8–2 (rarely to 4) mm wide, 6–15 (-20) cm long, adaxially glabrous, abaxially glabrous (or with hairs along the margin), to villous; leaf sheaths, glabrous or with varying amounts of long silky hairs and a tuft of longer hairs at the margins of the collar; ligule a fringe of straight hairs, 0.4–1.5 mm long (Fig. 2J).

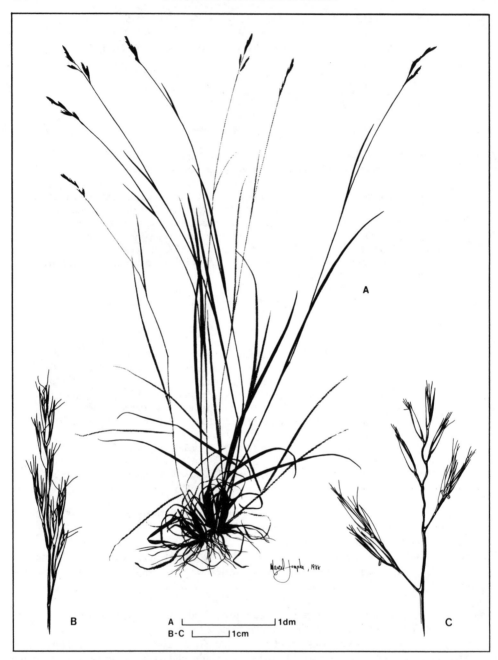

Fig. 1. *Danthonia spicata*, poverty-oat grass (*M. Jomphe* s.n. *5.VII.88*). A, habit; B. inflorescence as seen in cleistogamous form or chasmogamous form before and after anthesis; C, inflorescence of chasmogamous form at anthesis.

Inflorescence of two types: (a) Terminal inflorescence exerted from flag leaf sheath, paniculate, with (1–)5–8(–20) spikelets; branches spreading, or slightly reflexed at

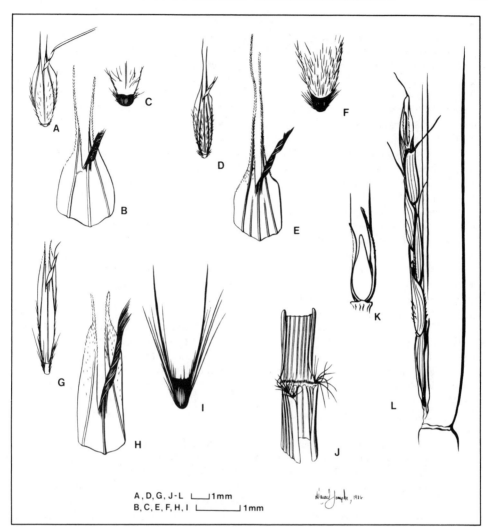

Fig. 2. *Danthonia*, oat grass. A, B & C, *D. spicata* (*W.G. Dore* s.n. *20.VII.71*): A, abaxial view of lemma; B, lemma apex; C, lemma callus. D, E & F, *D. compressa* (*S.J. Darbyshire 2040*): D, abaxial view of lemma; E, lemma apex; F, lemma callus. G, H & I, *D. intermedia* (*A.J. Breitung 1773*): G, abaxial view of lemma; H, lemma apex; I, lemma callus. J, K & L, *D. spicata*: J (cultivated from *W.G. Dore 21460*), adaxial view of ligule from culm leaf; K (*W.G. Dore* s.n. *20.VII.71*), common form of cleistogene spikelet with a single floret; L (cultivated from *W.G. Dore 21461*), large cleistogene spikelet with 6 florets attached to culm (leaf sheath removed).

anthesis but stiff and erect prior to and after anthesis (Fig. 1B–C). Spikelets 3–10 flowered, (7–)10–15 mm long; glumes lanceolate, acuminate, ± equal to subequal, usually surpassing florets, (7–)9–13(–15) mm long, chartaceus, (3–)5–7 nerves, glabrous; lemma ovate, rounded on back, 3.0–5(–6.5) mm long, 7 faint nerves, pubescent with long silky hairs over the back and especially along margins (medial hairs sometimes sparse, or rarely medially glabrous), apex bifid with 2 membranous, triangular to subsetaceous apical teeth to 2 mm long (¼ to ⅔ length of lemma body) (Fig. 2A–B); lemma awn (5 −) 6–7(−9) mm long, brown, arising dorsally from between the lemma teeth, geniculate between the lower and upper sections; palea as long as lemma body, glabrous, the 2 nerves carinate and scabrous to ciliate on upper half; anthers: in chasmogamous florets 1.0–2.2 mm long, dehiscent, with many pollen grains (thousands); in cleistogamous florets 0.2–0.3 mm long, indehiscent, with few pollen grains (hundreds); lodicules: in chasmogamous florets lodicules apically membranous, toothed or not and functional; in cleistogamous florets rudimentary or lacking, club-shaped, broad, non-membranous apex; grain ovate, to 2.0(−2.3) mm long, brown, loose in the floret. (b) Basal inflorences (referred to as cleistogenes) axial and enclosed by the lower culm leaf sheaths; usually consisting of a single, non-disarticulating spikelet of usually one (Fig. 2K) to several (Fig. 2L) modified cleistogamous florets with the lower culm nodes tending to have single-flowered cleistogenes and the upper nodes (where the internodes are longer) often with more than one floret per cleistogene. Spikelets with two setaceous or strap-like ciliate bracts; glumes absent; lemma ovate, sharply acute sometimes with a small awn to 2 mm long, coriaceus, 5–9 faint nerves, glabrous or with a few trichomes on keel; palea chartaceus (especially medially) to coriaceus at the margins, glabrous; anthers small, indehiscent; ovary apically glabrous. Grain ellipsoidovate, tightly enclosed by floret, to 2.5 mm long, brown.

A chromosome number of $2n = 36$ has been found in Canadian populations (Bowden 1960; Gervais 1981; Löve and Löve 1981) as well as in the United States (Myers 1947; de Wet 1954). Also reported for the United States is a count of $2n = 31$ (Gould 1975).

Anatomical features of *Danthonia* and related genera are described by Tomlinson (1985), and the features of *D. spicata* are described in detail by Metcalfe (1960).

(b) *Similar species* — Two other species of *Danthonia*, *D. compressa* Austin ex Peck and *D. intermedia* Vasey, might be confused with *D. spicata*, although neither are likely to be found as agricultural weeds. *Danthonia spicata* is more drought tolerant and occurs in nutrient-poorer soil than either *D. compressa* or *D. intermedia.*

In eastern Canada, *D. compressa* occurs in dry to mesic pastures and woodland edge habitat. Characteristics that distinguish *D. compressa* (Fig. 2D–F) from *D. spicata* include: panicle branches spreading after anthesis, versus branches stiffly erect; the leaves of vegetative shoots about half the length of culm, versus leaves usually much less than half the culm height; teeth more than 2 mm long and obviously ¾ or more the length of the lemma body (Fig. 2D–E), versus lemma teeth up to 2 mm long and obviously half or less the length of lemma body; and the pedicels of the spikelets on the lower panicle branch distinctly longer than the spikelet, versus pedicels shorter than to only slightly longer.

Danthonia intermedia occurs on cool native western grasslands at elevations up to alpine meadows and, in eastern Canada, in open boreal or alpine habitats (Cayouette and Darbyshire 1987). Features distinguishing *D. intermedia* (Fig. 2G–I) from *D. spicata* include: senescent leaves more or less straight, versus senescent leaves curling; lower lemmas 5–9 mm long, versus lemmas usually 4–5 (−6.5) mm long; lemma always glabrous dorsally (Fig. 2G–H) versus spreading hairs across the back (sometimes only a few hairs, or rarely dorsally glabrous); grain more than 2.3 mm long, versus less than 2.3 mm long.

In southeastern Newfoundland and southeastern Nova Scotia, *Danthonia decumbens* (L.) DC. in Lam. & DC. (*Sieglingia decumbens* (L.) Bernh.) has been introduced from Europe and is found in old pastures and disturbed, moist soils. *Danthonia decumbens* is, however, readily distinguished from other species of *Danthonia* by its lack of lemma awn.

(c) I. *Taxonomic Problems* — Fernald (1943) revised the *Danthonia spicata* group, recognizing three varieties (var. *spicata*, var. *longipila* Scribn. et Merr., and var. *pinetorum* Piper) as well as the species *D. allenii* Austin and *D. compressa* Austin. Boivin (1967) considered all of these taxa as part of the variation of *D. spicata* without recognizing any varieties. The treatment of Canadian *Danthonia* by Baum and Findlay (1973) and Findlay and Baum (1974) utilizes lodicule morphology (which is correlated to the breeding system) to produce a taxonomy that cuts across all other species concepts. Plants with similar breeding systems are combined regardless of gross morphology (see Section 8(a) for further details). The holotype of their *D. canadensis* Baum & Findlay is referred to *D. intermedia* of other treatments. Many specimens of *D. spicata* are cited as paratypes, all of which possess well-developed lodicules of chasmogamous terminal inflorescence florets. The name *D. spicata* was reserved for plants with rudimentary lodicules (cleistogamous terminal inflorescence florets) and no setae at the tip of the lemma (i.e. apical teeth not attenuate into a long point). Scoggan (1978) reported *D. compressa*, *D. spicata* var. *spicata* (including *D. allenii*) and *D. spicata* var. *pinetorum* from Canada. Butters and Abbe (1953), while recognizing var. *pinetorum*, discuss the variability and overlap of taxonomic characters used to distinguish var. *pinetorum* and *D. thermalis* from typical *D. spicata*. Robust plants, sometimes referred to as *D. allenii*, are the result of environmental disturbance either to the substrate (e.g. scarification, fire, etc.) or to circumstances resulting in late flowering (e.g. grazing) (Dore and McNeill 1980). Fernald (1950), however, considered *D. allenii* to be a hybrid, between *D. spicata* and *D. compressa*, and Hitchcock and Chase (1951) considered it synonymous with *D. compressa*. Boivin (1981) refers plants called *D. thermalis* to vigorous forms of *D. spicata*. The treatment by Dore and McNeill (1980), which was supported by observations on the taxa under uniform cultivation, recognizes *D. compressa* and *D. spicata* but treats var. *longipila*, var. *pinetorum* and *D. allenii* as part of the phenotypic variation in *D. spicata* . Most current authors do not recognize subspecific variation in *Danthonia spicata* taxonomically (e.g. Dore and McNeill 1980; Gould 1975; Voss 1972).

Phylogenetic relationships in the tribe Arundinaceae are conjectural and the circumscription of the genus *Danthonia* and its generic relatives are controversial (Tomlinson 1985; Clayton and Renvoize 1986 Conert 1987). Species of *Danthonia sensu stricto* from Europe, North America and South America form a cohesive group with *D. spicata* as the type species.

(c) II. *Genetic Variation* — A number of studies have been published on the genetic variation of *Danthonia spicata*. Clay, Kelley and various colleagues have examined genetic and phenotypic variation in a *D. spicata* population in Durham, North Carolina, for a number of characteristics including, competitive fitness (Clay and Antonovics 1985a,b; Kelley 1985; Antonovics et al. 1987; Kelley and Clay 1987), germination and seedling survival (Clay 1983a), cleistogene allocation (Clay 1982, 1983b; Clay and Antonovics 1985b), and fecundity (Clay and Antonovics 1985a,b; Antonovics et al. 1987). Scheiner and his colleagues, working in Michigan, have studied intra- and interpopulation variation in morphological, phenological, reproductive, physiological, and growth characteristics. Scheiner and Teeri (1987) showed that during succession after major environmental disturbance there is rapid genetic change of growth in response to light. The studies of Scheiner and Goodnight (1984), Scheiner et al. (1984), and Scheiner and Teeri (1986a,b, 1987) show small, but significant amounts of genotypic variation, but suggest that phenotypic plasticity is more important than genetic variation in microhabitat selection in successional habitats. Clay and Antonovics (1985b) found no allozyme heterozygosity in an unspecified number of enzyme systems of *D. spicata* from Durham, North Carolina. Foliage pubescence is genetically controlled in *D. spicata* (Dore and McNeill 1980), but variants do not seem to be correlated with habitat differences and may be found in mixed populations.

3. Economic Importance

(a) *Detrimental* — In eastern North America *Danthonia spicata* is asssociated with pastures in poor condition and "sterile" land. The presence of *D. spicata* in agricultural soils is an indication of depleted soil fertility (Georgia 1914; Muenscher 1955; Runnels and Schaffner 1931). It is of low forage value (Georgia 1914; Dore 1936; Kalmbacher and Waskko 1977) and generally unpalatable to cattle (Doyon 1968; Dore and McNeill 1980) due to its loosely rooted tufts being removed entirely with attached soil (Dore and Campbell 1949). It is a common, often dominant, grass in pastures of southern Quebec and the Maritime provinces (Dore 1936; Boulet 1946; Dore and Campbell 1949; Doyon 1968).

The light, sandy soils of preference in blueberry production in the Maritime provinces are also prone to colonization by *Danthonia spicata* (Lavoie 1968; Hall et al. 1979; Vander Kloet and Hall 1981; Yarborough and Bhowmik 1986). It is occasionally found as a weed in cultivated land (Palmer 1930), but is not a significant problem in crop fields.

(b) *Beneficial* — *Danthonia spicata* is very important as a spring forage for wildlife (Kalmbacher and Waskko 1977) and has value in protecting soils from erosion and nutrient depletion (Chichester 1977). As a pioneer species it will grow readily on mineral soils and withstands severe frost heaving.

(c) *Legislation* — Neither the Canadian Federal Seeds Act, nor any provincial regulations presently name *Danthonia spicata*.

4. Geographical Distribution
A New World species with the largest geographical range in the genus, *Danthonia spicata* is found from southern Greenland to southern Alaska, in all the provinces and territories of Canada (Fig. 3), south through the United States, except the southwestern states (Gould 1975), to eastern Mexico. West of the Great Lakes it is less widespread although generally locally common. Packer and Bradley (1984) include it in their list of rare vascular plants of Alberta. The

suggestion that *D. spicata* is adventive on Anticosti Island (Marie-Victorin and Rolland-Germain 1969) is based on a misunderstanding of the taxonomic significance and distribution of var. *pinetorum*.

5. Habitat
(a) *Climatic Requirements* — The distribution of *Danthonia spicata* indicates its wide environmental and climatic tolerances. The most significant factors limiting distribution in North America would appear to be moisture and temperature. In western and northern Canada *D. spicata* is absent from areas with precipitation rates of less than about 25–30 cm per year (Fig. 3). In southeastern Yukon and southwestern Northwest Territories, at the northern edge of the range, known populations are associated with areas of geothermal activity (Fig. 3).

(b) *Substrate* — The ecological range of *Danthonia spicata* is substantial, although generally it is found in open areas or open forest habitats on well-drained soils of low fertility. Substrate pH is of little significance as populations may be found on acid bedrock and sands of glacio-fluvial origin (Boulet 1946; Doyon 1968) or on the almost pure mineral soil of limestone barrens. Baker and Nestor (1979), studying pastures in West Virginia, found an increase in *D. spicata* populations with a decrease in soil pH, potassium and phosphorus. In the sand barrens and dry prairies of central Ontario the abundance of *D. spicata* is reduced in areas of increasing soil moisture (Reznicek and Maycock 1983). Voss (1972) states that in Michigan it is sometimes found in boggy or marshy places; however, it is probably restricted to drier microhabitats in such places.

Working in Yellowstone National Park, Wyoming, Sheppard (1971), noted the occurrence of *Danthonia thermalis* (= *D. spicata*) associated with zones of vegetation correlating to geothermal temperature gradients. Geothermal flux was also correlated to various soil conditions such as pH and fertility.

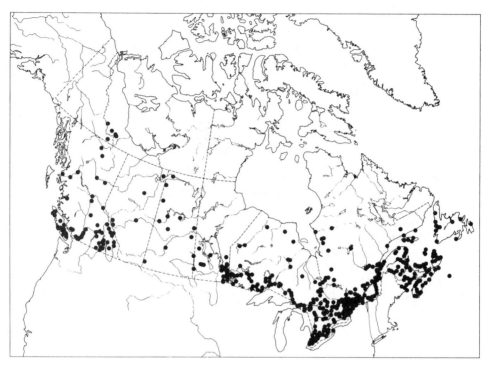

Fig. 3. Canadian distribution of *Danthonia spicata* compiled from specimens at the National Herbarium, National Museum of Natural Sciences, Ottawa (CAN) and the herbaria of The Biosystematics Research Centre, Agriculture Canada, Ottawa (DAO), Environment Canada Land Directorate Québec Region, Sainte-Foy (QFBE) and the University of British Columbia, Vancouver (UBC).

(c) *Communities in which the species occurs* — In eastern Canada, *Danthonia spicata* is abundant in deteriorated pastureland, along sandy roadsides and in abandoned fields (Dore and McNeill 1980). It may be the predominant grass in unimproved eastern pastures (Dore 1936). It is often a dominant in early successional stages of dry anthropogenic or second growth habitats (Doyon and Cayouette 1978; Clayden and Bouchard 1983). Generally it is a grass of "dry and sterile or rocky soil" (Hitchcock et al. 1939).

A number of phytosociological communities have been investigated and described from fields and pastures in southern Quebec where *D. spicata* is a major component (Doyon 1968; Deschênes and St.-Pierre 1978; Doyon and Clabault 1979; Payette and Lavoie 1971). The most common *D. spicata* pasture association described by Doyon (1968, 1975), Polytricho-Danthonietum spicatae (associates: *Hieracium pilosella, Agrostis tenuis, Polytrichum commune, Rumex acetosella, Panicum lanuginosum, H. aurantiacum, Solidago graminifolia, Cladonia* sp.) was considered to be anthropogenic. A *D. spicata*-dominated old field is described as an edaphic climax caused by mowing (Dore 1959). Swan (1970) described a more or less stable community dominated by *D. spicata* and *Solidago* spp. that invades abandoned fields of the northeastern United States and southeastern Canada. The occurrence and frequency of *D. spicata* has been studied through the succession of plant communities in southern Québec (Dansereau 1943, 1946, 1959; Doyon 1975). In natural habitats *D. spicata* is a pioneer colonizer of precambrian gneisses and granites with *Polytrichum* spp. and *Cladonia* spp. (Marie-Victorin 1964). Other habitats include: cliffs (Baldwin 1958; Larson and Batson 1979); slate ledges, river gravels, serpentine barrens (Scoggan 1950); rock outcrops (Looman and Best 1979); stable talus and calcareous river shores (Cayouette 1979); pine plantations (Cruise 1969); *Pinus contorta* forest (Breitung 1954); *Pinus banksiana* forest (Baldwin 1958; Clayden and Bouchard 1983; Voss 1972); *Quercus* spp. woods (Catling 1985), and post-fire forest communities (Cléonique-Joseph 1936; Lavoie 1968; Swan 1970; Scheiner 1983). In northern Michigan it persists for at least 80 yr through post-fire forest succession, where woods are initially dominated by *Populus grandidentata* and replaced by *Acer rubrum, Pinus strobus, Quercus rubra* and *Betula papyrifera* but declines in density in late post-disturbance successional stages (Scheiner 1988; Scheiner and Teeri 1981, 1986a).

6. History
Germination and colonization characteristics as well as tolerance of poor soils and low palatability to livestock results in *D. spicata* being "...one of the few native grasses that has become more successful under present land management than it seems to have been previously; most other species have declined under agriculture." (Dore and McNeill 1980.)

7. Growth and Development
(a) *Morphology* — *Danthonia spicata* grows as tufts of curled leaves with numerous, shallow, fibrous roots. A number of culms with inflorescences are produced by each tuft.

(b) *Perennation* — The life-form is referred to as semi-rosette hemicryptophytic. Overwintering is by tufts that spread vegetatively at a rate of 1–2 cm per year (Dore and McNeill 1980) by producing short but numerous tillers from the basal nodes of the shoots.

(c) *Physiological data* — As in other members of the subfamily Arundinoideae, *Danthonia spicata* utilizes the C_3 photosynthetic pathway. Studies on photosynthetic rates in Michigan by Scheiner et al. (1984) showed that the rate is intermediate between rates encountered between sun (early successional) and shade (late successional) species. They demonstrated that photosynthetic saturation occured at about 800 μE m^{-2} s^{-1}, or about 40% of the unshaded photosynthetic photon flux density (PPFD) at 12:00 h (noon). The photosynthetic saturation level is such that it is probably below the instantaneous PPFD most of the day. At 10 – 20% of full sunlight levels, growth and fecundity are greatly restricted (Scheiner and Teeri 1986b, 1987).

(d) *Phenology* — Germination of *Danthonia spicata* has not been studied in Canada, but occurs during mid- to late spring in North Carolina (Clay 1983a). There may be significant germination differences between the fruits of terminal inflorescence and cleistogene florets. In southern Canada, flowering of terminal inflorescences generally occurs in mid- to late May and early June with seed maturing in late June and July and rapidly shattering. Northern and western populations begin flowering later and continue through June. Diehl (1950) reports flowering in New England as intermittent during the summer. Grain maturation and dispersal of terminal inflorescence florets occurs 1–2 wk prior to the maturation of cleistogenes. Dispersal of mature cleistogene fruits may be further delayed as culm disarticulation does not always occur immediately after culm senescence.

(e) *Mycorrhizae* — *Danthonia spicata* is invaded by vesicular arbuscular endogonaceous mycorrhizal fungi. Root colonization of four collections of *D. spicata* from the Ottawa area (*Cayouette J86–13–1, C6695–1, C6696–1, C6697–1;* DAO) was very low, with hypae seeming to surround the root without penetrating it deeply. Different species of *Glomus* have been found in the rhizosphere, including *G. aggregatum* Schenk & Smith, *G. constrictum* Trappe (DAOM 196164), *G. fasciculatum* (Thaxter *sensu* Gerd.) Gerd. & Trappe *emend.* Walker & Koske, *G. geosporum* (Nicol. & Gerd.) Walker, *G. microaggregatum* Koske, Gemma & Olexia (DAOM 198932) and *G. mossae* (Nicol. & Gerd.) Gerd. & Trappe, although four collections of *D. spicata* (*Cayouette C6703-1, C6706-1, C6708-1, C6721-1;* DAO) showed no colonization at all (Y. Dalpé, pers. commun.).

8. Reproduction

(a) *Floral biology* — *Danthonia spicata* is self-compatible and highly autogamous. Clay (1983b, p. 842) described the reproductive system in *Danthonia* as ''a complex characteristic involving contrasting genetic systems, energetic investments, locations on the plant, dispersal potentials and seed morphologies between the cleistogamous and chasmogamous modes of reproduction.'' In a series of papers, Clay and his colleagues have described and quantified some of these features of the terminal inflorescence floret and cleistogene dimorphism of *D. spicata* (Clay 1982, 1983a,b, 1984; Clay and Antonovics 1985a,b; Clay and Jones 1984). Cleistogenes were first reported by Austin (1872) and described in *Danthonia* by Chase (1918) and those of *D. spicata* characterized in detail by Weatherwax (1928). In contrast to the terminal inflorescence, which is completely exert from the leaf sheath, cleistogenes are completely enclosed in the leaf sheath throughout their development and dispersal.

Asa Gray (1878) first reported the occurrence of cleistogamy in *Danthonia spicata* and was presumably referring to the cleistogenes with his statement, ''flowers...within the leaf-sheaths''. Cleistogamous and chasmogamous forms of the terminal inflorescence were first described by Hackel (1906). Although Hackel cited Gray (1878), his description of cleistogamy in *Danthonia* clearly does not include cleistogenes. Confusion over the chasmogamic or cleistogamic nature of

the aerial florets of the terminal inflorescence was also noted by Weatherwax (1928) when he described a cleistogamic form (with short anthers and rudimentary lodicules) and referred to the chasmogamous form illustrated in Gray's Manual (with long anthers). The examination and interpretation of Canadian *Danthonia* spp. by Baum and Findlay (1973) was based largely on terminal inflorescence floret lodicule characteristics. Herbarium specimens with either rudimentary lodicules (cleistogamous) or well-developed lodicules (chasmogamous) were found. Arguing that the nature of the lodicule reflects different breeding systems and genetic isolation of populations, they (Baum and Findlay 1973; Findlay and Baum 1974) relegate chasmogamous and cleistogamous forms to different species. W. G. Dore (Dore and McNeill 1980) pointed out that both chasmogamous and cleistogamous forms of the terminal panicle occur in *D. spicata,* sometimes in the same population.

A paper by Philipson (1986a), reporting on the reproductive form of greenhouse-grown material, reported spikelets of mixed cleistogamous and chasmogamous florets in the terminal inflorescence as did Hackel (1906) in other *Danthonia* species. This is in contrast with the hypothesis of genetic polymorphism of Dore and McNeill (1980) and Findlay and Baum (1974). Much material for Philipson's study, however, originated from well-known North American populations. Field observations of the population at Danford Lake, Quebec, indicate that plants produce one form or the other in their terminal inflorescences; not a mixture (W. G. Dore, pers. commun.). Similar observations have been reported in the literature from Bloomington, Indiana (Weatherwax 1928). The material studied by Philipson (1986a) from Durham, North Carolina, originated from partially or wholly infected seeds (see section 13) (K. Clay, pers. commun.). Clarification will require repetition of Philipson's work with material from a number of populations under natural conditions.

Philipsons' (1986a) contention that her findings invalidate the conclusions of Keith Clay's work on *Danthonia spicata* population genetics is false. Clay makes no assumption that chasmogamous flowers are all outcrossing (Clay and Antonovics 1985a,b). Although unable to quantify outcrossing rates in later studies (Clay and Antonovics 1985a,b), a preliminary outcrossing rate of less than 10% was estimated for chasmogamous terminal inflorescence florets (Clay 1982). His conclusions on the effects of the two types of inflorescences on population genetics and ecology are valid but possibly better understood by substituting "cleistogene" for Clay's use of "cleistogamous flower" or "CL" and "terminal inflorescence floret" for his term "chasmogamous flower" or "CH" (Clay 1982, 1983a,b, 1984; Clay and Antonovics 1985a,b; Clay and Jones 1984).

Confusion and controversy in the literature, spanning more than 100 yr, and the differences noted in various reproductive studies indicate the considerable variation in the reproduction systems of different populations of this wide-ranging species. Detailed studies throughout the geographic and habitat distribution will be required for a better understanding of the complex reproductive patterns documented so far.

(b) *Seed production and dispersal —* Reproduction in *Danthonia spicata* is entirely by seed (Muenscher 1955). Clay (1983a,b) found that populations at Durham, North Carolina, had seed set of virtually 100% in both terminal and cleistogene florets and that healthy plants produce an average of 200 florets. The proportion of cleistogene fruits was about 25%, although the figure varied (12–65%) between individuals and populations (Clay 1982, 1983a). The proportion of cleistogenes produced is also subject to environmental conditions such as grazing, mowing, cultivation and parasites (Clay 1982, 1983a). Clay (1983a) also found a correlation between habitat type and proportion of cleistogenes produced. A greater proportion of cleistogenes are produced in plants from higher elevations (mountains versus piedmont), disturbed areas (versus undisturbed areas) and woods (versus open areas).

The fruits of terminal inflorescence florets are heavier than cleistogene fruits, indicating greater food reserves (Clay 1983a). Scheiner and Teeri (1986b) found seeds of the terminal inflorescences usually fall within 1 m of the parent plant. Of the cleistogene fruits, those at the lowest internodes are usually just below the soil surface, where they remain to germinate in situ (Clay 1983a), while those of the upper nodes are dispersed by disarticulation of the dead culm.

The cleistogene diaspore (dispersal unit) comprises the cleistogene spikelet of one or more florets (enclosing the caryopsis) attached to a culm node and the apical internode, all enclosed by the persistent leaf sheath. Diaspores from the terminal inflorescence consist of the caryopsis, palea, lemma and rachilla internode. Most members of the genus have, as does *Danthonia spicata*, lemmas (terminal inflorescence) with a geniculate and spirally twisted awn arising from between the two apical teeth, and varying amounts of long, stiff, antrorsely pointing hairs. Simpson (1952) showed that the awns and hairs are important structures for dispersal and placement of the diaspore of *D. penicillata* (Labill) R.Br. ex Beauv. (= *Rytidosperma penicillata* (Labill.) Connor & Edgar).

(c) *Viability of seeds and germination — Danthonia* seed is highly dormant (Prince and Hodgdon 1946; Laude 1949) and, in Massachusetts, may remain viable in soil for several decades (Livingstone and Allessio 1968). Seed banks may persist in soils after aboveground populations have ceased to exist. Subsequent disturbance, especially fire, to the surface community or soil can stimulate germination (Abrams and Dickmann 1984; Scheiner 1988). Seeds of *D. spicata* may also pass through the digestive tract of cattle unharmed (Dore and Raymond 1942). Toole (1939) found that germination rates in *D. spicata* were enhanced (to 71%) equally by chilling (3°C for 2 mo) or sulphuric acid pretreatment. Such treatments may assist by removing gas restriction barriers of the seed coat (Toole 1939). High seedbed temperatures (10–35°C) and dilute potassium nitrate levels increased germination rates to various levels depending on pretreatment regime (Toole 1939).

Seedling survivorship may vary considerably in various habitats and successional stages (Scheiner 1988). Germination and seedling establishment studies at Durham, North Carolina, show that the proportion of establishing cleistogene to terminal floret progeny varies between populations but is relatively stable within a population from year to year unless major environmental disturbances occur (Clay 1983a). Differential establishment is due to many factors including differential production of parents, dispersal and germination behavior (Clay 1983a). Survivorship differences between cleistogene and terminal floret progeny were greatest at juvenile stages of development with insignificant differential survivorship of adults (Clay and Antonovics 1985a,b).

9. Hybrids

Interspecific hybrids have not been reported among native North American species of *Danthonia* (Knobloch 1968). Fernald (1950) suggested, however, that plants referable to *D. allenii* might be hybrids of *D. spicata* × *D. commpressa*.

10. Population Dynamics

Scheiner (1988) and Scheiner and Teeri (1981, 1986a,b, 1987) have examined *Danthonia spicata* populations along a forest successional gradient at Douglas Lake, Michigan. The persistence for more than 80 yr after canopy disturbance in aspen-pine woodland of this invader species is due to differential survivorship in a heterogeneous environment. Population size rises rapidly following canopy removal and slowly declines after the disturbance with the death of half the population on an average of every 2.2 yr (Scheiner 1988). As shade increases, surviving individuals of *D. spicata* are restricted to sites of higher than average light intensity and lower than average moisture. The early successional habitat of *D. spicata* is temporally unstable and this environmental instability selects for phenotypic flexibility rather than genotypic differentiation. The significant genetic differentiation between populations found by Scheiner and Teeri (1986b) was attributed to genetic drift. They argue that small population neighborhoods with low gene flow, extensive inbreeding and local seed dispersal have facilitated this genetic differentiation of populations. Population dynamics and survivorship along successional gradients is driven by habitat change (mainly canopy growth) rather than by genetic selection (Scheiner 1988).

Rapid changes in the genetic structure of populations can occur after major environmental disturbance. Populations in pine/hardwood forest after a fire rapidly change to post-fire light conditions with changes in morphology, reproduction, phenology and productivity (Scheiner and Teeri 1987). In the Douglas Lake population directional changes shifted growth characteristics by a standard deviation within two growing seasons.

Kelley (1985), Antonovics et al. (1987), and Kelley and Clay (1987) have shown that there was considerable variation in the growth response of various *Danthonia spicata* genotypes in competition with differing genotypes of *Anthoxanthum odoratum*. Those genotypes of *D. spicata* that were highly productive were most variable in their response to competition with differing genotypes of the competitor, thus being more unstable with environmental change. Those *D. spicata* genotypes with low productivity were more stable in their response to various genotypic environments. Thus a range of genotypes may remain in populations through microhabitat selection utilizing biotic components as parameters, as well as physical ones.

Population dynamics is also greatly affected by the fungal epiphyte, *Atkinsonella hypoxylon* (Peck) Tul. which will be discussed in Section 13.

11. Response to Herbicides and Other Chemicals

Of the five herbicides tested in a general vegetation control experiment in Pennsylvania, bromacil was found to be effective in *Danthonia spicata* control (Shipman 1974). Control was proportional with increasing applications (5.6, 11.2 and 22.4 kg ha^{-1}) was found to be most effective on sand-loam or clay-loam soils. A follow-up study of the same experimental sites 11 yr after initial application (Machlica and Shipman 1983) found the greatest herbicide reactions in the dominant grasses (*D. spicata, Phleum pratense* and *Poa pratensis*) to applications of fenuron (11.2 kg ha^{-1}), pelleted picloram (2.24 and 5.6 kg ha^{-1}) and wettable powder bromacil (22.4 kg ha^{-1}), eliminating grasses as the dominant species for at least two growing seasons. Grasses, including *D. spicata*, were controlled in blueberry populations in Maine with application of hexazinone at 2 kg ha^{-1} (Yarborough and Bhomik 1986).

12. Response to Other Human Manipulation

Danthonia spicata is a common invading species of mine spoils in West Virginia (Smith et al. 1971) and reclaimed strip mines in Pennsylvania (Hedin 1986). It is an ''increaser species'' under close grazing in dry pastures and an invader of abandoned fields (Dore and McNeill 1980). Muenscher (1955) recommended abandoning infested agricultural land as the presence of large *D. spicata* populations indicated a lack of soil fertility. Control in pastures is best effected by cultivation, fertilization and heavy reseeding (Georgia 1914; Runnels and Schaffner 1936).

13. Response to Parasites

(a) *Insects and other nondomestic animals* — *Danthonia spicata* is the primary host of the leaf hopper, *Latalus personatus* Beirne (A. Hamilton, pers. commun.). In Ottawa, Ontario, the butterfly, *Oeneis chryxus strigulosa* McDunnough has been reared from *D. spicata* (R. A. Layberry, pers. commun.). Two species of non-specialist grass aphids, *Geoica squamosa* Hart. and *Prociphilus erigeronensis* Thonas (Patch 1938) and a single chalcid wasp, *Harmolita danthoniae* Phillips (Phillips 1936), have also been reported as parasites of *D. spicata*.

(b) *Microorganisms and viruses* — A number of parasitic fungi have been reported on *Danthonia spicata* from Canada: *Ustilago residua* Clint., *Atkinsonella hypoxylon* (Peck) Diehl (anamorph named *Ephelis borealis* Ell. & Ev.), *Epichloe typhina* (Pers.: Fr.) Tul., *Pseudoseptoria stomaticola* (Bauml.) Sutton var. *stomaticola* and *Pyrenophora semeniperda* (Brittleb. & Adam) Shoem. (anamorph named *Drechsleria verticillata* (O'Gara) Shoem.) (Conners 1967; Ginns 1986). In the United States *Helminthosporium* sp., *Puccinia graminis* Pers., *Rhynchosporium secalis* (Oud.) J. J. Davis, and *Claviceps purpurea* (Fr.) Tul. have also been reported from *D. spicata* (United States Dep. Agric. 1960).

A common fungal disease of *Danthonia spicata*, caused by *Atkinsonella hypoxylon* (Peck) Diehl and known as choke or black stripe, belongs to the clavicipitaceous tribe Balansiae. Several genera and a number of species in this tribe have been described as endophytic or epiphytic on grasses and sedges (Diehl 1950). During the hosts' vegetative growth phases, dense mats of mycelia form on meristematic regions and in the gaps between young leaf bases. The terminal inflorescence is mechanically (and possibly physiologically) restricted and aborted by the formation of hypothallus (sclerotium) at the apex of developing culms (Clay and Jones 1984; Diehl 1950; Leuchtmann and Clay 1988). Although terminal inflorescence production was aborted in infected clones studied by Clay and Jones (1984), they showed that the fungus penetrates normally developing cleistogenes where it remains inactive around the embryo and embryo sac wall through seed dispersal and germination. Philipson and Christey (1985), however, report from greenhouse-grown material that the fungus (which they initially identified as *Ephelis* sp.) did not inhibit terminal inflorescence development and that hyphae invaded terminal inflorescence florets in a similar fashion to the cleistogenes. At least under some circumstances the alternation of epiphytic form on the host sporophyte with endophytic form on the host gametophyte may have no deleterious effect on the reproduction of *D. spicata*.

Diehl (1950) found that infected plants were generally dwarfed and failed to produce cleistogenes. Clay (1984), on the other hand, has shown that infected plants produce more cleistogenes than non-infected plants. Although reducing fecundity, infection is often manifested with increased vegetative vigor (Clay 1984). Philipson (1986b) reported that infected plants possessed a chimeric outgrowth of hyper-trophied integument tissue through the ovary's apical pore. An apical pore, or failure of the ovary wall to completely fuse, is present only in infected plants and the ribbon-like projections of integument are always surrounded by a ''weft'' of hyphal tissue of the parasite.

Many recent studies indicate a constitutive mutualism rather than a simple parasite-host relationship between fungi in the tribe Balansiae and many species of grasses and sedges. Strong competitive abilities of endophyte-infected clones have been shown in their greater productivity (Clay 1984, 1987a; Kelley and Clay 1987), greater seed set (Clay 1987a), greater seedling survival (Clay 1984, 1987a), wider range of responses to environmental heterogeneity (Antonovics et al. 1987; Kelley and Clay 1987), and greater resistance to herbivory compared with uninfected clones (Cheplick and Clay (1988) see also reviews by Clay (1987b, 1988) and Siegel et al. (1987)).

Resistance to herbivory of infected plants is presently considered to be primarily, although not exclusively, due to the production by the fungus of mycotoxins (Cheplick and Clay (1988), see also review by Clay (1988)). These compounds are dispersed throughout host tissues causing minimal direct effects to the host physiology while often significantly reducing herbivore performance.

No reports of viral or bacterial infection of *Danthonia spicata* have been located.

(c) *Higher Plant Parasites — Danthonia spicata* has been reported as a host to the generalist hemiparasite, *Pedicularis canadensis* L. (Piehl 1963). Other scrophulariaceous hemiparasites, such as *Melampyrum lineare* Desr., *Euphrasia stricta* Wolf and *Rhinanthus minor* L., which are often sympatric with *D. spicata*, may facultatively parasitize this grass.

ACKNOWLEDGMENTS

We would like to thank those people cited in the text for their personal communication and to E. Gavora, L. Bain, R. Foottit, and L. Lesage, for assistance in searching the literature, to M. A. Martin for the tedious work of typing, to M. Jomphe for Figs. 1 and 2, and to K. Clay, C. W. Crompton, J. H. Ginns, and S. I. Warwick for comments on earlier drafts.

Abrams, M. D. and Dickmann, D. I. 1984. Apparent heat stimulation of buried seeds of *Geranium bicknellii* on jack pine sites in northern lower Michigan. Mich. Bot. **23**: 81–88.

Alex, J. F., Cayouette, R. and Mulligan, G. A. 1980. Common and botanical names of weeds in Canada. Agriculture Canada, Ottawa, Ont. Publ. 1397. 132 pp.

Antonovics, J., Clay, K. and Schmitt, J. 1987. The measurement of small-scale environmental heterogeneity using clonal transplants of *Anthoxanthum odoratum* and *Danthonia spicata*. Oecologia (Berl.) **71**: 601–607.

Austin, C.F. 1872. *Danthonia* DC. Bull. Torrey Bot. Club. **3**: 21–22.

Baker, B. S. and Nestor, R. L. 1979. Forage and weed species and grazing management systems on permanent pastures in the Allegheny highlands of West Virginia. W. V. Agric. For. Exp. Sta. Bull. 670. 22 pp.

Baldwin, W. K. W. 1958. Plants of the Clay Belt of northern Ontario and Quebec. Natl. Mus. Can. Bull. 156. 324 pp.

Baum, B. R. and Findlay, J. N. 1973. Preliminary studies in the taxonomy of *Danthonia* in Canada. Can. J. Bot. **51**: 437–450.

Bingham, R. T. 1987. Plants of the Seven Devils Mountains of Idaho — an annotated checklist. US For. Serv. Gen. Tech. Rep. Int. INT-219 146 pp.

Boivin, B. 1967. Énumération des plantes du Canada. VI - Monopsides, (2ème partie). Nat. Can. (Qué). **94**: 471-528.

Boivin, B. 1981. Flora of the Prairie Provinces. A handbook to the flora of the provinces of Manitoba, Saskatchewan and Alberta. Part V. Gramineae. Provancheria (Mémoires de l'Herbier Louis-Marie, Faculté des Sciences de l'Agriculture et de l'Alimentation, Université Laval, Québec) 12 108 pp.

Boulet, L.-J. 1946. Les principaux caractères botaniques et écologiques de nos divers groupes de pâturages. Nat. Can. (Qué). **73**: 137-142.

Bowden, W. M. 1960. Chromosome numbers and taxonomic notes on northern grasses. III. Twenty-five genera. Can. J. Bot. **38**: 541-557.

Breitung, A. J. 1954. A botanical survey of the Cypress Hills. Can. Field Nat. **68**: 55-92.

Butters, F. K. and Abbe, E. C. 1953. A floristic study of Cook County, Northeastern Minnesota. Rhodora **55**: 116-154.

Catling, P. M. 1985. Description and analysis of the vascular flora of the Cataraqui Marsh area. Agric. Can. Tech. Bull. 1985-7E. 63 pp.

Cayouette, J. 1979. L'habitat de trente-quatre espèces vasculaires des milieux ouverts du secteur calcaire de la Rivière Shipsaw, Saguenay. M.Sc. Thesis, Université Laval, Québec. 371 pp.

Cayouette, J. and Darbyshire, S. J. 1987. La répartition de *Danthonia intermedia* dans l'est du Canada. Nat. Can. (Qué). **114**: 217-220.

Chase, A. 1918. Axillary cleistogenes in some American grasses. Am. J. Bot. **5**: 254-258.

Cheplick, G. P. and Clay, K. 1988. Acquired chemical defenses in grasses: the role of fungal endophytes. Oikos **52**: 309-318.

Chichester, F. W. 1977. Effects of increased fertilizer rates on nitrogen content of runoff and percolate from monolith lysimeters. J. Environ. Qual. **6**: 211-216.

Clay, K. 1982. Environmental and genetic determinants of cleistogamy in a natural population of the grass *Danthonia spicata.* Evolution **36**: 734-741.

Clay, K. 1983a. The differential establishment of seedlings from chasmogamous and cleistagamous flowers in natural populations of the grass *Danthonia spicata* (L.) Beauv. Oecologia (Berl.) **57**: 183-188.

Clay, K. 1983b. Variation in the degree of cleistogamy within and among species of the grass *Danthonia.* Am. J. Bot. **70**: 835-843.

Clay, K. 1984. The effect of the fungus *Atkinsonella hypoxylon* (Clavicipitaceae) on the repro-duction system and demography of the grass *Danthonia spicata.* New Phytol. **98**: 165-175.

Clay, K. 1987a. Effects of fungal endophytes on the seed and seedling biology of *Lolium perenne* and *Festuca arundinacea.* Oecologia (Berl.) **73**: 358-362.

Clay, K. 1987b. The effect of fungi on the interaction between host plants and their herbivores. Can. J. Plant Pathol. **9**: 380-388.

Clay, K. 1988. Fungal endophytes of grasses: a defensive mutualism between plants and fungi. Ecology **69**: 10-16.

Clay, K. and Antonovics, J. 1985a. Demographic genetics of the grass *Danthonia spicata:* success of progeny from chasmogamous and cleistogamous flowers. Evolution **39**: 205-210.

Clay, K. and Antonovics, J. 1985b. Quantitative variation of progeny from chasmogamous and cleistogamous flowers in the grass *Danthonia spicata.* Evolution **39**: 335-348.

Clay, K. and Jones, J. P. 1984. Transmission of *Atkinsonella hypoxylon* (Clavicipitaceae) by cleistogamous seed of *Danthonia spicata* (Gramineae). Can. J. Bot. **62**: 2893-2895.

Clayton, W. D. and Renvoize, S. A. 1986. *Genera Graminum.* Grasses of the World. Kew Bull. Addit. Ser. 13. 389 pp.

Clayden, S. and Bouchard, A. 1983. Structure and dynamics of conifer-lichen stands on rock outcrops south of Lake Abitibi, Quebec. Can. J. Bot. **61**: 850-871.

Cléonique-Joseph, F. 1936. Études de développement floristique en Laurentie. Contrib. Inst. Bot. Université Montréal 27. 246 pp.

Conert, H. J. 1987. Current concepts in the systematics of the Arundinoideae. Pages 239-250 *in* T.R. Soderstrom et al., eds. Grass systematics and evolution. Smithsonian Institute Press, Washington, D.C.

Conners, I. L. 1967. An annotated index of plant diseases in Canada. Canada Department of Agriculture, Ottawa, Ont. Publ. 1251. 381 pp.

Cruise J. E. 1969. A floristic study of Norfolk County, Ontario. Trans. R. Can. Inst. **35**:1-116.

Dansereau, P. 1943. L'érablière laurentienne. I. Valeur d'indice des espèces. Can. J. Res. Sect. C Bot. Sci. **21**: 66-93.

Dansereau, P. 1946. L'érablière laurentienne. II. Les successions et leurs indicateurs. Can. J. Res. Sect. C Bot. Sci. **24**: 235-291.

Dansereau, P. 1959. Phytogeographia laurentiana. II. The principal plant associations of the Saint Lawrence Valley. Contrib. Inst. Bot. Université Montréal 75. 147 pp.

Deschênes, J. M. and St-Pierre, J. C. 1978. Etude agro-écologique dans le comté de Rivière-du-Loup: aspect écologique. Can. J. Plant Sci. **58**: 117–128.

Diehl, W.G. 1950. *Balansia* and the Balansiae in America. U.S. Dep. Agric. Monogr. 4. 82 pp.

Dore, W. G. 1936. Pasture Studies X. Succession and variation in the botanical composition of permanent pastures. Sci. Agric. **16**: 569–590.

Dore, W. G. 1959. Grasses of the Ottawa District. Canada Department of Agriculture, Ottawa, Ont. Publ. 1049. 101 pp.

Dore, W. G. and Campbell, J. B. 1949. Weeds of Grassland. Agric. Inst. Rev. **4**: 95–97.

Dore, W. G. and McNeill, J. 1980. Grasses of Ontario. Agriculture Canada, Ottawa, Ont. Monogr. 26. 566 pp.

Dore, W. G. and Raymond, L. C. 1942. Pasture Studies XXIV. Viable seeds in pasture soil and manure. Sci. Agric. **23**: 69–79.

Doyon, D. 1968. La végétation des pâturages naturels de Saint-Ferréol et de Saint-Tite-des-Caps, Comté de Montmorency. Nat. Can. (Qué.) **95**: 367–391.

Doyon, D. 1975. Etude éco-dynamique de la végétation du comté de Lévis. Agric. Québec, Service de la Défense des Cultures, Mémoire 1. 428 pp.

Doyon, D. and Cayouette, R. 1978. Liste annotée des plantes du comté de Lévis, Québec. Ptéridophytes et Spermatophytes. Agriculture Québec, Service de Recherche en Défense des Cultures, Mémoire 2. 191 pp.

Doyon, D. and Clabault, G. 1979. Application de l'analyse factorielle des correspondances à l'étude des pâturages semi-naturels de la région de Québec. Nat. Can. (Qué.) **106**: 313–330.

Fernald, M. L. 1943. Notes on *Danthonia*. Rhodora **45**: 239–246.

Fernald, M. L. 1950. Gray's manual of botany. 8th ed. American Book Co., New York, N.Y. 1632 pp.

Findlay, J. N. and Baum, B. R. 1974. The nomenclatural implications of the taxonomy of *Danthonia* in Canada. Can. J. Bot. **52**: 1573–1582.

Georgia, A. E. 1914. Manual of Weeds. Macmillan Co., New York, N.Y. 593 pp.

Gervais, C. 1981. Liste annotée de nombres chromosomiques de la flore vasculaire du nord-est de l'Amérique. II. Nat. Can. (Qué.) **108**: 143–152.

Ginns, J. H. 1986. Compendium of plant disease and decay fungi in Canada 1960–1980. Agriculture Canada, Ottawa, Ont. Publ. 1813. 416 pp.

Gould, F. W. 1975. The grasses of Texas. Texas A.& M. University Press, College Stn., Tex. 653 pp.

Gray, A. 1878. *A review of:* Darwin, C. 1877. The different forms of flowers on plants of the same species. John Murray, London. 352 pp. *In:* Am. J. Sci. Arts, Ser. 3 **15**: 67–71.

Hackel, E. 1906. Über kleistogamie bei den Gräsern. Oesterr. Bot. Z. **56**: 81–88, 143–154, 180–186.

Hall, I. V., Aalders, L. E., Nickerson, N. L. and Vander Kloet, S. P. 1979. The biological flora of Canada. I. *Vaccinium angustifolium* Ait., Sweet Lowbush Blueberrry. Can. Field Nat. **93**: 415–430.

Hedin, B. 1986. Ecological recovery of minimally-reclaimed strip mines in northeastern Pennsylvania. Bull. N.J. Acad. Sci. **31**: 7.

Hitchcock, A.S. and Chase, A. 1951. Manual of the grasses of the United States. 2nd ed. U.S. Dept. Agric. Misc. Publ. 200. 1051 pp.

Hitchcock, A. S., Swallen, J. R., and Chase, A. 1939. *Danthonia* DC. North American Flora **17(8)**: 571–576.

Kalmbacher, R. S. and Waskko, J. B. 1977. Time, magnitude, and quality estimates of forage consumed by deer in woodland clearings. Agron. J. **69**: 497–501.

Kelley, S. E. 1985. The effects of neighbors as environments: characterization of the competitive performance of *Danthonia spicata* genotypes. Pages 203–221 *in* P. Jacquard et al., eds. Genetic differentiation and dispersal in plants. NATO ASI Series, Vol. G5.

Kelley, S. E. and Clay, K. 1987. Interspecific competitive interactions and the maintenance of genotypic variation within two perennial grasses. Evolution **41**: 92–103.

Knobloch, I. W. 1968. A check list of crosses in the Gramineae. East Lansing, Mich. 170 pp.

Larson, S. S. and Batson, W. T. 1979. The vegetation of vertical rock faces in Pickens and Greenville Counties, South Carolina, U. S. A. Castanea **43**: 255–260.

Laude, H. M. 1949. Delayed germination of California Oatgrass, *Danthonia californica*. Agron. J. **40**: 404–408.

Lavoie, V. 1968. La phytosociologie et l'aménagement des bleuetières. Nat. Can. (Qué.) **95**: 397–412.

Leuchtmann, A. and Clay, K. 1988. *Atkinsonella hypoxylon* and *Balansia cyperi*, epiphytic members of the Balansiae. Mycologia **80**: 192–199.

Livingstone, R. B. and Allessio, M. L. 1968. Buried viable seed in successional field and forest stands, Harvard Forest, Massachusetts. Bull.

Torrey Bot. Club **95**: 58–69.

Looman, J. and Best, K. F. 1979. Budd's Flora of the Canadian Prairie Provinces. Agriculture Canada, Ottawa, Ont. Publ. 1662. 863 pp.

Löve, Á. and Löve, D. 1981. Chromosome Number Reports LXX. Poaceae. Taxon **30**: 72.

Machlica, D. J. and Shipman, R. D. 1983. Succession on fields eleven years after applying herbicides. Proc. Northeast. Weed Sci. Soc. **37**: 120–123.

Marie-Victorin, F. 1964. Flore laurentienne. 2nd ed. by E. Rouleau. Presses de l'Université de Montréal, Montréal, Qué. 924 pp.

Marie-Victorin, F. and Rolland-Germain, F. 1969. Flore de l'Anticosti-Minganie. Presses de l'Université de Montréal, Montréal, Qué. 529 pp.

Metcalfe, C. R. 1960. Anatomy of the monocotyledons. I. Gramineae. Oxford University Press, Toronto, Ont. 731 pp.

Muenscher, W. C. 1955. Weeds. 2nd. ed. The MacMillan Co., New York, N.Y. 560 pp.

Myers, W. M. 1947. Cytology and genetics of forage grasses. Bot. Rev. **13**: 322–421.

Packer, J. G. and Bradley, C. E. 1984. A checklist of the rare vascular plants in Alberta. Prov. Mus. Alberta Nat. Hist. Occas. Paper 5. 112 pp.

Palmer, E. J. 1930. The spontaneous flora of the Arnold Arboretum. J. Arnold Arbor. Harv. Univ. **11**: 63–119.

Patch, E. M. 1938. Food-plant catalogue of the aphids of the world including Phylloxeridae. Maine Agric. Exp. Sta. Bull. 393. 431 pp.

Payette, S. and Lavoie, V. 1971. Relations sol-végétation en basse Péri bonka. 1. Les groupements végétaux. Nat. Can. (Qué.) **98**: 495–514.

Philipson, M. N. 1986a. A re-assessment of the form of reproduction in *Danthonia spicata* (L). Beauv. New Phytol. **103**: 231–243.

Philipson, M. N. 1986b. Integumentary projections through the apical pore of the ovary of *Danthonia spicata.* Phytomorphology **36**: 287–289.

Philipson, M. N. and Christey, M. C. 1985. An epiphytic/endophytic fungal associate of *Danthonia spicata* transmitted through the embryo sac. Bot. Gaz. **146:** 70–81.

Phillips, W. J. 1936. A second revision of the Chalcid flies of the genus *Harmolita (Isosoma)* of America north of Mexico, with descriptions of 20 new species. U.S. Dep. Agric. Tech. Bull. 518. 27 pp.

Piehl, M. A. 1963. Mode of attachment, haustorium structure, and hosts of *Pedicularis*

canadensis. Am. J. Bot. **50**: 978–985.

Prince, F. S. and Hodgdon, A. R. 1946. Viable seeds in old pasture soils. New Hampshire Agric. Exp. Sta. Tech. Bull. 89. 14 pp.

Reznicek, A. A. and Maycock, P. F. 1983. Compositon of an isolated prairie in central Ontario. Can. J. Bot. **61**: 3107–3116.

Runnels, H. A. and Schaffner, J. H. 1931. Manual of Ohio weeds. Ohio Agric. Exp. Sta. Bull. 475. 166 pp.

Scheiner, S. M. 1983. The persistence of *Danthonia spicata* during secondary succession. Diss. Abstr. Int. B Sci. Eng. **44**: 1001.

Scheiner, S. M. 1988. Population dynamics of a herbaceous perennial *Danthonia spicata* during secondary forest succession. Am. Midl. Nat. **119**: 268–281.

Scheiner, S. M. and Goodnight, C. J. 1984. The comparison of phenotypic plasticity and genetic variation in populations of the grass *Danthonia spicata.* Evolution **38**: 845–855.

Scheiner, S. M., Gurevitch, J. and Teeri, J. A. 1984. A genetic analysis of the photosynthetic properties of populations of *Danthonia spicata* that have different growth responses to light level. Oecologia (Berl.) **64**: 74–77.

Scheiner, S. M. and Teeri, J. A. 1981. A 53-year record of forest succession following fire in northern lower Michigan. Mich. Bot. **20**: 3–14.

Scheiner, S. M. and Teeri, J. A. 1986a. Microhabitat selection and the successional gradient of a forest grass. Can. J. Bot. **64**: 734–738.

Scheiner, S. M. and Teeri, J. A. 1986b. Phenotypic flexibility and genetic adaptation along a gradient of secondary forest succession in the grass *Danthonia spicata.* Can. J. Bot. **64**: 739–747.

Scheiner, S. M. and Teeri, J. A. 1987. Rapid genotypic change in a population of the grass *Danthonia spicata* following disturbance. Can. J. Bot. **65**: 1819–1823.

Scoggan. H. J. 1950. The flora of Bic and the Gaspé Peninsula, Québec. Natl. Mus. Can. Bull. 115. 399 pp.

Scoggan, H. J. 1978. The Flora of Canada. Part 2. Natl. Mus. Nat. Sci. (Ott.) Publ. Bot. **7**: 93–545.

Sheppard, J. S. 1971. The influence of geothermal temperature gradients upon vegetation patterns in Yellowstone National Park. Diss. Abstr. Int. B Sci. Eng. **32**: 1403.

Shipman, R. D. 1974. Soil-applied herbicides in the control of native broadleaf weeds and grasses. Proc. Northeast. Weed Sci. Soc. **28**: 331–334.

Siegel, M. R., Latch, G. C. M. and Johnson, M. C. 1987. Fungal endophytes of grasses. Annu. Rev. Phytopathol. **25**: 293–315.

Simpson, M. 1952. Value of the awn in establishing seed of *Danthonia penicillata* (Labill.) Palisot. N.Z. J. Sci. Technol. Sect. A **34**: 360–364.

Smith, R. M., Tryon, E. H., and Tyner, E. H. 1971. Soil development on mine spoil. W. V. Agric. Exp. Sta. Bull. 604T. 47 pp.

Swan, F. R., Jr. 1970. Post-fire response of four plant communities in south-central New York State. Ecology **51**: 1074–1082.

Tomlinson, K. L. 1985. Comparative anatomical studies in *Danthonia* sensu lato (Danthonieae: Poaceae). Aliso **11**: 97–114.

Toole, V. K. 1939. Germination of the seed of poverty grass, *Danthonia spicata*. J. Am. Soc. Agron. **31**: 954–965.

United States Department of Agriculture. 1960. Index of plant diseases in the US. U.S. Dep. Agric. Handb. 165. 531 pp.

Vander Kloet, S. P. and Hall, I. V. 1981. The biological flora of Canada. 2. *Vaccinium myrtilloides* Michx., Velvet-leaf Blueberry. Can. Field Nat. **95**: 329–345.

Voss, E. G. 1972. Michigan Flora. Part I. Cranbrook Inst. Sci., Bloomfield Hills, and Univ. Mich. Herb., Ann Arbor. 488 pp.

Weatherwax, P. 1928. Cleistogamy in two species of *Danthonia*. Bot. Gaz. **85**: 104–109.

de Wet, J. M. J. 1954. The genus *Danthonia* in grass phylogeny. Am. J. Bot. **41**: 204–211.

Yarborough, D. E. and Bhowmik, P. C. 1986. Effect of hexazinone on weeds and on Lowbush Blueberies in Maine. Proc. Northeast. Weed Sci. Soc. **40**: 165–166.

THE BIOLOGY OF CANADIAN WEEDS. 93.
Epilobium angustifolium L. (Onagraceae).

D. H. BRODERICK

Department of Plant Sciences, University of Western Ontario, London, Ontario, Canada N6A 5B7. Received 13 June 1988, accepted 11 Sept. 1989.

BRODERICK, D. H. 1990. The biology of Canadian weeds. 93. *Epilobium angustifolium* L. (Onagraceae). Can. J. Plant Sci. **70**: 247–259.

Fireweed (*Epilobium angustifolium* L.), a native herbaceous perennial, occurs across most of Canada. It is particularly abundant on recently disturbed ground in coniferous or mixed forest ecosystems and is a common weed of roadsides and waste areas, especially in areas with acidic soils. In some successionally advanced vegetation, however, widely spaced colonies with low stem densities may persist for long periods. Where growth of the species is prolific, seedling establishment of commercially important coniferous trees can be suppressed and the species can be a problem in perennial crops.

Key words: *Epilobium angustifolium*, fireweed, fire, forest succession, forest weeds

[La biologie des mauvaises herbes canadiennes. 93. *Epilobium angustifolium* L. (Onagracées).]
Titre abrégé: *Epilobium angustifolium* L. (Onagraceae).
L'épilobe à feuilles étroites (*Epilobium angustifolium* L.), une espèce herbacée indigène et vivace, se retrouve dans presque toutes les régions du Canada. Elle est particulièrement abondante dans les peuplements forestiers de résineux ou les peuplements mixtes récemment exploités et elle pousse également le long des routes et dans les terrains vagues, en particulier là où le sol est acide. Dans certains types de végétations successives avancées, les colonies fortement espacées et à tiges peu denses peuvent toutefois persister pendant de longues périodes. Lorsque sa croissance est abondante, cette mauvaise herbe peut empêcher l'implantation de résineux d'importance commerciale; elle peut également nuire aux cultures vivaces.

Mots clés: *Epilobium angustifolium*, épilobe à feuilles étroites, feu, succession en forêt, mauvaises herbes des forêts

1. Name
Epilobium angustifolium L. (Onagraceae; Evening primrose family; Onagracées); **fireweed**, great willowherb (Scoggan 1978) **épilobe à feuilles étroites** (Alex et al. 1980), bouquet rouge (Marie-Victorin 1964). In the European literature, the species is frequently referred to as *Chamaenerion angustifolium* (L.) Scop..

2. Description and Account of Variation
The species is an herbaceous perennial with erect leafy stems that may exceed 2 m in height and which arise each spring from buds formed the previous year on lateral roots.

The leaves are alternate, entire, 3–20 cm long, green above, pale and reticulate-veiny beneath, acuminate with a narrowed, sessile, to obscurely petiolate base. The racemes are elongate, bracted and commonly bear more than 15 somewhat zygomorphic flowers that are often subtended by leaves or bracts. The calyx is cleft to the summit of the ovary, and the four magenta to pink (rarely white) petals are 1–2 cm in length. The style is declined and pubescent at the base, and the slender 3–4 mm long stigmas are revolute at maturity. The eight stamens form a single series and are shorter than the style. The seed capsules are canescent, 2.5–8.0 cm in length, and each may contain many small light brown

Can. J. Plant Sci. **70**: 247–259 (Jan. 1990)

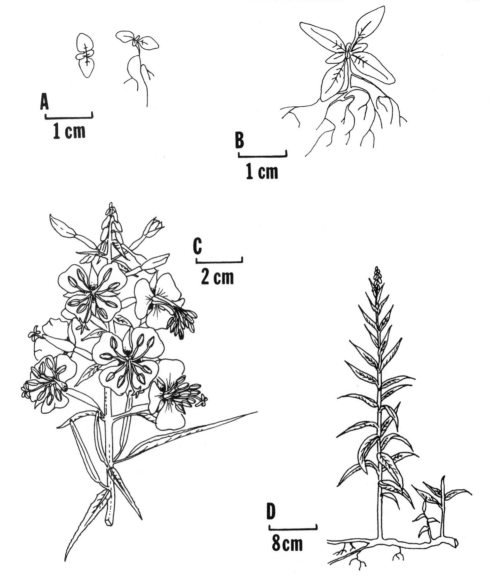

Fig. 1. Stages in the growth and development of *Epilobium angustifolium* L. A. seedling at the four-leaf stage. B. seedling at the eight-leaf stage. C. section of mature stem showing inflorescence. D. portion of mature plant with attached root system.

seed, 0.8–1.3 mm in length, capped with a tuft of hairs up to 13 mm long. Figure 1 depicts *Epilobium angustifolium* at various stages of development.

Epilobium latifolium L. is the species most likely to be confused with *Epilobium angustifolium* in Canada. Characteristics of *E.*

latifolium that distinguish it from *E. angustifolium* are: (1) stems — depressed, densely matted; (2) leaves — mostly opposite, thick and fleshy, glaucous, veinless, less than 8 cm in length; (3) racemes — usually less than 15 flowers, bracts not much reduced; (4) flowers — glabrous styles shorter than the stamens, short and thick stigma lobes.

The great intraspecific variation observed in *Epilobium angustifolium* may have both an environmental and genetic basis (Gleason 1963; Mosquin 1966; Myerscough 1980). Mosquin (1966) described two chromosomally different subspecies for North America. Individuals of the more northerly subspecies, *Epilobium angustifolium* ssp. *angustifolium* Mosquin (*n* = 18), is characterized by small- to medium-sized leaves which lack pubescence on the abaxial ribs and triporate pollen grains ranging in size from 62 to 85 μm. The tetraploid (*n*=36), and presumed autopolyploid (Mosquin 1967), spp. *circumvagum* Mosquin has small to very large leaves with glabrous to densely pubescent abaxial leaf ribs. The stems range from short to very tall and the flowers are usually large. The pollen grains had diameters ranging from 75 to 95 μm and were tri- or quadriporate. Scoggan (1978) recognized three forms within ssp. *angustifolium*: form *angustifolium* with roseate to purplish petals; form *albiflorum* (Dum.) Haussk. with white petals and sepals; and form *spectabile* (Simmons) Fern. with white petals and red sepals.

3. Economic Importance

a. *Detrimental* — In both western coniferous forests and the mixed forests of eastern Canada, *Epilobium angustifolium* is a common and sometimes dominant weed of logged and/or burned areas (Dyrness 1973; Bartos and Mueggler 1981). Where growth in conjunction with other invaders is prolific, seedling growth of such commercially important species as Douglas-fir may be suppressed (Peterson and Newton 1983). The species is also an alternate host of the rust, *Pucciniastrum Abieti-chamenerii* Kleb. (= *Pucciniastrum epilobii* Otth.), that causes needle rust in *Abies balsamea* L. (Goodwin 1930), and Ginns (1986) lists *E. angustifolium* as a host of 11 species of disease and decay fungi in Canada. At present, *E. angustifolium* does not seem to be a major weed of croplands in Canada, but it has been identified as a common weed of old fields in Quebec (Jobidon 1986), and it is one of the most persistent native weed species in grain and vegetable fields in Alaska (Conn and DeLapp 1983). Bailey and Hoogland (1984) reported *E. angustifolium*, among other species of *Epilobium*, to be an increasing problem in perennial crops in Great Britain.

b. *Beneficial* — Although the nectar production of the flowers is not very high (i.e. 1.55 mg sucrose equivalents per day (Bertsch 1983)), the number of flowers produced in some habitats make the species an important producer for the honey industry throughout most of its Canadian range (Mosquin 1966). Myerscough (1980) cites reports of honey production as high as 1000 kg ha^{-1} in the Soviet Union.

Epilobium angustifolium may prove to be a good species for artificial revegetation and land rehabilitation projects. It has been described as a dominant natural colonizer of oil spill sites in the arctic (Kimber et al. 1978; Walker et al. 1978; Kershaw and Kershaw 1986) and has been found on acidic coal spoils (Russell and La Roi 1986), mine wastes (Henderson et al. 1979) and along road cuts (Mosquin 1966). It produces new shoots from small root cuttings (van Andel 1974; Broderick 1980), making it suitable for transplanting. A low flammability rating also makes it a good candidate for land management treatments in areas prone to burning (Sylvester and Wein 1981).

Boivin and Benoit (1987) identified the coincidence of the first blooms of *Epilobium angustifolium* with captures of the first generation of the onion maggot (*Delia antiqua* Meign.) in south-western Quebec. They suggested that *E. angustifolium* thus represented a good visual indicator of the flights of this insect pest and would be useful in determining the time of pesticide applications.

In south-central British Columbia, Willms et al. (1980) found *Epilobium angustifolium* to be a preferred food of both deer and range cattle. Henderson et al. (1979) claimed the species is eaten in Canada by moose, caribou, muskrat and hares. The species can also be eaten by man and was used by the MicMac and Malecite Indians of the Atlantic Provinces (Chandler and Hooper 1979).

The species has aesthetic value as well. The flowering display is spectacular, and in the fall the foliage turns a deep red. These features and its great abundance in certain areas no doubt favored the selection of *Epilobium angustifolium* as the territorial flower of the Yukon Territory of Canada.

c. *Legislation — Epilobium angustifolium* is not listed in the Canada Seed Act or in the noxious weed acts of any province but Manitoba. In that province, fireweed is included in the schedule of noxious weeds (The Noxious Weeds Act of Manitoba 1970).

4. Geographical Distribution

Epilobium angustifolium is widespread in Canada, occurring in all the provinces and territories (Fig. 2). It is a circumboreal species (Hultén 1972) and has been recorded from 25° to 70° N and from sea level in the

central and northern portions of its range in western North America to 5000 m in the Himalayas (Mosquin 1966).

5. Habitat

a. *Climatic requirements — Epilobium angustifolium* tolerates a broad spectrum of climatic conditions (van Andel 1974; Myerscough 1980), although at the northern limits of its range it tends to be restricted to relatively sheltered sites away from the wind (Myerscough and Whitehead 1966) and at its southerly limits to montane environments (Mosquin 1966). Laboratory studies suggest that growth form and developmental patterns are not under direct photoperiod control, but day length, temperature, and dense shade were shown to affect the rate of development (Myerscough and Whitehead 1967).

b. *Substratum* — The species can grow in a wide variety of substrates. In northern Quebec, Henderson et al. (1979) found

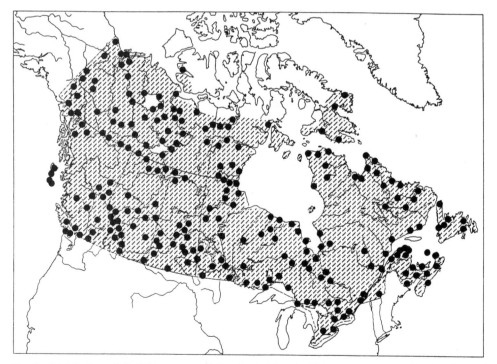

Fig. 2. Distribution of *Epilobium angustifolium* L. in Canada. The dots represent collection sites and the shaded area represents the probable range. (Redrawn from Mosquin 1966.)

populations on Gleysols, Brunisols, Podzols, Regosols and mine tailings. In Britain, *Epilobium angustifolium* can be found on non-calcareous gleyed soils, Podzols and Brunisols and mobile calcareous dunes (Myerscough 1980). In Holland, van Andel (1974) commonly found it on sand or sandy loams where pH values ranged from 3.7 to 5.6. An occasional specimen could be found in substrates with pH values as high as 8.0 – 9.0 (van Andel et al. 1978). While the species appears to grow best on soils that are relatively high in mineral nutrients (van Andel and Nelissen 1979; Myerscough and Whitehead 1967), van Andel and Nelissen (1979) and van Andel (1974) described it as a "nitro-resistant" species, capable of withstanding but not requiring high levels of nitrogen or mineral nutrients in general. Etherington (1984) found the species to lack tolerance to waterlogged soil, i.e. plants rooted under these conditions wilted within 12 h.

c. *Communities in which the species occurs* — In temperate regions, *Epilobium angustifolium* is a component of a wide variety of plant communities. It is most frequently associated with species colonizing recently disturbed ground: clear-cut areas (Dyrness 1973), forest fire sites (Mosquin 1966; Scotter 1971; Stark 1977; Broderick 1980; Bartos and Mueggler 1981; Dyrness and Norum 1983), roadsides (Mosquin 1966; Henderson et al. 1979), pumice plains (Wood and del Moral 1988), or urban waste areas (Salisbury 1942). In some disturbed sites *E. angustifolium* may be a dominant species during the early stages of succession (Brenchley and Heintze 1933; Bartos and Mueggler 1981; Dyrness and Norum 1983). In successionally advanced communities, the species may be restricted to such disturbed patches as caused by fallen trees (Hesselman 1917; Dyrness 1973). In some successionally advanced vegetation, however, widely spaced colonies with low stem densities may persist for long periods (Moss 1936; van Andel 1974). Van Andel and Nelissen (1979) report the occurrence of 35-yr-old "climax" stands of *E. angustifolium* in some sand dune habitats in Holland, and

Broderick (1980), in lichen woodlands in northern Quebec, found stems arising from roots at least 47 yr old. It is also a member of many tundra communities (Mosquin 1966; Wein and Bliss 1973).

6. History

Epilobium angustifolium is native to Canada. Mosquin (1967) considered it most likely that the tetraploid spp., *circumvagaum*, could have arisen through autopolyploidy in different sections of its range. The mountains of Wyoming and Montana, ice-free regions in Alaska and the land south of the margins of the continental ice sheets were probable Pleistocene refugia (Mosquin 1966). Recolonization of arctic Canada was probably from the Alaskan refugia, and recolonization of northeastern Canada was most likely from the south (Mosquin 1966).

7. Growth and Development

a. *Morphology and perennation* — Although seeds and seedlings may overwinter (Myerscough 1980), the mature plant functions as a geophyte. New aerial shoots arise each spring from buds formed late in the previous growing season along the often complex network of horizontal roots.

Annual bands of periderm produced within the vascular tissue of the roots may promote survival in environments no longer conducive to vigorous growth. According to Moss (1936), the living tissues of the roots may eventually be subdivided into discrete bands, each surrounded by layers of periderm. In Moss' view, compression and compartmentalization allows root survival without appreciable increase in diameter. In older roots, functional tissue can be reduced to a single living strand encircled by protective periderm layers. Periderm has also been observed to form in the fall at the base of senescing aerial shoots.

b. *Physiological data* — Myerscough and Whitehead ((1966, 1967), in their series of laboratory studies conducted in Britain, found the patterns and rates of growth and development *Epilobium angustifolium* to be influenced by temperature, nutrients, soil pH, and light intensity, but not photoperiod. Biomass production, for example, was not significantly different between plants grown in full sun versus 43% sunlight. The wider but thinner leaves of the shaded plants apparently compensate for lower light intensities. In Holland, seedlings grown at pH 3.5 made effective growth but at harvest yielded only about 20% of the biomass of seedlings grown at pH 5.0. *Epilobium angustifolium* tolerates a wide range of nutrient concentrations, and can utilize nitrate or ammonium ions with the latter preferentially absorbed (van Andel 1974; van Andel and Nelissen 1979). Both Stark (1977) and Dyrness and Norum (1983), in North America, found *E. angustifolium* to be an effective accumulator of mineral nutrients after forest fires.

Van Andel and Nelissen (1979) described a conservative system of internal mineral cycling for colonies growing in Holland. Within fully grown *Epilobium angustifolium* plants, 35 – 75% of the overall mineral content remained in the root system over the winter and some 40% of this pool was reused for shoot production in following years. No flowers were produced in natural soil to which sand had been added, but 33% of the plants grown in unmodified soil and 100% of the plants grown in fertilized soil produced flowers. According to van Andel and Vera (1977), vegetative growth of the species is dominant over sexual reproduction. The percentage of total plant biomass allocated to roots ranged from 60% at the lowest nutrient level to 46% at the highest. About 11% of the biomass of those plants that flowered was allocated to sexual reproduction, regardless of the soil nutrient status. This tight nutrient cycling and the dominance of vegetative growth were viewed as a means of maintaining a colony in environments of declining quality (van Andel and Vera 1977; van Andel and Nelissen 1979).

c. *Phenology* — In subarctic Quebec most stems of *Epilobium angustifolium* do not emerge until late May; maximum vegetative growth is reached in late July; flowers open in late July; and seeds are released in late August (Henderson et al. 1979; Broderick 1980). In more southerly regions of Canada, the phenological progression is similar to that in northern Quebec, but all growth stages begin about one month earlier (pers. obs.).

Myerscough (1980) noted for populations in England that root growth can be initiated at 4.5°C, and that root growth in the spring commonly preceded elongation of the shoot buds and the emergence of stems. Flower buds formed by mid-June and flowers were present from then until September; seed release began in late July. In England, Al-Mufti et al. (1977) observed few emergent shoots until early April when rapid shoot elongation ensued. By late July, standing crop dry matter reached about 600 g m^{-2}.

The phenological development of *Epilobium angustifolium* varies from habitat to habitat and from year to year. For example, shoots emerged earlier on the more disturbed habitats examined by Broderick (1980) and Henderson et al. (1979). None of the stems monitored by Broderick (1980) in recently burned and undisturbed woodland habitats flowered in 1978, but 6% of those in a burned site and 5% of the shoots in an undisturbed site flowered in 1979. Fruits were produced only in the burned site, where 4.2% of the flowering shoots produced seed capsules.

d. *Mycorrhiza* — Daft and Nicholson (1974) described a vesicular-arbuscular type of mycorrhizal association between an endomycorrhizal fungus, *Endogone* sp. (= *Glomus* sp.), and *Epilobium angustifolium* plants growing on coal mine spoils. They further described a second relationship with an unknown fungus that produced proportionately more of the ''tree-like'' arbuscular rather than ''bladder-like' vesicular structures inside the root.

8. Reproduction
a. *Floral biology* — Although the plants of *Epilobium angustifolium* are self-compatible (Mosquin 1966), the protandrous flowers

appear to promote cross pollination. Anthers dehisce within 24 h of the flower opening (Myerscough 1980), but stigmas remain closed and the style is strongly reflexed from the anthers for 2–3 d (Mosquin 1966). After the last anther dehisces and becomes deflexed, the style comes forward and the stigma opens (Mosquin 1966). The green, fleshy, slightly concave nectaries at the upper end of the ovaries (Swales 1979) produce nectar continuously from about one day after the flower opens until, in fertilized flowers, the floral parts are shed 4 or 5 d later (Mosquin 1966; Bertsch 1983). Mosquin (1966) reported populations with sterile flowers at the northern limits of the species range in Canada but attributed this to environmental effects.

Long distance aerial transport of the pollen seems unlikely as the grains are usually attached to the anther by viscine threads (Mosquin 1966). Insects appear to be the principal pollinators. Swales (1979) observed eight species of *Bombus* actively pollinating populations of *Epilobium angustifolium* in arctic Canada, and recorded floral visits by several Homopteran and Dipteran species, especially members of the Syrphidae. In northern Quebec, Henderson et al. (1979) reported floral visits by the bee, *Pyrosambus ternarius* (Say.), two Lepidopteran species, a member of the Cerambycidae, and various members of the Syrphidae, Tabanidae and Simuliidae. Galen and Plowright (1985) reported that *Bombus vagans* Smith, *B. terricola* Kirby and *B. perplexus* Cresson were pollinators in Canada. In Europe, Knuth (1908) and Myerscough (1980), reported floral visits by a similarly broad spectrum of insects.

Insects tend to visit first the lower and more mature flowers before moving upwards in a spiral fashion. Because of this behavior and the protandrous flower development, pollen reaching a receptive stigma is most likely to have been produced by a different plant or, at least, a different inflorescence (Myerscough 1980; Swales 1979).

b. *Seed production and dispersal* — Salisbury (1962) counted 300–500 seeds per capsule and calculated that a single plant might yield as many as 80 000 seeds per year. Individual seeds average about 0.034 mg (van Andel and Rozema 1974). Light seed and their tuft of hairs favor dispersal by wind. Myerscough and Whitehead (1966) reported a rate of fall in still air of $0.065-0.069$ m s^{-1}, and Solbreck and Andersson (1987) estimated that 20–50% of the seeds could be carried to at least 100 m above the ground and might commonly remain aloft for 10 h, perhaps travelling 100–300 km. Ridley (1930) observed that the tuft of hairs was not firmly attached, and that the seed could be released following slight contact with a solid object. Henderson et al. (1979) estimated a seed rain of up to 40 seeds m^{-2} in northern Quebec.

c. *Viability of seeds and germination* — Up to 100% of the seeds of *Epilobium angustifolium* collected from newly opened capsules in eastern Quebec germinated within 10 d of exposure to warm and moist conditions in the laboratory (Jobidon 1986). Van Andel (1974) reported that the seeds lack endosperm and are not innately dormant. The seeds can retain viability when stored indoors for 18 (Myerscough and Whitehead 1966) to 30 mo (van Andel 1974). Thompson and Grime (1979) found viable seeds in soil samples taken in Britain from late June until the following May. Seed germination patterns were studied in detail by Myerscough and Whitehead (1966). Their laboratory studies included varying regimes of light, soil moisture, atmospheric humidty, pH and mineral nutrients. The highest rates and levels of germination were obtained when seeds were sown on the surface of the soil under warm well lighted humid conditions. Germination was further enhanced by increased levels of mineral nutrients and by reduction in soil acidity. Van Andel's (1974) results parallel those of Myerscough and Whitehead (1966). After 13 d of observation, 15.0, 78.5, 81.0, and 86.0% of the seeds had germinated at 10, 10/20, 20, and 30°C, respectively. Oberbauer and Miller (1982) reported high germination levels when the substrate was at field water capacity but virtually no germination when the solution osmotic potentials were held at -1 bar. Jobidon (1986) reported that germination was inhibited by the presence of leachates from the foliage of coniferous tree species in eastern Quebec. In Europe, germination in the field mostly occurs in late summer (Myerscough 1980; van Andel and Nelissen 1981), but some seedlings have been observed in the spring in Britain (Myerscough and Whitehead 1967). Seedlings seem not to establish where underlain by living roots of *E. angustifolium* (Myerscough and Whitehead 1966; van Andel and Rozema 1974), and establishment is inhibited by fertilizer treatments (van Andel and Rozema 1974). Summerhayes and Williams (1926) found germination to be poor on a seedbed of raw humus, and Brenchley and Heintze (1933) noted improvement in germination when the seedbed of bare mineral soil was fertilized. An example of the level of seedling establishment that might occur in the field comes from the report of van Andel (1974) in Holland. Only 56 seedlings were established in the first year from 75 000 seeds sown at a density of 2500 seeds m^{-2} in a tract (5 × 6 m) of disturbed soil.

d. *Vegetative reproduction* — As the establishment of seedlings within mature stands of *Epilobium angustifolium* is, at best, rare, population maintenance and expansion in the field is largely by vegetative growth. In Emery's (1955) study, root cuttings as small as 2.5 × 1.5 mm were capable of producing adventitious buds within 3 wk, even if collected in their first year of growth. Emery (1955) found the number of buds eventually formed under laboratory conditions to be related more to the length rather than width of the cutting, and he noted that even 9-yr-old roots could produce buds. Moss (1936), in Alberta, observed that 20-yr-old roots were capable of sprouting in the field following disturbance. Van Andel (1974), in Holland, related the number of shoots produced to the amount of stored assimilates in the roots, but found no relationship between shoot production and root age. Root sections ranging in length from 4 to 32 cm were planted by Broderick (1980) at a 5-cm depth in an area of woodland in northern Quebec that had been burned a decade before. No shoots emerged from root sections less than 8 cm long. Fifty-five percent of the 8- and 16-cm root classes and 99% of the 32-cm root classes produced sprouts in the first year. Most of the roots re-sprouted in the second year, with one shoot from a 32-cm segment flowering and producing seeds.

Salisbury (1942) reported root extensions of up to 1 m per year in Britain, and van Andel (1975), in Holland, observed comparable growth. Broderick (1980) observed a similar pattern of vegetative expansion following fires in the woodlands of northern Quebec. Figure 3 shows the spatial distribution of stems and the age of basal roots for five colonies found in a woodland site burned 5 yr before. Four of the colonies had shoots emerging from roots which predated the disturbance and presumably sprouted following the fire. The entire root system of one colony (no. 4, Fig. 3) was exhumed and the roots were found to extend for several meters beyond the stems. Colonies exhumed on an adjacent unburned section of woodland consisted only of a very small number of stems emerging from fragmentary, often greatly decayed, root systems.

9. Hybrids
Myerscough (1980) reported that there were no natural hybrids between *Epilobium angustifolium* and any other species in Britain. Mosquin (1966) reported some natural hybridization between *E. angustifolium* and *E. latifolium* L. in the arctic and cites Böcher (1962) who found a sterile population in Greenland of what also appeared to be a hybrid of *E. angustifolium* and *E. latifolium*. Raven (1962) suggested that *E. angustifolium* and *E. conspermum* Hausskn. might hybridize in the Himalayas.

10. Population Dynamics
Populations of *Epilobium angustifolium* consist of one or more colonies producing shoots from a network of roots (van Andel 1975).

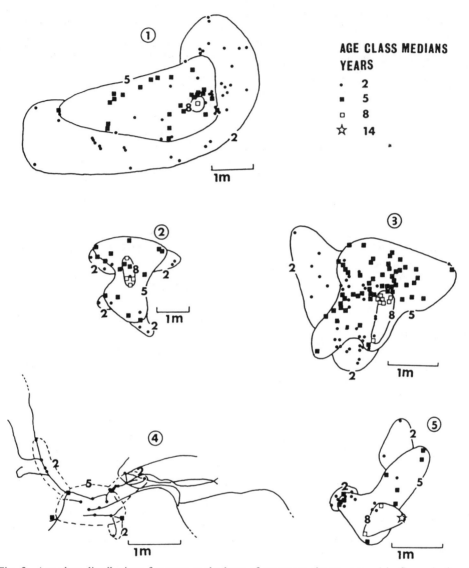

Fig. 3. Age-class distributions for roots at the base of emergent shoots mapped in five colonies of *Epilobium angustifolium* L. in a lichen-woodland burned five years previously in northern Quebec. The entire root system is traced in colony 4. (From Broderick 1980.)

Van Andel (1975) described an initial phase of vegetative expansion that might, depending on site conditions, last as long as 15 yr. Following the phase of expansion the growth of the root systems decreased and there was apparent emphasis on maintenance. Stem densities within the colonies studied by van Andel ranged from 61 to 112 stems m^{-2} and seemed to reflect root mass rather than age. Re-establishment failed to occur following the removal of the root system from a portion of a mature colony, and van Andel argued that at that point the mineral status of the soil had declined to a state where (re)expansion of the colony was no longer possible.

A burst of recruitment also seems to characterize *Epilobium angustifolium* populations colonizing vacant land in northern Quebec (Broderick 1980). Figure 4 shows root age-class distributions taken from two woodland habitats and their unburned counterparts. In the recently burned habitats, most of the stems were attached to roots which showed little sign of decay. In contrast, the roots in the adjacent unburned sites were attached to older, often highly decayed roots, many of which may have been far older than indicated by counts of the remaining periderm.

11. Response to Herbicides and Other Chemicals

The only detailed work on the sensitivity of *Epilobium angustifolium* to herbicide applications has been conducted in Britain by Bailey and Hoogland (1984). Bromacil and propyzamide applied as soil drenches at rates of 4 kg ha^{-1} provided complete control. Bromacil, oxadiazon oxyfluorofen applied to

foliage at rates of 1 kg ha^{-1}, mecoprop K salt at 4 kg ha^{-1}, 2,4-D amine at 2 kg ha^{-1}, triclopyr ester° at 0.05 kg ha^{-1}, and pentanochlor and chloropham at 1.7 and 0.84 kg ha^{-1} respectively, also provided complete control of *E. angustifolium*.

12. Response to Human Manipulation

Meyerscough and Whitehead (1967) reported the susceptibility of *Epilobium angustifolium* to damage from continual grazing, trampling or mowing.

13. Response to Parasites

a. *Insects* — Robinson (1979) listed *Aphis nivalis* Hille Rishambers, *A. varians* Patch and *Macrosiphum subarcticum* Robinson, a new species, as aphid species found on *Epilobium angustifolium* in northern Manitoba. MacGarvin (1982), lists a wide variety of phytophagous insects associated with *E. angustifolium* in Britain, including members of the Hemiptera (Psyllidae, Cercopidae, Aphidae, Miridae), Thysanoptera, Lepidoptera

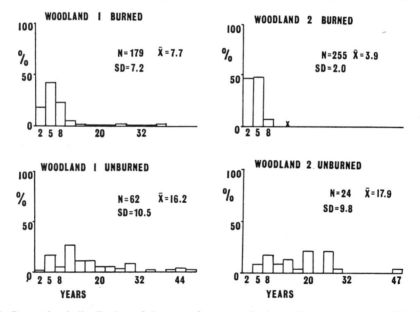

Fig. 4. Proportional distribution of the age of roots at the base of emergent stems of *Epilobium angustifolium* L. in burned and unburned woodland habitats at two sites in northern Quebec. The burning had occurred 10 years before the study at Woodland I and 5 yr before the study at Woodland II. (N = the number of roots examined; $\overline{X}$ = mean age in years; SD = standard deviation; x = a single specimen only. (From Broderick 1980.)

(Momphidae, Sphyngidae), Coleoptera (Nitulidae), Diptera (Cecidomyiidae) and Hymenoptera (Tenthridae). Myerscough (1980) reported a similar variety of insect associates in Britain.

b. *Micro-organisms* — Goodwin (1930) identified *Epilobium angustifolium* as an alternate host to the rust, *Pucciniastrum Abieti-chamenerii* Kleb. (= *Pucciniastrum epilobii* Otth.), that causes needle rust in *Abies balsamea*. Henderson et al. (1979) considered a species of *Puccinia* to be an important fungal parasite of the leaves and stem. Ginns (1986) listed 11 species of disease or decay fungi associated with *E. angustifolium* in Canada: *Cercospora montana* (Speg.) Sacc, *Dicostroma tosta* (Berk and Br.) Brockmann, *Ditopellopsis racemula* (Cooke and Peck) Barr, *Mycosphaerella chamaenerii* Savile, *Nectria pedicularis* (Tracy and Earle) Petrak, *Pistillaria typhuloides* (Peck) Burt, *Puccinia dioiceae* Magn., *Puccinia gigantea* Karst., *Pucciniastrum epilobii* Otth. (= *Pucciniastrum Abieti-chamenerii* Kleb.), *Pucciniastrum pustulatum* Diet. (causes needle rust of *Abies balsamea* L. and *A. lasiocarpa* (Hook.) Nutt.) and *Sydowiella fenestrans* (Duby) Petrak.

ACKNOWLEDGMENTS

I thank the Natural Science and Engineering Research Council of Canada for financial assistance through an operating grant to Dr. P. B. Cavers of the Department of Plant Sciences, The University of Western Ontario. My thanks are also offered to Marguerite Bough for assistance in preparing the figures. In addition I wish to thank Dr. P. G. Holland of the Department of Geography, University of Otago, New Zealand, and two anonymous reviewers for very helpful criticisms of earlier manuscripts. The author, however, bears full responsibility for any errors and omissions.

Al-Mufti, M. M., Sydes, C. L., Furness, S. B., Grime, J. P. and Band S. R. 1977. A quantitative analysis of shoot phenology and dominance in herbaceous vegetation. J. Ecol. **65**: 759–791.

Alex, J. F., Cayouette, R. and Mulligan, G. A. 1980. Common botanical names of weeds in Canada. Agriculture Canada, Ottawa, Ont., Publ. 1397. 132 pp.

Bailey, J. A. and Hoogland, D. 1984. The response of *Epilobium* species to a range of soil and foliar acting herbicides. Asp. Appl. Biol. **8**: 43–52.

Bartos, D. L. and Mueggler, W. F. 1981. Early succession in aspen communities following fire in western Wyoming. J. Range Manage. **34**: 315–318.

Bertsch, A. 1983. Nectar production of *Epilobium angustifolium* L. at different air humidities; nectar sugars in individual flowers and the optimal foraging theory. Oecologia (Berlin) **59**: 40–48.

Böcher, T. W. 1962. A cytological and morphological study of the species hybrid *Chamaenerion angustifolium* × *Chamaenerion latifolium*. Botanisk Tidsskrift **58**: 1–34.

Boivin, G. and Benoit, D. L. 1987. Predicting onion maggot (Diptera: Anthomyiidae) flights in southwestern Quebec using degree days and common weeds. Phytoprotection **68**: 65–70.

Brenchley, W. E. and Heintze, S. G. 1933. Colonization by *Epilobium angustifolium*. J. Ecol. **21**: 101–120.

Broderick, D. H. 1980. The establishment and maintenance of fireweed in disturbed and undisturbed sites at Schefferville. MSc. Thesis, Department of Geography, McGill University, Montreal, Que. pp. 162.

Chandler, R. F. and Hooper, S. W. 1979. Herbal remedies of maritime Indians.: A preliminary screening. Can. J. Pharmaceut. Sci. **14**: 103–106.

Conn, J. J. and DeLapp, J. A. 1983. Changes in weed-species assemblages with increasing field age. Agroborealis **15**: 39–41.

Daft, M. J. and Nicholson, T. H. 1974. Arbuscular mycorrhizas in plants colonizing coal wastes in Scotland. New Phytol. **73**: 1129–1138.

Dyrness, C. T. 1973. Early stages of plant succession following logging and burning in the western Cascades of Oregon. Ecology **54**: 57–69.

Dyrness, C. T. and Norum, R. A. 1983. The effects of experimental fires on black spruce forest floors in interior Alaska. Can. J. For. Res. **13**: 879–893.

Emery, A. E. H. 1955. The formation of buds on the roots of *Chamaenerion angustifolium* (L.) Scop. Phytomorphology **5**: 139–145.

Etherington, J. R. 1984. Comparative studies on plant growth and the distribution in relation to waterlogging. X. Differential formation of adventitious roots and their excision in *Epilobium hirsutum* and *Chamaenerion angustifolium*. J. Ecol. **72**: 389–404.

Galen, C. and Plowright, R. C. 1985. The effects of nectar level and flower development on pollen carry-over in inflorescences of fireweed (*Epilobium angustifolium*) (Onagraceae). Can. J. Bot. **63**: 488–491.

Ginns, J. H. 1986. Compendium of plant disease and decay fungi in Canada, 1960 to 1980. Ottawa Research Branch, Series A., Agriculture Canada, Ottawa, Ont. Publ. v. 1813. 416 pp.

Gleason, H. A. 1963. The new Britton and Brown illustrated flora of the northeastern United States and adjacent Canada. Vol. 2. Hafner, New York, N.Y. pp. 655.

Goodwin, W. 1930. Fungal diseases of plants in agriculture, horticulture and forestry. Balliere, Tindel, and Co., London, U.K. 526 pp.

Henderson, G., Holland, P. G. and Werren, G. L. 1979. The natural history of a subarctic adventive: *Epilobium angustifolium* L. (Onagraceae) at Schefferville, Quebec. Nat. Can. **106**: 425–437.

Hesselman, H. 1917. Papers in Meddelanden från statens skogsförsöksanstalt. (rev. in J. Ecol. **7**: 210–213, 1919).

Hultén, E. 1972. Outline of the Arctic and Boreal biota during the Quaternary Period. Wheldon and Wesley, New York, N.Y. pp. 168.

Jobidon, R. 1968. Allelopathic potential of coniferous species to old-field weeds in Eastern Canada. For. Sci. **32**: 112–118.

Kershaw, G. P. and Kershaw, L. J. 1968. Ecological characteristics of 35-year-old crude-oil spills in tundra plant communities of Mackenzie Mountains, Northwest territories, Canada. Can. J. Bot. **64**: 2935–2947.

Kimber, A. J., Pulford, I. D. and Duncan, H. J. 1978. Chemical variation and vegetation distribution on a coal waste tip. J. Appl. Ecol. **15**: 627–633.

Knuth, P. 1908. Handbook of flower pollination. Vol. II. Oxford University Press, London, U.K. 703 pp.

MacGarvin, M. 1982. Species-area relationships of insects on host plants: Herbivores on rosebay willowherb. J. Anim. Ecol. **51**: 207–223.

Marie-Victorin, Fr. 1964. Flore Laurentienne. University of Montreal, Montreal, Que. pp. 925.

Mosquin, T. 1966. A new taxonomy for *Epilobium angustifolium* L. (Onagraceae). Brittonia **18**: 167–188.

Mosquin, T. 1967. Evidence for autopolyploidy in *Epilobium angustifolium* (Onagraceae). Evolution **21**: 713–719.

Moss, E. H. 1936. The ecology of *Epilobium angustifolium* with particular reference to the rings of periderm in the wood. Am. J. Bot. **23**: 114–120.

Myerscough, P. J. 1980. Biological flora of the British Isles. *Epilobium angustifolium* L. (*Chamaenerion angustifolium* (L.) Scop.). J. Ecol. **68**: 1047–1074.

Myerscough, P. J. and Whitehead, F. H. 1966. Comparative biology of *Tussilago farfara* L., *Chamaenerion angustifolium* L., *Epilobium monatum* L. and *Epilobium adenocaulon* Hausskn. I. General biology and germination. New Phytol. **65**: 192–210.

Myerscough, P. J. and Whitehead, F. H. 1967. Comparative biology of *Tussilago farfara* L., *Chamaenerion angustifolium* L., *Epilobium monatum* L. and *Epilobium adenocaulon* Hausskn. II. Growth and ecology. New Phytol. **66**: 758–823.

Oberbauer, S. and Miller, P. C. 1982. Effect of water potential on seed germination. Holarctic Ecol. **5**: 218–220.

Peterson, T. D. and Newton, M. 1983. Growth of Douglas-fir following release from snowbush and forbs in the Oregon Cascades. (Abstr.) *In* Proceedings of the Western Society of Weed Science. Chapman International Co., Milltown, Mt. From: Weed Abstracts (1984) **33**: 73 (No. 692).

Raven, P. H. 1962. The genus *Epilobium* in the Himalaya region. Bulletin of the British Museum (Natural History), Botany **2**: 325–382.

Ridley, H. N. 1930. The dispersal of plants throughout the world. Reeve, Ashford. pp. 774.

Robinson, A. G. 1979. Annotated list of aphids (Homoptera: Apidae) collected at Churchill, Manitoba with the description of new species. Can. J. Entomol. **111**: 447–458.

Russell, W. B. and La Roi, G. H. 1986. Natural vegetation and ecology of abandoned coal-mined land, Rocky Mountain foothills, Alberta, Canada. Can. J. Bot. **64**: 1286–1298.

Salisbury, E. J. 1942. The reproductive capacity of plants. Bell, London, U.K. pp. 244.

Salisbury, E. J. 1962. Weeds and aliens. Collins London, U.K. 384 pp.

Scoggan, H. J. 1978. The flora of Canada. Part IV. Dicotyledoneae (Loasaceae to Compositae). National Museums of Canada Publications in Biology, No. 7 (1). pp. 1117–1711.

Scotter, G. W. 1971. Fire, vegetation, soil and barren-ground caribou in northern Canada. *In* C. W. Slaughter et al. eds. Fire in the northern environment—a symposium. Pacific Northwestern Forest and Range Experiment Station. 275 pp.

Solbreck, C. and Andersson, D. 1987. Vertical distribution of fireweed, *Epilobium angustifolium*, seeds in the air. Can. J. Bot. **65**: 2177–2178.

Stark, L. M. 1977. Fire and nutrient cycling in a Douglas fir/larch forest. Ecology **58**: 16–30.

Summerhayes, V. S. and Williams, P. H. 1926. Studies on the ecology of woodland heaths. II. Early stages in the recolonization of felled pinewood at the Oxshot Heath and Fisher Common, Surrey. J. Ecol. **14**: 203–243.

Swales, D. E. 1979. Nectaries of certain Arctic and Subarctic plants, with notes on pollination. Rhodora **81**: 363–407.

Sylvester, T. W. and Wein, R. W. 1981. Fuel characteristics of arctic plant species and simulated community flammability by Rothermal's model. Can. J. Bot. **59**: 898–907.

Thompson, K. and Grime, J. P. 1979. Seasonal variation in the seedbanks of herbaceous species in ten contrasting habitats. J. Ecol. **67**: 893–921.

van Andel, J. 1974. An ecological study of *Chamaenerion angustifolium* (L). Scop. Ph.D. Thesis, Free University, Amsterdam. Graduate Press, Amsterdam, The Netherlands. pp. 85.

van Andel, J. 1975. A study on the population dynamics of the perennial plant species *Chamaenerion angustifolium* (L.) Scop. Oecologia (Berlin) **19**: 329–337.

van Andel, J., Bos, W. and Ernst, W. 1978. An experimental study on two populations of *Chamaenerion angustifolium* (L.) Scop. (=*Epilobium angustifolium* L.) occurring on contrasting soils, with particular reference to bicarbonate. New Phytol. **81**: 763–772.

van Andel, J. and Nelissen, H. J. M. 1979. Nutritional status of soil and plant species in several clearings in coniferous woods compared to that in two related habitats. Vegetatio **39**: 115–121.

van Andel, J. and Nelissen, H. J. M. 1981. An experimental approach to the study of species interference in patchy vegetation. Vegetatio **45**: 155–163.

van Andel, J. and Rozema, J. 1974. Reproduction from seed within existing populations of *Chamaenerion angustifolium* (L.) Scop. Plant Soil **41**: 415–419.

van Andel, J. and Vera, F. 1977. Reproductive allocation in *Senecio sylvaticum* and *Chamaenerion angustifolium* in relation to mineral nutrition. J. Ecol. **65**: 747–758.

Walker, D. A., Webber, P. J., Everett, K. R. and Brown, J. 1978. Crude and diesel oil spills on plant communities at Prudhoe Bay, Alaska, and the derivation of oil spill sensitivity maps. Arctic (31): 242–259.

Wein, R. W. and Bliss, L. C. 1973. Changes in arctic *Eriophorum* tussock communities following fire. Ecology **54**: 845–852.

Willms, W., McLean, A., Tucker, R. and Ritcey, R. 1980. Deer and cattle diets on summer range in British Columbia. J. Range Manag. **33**: 55–59.

Wood, D. W. and del Moral, R. 1988. Colonizing plants on the pumice plains, Mount St. Helens, Washington. Am. J. Bot. **78**: 1228–1237.

THE BIOLOGY OF CANADIAN WEEDS. 94.
Sonchus arvensis L.

WANDA K. LEMNA and CALVIN G. MESSERSMITH

Crop and Weed Sciences Department, North Dakota State University, Fargo, North Dakota, 58105 USA. Received 10 Aug. 1988, accepted 18 Dec. 1989.

LEMNA, W. K. AND MESSERSMITH, C. G. 1990. The biology of Canadian weeds. 94. *Sonchus arvensis* L. Can. J. Plant Sci. **70**: 509–532.

Perennial sow-thistle (*Sonchus arvensis* L.) was introduced into North America from Europe and Asia and is distributed widely throughout the Canadian provinces. Two varieties are common; var. *arvensis* and var. *glabrescens* differ morphologically in the presence or absence of glandular hairs on peduncles and involucral bracts, respectively. Both varieties are common along roadsides and river and lake shores and in waste areas and cultivated fields throughout their introduced and native ranges. The perennial nature and ability to spread both by spreading roots and by seed make these weeds difficult to control. Details on the morphology, cytology, distribution, reproductive and population biology, and control methods are reviewed.

Key words: Distribution, perennial sow-thistle, smooth perennial sow-thistle, weed biology

[La biologie des mauvaises herbes Canadiennes. 94. *Sonchus arvensis* L.]
Titre abrégé: *Sonchus arvensis* L.
Le laiteron des champs (*Sonchus arvensis* L.) et le laiteron des champs glabre (*S. arvensis* var. *glabrescens* Guenth., Grab. & Wimm.) est une espèce commune dans les provinces Canadiennes, ayant été introduite en Amerique du Nord de l'Europe et de l'Asie. Du point de vue morphologique, *S. arvensis* var. *glabrescens* se distingue de *S. arvensis* surtout par son manque de poils glandulaires sur les pédoncules et sur les écailles de l'involucre. Le laiteron et le laiteron glabre sont très répandus dans leurs habitats indigènes et dans les zones ou ils ont été introduits; ils se rencontrent le long des routes et des cours d'eau, au bord des lacs, dans les terrains négligés et dans les champs cultivés. A cause de son caractère vivace et de sa capacité de se mulitplier par des racines végétatives ou horizontales, cette mauvaise herbe est difficile à controler. L'article comprend une révision de la morphologie, la cytologie, la distribution, les caractères écologiques et biologiques et les methodes de contrôle.

Mots cles: Distribution, laiteron des champs, laiteron des champs glabre, la biologie des mauvaises herbes

1. Name

Sonchus arvensis L. — **perennial sow-thistle** (Ferron and Cayouette 1975), creeping sow-thistle, field sow-thistle (Frankton and Mulligan 1987), milk thistle, field milk thistle, corn sow-thistle (Tullis 1924; Korsmo 1954,) swine-thistle, tree sow-thistle, dindle, gutweed (Boulos 1973); **laiteron des champs** (Alex et al. 1980), boquet jaune, crève-z-yeux, florent, laiteron, laiteron vivace, roi des champs (Ferron and Cayouette 1975), Compositae, composite family, Composées.

2. Description and Account of Variation

Vigorous, deep-rooted perennial herb; reproducing by seeds, by vertical, thickened roots, and by cylindrical, horizontal, spreading roots; entire plant filled with milky latex.

Stems erect, 30–180 (most commonly 60–150) cm high, 3–10 mm diameter; hollow; branched, number varying from two to many per plant; lower stem glabrous with conspicuous, stalked, gland-tipped hairs on upper stems and peduncles; hairs extending to 18 cm below involucre (Pretz 1923); peduncle 20–80 mm long, 1.5 mm diameter, thicker toward head. Leaves crowded on lower stem, sparse on upper; variable from nearly entire to deeply pinnatifid, when lobed, 2–5 (occasionally 7) lobes on each side, usually with tip lobe longer or broadly triangular; lobes more or less triangular often curving backward; leaf margins spinulose; rosette leaves 5–15 cm long, 2–4 cm wide, narrowing to winged stalk; cauline leaves 5–30 cm long, 2–10 cm wide, alternate, sessile, bases clasping stem with rounded basal lobes; upper leaves greatly reduced, sparse, and often unlobed. Heads (capitula) 3–5 cm diameter when open; arranged in loose, terminal, cymose-type clusters; phyllaries or involucral bracts, 38–50; narrowly lanceolate, in three imbricate row; dark green or lead-colored, sometimes pale with white margins; outer phyllaries 6–10 cm long, 1.5 mm wide, becoming swollen at base with maturity; hairy; glandular; inner phyllaries 12–15 mm long, 1–2 mm wide. Flowers 150–240 per head; perfect; all fertile; corolla 18–26 mm long, yellow to bright yellow-orange; corolla petals fused at base into cylinder 9–14 mm long, spreading out above into ligulate corolla 9–12 mm long, 2 mm wide; anthers 4 mm long, 0.5 mm wide; style branches yellow to brown, 1–2.5 mm long. Achene, 2.5–3.5 mm long, 1–1.5 mm wide, dark brown, less frequently light brown to golden yellow; compressed; beakless; elliptical; tapering toward each end; upper end truncate where pappus attached, 5–7 distinct lengthwise ribs on each side; ribs strongly cross-ridged; pappus white; four times longer than achenes; composed of thin, soft, flexible hairs and a few stiff, straight bristles; mostly persistent but sometimes easily detached. Morphological characteristics of an achene, seedling, rosette, and flowering plant of *S. arvensis* are shown in Fig. 1.

The above descriptions are based on Stevens (1924), Reed (1970), Boulos (1960, 1973) and Frankton and Mulligan (1987) unless otherwise indicated. Detailed descriptions of leaf variation (Bell et al. 1968), leaf venation (Banerjee 1978), leaf anatomy (Banerjee 1978; Korsmo 1954), stem and root anatomy (Korsmo 1954), pappus characteristics (Boulos 1960), glandular hairs (Korsmo 1954), and pollen morphology (Saad 1961) are available.

The species is commonly divided taxonomically into two varieties, *S. arvensis* L. var. *arvensis*, which fits the description given above, and *Sonchus arvensis* var. *glabrescens*, which lacks the glandular hairs on peduncles and involucres (Fig. 2) (Shumovich and Montgomery 1955; Skalinska et al. 1971; Boulos 1973). Hence, *S. arvensis* var. *glabrescens* commonly named smooth perennial sow-thistle [(laiteron des champs glabre (Alex et al. 1980)]. The term "glabrous", used widely to describe the variety, is not strictly correct because buds do possess a deciduous woolly tomentum that forms white tufts at the base of phyllaries and upper peduncles (Lousley 1968). This pubescence often is lost by the time the flowers open.

The taxonomic rank of the glabrous type remains controversial (Skalinska et al. 1971; Boulos 1973). Some authors rank it as a separate species, *S. uliginosus* Bieb., while others treat it as a variety *S. arvensis* var. *glabrescens* [= *S. arvensis* var. *laevipes* Koch; *S. arvensis* subsp. *uliginosus* (Bieb) Beguinot]. This article will use *S. arvensis* to identify the species as a whole and will use *S. arvensis* var. *arvensis* and *S. arvensis* var. *glabrescens* to identify the glandular and glabrous varieties, respectively, when the varieties have been distinguished in the literature.

No morphological characters other than the presence or absence of glandular hairs seem consistently reliable to distinguish the two varieties (Shumovich and Montgomery 1955; Boulos 1961). Lousley (1968) reported that the capitula of *S. arvensis* var. *glabrescens* from British and North American specimens generally were longer and more slender and that the inflorescence exhibited a stronger subumbellate character compared to the shorter, wider capitula and more marked dichotomous branching inflorescences of *S. arvensis* var. *arvensis*.

Cytogenetic analyses have not alleviated the confusion. Early reports that *S. arvensis* var. *arvensis* had a chromosome number $2n = 64$ have not been substantiated in later studies (Boulos 1961; Skalinska et al. 1971). Early studies (Schumovich and Montgomery 1955; Mulligan 1957) found glandular and glabrous specimens from Canada to be hexaploid $(2n = 54)$ and tetraploid $(2n = 36)$, respectively. Love and Love (1961) reported the same chromosome numbers from European specimens. Jalas and Pellinen (1985) identified glandular plants from Scandinavia with either $2n = 36$ or $2n = 54$, while glabrous plants were $2n = 36$. Plants with chromosome number $2n = 45$ were also found; these were thought to be F_1 hybrids between the two varieties (Shumovich and Montgomery 1955). A series of aneuploids were also obtained (see Section 9).

The hybrids occasionally differed from the typical glandular variety by having reduced numbers of glandular hairs or slightly altered bud shape, but distinguishing between the glandular variety and hybrids based on morphology alone was often impossible. Complex natural populations probably exist that contain the two major varieties $(2n = 36$ and $2n = 54)$, F_1 hybrids $(2n = 45)$, backcrosses, and hybrid intercrosses. Boulous (1961) concluded for simplicity that all varieties and hybrids should be considered as races of *S. arvensis* L. with a basic genome of $X = 9$.

Sonchus arvensis var. *glabrescens* $(2n = 36)$ is an allotetraploid with diploid-type chromosome pairing as indicated by normal bivalent chromosome associations and by lack of quadrivalent associations (Hsieh et al. 1972). The genomes $(X = 9)$ are not alike but apparently have one or two partially homologous chromosomes.

Additional varieties of *S. arvensis* L. have been reported in Europe. *S. arvensis* var. *maritimus* G. F. W. Mey, a smooth variety with chromosome number $2n = 54$ (Jalas and Pellinen 1985) occurs in coastal dune habitats of The Netherlands (Pegtel 1973, 1974). This variety is excluded from arable inland areas and differs genetically from the inland var.

arvensis by having more waxy, prickly, and irregularly indented leaves. Some authors suggest that specimens similar to *S. arvensis* found from Afghanistan and Pakistan eastward to China and Japan should be treated as a subspecies, *S. arvensis* subsp. *brachyotus* (DC) Kitamura (Peschken 1982). However, Boulos (1961, 1973) maintains that this variant should be classified as *S. brachyotus* DC. or *S. wightianus* DC.

Sonchus arvensis can be distinguished from the two annual sow-thistles that occur in Canada, *S. asper* (L.) Hill (spiny annual sow-thistle) and *S. oleraceus* L. (annual sow-thistle), by growth habit and somewhat by floral, achene, and leaf characteristics (Hutchinson et al. 1984). Annual sow-thistles lack spreading roots and have involucres that are smaller (1.5–2.5 cm diameter) when open than *S. arvensis*. The corolla of *S. oleraceus* is paler yellow than that of *S. arvensis*. The achenes of *S. arvensis* are strongly ribbed and beakless, whereas the achenes of *S. asper* are smooth, strongly compressed, and more or less winged. *S. arvensis* generally has longer leaves with smaller, rounded auricles compared to the prominent, rounded auricles of *S. asper* and the sharply acute and obliquely descending auricles of *S. oleraceus*. In addition, the leaf margins of *S. asper* are more undulant and spiny when compared to *S. arvensis*.

Sonchus arvensis is similar vegetatively to prickly lettuce (*Lactuca scariola* L.) and to blue lettuce ([*L. pulchella* (Pursh) DC.]). However, prickly lettuce possesses stiff, sharp prickles on the lower midvein surface that are lacking in *S. arvensis* and blue lettuce has blue flowers, beaked achenes, and lacks prickles on leaf edges (Frankton and Mulligan 1987).

3. Economic Importance

(a) *Detrimental* — *Sonchus arvensis* is locally common in various cereal and oilseed crops of the northern prairies of Canada and the United States (Peschken et al. 1983) and is regarded as a serious weed problem in several countries, including Hungary, Norway, Poland, and the Soviet Union (Holm et al. 1979). Economic losses from perennial sow-thistle infestations result from reduced crop

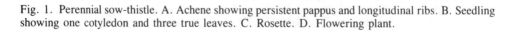

Fig. 1. Perennial sow-thistle. A. Achene showing persistent pappus and longitudinal ribs. B. Seedling showing one cotyledon and three true leaves. C. Rosette. D. Flowering plant.

Fig. 2. A. Peduncle and flower of *S. arvensis* var. *arvensis* showing glandular hairs. B. Peduncle and flower of *S. arvensis* var. *glabrescens* showing lack of glandular hairs. Both photos were taken from herbarium material.

yield, increased cultivation and herbicide expense, and land depreciation.

Sonchus arvensis was ranked among the 15 most abundant weeds in fields surveyed in Alberta (Thomas and Wise 1986a), Manitoba (Thomas and Wise 1984, 1988), and Saskatchewan (Thomas and Wise 1983, 1987a). The weed tended to be more abundant in barley and oats than in wheat (Thomas and Wise 1983, 1987a 1988) and was more abundant in winter wheat than in spring wheat (Thomas and Wise 1986d, 1987b). *S. arvensis* was found in 21 and 67% of Saskatchewan mustard and dry pea fields, respectively, but only in 5 and 14% of lentil and sunflower fields, respectively (Thomas and Wise 1986b,c). In the United States, *S. arvensis* was found in 11% of surveyed fields at a mean density of 5.5 plants m^{-2} in a survey of small grain, flax, and sunflower in North Dakota (Dexter et al. 1981).

The uniformity (percentage of quadrats within fields containing *S. arvensis*) in infested fields is low compared to its frequency (percentage of fields surveyed containing *S. arvensis*) (Thomas and Wise 1986a, 1987a, 1988). *Sonchus arvensis* occurred in 39% of rapeseed fields in Saskatchewan and Manitoba but only infested 7% of the rapeseed hectares (Peschken et al. 1983). *Sonchus arvensis* occurred in 57% of pedigreed alfalfa seed fields in Manitoba but was not distributed uniformly (Goodwin et al. 1986).

Recent surveys indicate that *S. arvensis* may be decreasing in cereal and oilseed crops in Manitoba and Saskatchewan (Thomas and Wise 1987a, 1988). The frequency of occurrence was 24 and 11%, and field uniformity was 5 and 2% in fields surveyed in Saskatchewan from 1976 to 1979 and in 1986, respectively (Thomas and Wise 1983, 1987a). Similarly, *S. arvensis* frequency in Manitoba fell from 43 to 30%, and field uniformity fell from 9 to 6% in surveys taken in 1978 to 1981 and in 1986, respectively (Thomas and Wise 1984, 1988). This trend corresponded to an overall decrease in weed populations in cereal and oilseed crops.

Data quantifying competition from *S. arvensis* are limited. Rapeseed yield in Saskatchewan

was reduced by 12 and 18% at densities of 5 and 10 shoots *S. arvensis* m^{-2}, respectively (Peschken 1981). The average annual yield loss of rapeseed due to *S. arvensis* was estimated to be 9.4 and 6.1 million kg, and monetary losses were estimated at $2.6 and $1.7 million annually in Saskatchewan and Manitoba, respectively (Peschken et al. 1983). The total annual loss in Alberta, Saskatchewan, and Manitoba due to *S. arvensis* in rapeseed fields was estimated at $6.7 million. *S. arvensis* densities of 3 to 15 plants m^{-2} reduced spring wheat yield by 4.5 to 27% in western U.S.S.R. (Shashkov et al. 1977). *Sonchus arvensis* densities of 14 and 27 shoots m^{-2} reduced spring wheat yield by 15 and 45%, respectively, in 1 yr in North Dakota (Schimming and Messersmith, unpubli. data, 1986).

Sonchus arvensis is a host of several economically important plant pests and parasites (see Section 13 for further details).

(b) *Beneficial* — *Sonchus arvensis* is acceptable as a livestock feed, and patches of the weed were cut for hay or were pastured as an early control measure (Batho 1936; Stevens 1926). The plant is an excellent feed for foraging animals such as rabbits (Szczawenski and Turner 1978). *Sonchus arvensis* has equal or higher in vitro digestible dry matter, micro- and macromineral content and crude protein and lower neutral detergent fiber compared to alfalfa (Martin et al. 1987). Dry *S. arvensis* was about 10% crude protein by weight (Buchanan et al. 1978a,b). However, the palatability of *S. arvensis* to lambs was lower compared to alfalfa and grasses, and infestations of the weed in pastures and hayfields may decrease overall forage feeding value (Martin et al. 1987).

Roasted roots of *S. arvensis* have been used like chicory root as an additive to or a replacement for coffee (Boulos 1973), and young, tender leaves can be eaten raw in salads or cooked (Szczawinski and Turner 1978). Most of the latex of *S. arvensis* is composed of oil (about 5% of the total weight), and the plant may be a potential crop for oil or hydrocarbon production (Buchanan et al.

1978a,b). *Sonchus arvensis* is a good source of pentacyclic triterpenes, which may become important in the pharmaceutical industry (Hooper and Chandler 1984).

(c) *Legislation* — *Sonchus arvensis* was declared a primary noxious weed in the Canadian Seed Act (Agriculture Canada 1967) and was listed as a noxious weed in the Weed Acts of Alberta, British Columbia, Manitoba, Nova Scotia, Ontario, Quebec, and Saskatchewan (anonymous 1979, 1985, 1987, 1988, 1986, 1984a, 1984b, respectively).

4. Geographical Distribution

Both *S. arvensis* var. *arvensis* and *S. arvensis* var. *glabrescens* were introduced into North America and are established widely throughout Canada. Groh (1942) reported that *S. arvensis* var. *glabrescens* was sparse in eastern Canada and that *S. arvensis* var. *arvensis* was sparse west of Lake Superior. Both varieties occur throughout Canada (Figs. 3, 4). However, *S. arvensis* var. *glabrescens* was more common in Alberta, Saskatchewan, Manitoba, and western Ontario than was *S. arvensis* var. *arvensis*, which constituted a large proportion of the specimens examined from eastern Ontario to Newfoundland.

Sonchus arvensis is locally frequent to occasional throughout the northern United States but is rare in the southern, central, and southwestern states (Reed 1970). Gleason and Cronquist (1967) reported that var. *arvensis* was more common than var. *glabrescens* along the Atlantic states and that the latter was more common west of the Appalachians. Both varieties occur in Alaska (Fernald 1950; pers. obs.).

Sonchus arvensis is found throughout Europe, western Asia, and Iceland (Boulos 1961, 1973). It is distributed in Europe and Asia from Scandanavia south to Italy and west to western U.S.S.R. (west and north of the Caspian Sea). *Sonchus arvensis* is common in northwestern Europe, less common in central Europe, and rare in southern Europe (Boulos 1973). It occurs in South America, New Zealand, and Australia (Pegtel 1973; Peschken 1982).

5. Habitat

(a) *Climatic requirements* — *Sonchus arvensis* is widely distributed in temperate regions and is absent from the tropics. Neither the climatic conditions required for successful establishment nor the conditions, if any, favoring var. *arvensis* over var. *glabrescens* have been established.

(b) *Substratum* — *Sonchus arvensis* is adapted to many soil types, but most references indicate that it prefers low, fine-textured soils and that it does not thrive on dry, coarse-textured sand (Frankton and Mulligan 1987; Korsmo 1954; Stevens 1924). The weed occurred more frequently on loam (moderately fine to moderately coarse textured) compared to heavy clay (fine textured), sandy, or gravelly soils (Thomas and Wise 1983, 1986b). The role of soil type in determining distribution is unclear because the rainfall patterns closely follow shifts in soil type. Generally, *S. arvensis* is located in regions of the prairie provinces that receive the most precipitation. One variety, *S. arvensis* var. *maritimus*, has adapted in The Netherlands to coastal dune sands that contain only small amounts of nitrate, phosphorus, humus, and clay (Pegtel 1973, 1974).

Sonchus arvensis seems to prefer slightly alkaline or neutral soils and does not thrive in acid soils, salt marshes, or highly alkaline areas (Groh 1942; Stevens 1924). Greenhouse-grown plants had 44% less total dry weight when grown at pH 5.2 compared to 7.2 (Zollinger and Kells 1987).

Sonchus arvensis was more frequent on Dark Gray Chernozemic soils in Saskatchewan and Manitoba compared to Black, Dark Brown, and Brown Chernozemic soils and Gray Luvisolic soils (Thomas and Wise 1987a, 1988). *Sonchus arvensis* is more common in Alberta on soils of the Davis series (Orthic Gray Wooded, medium textured, well drained) compared to other soil complexes (Leith complex, Boyer complex, and Tangent series) (Thomas and Wise 1986a).

Sonchus arvensis is adapted to nonsaline or moderately saline soils with a soil water potential of greater than -1.0 MPa (Guy and

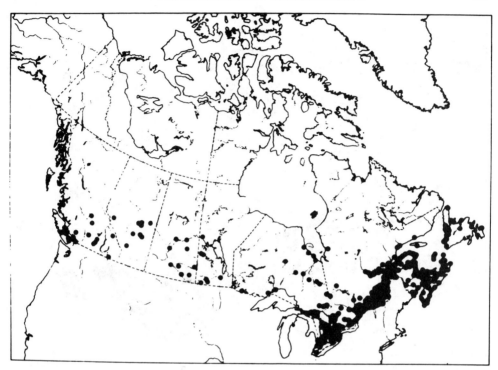

Fig. 3. Distribution of *Sonchus arvensis* var. *arvensis* in Canada based on herbaria specimens from ACAD, CAN, DAOM, DAS, HAM, LKHD, MT, NBM, NFLD, NSAC, PMAE, QFA, QUE, SASK, SCS, SFS, TRTE, UBC, USAS, UVIC, UWO, WIN, and WOCB, and on information provided by ALTA, QK, UNB, V, and WAT [herbarium abbreviations as in Holmgren et al. (1981)].

Reid 1986). The plant was the major species in Alberta along a salinity gradient when the soil water potential was from −0.5 to −0.2 MPa and when the soil moisture content ranged from 19 to 24%. *Sonchus arvensis* was replaced rapidly by *Hordeum jubatum* as the soil water potential fell below −0.25 MPa, and the density of *S. arvensis* fell to zero at soil water potentials of −0.75 to −1.0 MPa.

Sonchus arvensis prefers loose, coarse soils (Njos 1982). Infestations were greater in wet (soil moisture tension of 5 MPa or less), cultivated, noncompacted soils compared to wet, artificially compacted soils. The weed was not found in noncompacted or compacted soils with soil moisture tensions of 7 to 50 MPa. Mokshin (1978) suggested that spreading

roots of *S. arvensis* are forced to the surface where prolonged use of minimum cultivation leads to soil compaction. Regrowth ceased from 10 cm deep as the soil density increased from 0.9 to 1.3 g cm⁻³.

Sonchus arvensis var. *glabrescens* invaded the hydrophytic communities of the Saline Gleysol subgroup associated with saline seep areas of Saskatchewan in dry years when seedlings could establish along the shores of normally flooded areas (Dodd and Coupland 1966). The plant occurred in low frequency (< 1 to 11% of total basal area) in halophytic communities of the Saline Meadow subgroup, which were characterized by fluctuating but generally high soil water content. *Sonchus arvensis* var. *glabrescens* occurred more frequently in Saline Meadow

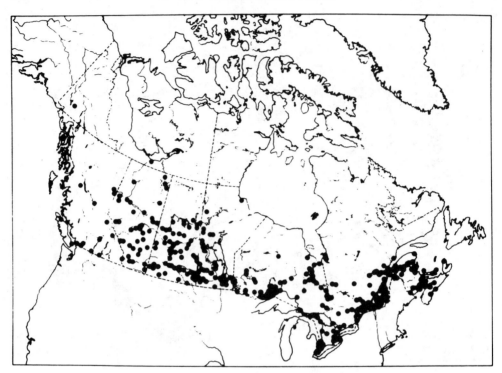

Fig. 4 Distribution of *Sonchus arvensis* var. *glabrescens* in Canada from herbaria specimens determined as described in Fig. 3.

subgroups with relatively low soil salt concentration. In addition, this variety occurred with 20% frequency in semi-halophytic communities in medium-textured soils of the Saline Calcareous Chernozem subgroup, which were located on the drier peripheries of saline depressions that did not develop salt crusts.

(c) *Communities in which the species occurs* — *Sonchus arvensis* occurs in cultivated fields of both small grains and row crops, in disturbed areas, waste grounds, meadows, sloughs, woods, and lawns, and along roadsides, streets, beaches, ditches, and river and lake shores (Stevens 1924; Korsmo 1954; Montgomery 1955; Reed 1970; Shumovich and Montgomery 1955; Frankton and Mulligan 1987).

Major species associated with *S. arvensis* var. *glabrescens* in halophytic or semi-halophytic communities near saline depressions in Saskatchewan included *Achillea lanulosa* Nutt., *Antennaria microphylla* Greene, *Aster ericoides* L., *Distichlis stricta* (Torr.)Rydb., *Glycyrrhiza lepidota* (Nutt.) Purshl., *Hordeum jubatum* L., *Muhlenbergia richardsonis* (Trin.)Rydb., and *Solidago nemoralis* Ait. (Dodd and Coupland 1966). *Sonchus arvensis* was found with 50, 57, 20, and 11% frequency in dryland saline areas of central Saskatchewan, Manitoba, central Alberta, and southern Alberta, respectively, in association with species such as *Aster brachyactis* Blake, *Atriplex patula* var. *subspicata* (Nutt.) S. Wats., *Grindelia squarrosa* (Pursh)Dunal, *Kochia scoparia* (L.)Schrad.,

Puccinellia nuttalliana (Schulte) Hitche., *Salicornia rubra* Nels., and *Suaeda calceoliformis* (Hook.)Torr. (Braidek et al. 1984). The weed occurred in alfalfa seed fields in Manitoba in association with other perennial weeds including *Agropyron repens (L.) Beauv.*, *Cirsium arvense* (L.)Scop., and *Taraxacum officinale* Weber in Wiggers (Goodwin et al. 1986).

6. History

Sonchus arvensis originated in Europe and western Asia (Shumovich and Montgomery 1955; Frankton and Mulligan 1987) and was probably introduced into North America as a seed contaminant (Long 1922). Newly established plants likely spread by railroads and threshing machines or in contaminated crop seed, packing materials, or hay (Harrison 1916).

Sonchus arvensis var. *arvensis* was first reported in North America in 1814 from Pennsylvania (Pursh 1814; Shumovich and Montgomery 1955) and the earliest collection of var. *glabrescens* in North America was from Maine in 1894. Additional collections were reported from Massachusetts and Ohio as early as 1902 (Fernald and Wiegand 1910).

Both varieties probably became established in Manitoba around 1890 (Fernald and Wiegand 1910). Infestations of *S. arvensis* var. *glabrescens* in the Peace River District of Alberta, British Columbia and the northern Great Plains of the United States probably originated from Manitoba (Porter and Stevens 1919; Groh 1942). *Sonchus arvensis* was not considered a serious pest in eastern Canada in the early 1900s but became a serious weed problem in Manitoba by 1910 (Harrison 1916).

7. Growth and Development

(a) *Morphology* — The subterranean spreading roots are the major means of vegetative propagation and enable the plant to colonize new areas rapidly and to persist despite cultivation and other disturbances. These roots, frequently 0.25–0.5 cm in diameter (rarely exceeding 1 cm) (Stevens 1924), are found from 5–12 cm below the

surface (Arny 1932). They originate from short, spindle-shaped, somewhat branched primary roots (Korsmo 1954). Additional root branches can form from preexisting spreading roots or from adventitious roots that develop from underground portions of aerial stems. Vertical roots can penetrate 2 m deep and can produce vegetative buds as deep as 50 cm below the soil surface (Stevens 1924; Arny 1932).

Sonchus arvensis forms a rosette early in development, which provides a large photosynthetic area (Pegtel 1973). The net assimilation rate of the coastal ecotype (*S. arvensis* var. *maritimus*) in The Netherlands is reduced compared to *S. arvensis* var. *arvensis*, which was attributed to inadequate rosette formation. *Sonchus arvensis* forms its flower stalk quickly and branches readily when not crowded (Stevens 1924).

Hooked cells at the tips of pappus hairs allow the pappus to cling to clothes, animal fur, and other objects (Fig. 1A) (Boulos 1960). The pappus, which generally remains attached to the achene (Peschken 1981), is a mechanism for wind dispersal. The maximum dispersal distance of *S. arvensis* achenes at wind speeds of 5, 11, and 16 km h^{-1} was 3, 7, and 10 m, respectively (Sheldon and Burrows 1973). The arrangement of pappus filaments on achenes offers greater resistance to air, thereby providing greater dispersal potential than more open pappus arrangements of other composites, such as *Taraxacum officinale* and *Senecio* spp.

(b) *Perennation* — New shoots develop from buds that overwinter on vertical or spreading roots or on basal portions of aerial stems (Hakansson 1982; Pegtel 1973). The weed also overwinters as seed.

(c) *Physiological data* — *Sonchus arvensis* is a C$_3$ plant (Pegtel 1973; Guy and Reid 1986) that is adapted to moist, sunny locations in temperate areas. *Sonchus arvensis* growth by greenhouse-grown plants was correlated positively with increasing soil moisture potentials (Zollinger and Kells 1987). Plants grown at saturation (0 MPa) had greater leaf and capitula number, increased plant height, and greater dry weight compared to plants grown at field capacity (-0.033 MPa). Severe growth inhibition occurred when plants were grown in soils drier than -0.033 MPa. Also, a decrease in leaf number, plant height and weight, and an increase in rosette diameter were observed as the light intensity was reduced from about 1000 to 200 μE m^{-2} s^{-1}. Overwintering roots of *S. arvensis* were not severely injured by temperatures above $-16°C$ in laboratory experiments, but few roots survived exposure to $-20°C$ (Schimming and Messersmith 1988).

Carbohydrate reserves in *S. arvensis* are stored in parenchymatous cells and are composed mainly of polysaccharides; inulin is the primary storage carbohydrate and there is little or no starch (Pegtel 1973; Stevens 1924). Carbohydrate, excluding cellulose, comprised about 40% of the dry weight of roots from mid-May to November in Minnesota (Arny 1932). The content of mono-, di-, and polysaccharides in underground storage tissue fluctuates with growth cycle. The percent of carbohydrate in a readily available form decreased from late April (90%) to beginning bloom (75%). This percent water-soluble carbohydrates increased into late fall (post-bloom) (Arny 1932; Pegtel 1974) and decreased slightly during the winter because of catabolism (Hakansson 1969; Pegtel 1974). The same trends were observed with percent total organic nitrogen (Arny 1932).

At all growth stages, water-soluble carbohydrate content was greater (30–50%) in roots than shoots (10–20%), but nitrogen content was greater in shoots (1–4%) than in roots (0.5–2%) (Hakansson 1969). *Sonchus arvensis* had a relatively high sodium (705 $\pm$ 372 μM g^{-1} dry weight) and calcium (427 $\pm$ 89 μM g^{-1} dry weight) content compared to other common plants in moderately saline areas of Alberta, but the potassium content was highly variable (Guy and Reid 1986).

In experiments using $^{14}CO_2$, assimilates were translocated to the root system during the rosette stage and to the branches, leaves, and flower buds during stem elongation (Fykse 1974). Translocation to the root system from rosette leaves resumed after flowering, while translocation from stem leaves was always acropetal. Assimilates moved readily throughout the root system if plants only had one shoot, but movement was confined primarily to the root tissue between shoots when more than one shoot was present on a root branch.

Translocation of herbicides in *S. arvensis* seems to be governed by factors other than assimilate movement. ^{14}C-MCPA and ^{14}C-clopyralid translocated freely among rosette leaves but neither herbicide moved readily to the roots (Fykse 1975; Devine and Vanden Born 1985). The greatest downward translocation of ^{14}C-MCPA occurred when treated plants had 5–7 rosette leaves 12–15 cm long (Fykse 1976). Absorption of ^{14}C-clopyralid and ^{14}C-chlorsulfuron in plants treated at the 8–10 leaf stage was 85 and 30%, respectively (Devine and Vanden Born 1985). Then 50% of absorbed ^{14}C-clopyralid translocated to the upper shoot, but over 90% of ^{14}C-chlorsulfuron remained with the treated leaf.

Oven-dry *S. arvensis* had a crude protein, oil, and polymeric hydrocarbon (natural rubber and wax) content of about 10, 5, and 0.6%, respectively (Buchanan et al. 1978a,b). The lipid fractions of fresh herbaceous *S. arvensis* were identified as monoacyl galactosylglycerol, diacyl galactosylglycerol, and diacyl digalactosylglycerol (Baruah et al. 1983). Five phenolic flavones, apigenin 7-glucuronide, luteolin 7-glucoside, luteolin 7-glucuronide, luteolin 7-rutinoside, and luteolin 7-glucosylglucuronide, and two coumarins, scopoletin and aesculetin, have been isolated from *S. arvensis* var. *glabrescens* (Mansour et al. 1983). Cynaroside, isocynaroside, quercetin, quercimetrin, chrysoeriol, isorhamnetin, and sonchoside have been isolated from *S. arvensis* flowers (Bondarenko et al. 1978).

(d) *Phenology* — Shoots and new roots in established stands begin to develop when the soil starts to warm, which is in late April in many areas where *S. arvensis* occurs (Hakansson 1969; Stevens 1924). Most shoots develop from within the top 10 cm of soil, but deeper emergence is possible (Hakansson

1969). Small reddish or purplish leaves begin to appear from shallow roots around 1 wk after initial growth (Stevens 1924), and adventitious root development begins 3 to 4 wk later. Initial thickening of new roots begins when the plants have 5–7 leaves (Hakansson 1969; Hakansson and Wallgren 1972a). Secondary thickening proceeds quickly, and spreading roots of 4 mm diameter and over 200 cm long can be detected by 3 mo after initial growth (Stevens 1924). Thickening of new roots ceases by mid-summer. New shoots develop from roots 2–3 mm diameter until late summer. Plants are injured by light frosts, and leaves and stems are killed by freezing temperatures.

Flowering stems begin to develop when plants have 12–15 leaves (Hakansson 1969; Stevens 1924). Flowering begins around 1 July in the northern United States and continues until the plants are frosted, although most flowering is complete by late summer (Stevens 1924). The time required from flowering to fruit maturation is about 10 days.

Seed germination does not begin until the soil has warmed, and most seedlings do not emerge until mid- to late-May in Saskatchewan, in the Great Plains of the United States, and Europe. Chepil (1946) reported germination until late July in Saskatchewan, but no achenes sown in summer in Great Britain emerged in the fall (Roberts and Neilson 1981). Seedlings will grow slowly for about 2 wk until leaves are about 3 cm long (Chepil 1946; Stevens 1924), but they develop rapidly thereafter, and the reproductive ability of spreading roots is established quickly. Most seedlings do not flower the first year, but flowering in late summer is possible from some first-year seedlings under favorable environments (Hakansson and Wallgren 1972a; Stevens 1924).

(e) *Mycorrhiza* — No information on mycorrhiza is available.

8. Reproduction

(a) *Floral biology* — Flowers of *S. arvensis* are perfect and generally self-incompatible (Derscheid and Schultz 1960). Seeds produced by self pollination are generally shriveled and nonviable (Derscheid and Schultz 1960; Stevens 1924).

Flowers nearest the edge of the head are the first to open and to mature (Derscheid and Schultz 1960). *S. arvensis* is pollinated by insects, e.g., honeybees and other bees, hover flies, and blister beetles (Stevens 1924). Flowers generally open 2–3 h after sunrise and close near noon, but opening and closing is hastened by high temperatures and is delayed by cool temperatures or cloudy conditions.

(b) *Seed production and dispersal* — Heads contain between 150 and 240 fertile flowers (Boulos 1973), but the number of achenes produced varies widely among heads, plants, and locality. The variability likely results from several factors, including environmental conditions and the availability of suitable pollinators (Stevens 1924).

Sonchus arvensis can typically produce an average of 30 achenes per head and up to 50 000 achenes per 0.9 m^2 (Dorph-Peterson 1924; Stevens 1924). One main stalk with relatively little competition produced 62 heads and 9750 well-developed achenes in North Dakota (Stevens 1932). In South Dakota, artificially cross-pollinated heads from greenhouse- and field-grown plants produced about 50 achenes per head, but the number of achenes per head in natural populations varied from 20 to 40 or from 60 to 80 depending upon the year (Derscheid and Schultz 1960). European specimens growing in competition with oats produced an average of 3000 achenes per plant (Dorph-Peterson 1924). Mature achenes weighed from 0.38 to 0.5 g per 1000 achenes (Stevens 1932).

Wind is the primary agent for achene dispersal (Stevens 1924). Achenes also can adhere to animals, vehicles, farm implements, etc. The special characteristics of the pappus that allow the achenes to disperse were discussed in Section 7. Seeds also are dispersed as contaminants in crop seed or hay.

(c) *Viability of seeds and germination* — *Sonchus arvensis* achenes are capable of germination about 5 d after pollination (Stevens 1924; Kinch and Termunde 1957; Derscheid and Schultz 1960). Viability increased from low to none at 4 d after flowering to a maximum at 7–9 d after flowering. Stevens (1924) suggested that achenes may continue to mature on mowed stems if the tissue remains moist. Achenes do not exhibit appreciable endogenous dormancy, and many can germinate immediately or shortly after maturity (Dorph-Peterson 1924). About 80% of achenes that germinated in the field during a 3–5 yr period germinated during the first year (Brenchley and Warington 1930; Roberts and Neilson 1981). Of the total number of seedlings that emerged after 3 yr, 43, 67, and 87% emerged during the first year in clay, loam, and sandy loam soils, respectively (Chepil 1946).

Viability is relatively high (70–90%) in germination tests, but seedling survival in the field is low (Kinch and Termunde 1957; Derscheid and Schultz 1960). Only about 12% of achenes planted in the fall in Saskatchewan produced seedlings the following spring (Chepil 1946). Viability of achenes after 3 yr was 38, 20, and 10% for clay, loam, and sandy loam, respectively. Viability in storage seems to depend upon storage conditions (Gupta and Murty 1986). Viability was maintained for 18 mo for achenes stored in a desiccator at 5–7°C and was reduced (<16 mo) by higher temperatures and higher humidity. Germination of achenes was 80, 62, and 19% after storage in glass bottles for 0, 48, and 60 mo, respectively (Bruns 1965). However, achenes were 100% decomposed after only 3 mo storage in fresh water.

Most reports indicate that temperatures from 25 to 30°C are optimal for germination (Stevens 1924; Hakansson and Wallgren 1972a; Pegtel 1972; Zilke and Derscheid 1959). Achenes germinate poorly (<5%) below 20°C and above 35°C, but alternating temperatures are more favorable for germination than constant temperatures if temperatures above 25°C are included in the cycle (Stevens 1924; Hakansson and Wallgren 1972a; Pegtel 1973).

Sonchus arvensis achenes apparently do not require light for germination, but light may stimulate germination. Germination was less (50%) for achenes germinated in soil than on moist filter paper (80%) and was greater in diffuse laboratory light than in complete darkness (Pamadasa and Kangatharalingan 1977). Germination of *S. arvensis* var. *arvensis* was greatly reduced without light, but germination of *S. arvensis* var. *maritimus* was not affected (Pegtel 1973). The effect of light on germination of *S. arvensis* was greater at 25 and 35°C than at 30°C.

Achenes seem to require a continual water supply for germination, but desiccation of germinating achenes may not reduce viability (Pemadasa and Kangatharalingan 1977). Drying of seeds initially exposed to water for 5 d substantially delayed germination in the laboratory but did not reduce the final germination percentage after rewetting. Better germination of achenes occurred with the pappus placed upward, considered the normal landing state, as compared to the pappus downward, 83 and 32%, respectively; this was attributed to increased achene hydration in the normal landing position.

Both germination and emergence were reduced by increased burial depth, but depth affected emergence more than germination (Permadasa and Kangatharalingan 1977). No achenes sown in the greenhouse produced seedlings that emerged from greater than 3-cm seeding depth, and the rate of emergence decreased rapidly at depths greater than 0.5 cm (Hakansson and Wallgren 1972a). The emergence from achenes planted at 0. 0.5, 1, 2, and 3 cm was 30, 36, 12, 2.3, and 0.3%, respectively, after 104 d.

Seedlings survive best in areas with protective plant cover or litter and high moisture as compared with open, cultivated soil (Stevens 1924, 1926; Pegtel 1974). Thus, seedlings are often only found along pond, ditch, or field margins, or in lawns, meadows, or uncultivated fields. The species may show increased seedling establishment under irrigated systems (Peschken 1981).

(d) *Vegetative reproduction — Sonchus arvensis* reproduces vegetatively from buds that develop on spreading and vertical roots and on underground portions of aerial stems. Thickened roots develop as a result of secondary growth of original fibrous roots (Hakansson 1982) and begin to show reproductive capacity when they thicken to 1–1.5 mm (Hakansson 1969). This occurs on vertical primary roots when seedlings reach the 4-leaf stage and on spreading roots when seedlings have 6–7 photosynthetic leaves. One-month-old seedlings can have 7–8 leaves with spreading roots 10–15 cm long and 1.5 mm thick. Spreading roots from 60–100 cm long and vertical roots that penetrate 50 cm can develop from seedlings within 4 mo after emergence (Stevens 1924).

The rate of vegetative spread from the border of a clone varied from 0.5 to 2.8 m per year depending upon the clone in North Dakota (per. obs., 1987). Spreading roots 90–100 and 140–150 cm long were found on 30 June and 10 July, respectively, from root sections planted the previous fall in Sweden (Hakansson 1969). The average total length of spreading roots decreased to 100–120 cm by mid-November due to necrosis of the thinner portions of thickened roots. The maximum diameter of spreading roots in November was 4–5 mm, and few roots were detected with a width less than 1.5 mm. *Sonchus arvensis* clones in the field produced from 8 to 170 new shoots per 1.4 m^2 in 1 yr in North Dakota (Bell et al. 1973a). Shoot production variability among clones was related directly to the rate of spreading root growth and to the number of buds per root.

The minimum dry weight of roots occurs when the aerial shoots have 5–7 leaves (Hakansson 1969; Hakansson and Wallgren 1972a). This stage occurs prior to initiation of pronounced thickening in new roots and is the stage of minimum capacity for regeneration after soil disturbance (Hakansson and Wallgren 1972a). A second period of low regenerative ability occurs when stem and aerial shoots elongate and flower stalks develop.

The rate of shoot emergence is directly related to dry matter content of thickened roots in the spring and early summer (Pegtel 1974). Vegetative growth is inhibited in autumn, and shoot emergence from newly produced thickened roots ceases in late summer (Hakansson 1969; Henson 1969). *Sonchus arvensis* in Sweden exhibited an innate dormancy that restricted formation of new shoots and roots from bases of shoots and from new and old roots in late summer and fall even if the roots were fragmented (Hakansson 1982; Hakansson and Wallgren 1972a). Dormancy was broken after a few weeks of low temperatures, i.e., 1 mo at 2°C, and was overcome in the field before spring. The dormant period may develop in response to decreasing temperatures, senescence of top growth, or decreasing daylength (Henson 1969; Pegtel 1974).

Vegetative reproduction of *S. arvensis* accounts for persistence of the plant under cultivation. Plants can be produced from root sections less than 2.5 cm long if well-developed buds are present, and sections less than 1 cm long can produce plants that flower within 1 yr (Stevens 1924; Hakansson and Wallgren 1972a).

9. Hybrids

Sonchus arvensis var. *arvensis* ($2n = 54$) and var. *glabrescens* ($2n = 36$) can be crossed reciprocally to produce F$_1$ hybrids with $2n = 45$) (Shumovich and Montgomery 1955). Backcrossing of F$_1$ hybrids with parents and intercrossing among F$_1$ hybrid siblings have been demonstrated. Backcrosses of F$_1$ hybrids with var. *glabrescens* gave plants with $2n = 37$ to 43, while backcrosses with var. *arvensis* yielded plants with $2n = 48$. Intercrossing of natural and experimental F$_1$ hybrids produced plants with $2n = 40$, 43, 45, and 46. Naturally occurring hybrids ranging from $2n = 38$–52 have been detected in areas where both var. *arvensis* and var. *glabrescens* occur.

Hybrids have been made artificially of *S. arvensis* var. *glabrescens* with *S. oleraceus* and *S. asper* (Alam 1972; Hsieh et al. 1972; Bell et al. 1973a). F$_1$ hybrids between *S. arvensis* var. *glabrescens* ($2n = 36$) and *S. oleraceus* ($2n = 36$) had a chromosome number of $2n = 36$ and were intermediate for most morphological characteristics between the two parents (Alam 1972; Hsieh et al. 1972). F_1 hybrids were highly sterile and produced few pollen grains and achenes, and these achenes produced only weak plants that did not flower. The number of root buds on F_1 plants was only 20–30% of the perennial parent (Alam 1972), and the F_1 plants produced only 5 to 10% as many new shoots from spreading roots (Bell et al. 1973a). However, F_1 hybrids exhibited greater resistance to 2,4-D, dicamba, and picloram compared to var. *glabrescens* and appeared similar to *S. oleraceus* in this respect (Alam 1972; Bell et al. 1973a).

Crosses between *S. arvensis* var. *glabrescens* ($2n = 36$) and *S. asper* ($2n = 18$) had chromosome numbers of $2n = 27$, were intermediate in height between parents, and had leaf characteristics that more closely resembled *S. asper* (Hsieh et al. 1972). A cross between *S. arvensis* and *S. palustris* L. was reported in Europe but has not been substantiated (Lewin 1975). Hybrids of *S. arvensis* and var. *maritimus* G.F.W. Mey with morphological characteristics intermediate between the two parents can be produced easily artificially but are rare under natural conditions (Pegtel 1973).

10. Population Dynamics

A single plant of *S. arvensis* can form a large patch of stems through vegetative propagation of the root system as described in Section 8 (Stevens 1924). Seed production in isolated patches is poor probably because of self-incompatibility. The maximum age of reproductive roots is not known but is a least 2 yr (Hakansson 1969). Vertical roots rarely live beyond the second year (Stevens 1924).

Observations in Austria and Sweden suggest that *Sonchus* sp., including *S. arvensis*, occur almost exclusively as early successional inhabitants on recently disturbed sites (Schroeder 1973). Other plant species, such as *Artemesia* sp., *Crepis* sp., and grasses, displace *Sonchus* sp. from disturbed sites within 2 or 3 yr. The erratic occurrence of newly disturbed sites

results in a continuously changing distribution pattern and leads to stands of *Sonchus* sp. that are isolated from each other.

Sonchus arvensis often is listed as a highly aggressive weed, but the mode of competition generally is unknown. The weed appears to accumulate potassium and may compete with alfalfa for potassium (Martin et al. 1987). The content of nitrogen, phosphorus, potassium, magnesium, and iron was greater for *S. arvensis* than for winter wheat, and the content of potassium, calcium, and sodium was greater for the weed than for spring barley (Malicki and Berbeciowa 1986). However, the total mineral uptake (mg plant^{-1}) of most nutrients did not differ among the weed and the crops. *Sonchus arvensis* was considered a vigorous competitor for removing minerals from winter wheat, spring barley, and sugarbeet soils but was not considered among the worst competitors in rapeseed.

Very little is known about allelopathic effects of *S. arvensis* on crops. Leaf and stem extracts of *S. arvensis* reduced root growth of wheat seedlings but did not reduce epicotyl length or dry weight (Bhatia et al. 1982). In contrast, extracts from root tissue appeared to stimulate wheat root growth.

11. Response to Herbicides and Other Chemicals

Sonchus arvensis is relatively resistant to many common broadleaf herbicides compared to most annual broadleaf weeds. Thus, the best systems for control often include a combination of cultural and chemical treatments that are designed to reduce competition, prevent seed production, and reduce the reproductive capacity of roots (Derscheid and Parker 1972; Fryer and Makepeace 1982).

Herbicide recommendations for *S. arvensis* control after harvest include amitrole at 4.4–4.9 kg a.i. ha^{-1} and dicamba at 1.2 kg ae ha^{-1}, for summerfallow include MCPA amine and sodium salt at 1.1 kg ae ha^{-1} and 2,4-D amine at 1.1 kg ae ha^{-1}; and for spot treatment include dicamba at 1.2 kg ha^{-1}, glyphosate at 2.5–4.3 kg ae ha^{-1}, and dicamba plus glyphosate at 0.6 plus 0.6 kg ha^{-1} (Manitoba Agriculture 1989).

Auxin-type herbicides are the primary chemicals. *Sonchus arvensis* is moderately susceptible to auxins such as 2,4-D, 2,4-DB, and MCPA in the seedling stage, and established stands are moderately resistant (Fryer and Makepeace 1982). Growth of aerial portions can be retarded by auxin-type herbicides, and flowering can be suppressed completely if the plant is treated early when growth is vigorous (May and Smith 1977; Fryer and Makepeace 1982).

Postharvest treatments are recommended if the herbicide is applied at least 1 wk before the first frost (Derscheid and Parker 1972). However, single treatments are unlikely to provide eradication. Auxin-type herbicides with soil activity, e.g., picloram, dicamba, or clopyralid, are sometimes applied above rates recommended on cereal crops for eradication in small areas. Spray solutions with good wetting ability are necessary for effective control because of the waxy leaf characteristics.

The growth stage at application influences the efficacy of auxin-type herbicides (Vidme 1961). 2, 4-D amine and MCPA at 1 and 3 kg ha^{-1} were most effective in greenhouse experiments when treated plants had large rosettes at the early bud stage. Both chemicals provided greater reduction in root weight when applied at the late rosette stage compared to the late bud stage. Most *S. arvensis* shoots on arable lands do not emerge until late spring, and many escape early herbicide treatment of crops (May and Smith 1977; Boyall 1983).

Clones of *S. arvensis* in field and greenhouse studies responded differently to 2,4-D, dicamba, and picloram varying from highly susceptible to highly resistant (Bell et al. 1968, 1973b; Alam 1972). No evidence indicates that herbicide-resistant populations are increasing in the field (Bell et al. 1968, 1973b).

Information on *S. arvensis* control with nonauxin herbicides is limited. Glyphosate at 1.4 and 2.2 kg ha^{-1} has been used successfully as a pre-harvest treatment in Britain

Keeffe 1980). However, glyphosate fall-applied generally was less effective than auxin-type herbicides fall-applied (Schimming 1987).

Sonchus arvensis is susceptible to atrazine at 17 and 22 kg ha^{-1}, simazine at 22 kg ha^{-1}, bromacil at 5.6 and 12 kg ha^{-1}, and monuron and diuron at 18 and 27 kg ha^{-1} (Fryer and Makepeace 1982). Dichlobenil at 2.2 and 4.5 kg ha^{-1} used for 4 successive yr has reduced *S. arvensis* in alfalfa (Waddington 1980). Some sulfonylurea herbicides (DPX-L5300 and metsulfuron) provided control similar to auxin-type herbicides, but chlorsulfuron provided poor control (Schimming 1987). Contact herbicides such as bromoxynil are unlikely to be effective at rates used for annual weed control (Terry and Wilson 1964) and have been antagonistic when used with auxin-type herbicides; this likely is due to reduced herbicide translocation (Vidme 1961).

12. Response to Other Human Manipulations

Tillage generally reduces *S. arvensis* stands, but its effectiveness depends upon plant growth characteristics at the time of tillage and the type of tillage being used. Growth of *S. arvensis* after plant burial to simulate tillage was correlated positively with dry matter, water-soluble carbohydrates, and nitrogen content in vegetative roots (Arny 1932; Hakansson 1969). Plants tolerated burial least at the 6-leaf-rosette stage, which was the stage of minimum dry weight just prior to secondary root thickening (Hakansson 1969; Hakansson and Wallgren 1972a).

The 7- to 9-leaf-rosette stage seemed to be the critical stage for tillage to reduce the reproductive capacity of roots (Hakansson 1969). Defoliation was less effective than burial for reducing infestations (Hakansson and Wallgren 1972a), suggesting that mowing would not be as effective as tillage for control. However, pasturing infested land effectively reduces stands because the weed is palatable to both cattle and sheep (Tullis 1924).

The efficacy of tillage depending upon the depth of burial and the degree of *S. arvensis* root breakage. Plant tissue did not survive desiccation when not buried and emerged best when buried 2.5 cm deep (Hakaansson and Wallgren 1972a,b). Emergence decreased gradually with increased burial depth, and less than 10% of root sections produced shoots if buried 30 cm deep. Increased root breakage increased the proportion of buds that formed shoots and resulted in greater use of food reserves (Hakansson and Wallgren 1972b; Hakansson 1982). Emergence of shoots was greater from long compared to short root sections regardless of planting depth, and shoots produced from shorter sections were usually less vigorous and slower to emerge.

Combinations of tillage plus other cultural practices or herbicides applied regularly have controlled *S. arvensis* (Derscheid et al. 1961; Derscheid and Parker 1972). For example, cultivation three times before seeding a close-drilled crop such as soybeans, forage sorghum, sudangrass, or buckwheat followed by fall plowing and subsequent fall cultivation reduced stands 70-80% in South Dakota. Infestations have been reduced 80-90% by spring cultivation followed by establishment of alfalfa or a perennial grass. Fallow systems can reduce *S. arvensis* stands and are most effective if started in the fall and continued until the subsequent fall. Cultivation during fallow every 3 wk during good growing conditions or every 4 wk during hot, dry weather reduced stands 75-90% in 1 yr. Over 99% of plants were eliminated with spring plowing followed by cultivation at 2- to 4-wk intervals throughout the summer.

13. Response to Parasites

(a) *Insects and other nondomestic animals*
INSECTS. Schroeder (1973) lists 53 insect species that feed on *Sonchus* sp. in Europe; 21 species are polyphagous, six are restricted to the family Compositae, 20 are restricted to the subfamily Chichoriodeae, and only six are restricted to the genus *Sonchus*. The latter include four species that are endophytic in flower heads, *Contarinia schlechtenmdaliana* Rubs (Diptera), *C. sonchi* F. Loew (Diptera), *Tephritis dilacerata* H. Loew (Diptera), and

Pegohylemyia sonchi Hardy (Diptera); one species external on stems and leaves, *Nasonovia compositella* Theob.(Homoptera); and one species endophytic in leaves, *Cystiphora sonchi* F. Loew (Diptera). Only three of these species, *Contarinia sonchi*, *T. dilacerata*, and *P. sonchi* were found on *S. arvensis* in a 3-yr study in Austria and the Swiss Jura. Other insects not specific for the genus *Sonchus* that were found on *S. arvensis* included *Ensina sonchi* L. (Diptera), *Eucosma eypallidana* Haworth (Lepidoptera), *Eucosma* (?)sp. (Lepidoptera), *Dactynotus sonchi* L. (Homoptera), *Hyperomyzus lactucae* L. (Homoptera), *Liriomyza andivae* Hg. (Diptera), and *Phytomyza atricornis* Meig. (Diptera). *Ensira sonchi*, *Tephritis dilacerata* and *Eucosma* (?) sp. attacked only 5-8, 3-6, and 3-15% of flower heads of the weed, respectively. All other insects were rare (see Schroeder (1973) for complete listing).

No significant damage to *S. arvensis* caused by insect feeding on or in roots was observed, and no effective stem miner was found. Schroeder (1973) concluded that prospects for an effective biological control outside of the native distribution was slight but suggested *Tephritis dilacerata*, *Eucosma* (?)sp., and *Cystiphora sonchi* as candidates for oviposition and feeding tests. *Tephritis dilacerata* and *Cytiphora sonchi* have been studied for biological control of *S. arvensis* in Canada (Williamson 1984).

Tephritis dilacerata, which occurs throughout northern and central Europe, is reported most frequently on *S. arvensis*, but *S. asper* and *S. oleraceus* can serve as hosts (Berube 1978a,b). The larvae of *T. dilacerata* develop internally on flower heads where feeding stimulates swelling of the involucral base and twisting of the upper portion of bracts to produce button-like floral galls (Berube 1978a; Shorthouse 1980). The larvae prevent seed production in infested heads and act as a nutritive sink that may reduce seed production on other heads of the same plant (Shorthouse 1980). Existing *S. arvensis* infestations are unlikely to be reduced by this pest (Peschken 1979). *Tephritis diacerata* was released in Saskatchewan, Alberta, Quebec, and Prince Edward Island in 1979, 1980, and 1981 (Williamson 1984), but it did not become established (Peschken 1981; Peschken and Derby, pers. commun.).

Cystiphora sonchi, a leaf-gall fly native to Europe, has only *S. arvensis, S. asper, S. oleraceus,* and *S. maritimus* L. as hosts (Peschken 1981, 1982). Adult *C. sonchi* lay eggs through stomata on the undersides of leaves, and larvae form dark red or green galls about 5 mm diameter (DeCleck and Steeves 1988; Peschken 1982). High populations would be necessary for serious damage. Three generations of the insect occur in Czechoslovakia with peak populations in June, August, and September (Skurava and Skuhravy 1973); three generations probably also occur in Canada (DeClerck and Steeves 1988). *Cystiphora sonchi* was released in Saskatchewan, Alberta, Manitoba, and Quebec in 1981–1982 (Peschken 1981; Williamson 1984), and in 1984–1986 in Nova Scotia (Peschken and Derby, pers. commun.). The fly has survived from 1–6 yr on two release sites in Saskatchewan, one site in Alberta and Manitoba, and two sites in Nova Scotia. No reduction of weed population has been observed.

Permission has been granted in Canada for release of a leaf mining insect, *Liriomyza sonchi* Hendel (Diptera), from Europe (Peschken and Derby 1988). Adults of *L. sonchi* deposit eggs singly through the upper epidermis of the leaf, and the leaves form a blotch mine within the leaf tissue.

OTHER ANIMALS *Sonchus arvensis* is susceptible to root-knot nematode, *Meloidogyne incognita* (Kofoid and White) Chitwood, in the United States (Gaskin 1958) and to the cyst-forming nematode, *Heterodera sonchophila,* Estonia (Kirjanova et al. 1976). *Heterodera sonchophila* was considered a highly specialized plant parasite and seemed highly pathogenic to seedlings in the field. Root lesions caused by the nematode *Pratylenchus penetrans* (Cobb) Filip & Stek., a lesion-forming nematode pathogenic to tobacco, strawberry, cherry, and other crops, were found on *S. arvensis* in southern Ontario

strawberry plantations (Townshend and Davidson 1960).

(b) *Microorganisms and viruses*

FUNGI. Three species of fungi apparently are specific for *S. arvensis* in Canada, *Marssonina sonchi* Dearn. & Bisby, *Septoria sonchiarvensis* Dearn. & Bisby, and *S. sonchifolia* (Conners 1967). Also, the following fungi have occurred on *S. arvensis*: leaf spots, *Alternaria sonchi* J. J. Davis (USDA 1960); downy mildew, *Bremia lactucae* Regel (USDA 1960); on dead stems, *Leptosphaeria doliolum* (Pers) de Not., *Phialea cyathoidea* Bull. ex Gill., *Sclerotium* sp., and *Sporocybe tessulata* Sacc. (Conners 1967); on diseased roots, *Fusarium oxysporum* Schlecht., *Rhizoctonia solani* Kuhn (Conners 1967); and *Sclerotinia sclerotiorum* (Lib.) dBy. (USDA 1960; Conners 1967) and rust, *Coleosporium sonchi arvensis* (Pers.) Lev. (USDA 1960).

VIRUS. Aster yellows virus (*Chlorogenus callistephi* Holmes) has occurred on *S. arvensis* in Canada and the United States (USDA 1960; Conners 1967). *Sonchus arvensis* shows a systemic reaction to potato virus N when leaves are artificially inoculated (Agur 1975). The weed may be an overwintering host for this virus, which is pathogenic on potato and other vegetables and horticultural plants in Estonia.

BACTERIA. *Sonchus arvensis* was susceptible to *Pseudomonas solanacearum* E.F.S. in artificial inoculation tests (Joshi et al. 1976). the organism caused wilting symptoms, but plants recovered from wilt in the evening in the field. This ubiquitous bacterium causes wilt on several economically important crops, including tomato and potato, and may be perpetuated in the field by *S. arvensis*.

Agriculture Canada. 1967. Seed act and regulations. Queen's Printer, Ottawa, Ont. 50 pp.

Agur, M. 1975. The host range of the potato virus N. Eesti NSV Tead. Akad. Toim. Biol. **24:** 151–161.

Alam, S. 1972. Morphology, cytology, crossability and herbicide reaction of *sonchus arvensis* L.,

Sonchus oleraceus L., and their hybrids. Bangladesh J. Bot. **1**: 179–184.

Alex, J. F., Cayouette, R. and Mulligan, G. A. 1980. Common and botanical names of weeds in Canada/Noms populaire et scientifiques des plantes nuisibles du Canada. Canada Department Agriculture, Ottawa, Ont. Publ. 1397 (rev.). 132 pp.

Anonymous. 1979. The weed control act. Queen's Printer, Edmonton, Alta.

Anonymous. 1984a. Abus prejudiciables a l'agriculture — Mauvaises berbes. Govern. Quebec A-2. Quebec, Que.

Anonymous. 1984b. An act respecting noxious weeds. Queen's Printer, Regina, Sask.

Anonymous. 1985. Weed control act. Queen's Printer, Victoria, B.C.

Anonymous. 1986. Weed control act. Ministry of the Attorney General. Queen's Printer, Toronto, Ont.

Anonymous. 1987. The noxious weed act. Queen's Printer, Winnipeg, Man.

Anonymous. 1988. Weed control act. Queen's Printer, Halifax, Nova Scotia.

Arny, A. C. 1932. Variations in the organic reserves in underground parts of five perennial weeds from late April to November. Univ. Minnesota Agric. Exp. Stn. Tech. Bull. 84. 28 pp.

Banerjee, G. 1978. Foliar venation of *Sonchus arvensis*. Curr. Sci. **47**: 26–27.

Baruah, P., Baruah, N. C., Sharma, R. P., Baruah, J. N., Kulanthaivel, P. and Herz, W. 1983. A monoacyl galactosylglycerol from *Sonchus arvensis*. Phytochemistry **22**: 1741–1744.

Batho, G. 1936. Sow thistle control. Manitoba Dep. Agric. Circ. 115. Winnipeg, Man. 7 pp.

Bell, A. R., Nalewaja, J. D., Alam, S., Schooler, A. B. and Hsieh, T. S. 1973a. Herbicide response and morphology of interspecific sowthistle crosses. Weed Sci. **21**: 189–193.

Bell, A. R., Nalewaja, J. D. and Schooler, A. B. 1973b. Response of perennial sowthistle selections to herbicides. Crop Sci. **13**: 191–194.

Bell, A. R., Nalewaja, J. D., Schooler, A. B. and Alam, S. 1968. Variations in shape of perennial sowthistle. North Dakota Farm Res. **25**(4): 6–7.

Berube, D. E. 1978a. Larval descriptions and biology of *Tephritis dilacerata* [*Dip.: Tephritidae*], a candidate for the biocontrol of *Sonchus arvensis* in Canada. Entomophaga **23**: 69–82.

Berube, D. E. 1978b. The basis of host plant specificity in *Tephritis dilacerata* and *T. formosa* [*Dipt. Tephridtidae*]. Entomophaga **23**: 331–337.

Bhatia, R. K., Gill, H. S. and Mehra, S. P. 1982. Allelopathic potential of some weeds on wheat. India J. Weed Sci. **14**: 108–114.

Bondarenko, V. G., Glyzin, V. I. and Shelyuto, V. L. 1978. Sochoside — A new flavonoid glycoside from *Sonchus arvensis*. Chem. Nat. Compd. **14**: 340.

Boulos, L. 1960. Cytotaxonomic studies in the genus *Sonchus*. 2. The genus *Sonchus*, a general systematic treatment. Bot. Not. **113**: 400–420.

Boulos, L. 1961. Cytotaxonomic studies in the genus *Sonchus*. 3. On the cytotaxonomy and distribution of *Sonchus arvensis* L. Bot. Not. **114**: 57–64.

Boulos, L. 1973. Revision systematique du genre *Sonchus* L. s.l. IV. Sous-genre 1. *Sonchus*. Bot. Not. **126**: 155–196.

Boyall, L. A. 1983. The control of perennial weeds. Pages 141–170. *In* W. W. Fletcher, ed. Recent advances in weed research. May & Baker, Ltd., Ongar, Essex, U.K.

Braidek, J. T., Fedec, P. and Jones, D. 1984. Field survey of halophytic plants of disturbed sites on the Canadain prairies. Can. J. Bot. **64**: 745–751.

Brenchley, W. E. and Warington, K. 1930. The weed seed population of arable soil I. Numerical estimation of viable seeds and observations on their natural dormancy. J. Ecol. **18**: 235–272.

Bruns, V. F. 1965. The effects of fresh water storage on the germination of certain weed seeds. Weeds **13**: 38–39.

Buchanan, R. A., Cull, I. M., Otey, F. H. and Russell, C. R. 1978a. Hydrocarbon- and rubber-producing crops. Econ. Bot. **32**: 131–145.

Buchanan, R. A., Otey, F. H., Russell, C. R. and Cull, I. M. 1978b. Whole-plant oils, potential new industrial raw materials. J. Am. Oil Chem. Soc. **55**: 657–662.

Chepil, W. S. 1946. Germination of weed seeds I. Longevity, periodicity of germination, and vitality of seeds in cultivated soil. Sci. Agric. **26**: 307–346.

Conners, I. L. 1967. An annotated index of plant diseases in Canada and fungi recorded on plants in Alaska, Canada, and Greenland. Canada Department of Agriculture, Ottawa, Ont. Publ. 1251, 381 pp.

DeClerck, R. A. and Steeves, T. A. 1988. Oviposition of the gall midge *Cystiphora sonchi* (Bremi) (Diptera: Cecidomyiidae) via the stomata of perennial sowthistle (*Sonchus arvensis* L.). Can. Entomol. **120**: 189–193

Derscheid, L. A., Nash, R. L. and Wicks, G. A. 1961. Thistle control with cultivation, cropping, and chemicals. Weeds **9**: 90–102.

Derscheid, L. A. and Parker, R. 1972. Thistles, Canada thistle and perennial sowthistle. South Dakota Coop. Ext. Serv. Fact Sheet, F. S. 450.

Derscheid, L. A. and Schultz, R. E. 1960. Achene development of Canada thistle and perennial sowthistle. Weeds **8**: 55–62.

Devine, M. D. and Vanden Born, W. H. 1985. Absorption, translocation, and foliar activity of clopyralid and chlorsulfuron in Canada thistle (*Cirsium arvense*) and perennial sowthistle (*Sonchus arvensis*). Weed Sci. **33**: 524–530.

Dexter, A. G., Nalewaja, J. D., Rasmusson, D. D. and Buchli, J. 1981. Survey of wild oats and other weeds in North Dakota, 1978 and 1979. North Dakota Agric. Exp. Sta. Res. Rep. 79. 80 pp.

Dodd, J. D. and Coupland, R. T. 1966. Vegetation of saline areas in Saskatchewan. Ecology **47**: 958–968.

Dorph-Peterson, K. 1924. Examinations of the occurrence and vitality of various weed seed species under different conditions, made at the Danish State Seed Testing Station during the years 1896–1923. 4th Int. Seed Testing Conf., Cambridge, U.K. pp. 124–138.

Fernald, M. L. 1950. Gray's manual of botany. American Book Co., New York, N.Y.

Fernald, M. L. and Wiegand, K. M. 1910. A summer's botanizing in eastern Maine and western New Brunswick. Rhodora **12**: 101–146.

Ferron, M. and Cayoutte, R. 1975. Noms des mauvaises herbes du Québéc. 3rd ed. Agriculture Québéc, Québéc, Qué. Publ. QA38 R4-4, 113 pp.

Fleeker, J. and Steen, R. 1971. Hydroxylation of 2,4-D in several weed species. Weed Sci. **19**: 507–510.

Frankton, C. and Mulligan, G. A. 1987. Weeds of Canada. Agric. Canada, NC Press, Toronto, Ont. Publ. 948. 217 pp.

Fryer, J. D. and Makepeace, R. J. 1982. Weed control handbook. II. Recommendations; including plant growth regulators. 7th ed Blackwell, Oxford, U.K. 424 pp.

Fykse, H. 1974. Research on *Sonchus arvensis* L. 1. Translocation of [14]C- labelled assimilates. Weed Res. **14**: 305–317.

Fykse, H. 1975. Research on *Sonchus arvensis* L. 2. Translocation of [14]C- MCPA under various conditions. Weed Res. **15**: 165–170.

Fykse, H. 1976. Research on *Sonchus arvensis* L. 3. Metabolism of MCPA. Weed Res. **16**: 309–316.

Gaskin, T. A. 1958. Weed hosts of *Meloidogyne incognita* in Indiana. Plant Dis. Rep. **42**: 802–803.

Gleason, H. A. and Cronquist, A. 1967. Manual of vascular plants of northeastern United States and adjacent Canada. Van Nostrand, Princeton, N.J. 810 pp.

Goodwin , M. S., Morrison, I. N. and Thomas, A. G. 1986. A weed survey of pedigreed alfalfa seed fields in Manitoba. Can. J. Plant Sci. **66**: 413–416.

Groh, H. 1942. Perennial sowthistle and its smooth variety in Canada. Sci. Agric. **23**: 127–130.

Gupta, R. D. and Murty, Y. S. 1986. Studies on seed storage and viability in some weed seeds of family Asteraceae. Seed Res. (New Delhi) **14**: 115–125.

Guy, D. R. and Reid, D. M. 1986. Factors affecting 13C/12C ratios of inland halophytes. II. Ecophysiological interpretations of patterns in the field. Can. J. Bot. **64**: 2700–2707.

Hakansson, S. 1969. Experiments with *Sonchus arvensis* L. I. Development and growth and response to burial and defoliation in different developmental stages. Lantbrukshogsk. Ann. **35**: 989–1030.

Hakansson, S. 1982. Multipication, growth, and persistence of perennial weeds. Pages 123–135 *in* W. Holzner and M. Numata, eds. Biology and ecology of weeds. The Hague, The Netherlands.

Hakansson, S. and Wallgren, B. 1972a. Experiments with *Sonchus arvensis* L. II. Reproduction, plant development and response to mechanical disturbance. Swed. J. Agric. Res. **2**: 3–14.

Hakansson, S. and Wallgren, B. 1972B. Experiments with *Sonchus arvensis* L. III. The development from reproductive roots cut into different lengths and planted at different depths, with and without competition from barley. Swed. J. Agric. Res. **2**: 15–26.

Harrison, T. J. 1916. Control of the sow thistle in Manitoba. Man. Farmer's Library, Man. Dep. Agric. Bull. 4. Winnipeg, Man. 34 pp.

Henson, I. E. 1969. Studies on the regeneration of perennial weeds in the glasshouse I. Temperate species. Weed Res. Organiz. Tech. Rep. **12**: 1–23.

Holm, L., Pancho, J. V., Herberger, J. P. and Plucknett, D. L. 1979. A geographic atlas of world weeds. John Wiley & Sons, New York, N.Y. 391 pp.

Holmgren, P. K., Keuken, W. and Schofield, E. K. 1981. Index herbariorum. Part I. The herbaria of the world. 7th ed. (Regnum Veg. 106) Ousthock, Schetema and Holkema, Utrecht, The Netherlands. 452 pp.

Hooper, S. N. and Chandler, R. F. 1984. Herbal remedies of the Maritime Indians: phytosterols and triterpines of 67 plants. J. Ethnopharm. **10**: 181–194.

Hsieh, T. S., Schooler, A. B., Bell, A. and Nalewaja, J. D. 1972. Cytotaxonomy of three *Sonchus* species. Am. J. Bot. 59: 789–796.

Hutchinson, I., Colosi, J. and Lewin, R. A. 1984. The biology of Canadian weeds. 63. *Sonchus asper* (L.) Hill and *S. oleraceus* L. Can. J. Plant Sci. 64: 731–744.

Jalas, J. and Pellinen, K. 1985. Chromosome counts on *Erigeron, Hieracium, Pilosella* and *Sonchus*, mainly from Finland. Ann. Bot. Fenn. 22: 45–47.

Joshi, L. K., Kulkarni, S. N. and Keshwal, R. L. 1976. Two new weed hosts of *Pseudomonas solanacearum*. JNKVV Res. J. 10(suppl.): 81–82.

Kinch, R. C. and Termunde, D. 1957. Germination of perennial sow thistle and Canada thistle at various stages of maturity. Proc. Assoc. Off. Seed Analysts N. Am. 47: 165–166.

Kirjanova, J., Krall, E. and Krall, H. 1976. The sowthistle cyst nematode *Heterodera sonchophila* n. sp. (Nematoda: Heteroderidae) from Estonia. Izv. Akad. Nauk Est. SSR Ser. Biol. 25: 305–315.

Korsmo, E. 1954. Anatomy of weeds. Kirstes Boktrykkeri, Oslo, Norway.

Lewin, R. A. 1975. *Sonchus* L. Pages 432–433. *in* C. A. Stace, ed. Hybridization and the flora of the British Isles. Academic Press, London, U.K.

Long, B. 1922. *Sonchus uliginosus* occurring in Philadelphia area. Torreya 22: 91–98.

Lousley, J. E. 1968. A glabrous perennial *Sonchus* in Britian. Proc. Bot. Soc. Br. Isles 7: 151–157.

Love, A. and Love, D. 1961. Chromosome number of central and northwest European plant species. Opera Bot. 5: 1–580.

Malicki, L. and Berbeciowa, C. 1986. Uptake of more important mineral components by common field weeds on loess soils. Acta Agrobot. 39: 129–142.

Manitoba Agriculture. 1989. Perennial weed control, perennial thistles. Pages 123–124 *in* 1989 Guide to chemical weed control. Winnipeg, Man.

Mansour, R. M. A., Saleh, N. A. M. and Boulos, L. 1983. A chemosystematic study of the phenolics of *Sonchus*. Phytochemistry 22: 489–492.

Martin, G. C., Sheaffer, C. C. and Wyse, D. L. 1987. Forage nutritive value and palatability of perennial weeds. Agron. J. 79: 980–986.

May, M. J. and Smith, J. 1977. Perennial weeds and their control on organic soils. ADAS Quarterly Rev. 27: 146–154.

Mokshin, V. S. 1978. Characteristics of growth of thistle root systems with minimum tillage. Sib.

Vestnik Sel'skokhozyaistvennoi Nauki No. 6: 13–17. Taken from Weed Abstr. 1980. 20: 4135.

Mulligan, G. A. 1957. Chromosome numbers of Canadian weeds. Can. J. Bot. 35: 779–789.

Njos, A. 1982. Effects of soil cultivation and compaction on grain crops and weeds — interactions with nitrogen fertilizer. Proc. 9th Conf. Soil & Till. Res. Organiz. pp. 323–328.

O'Keeffe, M. G. 1980. The control of *Agropyron repens* and broad-leaved weeds pre-harvest of wheat and barley with the isopropylamine salt of glyphosate. Proc. Br. Weed Contr. Conf. 1: 53–60.

Pegtel, D. M. 1972. Effects of temperature and moisture on the germination of two ecotypes of *Sonchus arvensis* L. Acta Bot. Neerl. 21: 48–53.

Pegtel, D. M. 1973. Aspects of ectoypic differentiation in the perennial sowthistle. Acta Hortic. 32: 55–71.

Pegtel, D. M. 1974. Effects of crop rotation on the distribution of two ecotypes of *Sonchus arvensis* L. in The Netherlands. Acta Bot. Neerl. 23: 349–350.

Pemadasa, M. A. and Kangatharalingan, N. 1977. Factors affecting germination of some composites. Ceylon J. Sci. Biol. Sci. 12: 157–168.

Peschken, D. P. 1979. Host specificity and suitability of *Tephritis dilacerata* [Dip.: Tephritidae]: A candidate for the biological control of perennial sow-thistle (*Sonchus arvensis*) [Compositae] in Canada. Entomophaga 24: 455–461.

Peschken, D. P. 1981. *Sonchus arvensis* L., perennial sow-thistle, *S. oleraceus* L., annual sow-thistle and *S. asper* (L.) Hill, spiny annual sow-thistle (Compositae). Pages 205–209 *in* J. S. Kelleher and M. A. Hulme, eds. Biological control programmes against insects and weeds in Canada 1969–1980. Commonwealth Agric. Bureaux, Slough, U.K.

Peschken, D. P. 1982. Host specificity and biology of *Cystiphora sonchi* [Dip: Cecidomyiidae], a candidate for the biological control of *Sonchus* species. Entomophaga 27: 405–416.

Peschken, D. P. and Derby, J. L. 1088. Host specificity of *Liriomyza sonchi* Hendel (Diptera: Agromyzidea), a potential biological agent for the control of weedy sow-thistles, *Sonchus* spp. in Canada. Can. Entomol. 120: 593–600.

Peschken, D. P., Thomas, A. G. and Wise, R. F. 1983. Loss in yield of rapeseed (*Brassica napus, B. campestris*) caused by perennial sow-thistle (*Sonchus arvensis*) in Saskatchewan and Manitoba. Weed Sci. 31: 740–744.

Porter, W. R. and Stevens, O. A. 1919. Sow thistle and other weeds of similar habits. North Dakota Agric. Coll. Circ. 18. 12 pp.

Pretz, G. W. 1923. Additional notes on *S. uliginosus*. Torreya **23**: 79–85.

Pursh, F. 1814. Florae Americae Septentrionalis. Strauss & Cramer GmbH, 6945 Hirschberg 2, Germany. 501 pp.

Reed, C. F. 1970. Selected weeds of the United States. USDA Agric. Handb. 366, U.S. Gov. Print Office, Washington, D.C. 463 pp.

Roberts, H. A. and Neilson, J. E. 1981. Seed survival and periodicity of seedling emergence in twelve weedy species of Compositae. Ann. Appl. Biol. **97**: 325–334.

Saad, S. I. 1961. Pollen morphology in the genus *Sonchus*. Pollen Spores **3**: 247–260.

Schimming, W. K. 1987. Postemergence control of perennial sowthistle and freezing resistance of overwintering buds of four perennial weed species. M. S. Thesis, North Dakota State University, Fargo, N.D. 88 pp.

Schimming, W. K. and Messersmith, C. G. 1988. Freezing resistance of overwintering buds of four perennial weeds. Weed Sci. **36**: 568–573.

Schroeder, D. 1973. The phytophagous insects attacking *Sonchus* spp. (Compositae) in Europe. Proc. 3rd Int. Symp. Biol. Control Weeds. Montpellier, France, Commonwealth Inst. Biol. Control Misc. Publ. **8**: 89–96.

Shashkov, V. P., Kolmakov, P. P., Volkov, E. D. and Trifonova, L. F. 1977. The influence of rhizomatous weeds in spring wheat crops on the utilization of nitrogen, phosphorus, and potassium. Agrokhimiya **14**: 57–59. Taken from Weed Abstr. 1977. **26**: 3373.

Sheldon, J. C. and Burrows, F. M. 1973. The dispersal effectiveness of the achene-pappus units of selected Compositae in steady winds with convection. New Phytol. **72**: 665–675.

Shorthouse, J. D. 1980. Modification of the flower heads of *Sonchus arvensis* (family Compositae) by the gall former *Tephritis dilacerata* (order Diptera, family Tephritidae). Can. J. Bot. **58**: 1534–1540.

Shumovich, W. and Montgomery, F. H. 1955. The perennial sowthistle in northeastern North America. Can. J. Agric. Sci. **35**: 601–605.

Skalinska, M., Jankun, A. and Wcislo, H. 1971. Studies in chromosome numbers of Polish angiosperms. Eighth contribution. Acta Biol. Cracov. **14**: 55–102.

Skuhrava, M. and Skuhravy, V. 1973. Gallmucken und ihre Gallen aud Wildpflazen. Ziemsen, Wittenberg Lutherstadt. 118 pp.

Stevens, O. A. 1924. Perennial sow thistle growth and reproduction. North Dakota Agric. Exp. Sta. Bull. 181. 44 pp.

Stevens, O. A. 1926. The sow thistle. North Dakota Agric. Exp. Sta. Circ. 32. 16 pp.

Stevens, O. A. 1932. The number and weight of seeds produced by weeds. Am. J. Bot. **19**: 784–794.

Szczawenski, A. F. and Turner. N. J. 1978. Edible garden weeds of Canada. Nat. Mus. Nat. Sci. Ottawa, Ont. 184 pp.

Terry, H. J. and Wilson, C. W. 1964. A field study of the factors affecting the herbicidal activity of ioxynil and bromoxynil and their tolerance by cereals. Weed Res. **4**: 196–215.

Thomas, A. G. and Wise, R. F. 1983. Weed surveys of Saskatchewan cereal and oilseed crops from 1976 to 1979. Weed Survey Ser. Agric. Can. Res. Sta., Regina, Sask. Publ. 83-6, 260 pp.

Thomas, A. G. and Wise, R. F. 1984. Weed surveys of Manitoba cereal and oilseed crops 1978, 1979, and 1981. Weed Survey Ser. Agric. Can. Res. Sta, Regina, Sask. Publ. 84-1, 230 pp.

Thomas, A. G. and Wise, R. F. 1986a. Fort Vermilion area of Alberta weed survey in cereal and oilseed fields 1985. Weed Survey Ser. Agric. Can. Res. Sta., Regina, Sask. Publ. 86-4, 98 pp.

Thomas, A. G. and Wise, R. F. 1986b. Weed survey of Saskatchewan mustard, lentil and dry pea crops 1985. Weed Survey Ser. Agric. Can. Res. Sta., Regina, Sask. Publ. 86-2, 157 pp.

Thomas, A. G. and Wise, R. F. 1986c. Weed survey of Saskatchewan sunflower fields 1985. Weed Survey Ser. Agric. Can. Res. Sta., Regina, Sask. Publ. 86-1, 50 pp.

Thomas, A. G. and Wise, R. F. 1986d. Weed survey of Saskatchewan winter wheat fields 1985. Weed Survey Ser. Agric. Can. Res. Sta., Regina, Sask. Publ. 86-3, 85 pp.

Thomas, A. G. and Wise, R. F. 1987a. Weed survey of Saskatchewan cereal and oilseed crops 1986. Weed Survey Ser. Agric. Can. Res. Sta., Regina, Sask. Publ. 87-1, 251 pp.

Thomas, A. G. and Wise, R. F. 1987b. Weed survey of Saskatchewan winter wheat fields 1986. Weed Survey Ser. Agric. Can. Res. Sta., Regina, Sask. Publ. 87-2, 99 pp..

Thomas, A. G. and Wise, R. F. 1988. Weed survey of Manitoba cereal and oilseed crops 1986. Weed Survey Ser. Agric. Can. Res. Sta., Regina, Sask. Publ. 88-1, 201 pp.

Townshend, J. L. and Davidson, T. T. 1960. Some weed hosts of *Pratylenchus penetrans* in premier strawberry plantations. Can. J. Bot. **38**: 267–273.

Tullis, M. P. 1924. The control of sow thistle. Dep. Agric. Saskatchewan, Regina, Sask. Bull. 58. 8 pp.

United States Department of Agriculture. 1960. Index of plant diseases in the United States. Agric. Handb. 165. Agric. Res. Ser., U.S. Gov. Print. Office, Washington, D.C. 531 pp.

Vidme, T. 1961. Control of *Sonchus arvensis* L. with chemicals. Weed Res. **1**: 275–288.

Waddington, J. 1980. Chemical control of dandelion (*Taraxacum officinale*) and perennial sowthistle (*Sonchus arvensis*) in alfalfa (*Medicago sativa*) grown for seed. Weed Sci. **28**: 164–167.

Williamson, G. D. 1984. Insect liberations in Canada. Parasites and predators 1981. Liberation Bull. 45. Agriculture Canada, Ottawa, Ont.

Zilke, S. and Derscheid, L. A. 1959. Effects of environmental factors on thistle seed germination. Proc. Joint Meet. 16th North Cent. Weed Control Conf. and West. Canada Weed Control Conf. **16**: 20–21.

Zollinger, R. K. and Kells, J. J. 1987. Edaphic and environmental factors affecting the growth and development of perennial sowthistle (*Sonchus arvensis* L.). Proc. North Cent. Weed Control Conf. **42**: 1.

THE BIOLOGY OF CANADIAN WEEDS. 95. *Ranunculus repens*

J. LOVETT-DOUST[1], L. LOVETT-DOUST[1], and A. T. GROTH[2]

[1]*Biological Sciences, University of Windsor, Windsor, Ontario, Canada N9B 3P4; and, [2]Biological Sciences, Mount Holyoke College, South Hadley, MA 01075 U.S.A.*
Received 23 Aug. 1989, accepted 21 Apr. 1990.

LOVETT-DOUST, J., LOVETT-DOUST, L. AND GROTH, A. T. 1990. The biology of Canadian weeds. 95. *Ranunculus repens*. Can. J. Plant Sci. **70**: 1123–1141.

Ranunculus repens L. (creeping buttercup) is a common weed in the Maritimes, Ontario and Quebec, as well as British Columbia. A review of the literature on the biology of the species is presented. *Ranunculus repens* can develop large spreading clones as it produces ramets on stolons, and readily regenerates from root fragments. It is therefore particularly resistant to cultivation as a weed control strategy. It is, in addition, partially, or fully resistant to many herbicides, and its seeds show dormancy and sustained viability in the seed bank. Several investigations have been carried out on the population dynamics of this species, and its responses to light and nutrient treatments have been described.

Key words: Weed biology, *Ranunculus repens*, creeping buttercup

[Biologie des mauvaises herbs canadiennes. *Ranunculus repens*.]
Titre abrégé: *Ranunculus repens* L.
Ranunculus repens L. (rénoncule rampante) est une mauvaise herbe répandue dans les Maritimes, en Ontario, au Québec et en Colombie-Britanique. Nous vous présentons une revue de la documentation sur la biologie de cette espèce. *Ranunculus repens* peut développer de larges clones rampants, car elle produit des ramettes sur les stolons et se régénère facilement à partir des fragments racinaires. Elle est donc particulièrement résistante au labour utilisé comme méthode de lutte. Elle est en outre partiellement ou entièrement résistante à bon nombre d'herbicides, et ses semences affichent une période de dormance et une viabilité soutenue dans la banque de semences. Plusieurs études ont été effectuées sur la dynamique de la population de cette espèce et ses réactions à la lumière et à l'apport d'éléments nutritifs ont été étudiées.

Mots clés: Biologie des mauvaises herbes, *Ranunculus repens*, renoncule rampante

1. Names
Ranunculus repens L. — **creeping buttercup** or **rénoncule rampante** (Alex et al. 1980); bassin d'or, bassinet, petite douve, pied-de-poule, rénoncule couchée, rénoncule flammette (Ferron and Cayouette 1971).
Ranunculaceae, Crowfoot family, Rénonculacées.

2. Description and Account of Variation
(a) *Description* — The following description includes information from Ray (1886), Muenscher (1955), Gleason (1952), Harper

(1957, 1958), Clapham et al. (1962), Tutin et al. (1964), Calder and Taylor (1968), Frankton and Mulligan (1970), Darlington and Brown (1975), Coles (1977), Clegg (Lovett Doust) (1978), and Lovett Doust (1981a).

Ranunculus repens L. is a perennial herb with a short (1–2 cm) vertical caudex (swollen stem base) with up to 25 long stout adventitious roots (Fig. 1). Strong leafy epigeal stolons (not fistulose, usually with appressed hairs, nearly glabrous to densely hirsute; 0.7–2.0 mm in diameter) are formed in the leaf axils. These readily root at nodes, even when there is no direct contact with the soil.

Fig. 1. Morphology of *R. repens* showing: (a) rooting node with daughter rosette, (b) long petiolule of central leaf lobe, (c) seed head with achenes (reproduced by permission, from Alex and Switzer (1976)).

Internodes vary in length, depending on environmental conditions (see Lovett Doust (1981a,b,c) and (1987)). Flowering stems erect, 15–65 cm high, leafy and hairy. Leaves on stolons alternate, one per node; axillary shoots at leaf nodes later form compact rosettes (ramets, *sensu* Harper (1977)). Basal and lower stem leaves stalked, triangular-ovate to deltoid-cordate, pinnately compound with three lobes. Middle lobe has long-stalked

petiolule and projects beyond the others. Lobes further divided into three toothed segments, distal lobes mostly acute. Dissection varies according to position and time of leaf formation (less dissection in leaves formed early in the season or young seedlings). Leaf blades 1.5–6 cm long, 2–8 cm broad, with middle petiolule (in basal and lower cauline leaves) up to 4 cm long; lateral petiolules (again in basal and lower cauline leaves) up to 2 cm long. Petioles 4–25 cm long, hirsute to subglabrous. Upper leaves sessile with narrow ± entire segments. Leaves usually dark green, occasionally dark green with light spots.

Flowers produced on erect stolons and, often, in the axil of the penultimate leaf. Flowers are 2–3 cm diameter, perfect, regular and usually solitary (Fig. 3). Less commonly they occur in corymb-like inflorescences. Flower pedicels are 2–10 cm long, pubescent. Pilose sepals, usually five, greenish in colour, acute, spreading, separate and not reflexed, 5–7 mm long, 3–4 mm broad, and 2/5 of the length of the petals, are deciduous, soon after flower opens. Petals are 6–9 or even more (var. *pleniflorus* Fern.), with some staminoidia rarely forming a "double" corolla. Petals cuneate-obovate (about 2/3 as broad as long) in shape, suberect, golden yellow, glossy, 7–15 mm long, about 5–10 mm broad. Nectary scale glabrous, free laterally for 2/3 of its length, 1–1.3 mm long and truncate. Stamens 30–80, fewer in "double" flowers, with anthers 1–2 mm long. Carpels numerous, separate, with short recurved styles. Stigma forms a beak-like structure which enlarges after pollen has been shed from the stamens, favouring cross-pollination. Receptacle subglobose ovoid, up to 4 mm long, pubescent or rarely glabrous. Carpel develops into a dry, indehiscent fruit (achene). Achenes 20–50, in subglobose head 6–7 mm in diameter; obliquely obovate to rotund in outline, one edge more curved than the other, and flattened sideways so that the cross section is narrowly oval (Fig. 3), pointed at the edge terminating in an indistinct winged margin; obliquely placed, curved beak at tip, the base being truncate and broadly extended. Achene surface glabrous, unevenly porous, and colored light to dark brown. Achene 2–3.5 mm long, and up to 2.2 mm broad, beak 0.7–1.2 mm long. Achenes eventually dry and separate from the cone-shaped hairy receptacle for dispersal. Ovary 1 mm, ovule 0.3 mm, fruiting head 4×4 mm.

Ranunculus repens is normally tetraploid based on $x=8$ (Larter 1932; Federov 1974), with $2n = 32$ chromosomes (e.g. numerous accounts in Moore (1973, 1977); in the Queen Charlotte Islands (Taylor and Mulligan 1968); in Yugoslavia, Finland, Italy (Marchi 1971) and the Soviet Union (Pervova and Gershunina 1976; Lavrenko and Serditov 1986). There also appears to be a diploid ($2n=16$) race of *R. repens* in Europe (Harper 1957; Kuzmanov and Kozuharov 1969), and Japan (Matsuura and Suto 1935). Pervova et al. (1971) report the presence of aneuploid cells in the root meristem, including $2n=16$, 18, 20, 24, and 28; an unusual count of $2n=14$ was reported by Scott (1974), but see Section 2b, below.

(b) *Morphological characters* — Two congeneric species present in Canada that could be confused with *Ranunculus repens* are *Ranunculus acris* L. and *Ranunculus bulbosus* L. The long-stalked petiolule of *R. repens* is an important character distinguishing the species from its close relatives, *R. acris* and *R. bulbosus* (see Fig. 2). Other species may resemble *R. repens*, e.g., *R. scleratus* L., *R. septentrionalis* Poir., *R. fascicularis* Muhl. and perhaps *R. arvensis*. The distributions and general descriptions of these species are available in Gleason (1952). Coles (1977) states that *R. repens* can be distinguished from all other members of section *Ranunculus* in Europe because of its production of large numbers of creeping stolons which root at the nodes. The same is generally true of *R. repens* in Canada, but Frankton and Mulligan (1970) point out that *R. repens* var. *erectus* DC., which lacks stolons, can be difficult to distinguish from *R. acris*, except that the leaflets are distinctly petiolulate in *R. repens* (Fig. 2). *Ranunculus acris* can also be distinguished from *R. repens* by chromosome number, *R. acris* having a base number $x=7$ with $2n=28$ (Larter 1932). This distinction suggests that Scott's (1974) report of $2n=14$ for *R. repens* may have been based on *R. acris* material. *Ranunculus bulbosus* is easily distinguished from *R. repens* because of its distinctly thickened and cormose base, and because the sepals in *R. bulbosus* are generally somewhat reflexed while they are not reflexed in *R. repens*.

(c) *Intraspecific variation* — *Ranunculus repens* is a relatively variable species (Lawson 1884;

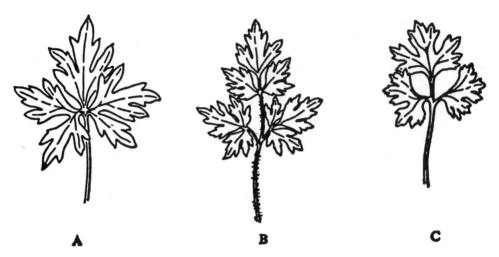

Fig. 2. Leaves of *Ranunculus*: (A) *R. acris*, (B) *R. repens*, (C) *R. bulbosus* (from Harper 1957).

Fernald 1950), and a number of varieties have been described for North America. Fernald listed five varieties (var. *villosus* (Lamotte); var. *glabratus* (DC); var. *erectus* (DC); var. *linearilobus* (DC) and var. *pleniflorus* (Fern.)) besides the typical form. He also developed a key to distinguish between them (Fernald 1950).

Benson (1954) agreed that var. *glabratus* DC. (which "occupies northern ecological niches [in Europe] similar to those it has taken over in the northern regions of North American"), var. *pleniflorus* Fern. and var. *repens* were valid, but that the other alleged varieties (in North America) "....are simply a few of the many biotypes to be found in the general population of *R. repens* in Europe". Gleason and Cronquist (1963) agree with Benson (1941, 1948, 1954) in considering three varieties only: var. *pleniflorus* Fern., var. *glabr*. *'s* DC., and var. *repens*. Hitchcock et al. (1964) and Boivin (1967) do not recognize var. *glabratus* DC., and consider only the double-flowered var. *pleniflorus* Fern. together with var. *repens*. Scoggan (1978) included the same varieties as Fernald (1950), except for var. *linearilobus* DC, and Frankton and Mulligan (1970) recognized *R. repens* var. *erectus* DC. (see Section 2b above).

Benson's (1954) view that "These minor biotypes .... are not taxa." is supported by breeding experiments involving plants from widely separated localities in Europe that showed them to be completely interfertile (Coles 1977).

Pervova and Gershunina (1976) studied intraspecific variability in *R. repens* through a "common garden" experiment, involving plants raised from seed. They found stable "phenorhythms", level of vegetative productivity, absence of feathering on the leaf epidermis and "response to environmental conditions". Density of leaf feathering, number of stomata per unit of leaf surface and cell size on the lower epidermis were regarded as variable characters.

In contrast, in a study of local specialization, Lovett-Doust (1981b), performed a series of reciprocal transplants and replants of ramets between woodland and grassland sites and found that *R. repens* transplanted in alien sites failed to maintain several "ecotypic" differences including leaf birth and death rates and stolon internode length. Van Den Berg et al. (1985) investigated apparent differences between *R. repens* populations exposed to different hay-mowing selection regimes, and found that seedlings derived from these contrasting conditions did not retain their differences when grown in a common garden.

In conclusion, while the full range of biotypes encountered in Europe may not be represented in North America, there is, as far as we can assess, little to support the application of varietal status to any of the five varieties distinguished by Fernald (1950). Reciprocal transplant-replant studies following the protocol of Lovett Doust 1981b, and common garden studies, as well as evaluation of crossability, would help to clarify the taxonomic status and variability of this species in Canada.

(d) *Illustrations* — The morphology of *R. repens* is illustrated for an adult plant, flowers and seedlings in Figs. 1, 3, and 4, respectively, and the annual cycle of clonal growth is shown in Fig. 5.

3. Economic Importance

(a) *Detrimental* — *Ranunculus repens* is a common weed of pastures, lawns and waste places, as well as arable land and forage crops in Canada (e.g. Hughes 1971). It contains a small percentage of toxic cardiac glycosides. These cause salivation, diarrhoea, and signs of abdominal pain in cattle and sheep, and the symptoms usually persist for 14 d (Shearer 1938). Plants of *R. repens* are generally distasteful to grazing animals, and will be rejected if better foliage is present. Harper (1958) and Darlington and Brown (1975) disagree, suggesting that the amount of glycoside in *R. repens* is so low that it does not affect palatability.

Schipstra (1957) associated potassium deficiency in rye (*Secale cereale*) with the impact of *R. repens*. Schipstra (1957) interpreted leaf dieback of the rye plants as being due to sequestering of minerals and nutrients by the weed. Hatfield (1970) described *R. repens* as a species which seriously depletes the ground of potassium and other elements. He further proposed that the root secretes a toxin causing neighbouring plants to suffer from a nitrogen deficiency. Hatfield (1970) gave no evidence to support this claim of allelopathic action, but see Section 7c, below.

(b) *Beneficial* — On sand dunes, *R. repens* helps stabilize the substrate when adequate moisture is present, although it is rarely a pioneer colonizer there (Harper 1957). Turner (1984) has studied ethnobotanic aspects of the Ranunculaceae; protanenomonin is thought to be the active principle in the use of the family (including *R. repens*) as external poultices for boils, cuts, abrasions and other skin sores. Extracts of *Ranunculus repens* failed to show antiviral properties (Husson et al. 1986).

Ranunculus leaves have been found in the crops of redlegged partridge (*Alectoris rufa* L.), Hungarian partridge (*Perdix perdix* L.), and the pheasant, *Phasianus colchicus* L. Large quantities of seed are also eaten by these three species and by the woodpigeon, *Columba palumbus palumbus* L.; most, if not all, of these seeds are digested. Chickens and geese readily eat *Ranunculus* leaves (Harper 1957).

(c) *Legislation* — *Ranunculus repens* is not listed as a noxious weed in Alex and Switzer (1976) or in the 1986 issue of the (Ontario) Weed Control Act. It was previously listed in the Seeds Act and Regulations for Canada (in 1964), but is not found in more recent editions.

4. Geographic Distribution

Ranunculus repens has been introduced to the United States and Canada where it is distributed in a broad band extending mainly between 38° and 50°N. In Canada, *R. repens* occurs in all the provinces, but not the Yukon and Northwest Territories. The species is most common in the Maritime provinces, Quebec, Ontario and coastal British Columbia (Fig. 6). *Ranunculus repens* is generally distributed over Europe including northernmost Norway, and extends into the Faroes, Iceland, and the south and west coasts of Greenland (Coles 1977). It has not been recorded from northern European Russia, Greece, or Albania, but is present in Romania, Bulgaria, and Yugoslavia. It has been recorded from the mountains of Morocco and Algeria and from the Nile delta. Coles (1977) reports that it is also found in Siberia and Japan, but Harper (1957) suggested that these identifications should be checked. It has also been introduced to much of Central and South America and

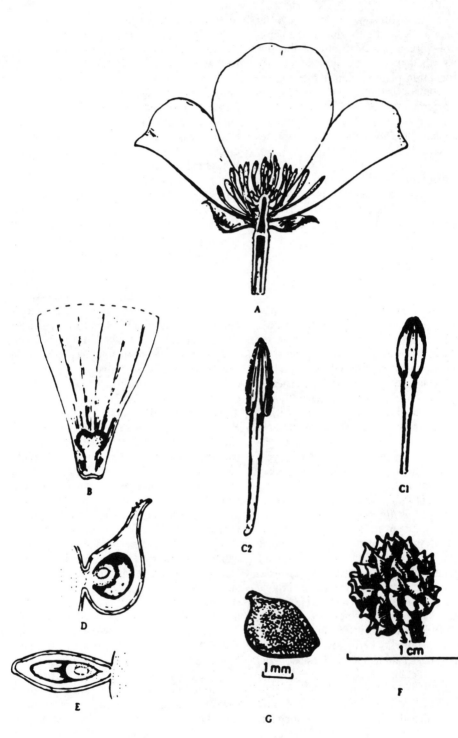

to New Zealand and Australia (Harper 1957; Coles 1977; Auld and Medd 1987).

5. Habitat

(a) *Climatic requirements — Ranunculus repens* can tolerate most weather conditions in temperate latitudes, except for prolonged dry periods. It will survive through the winter as a rosette with a caudex and roots (e.g. as in southern British Columbia), or simply as caudex and roots (e.g. as in Ontario), depending on the severity of winter conditions (L. Lovett Doust, personal observations).

(b) *Substratum — Ranunculus repens* is usually found in heavy wet clay soils and can withstand waterlogging. It is a problem weed on well-watered lawns (Alex and Switzer 1976). It can also thrive in sand or gravel if adequate moisture is present. It occurs on calcareous soils, but seems less able to tolerate high acidity (Harper 1957, review of Canadian herbarium specimen data).

(c) *Communities in which the species occurs — Ranunculus repens* is usually found in early successional communities. It is an important member of four major community types (survey of herbarium specimen data, Harper (1957)):

(1) Disturbed soils, including arable lands: it is especially common among grain crops but can also be found in gardens and among other crops including forage. It is a pioneer colonizer of ploughed land or of smaller disturbed sites.

(2) Grassland communities: it tolerates trampling and grazing but is rare on light well-drained soils.

(3) Aquatic and semi-aquatic communities: according to data provided on the herbarium specimens we examined, *R. repens* is common in swamps and along the margins of ponds, rivers, and ditches. It is able to tolerate some salinity and is found on beaches, in salt marshes, and on the margins of tidal estuaries.

(4) Woodlands: it is restricted to clearings, forest margins, and along paths where light conditions are adequate.

6. History

There seems to be little question that *Ranunculus repens* in Canada was naturalized from Europe and spread rapidly in the wake of the pioneers. Rousseau (1968) calls *R. repens* a "plante adventice", an adventitious or casual colonizer of North America. He also noted that the earliest mention of *R. repens* in Quebec was in 1821 where it was described as common in the vicinity of Montreal. Godwin (1975) states that *R. repens* "belongs to Hulten's category of 'circumpolar plants strongly spread by cultivation' ". Gilkey (1957) even suggested that *R. repens* may have been introduced as a garden plant or ornamental because of its aesthetic value. In contrast, Montgomery (1964) has proposed that *R. repens* could be indigenous to some parts of Canada, but he gave no locations, or supporting evidence for this contention.

7. Growth and Development

(a) *Morphology — Ranunculus repens* produces ramets (clones) and perennates through stolons (runners). These stolons can cover a considerable area in a short time (See Salisbury (1964) and Section 8d, below). At nodes along

---

Fig. 3. Flower and infructescence of *R. repens* (redrawn from Darlington and Brown 1975 and Hickey and King 1988).
   A. L.S. of the flower with two of the five petals removed, exposing the numerous free carpels surrounded by numerous, spirally arranged stamens. Sepals: 9×4 mm; petals 16×12 mm.
   B. Petal base, with pocket-like nectary situated on the ventral surface.
   C. Stamen. C1: upper portion of young stamen, showing two-celled anther prior to dehiscence. C2: the whole stamen after dehiscence of anther. Anthers: 2.25–2.5 mm; filaments: 5.5 mm.
   D,E. Carpel, L.S. and T.S., respectively, showing a single anatropous ovule on a basal placenta.
   F. Fruiting head.
   G. Carpel removed soon after fertilization, showing the enlarged stigma. (From Hickey and King (1988), Darlington and Brown (1975)).

1 cm

Fig. 4. Seedling of *R. repens,* viewed from above. Germination is epigeal and the pericarp often covers the glabrous, deep green cotyledons. A temporary well-branched primary root may extend 30 cm into the ground, but as the first leaves develop, adventitious roots form at the first foliar node and replace the hypocotyl and primary root system (redrawn from Chancellor (1966)).

the stolon adventitious roots may form, and in the axil of each leaf a rosette of leaves, or daughter ramet may form. The stolon internodes wither in the fall after the ramets have formed their own roots and leaves, and the ramets then become physiologically independent (see Fig. 5). The relationship between changes in the shoot apex (from vegetative, to transitional to flowering) and changing phyllotaxy in *R. repens* was investigated by Meichenheimer (1979).

(b) *Perennation — Ranunculus repens* usually overwinters as individual rosettes of leaves, daughter ramets having separated from the parent plants in fall. Some plants die back to ground level in winter but are capable of producing new leaves in the spring. In others, a few leaves will persist under snow or among leaf litter (Lovett Doust 1981a). The short stout caudex stores nutrients which will accelerate growth in spring. Sarukhán and Harper (1973) referred to this structure as a rhizome, but it is more correctly called a caudex. Of course the species can also overwinter as seeds (see Section 8b, below).

(c) *Physiological data* — Ginzo and Lovell (1973a) reported that while export of photosynthate is bidirectional between parent and daughter rosettes, the predominant direction is from parent to daughter. Controlled experiments have shown that increased nitrogen levels result in an increased shoot:root ratio, and also in increased stolon branching and dry weight; however, primary stolon length is not significantly affected by nitrogen level (Ginzo and Lovell 1973b; Lovett Doust 1987).

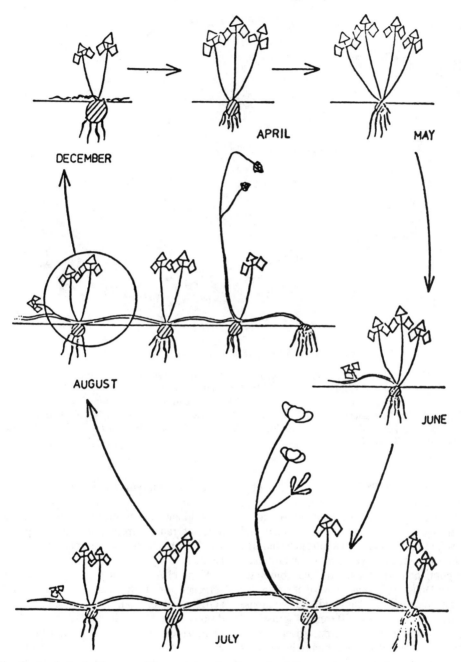

Fig. 5. A schematic diagram of the annual cycle of growth of *Ranunculus repens*: in spring regrowth from last year's rosette allows the development of a parent rosette. Stolons extend from leaf axils in late spring. These leaf-bearing stolons root at the nodes, forming daughter rosettes. By winter the stolon connections have atrophied and the species overwinters as a few old leaves (this occurs in southern British Columbia), or is reduced to a shoot apex at ground level (e.g. in southern Ontario). (From Clegg (Lovett Doust) (1978)).

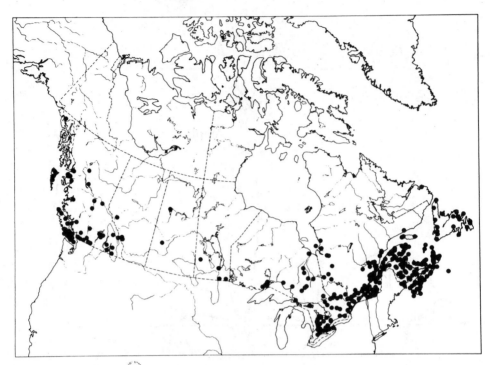

Fig. 6. The distribution of *R. repens* in Canada. This map is based on herbarium specimens in the following herbaria (see Holmgren et al. (1981) for detailed addresses): ACAD, APM, CAN, CDA, CDFN, Concordia University, DAL, DAO, DAVFP, Fort Qu'Appelle Herbarium Sask., HAM, Lands Directorate Ste. Foy Quebec, LKHD, MMMN, MT, MTMG, NBM, NFLD, NSAC, NSPM, PFES, QFA, QFB, QUE, RIM, SAFB, SASK, SCFQ, SFS, SLU, SSFM, TRT, UAC, UBC, UNB, UVIC, UWO, V, WAT, WIN, WNRE.

Lovett Doust (1987) has suggested that moisture, rather than light or nutrient level, may be the proximate determinant of stolon internode length in *R. repens*. Ginzo and Lovell (1973b) found that a nitrogen shortage results in a greater investment in root biomass as compared to stolon and leaf biomass. Lovett Doust (1987) has shown that a shortage of nutrients affects grassland and woodland clones of *R. repens* differently: grassland plants invest more in parent rosette roots while woodland plants invest more in the roots of daughter rosettes.

In a grid different nutrient regimes Sutherland (1990) found that more ramets of *R. repens* grew in the higher nutrient patches. This was because parent ramets in high nutrient locations produced more primary stolons. Parent ramets in low nutrient patches produced fewer primary stolons, but these were longer and more likely to branch. As a result ramets from low nutrient parents were more likely to be placed in other patches.

A number of "marsh" species were screened for alcohol dehydrogenase (ADH) activity under natural waterlogged conditions in the U.K. (Smith et al. 1986). Roots of *R. repens* in waterlogged soil had ADH activity 4.2 times that in dry soil, and produced ethanol as their major fermentation product in these roots. The physiological relevance of this remains unclear. Triglochinin was the major cyanogenic glycoside of *R. repens* collected in spring (Tjon Sie Fat 1979). This substance is accompanied by dhurrin and a third glycoside. In fall, leaves of *R. repens* no longer contained triglochinin; dhurrin was the main cyanogenic substance. The author also described cyanogenic polymorphism in *R. repens*. In a survey of potentially allelopathic phenolic compounds in soil, Whitehead et al. (1982) found high quantities of p-hydroxybenzoic acid under *R. repens*, i.e. more than 400 μg g^{-1} of soil organic carbon.

(d) *Phenology* — In the spring new leaves develop from the overwintered rosettes. Stolon production commences and continues until late summer at which time stolons begin to wither. Separation (or effective separation) of daughter ramets from the parent rosette is complete by fall. Flowering in Ontario occurs from April-July (Alex and Switzer 1976), and in British Columbia from April-August (L. Lovett Doust, personal observation). Seed germination usually occurs in late spring; fall germination in natural populations is rare in the U.K. (Harper 1957; Sarukhan and Harper 1973; Lovett Doust 1981a) and in Canada (L. Lovett Doust, personal observation).

(e) *Mycorrhizae* — None has been reported; in a survey of material from eight North Wales populations, no evidence of mycorrhizae was found (L. Lovett Doust, unpublished).

8. Reproduction

(a) *Floral Biology* — *Ranunculus repens* has hermaphroditic chasmogamous flowers that are insect-pollinated. The flowers are visited by *Apis mellifera* L., the honey bee, by all Syrphidae flying at the time of flowering (Harper 1957), and by butterflies, moths, bugs, and beetles (Harper 1958). Breeding experiments testing for self-sterility in *R. repens* resulted in seed development in 10% of the cases, but each seed head produced only one or two achenes, indicating that a small degree of selfing may occur (Coles 1977). Apomixis (agamospermy) was not seen under intraspecific pollination, but it was observed, occasionally, when pollen of other (*Ranunculus*) species was used.

(b) *Seed production and dispersal* — Sarukhán (1974), studying a grassland population of *R. repens* in Wales, found that more than half the plants produced only one flower and that no plant produced more than five. Each flower produced 20 or fewer seeds and the maximum number of seeds produced on a single plant was 77. A quarter (25%) of the plants which flowered set seed. Intensity of grazing severely affected amount of seed set.

Seeds are dispersed by wind, in the dung of birds and farm animals which have ingested the seeds, by small rodents which store the seeds for winter food, and by humans (Darlington and Brown 1975). In a quaint study, Darlington and Brown found that 11% of germinated seeds found in the trouser cuffs of boys who regularly walk through fields were *R. repens*. They also found significant numbers of viable seeds in soil retained between tire treads.

(c) *Viability of seeds and germination* — In rough lawns in southwestern Ontario, where *R. repens* was present at relatively low densities in the sward (2–3 rosettes per m^2) the number of viable seeds in the seed bank was also low (0–32 seeds per m^2, L. Lovett Doust, unpublished data.) In Wales, U.K., Chippendale and Milton (1934) reported a buried seed population of between 90 and 11 400 seeds per m^2 in permanent heavily grazed pastureland, while Sarukhán (1974) found 0–572 seeds per m^2 in a lightly to heavily grazed field. Lovett Doust (1981a) reported about 1000 viable seeds per m^2 in 12-yr-old mown grassland, in Wales. Seed numbers in the seed bank have not been recorded for woodlands. Williams (1984), conducting studies in England, found more than 12 000 seeds per m^2 in the uppermost 15 cm of soil. *Ranunculus repens,* though well represented in the seed bank, was rare in the sward. In a study in the Netherlands, two flushes of seedling emergence, in spring and fall, were described by Van Den Berg et al. (1985). However, there are few opportunities for emergence in closed turf or pasture, and most seedlings in such situations were noted in spring (see Section 7d above).

Edward (1971) suggested that viability of
R. repens seeds is better preserved under acid
or water-soaked soil conditions. Seeds in the
seed bank appeared to have fairly long half-
lives ("half viability periods", *sensu* Roberts
and Boddrell (1986)), with no significant seed
mortality in the first year (Sarukhán 1974).
In seed "populations" set up and monitored
in the soil by Sarukhán (1974), 38–50% of
seeds suffered predation, 6–9% germinated,
22–44% had enforced dormancy, while
3–4.2% had induced dormancy. The decayed
fraction varied from 2 to 10.1%. Exposure
to light promotes germination of *R. repens*,
while the burial of seed enforces dormancy
(Harper 1957). In England, Williams (1983)
found all *R. repens* seeds to be highly dormant; germination was protracted, and in a
comparison of the survival of several species,
the greatest survival after 15 mo was seen in
R. repens (69%). More recently, in England,
Roberts and Boddrell (1986) tracked seed
survival and seedling emergence in *R. repens*.
Ranunculus repens seedlings appeared sporadically over most of the year, and seeds of
R. repens showed the greatest survival in
the seed bank (compared to other species
studied); emergence in the 5th year after
establishment of the experiment accounted for
4% of the seeds sown of this species.

(d) *Vegetative reproduction* — In spring,
lateral stolons are produced in the axils
of leaves of overwintering rosettes, and stolon
production continues until late summer when
the stolons begin to wither. These stolons
may produce daughter ramets at their rooting nodes. Lovett Doust (1981a) found that
in adjacent woodland and grassland communities in Wales, about 27% of *R. repens*
plants were stoloniferous. The average
number of ramets produced per annum was
found to be 4.6 for woodland and significantly less, 4.0 for grassland stoloniferous
plants. On bare ground stolons may spread
rapidly; as an extreme example, Salisbury
(1964) reported a plant with 35 rooting nodes,
23 of which produced flowering ramets
in a single season. In contrast, in a demographic comparison of woodland and grassland

communities, only parent rosettes succeeded
in flowering (Lovett Doust 1981a).

Even if there is a large viable seed bank,
recruitment of *R. repens* seedlings in established grassland and woodland communities
is rare, and few of these seedlings survive.
In such sites the main source of population increase and maintenance is vegetative
(Sarukhán 1974; Soane and Watkinson 1979;
Lovett Doust 1981a).

9. Hybrids

Experimental crosses between *R. repens* and
a wide range of other *Ranunculus* species
produced only a few seeds in some cases, and
these were shown to have formed through
apomixis (see Coles (1977)). No close hybrids
have been recorded for *R. repens*.

10. Population Dynamics

Ranunculus repens is possibly one of the
best studied weeds, from the demographic
perspective. Harper first described the micro-
distribution of *Ranunculus* species in plough
furrows (Harper and Sagar 1953) and one
of the earliest detailed studies in plant
demography was carried out on three buttercup species by Sarukhán (1971). He mapped
plants in a grazed field, and tracked their
germination or production of rosettes, growth
and death over a period of 48 mo. A later
study of *Ranunculus repens* in Wales (Lovett-
Doust 1981a) showed that populations of
buttercups in both grassland and open woodland followed a similar seasonal pattern. They
remained remarkably stable from year to
year, although the density of woodland plants
was significantly greater than that of grassland plants. This suggests self-regulation
at a carrying capacity that varies according
to environmental factors. The average calculated time for complete turnover of rosette
populations was 2.17 years for woodland
and not significantly different at 2.27 years
for grassland rosettes (Lovett Doust 1981a).
Sarukhán and Harper (1973) recorded a
turnover time for rosettes in pasture of
2.18 yr.

Soane and Watkinson (1979) modelled
the population dynamics of *R. repens* and

found little evidence for selection among families of ramets or against new seedling recruits. Although the number of new seedlings was low, this recruitment could play a significant role in determining the number of genets represented in the population (Soane and Watkinson 1979).

Rosette density of *R. repens* increases with increased grazing (Sarakhán 1974). However, the number of seeds per primary rosette was higher in lightly grazed than in heavily grazed areas. Mowing had an effect opposite to that of grazing; populations of rosettes were found to be 2.5 times greater in an unmown strip of field when compared to a mown strip of the same field (Harper 1958).

Stolon production and the average length of stolon internodes seem to vary between populations (Lovett-Doust 1981a). Strategies of clonal spread may be described as either guerrilla, in which widely spaced ramets are produced and rapid spread is achieved, or phalanx in which lateral spread is less rapid but current position is consolidated (Lovett Doust 1981a). *Ranunculus repens* is very plastic in stolon production and internode length, and thus can express a range of strategies along the phalanx-guerrilla continuum depending upon local conditions. In Lovett Doust's study (1981a), buttercups in open woodland seemed to follow a more guerrilla growth form with longer stolon internodes than those of buttercup clones in the neighboring 12-year-old grassland.

Darlington and Brown (1975) have suggested that light intensity affects the length of stolon internodes, longer internodes being produced under shady conditions; an etiolation response. However, our experiments (Lovett Doust 1987) under controlled conditions indicate that internode length is neither a function of light intensity (etiolation), nor is it a symptom of "foraging" for sparse nutrients. There are indications that moisture level is a major factor affecting stolon internode length (Lovett Doust 1987), and we are conducting experiments to test this hypothesis. Alternatively, stolon internode length may be influenced by the intensity of local competition.

11. Response to Herbicides and Other Chemicals

North American research. In general, weed control strategies suitable for *R. repens* are expressed in perennial weed control guidelines for individual provinces (e.g. Saskatchewan Department of Agriculture 1966; Manitoba Department of Agriculture 1987). *Ranunculus repens* is very sensitive to translocated herbicides such as 2,4-dichloro-phenoxy-acetic acid (2,4-D) (Peabody and Swan 1976). Today MCPA is more generally recommended (e.g. Ontario Department of Agriculture 1988). In British Columbia, Levesque et al. (1987) found that spraying weeds with glycophosphate led to a significant ($P < 0.05$) level of colonization of *R. repens* roots by *Fusarium* spp. Crops subsequently sown in the field were not adversely affected. However, glycophosphate is a broad spectrum herbicide that can lead to root-rot-like damage in crops. In British Columbia, *R. repens* is found in various crops (Hughes 1971). In lawns and turf it is treated with mecoprop at 1.1 kg a.i. (active ingredient) ha^{-1} made up as 2.37 L of a product containing 179 g (a.i.) per litre of compitox; or MCPA at 1.23 kg (a.i.) ha^{-1}. To control the species as top growth in grain 0.84 kg ha^{-1} MCPA are applied. In establishing white clover, MCPA is best applied at 0.84–1.12 kg ha^{-1} at the early bud stage of the rosette. Injury of white clover will occur, but it will recover (other legumes will not). The treatment may, unfortunately, mask the flavour of wilting, poisonous weeds and make them more palatable to stock. When *R. repens* appears as seedlings among grasses, MCPA can be applied at 1.12–2.24 kg ha^{-1}. Weeds are treated in the early bud stage, and one should avoid the early flowering stage of the grass. In the Atlantic provinces, the control strategy for *R. repens* is similar to that in British Columbia, with herbicide being applied in early spring, or in September (Canadian Department of Agriculture 1958). Ordinarily this is done following grazing so that damage to clover is minimized.

In Ontario the response of *R. repens* to foliar sprays has been assessed (Ontario Department of Agriculture 1988). The species is coded as follows: S = susceptible, I = intermediate in reaction, and R = resistant, for each of the herbicides listed: 2,4-D (I-R); MCPA (S-I); 2,4-DB/MCPB (I, I-R); Mecoprop (I); Dicambra (I). In pastures MCPA applied at 1.1 kg ha^{-1} in June, and again in early September achieves control (MCPA at 500 g L^{-1}, 2.2 L ha^{-1}).

European research. Napropamide at 4.5 kg ha^{-1} kept plots of strawberry plants free of *R. repens;* a mixture of 1 kg pendimethalin and 2.3 kg napropamide ha^{-1} also gave excellent weed control in Ireland (Rath 1987). Winter applications of oxadiazon and oxyfluorfen lacked selectivity. Tramat (ethofumesate) at 7.5 L ha^{-1}, applied in mid-November, gave excellent control of *R. repens*. In Germany, a lower application, of 5 L ha^{-1}, also gave excellent (91–100%) control of *R. repens* (Triebel 1986) while fluoroxypyr at a rate of 360 g ha^{-1} gave only 28.5% control of the species (Schlotter et al. 1986). When application of 4.45 kg of asulam ha^{-1} was followed by raking of the litter, *R. repens* was able to spread (Sparke and Williams 1986).

Ranunculus repens is resistant to chloroxuron, chlorprophamphus fenuron, 2,4-DES, lenacil, terbacil, bromacil, trietrazine with simazine, and moderately resistant to dichlobenil, chlorthiamid, diuron, simazine, and atrazine when these are used to control weeds among ornamental crops (Fryer and Makepeace 1977). These authors have tabulated recommendations for the control (with paraquat, aminotriazole, MCPB-salt, simazine, and MCPA-salt) of *R. repens* found among edible crop species. *R. repens* is moderately susceptible to prsopyzamide and controlled well by MCPA-salt, 2, 4-D-amine, MCPB-salt, 2, 4-DB-salt, mecoprop-salt, and dichlor-prop-salt (Fryer and Makepeace 1977). Strykers and van Himme (1971) found that *R. repens* was resistant to rondom [sodium 2,2,3,3-tetrafluoropropionate (at 5 kg ha^{-1}) plus atrazine (1) and amitrol-T (aminotriazole + ammonium thiocyanate) at 2.5 kg ha^{-1}.

12. Response to Other Human Manipulation

Fryer and Makepeace (1977) report that plants of *R. repens* may be weakened by cultivation or dicing, but cut parts of the caudex and sections of stolon are capable of regeneration and causing population increase (Harper 1957; Darlington and Brown 1975; Lovett Doust 1981c). Ploughing provides ideal conditions for the germination of seed and the subsequent rapid spread of *R. repens*, especially if this species can establish itself prior to the crop species (Harper 1957). In the U.S.A., Muenscher (1955) has, however, suggested that infested fields should be ploughed, and followed with a clean cultivated crop for 2 yr.

In an experiment where replicate clones were either left intact, or had the stolon connections between ramets severed, Lovett Doust (1981c) found that severed grassland clones grew significantly less than intact grassland clones, whereas woodland clones did not differ in total biomass. In both populations severed clones distributed proportionately more biomass to inflorescences and ramet caudices, and less to stolons. This pattern suggested that belowground competition became more intense when stolons had been severed. The grassland clones appeared to be less tolerant of intraclonal competition; this is in agreement with the field observation that few of their neighbor "contacts" are with members of their own clone or species, but are rather, for the most part, with neighboring grasses. Woodland plants, which did have a selective history of intraspecific and intraclonal contacts, were more tolerant of intraclonal competition, even when connections between ramets had been lost.

Grazing effects were discussed in Section 10, above. Van Den Berg et al. (1985) raised plants from seed, gathered from populations of *R. repens* in the Netherlands which had, for several years, been subjected to three different hay-making schedules (July; July and September; September). These seed progeny exhibited differences which were interpreted as genetic specialization to the previous hay-making regime. The population cut in July seemed to maintain itself through sexual reproduction, (although this is an experimental result, and it is unlikely that establishment from seed would be important in a permanent hayfield). The population cut in September maintained itself through clonal growth since ramets are independent from the end of August. The July/September population seemed intermediate. Bakker (1987) found that disturbance caused by haymaking or grazing without fertilizer application led to increases in species diversity (including an increase in the presence of the weed, *Ranunculus repens*) as a result of canopy changes, and not as a result of nutrient removal. Kolbe (1987) found that, in apple orchards, cutting of the turf eight times markedly reduced *R. repens* populations, whereas straw mulching led to high *R. repens* populations.

A top-dressing of fertilizer employed to stimulate grass growth will usually result in a reduction of *R. repens* plants (Fryer and Makepeace 1977). A comparative survey of fertilized upland grassland in England and Wales made in 1970–1972 and again in 1986 indicated that sown grasses such as *Lolium perenne* had increased, while *Ranunculus* species had declined (Hopkins et al. 1988).

13. Response to Parasites

Fungal parasitic damage to *R. repens* has been documented for Canada (Ginns 1986), but we have been unable to find reports of parasitism of *R. repens* by insects in North America.

(a) *Insects and other nondomestic animals —* (based mostly on accounts in Harper (1957) and Smith and Harper (1957), for European observations). The nematode *Aphelenchoides ritzema-bosi* (Schwartz 1911) Steiner & Buhrer 1932 attacks stems and leaves. Thrips occasionally attack leaves or petals but rarely do significant damage; most species found on *R. repens* in large numbers are in the process of migrating to or from their primary host plant. There is no documentation on the species of primary hosts, so implications for crop species are not known. Species of *Ranunculus* serve as the secondary host for aphids which

are found on leaves and inflorescences, and the species *Thecabius affinis* (Kaltenbach 1843) produces a woolly mass of threads on old leaves which often results in leaf rot. It also damages the young (adventitious) roots arising from stolons. *Thecabius affinis* has two forms, one with a life cycle involving the alternation of one amphigonous, and several parthenogenetic, generations (Dolgova 1971). The second form has an incomplete life cycle on the roots of *R. repens*, and is continuously parthenogenetic. *Ranunculus repens* was identified as a new host of the American serpentine leafminer, *Liriomyza trifolii* (Burgess), at the Efford Experimental Horticultural Station, in Hampshire, England (Powell 1981); there are no reports in the literature of this leafminer on *R. repens* in North America. Of the Hymenoptera, several members of the Tenthredinidae produce larvae which infest *R. repens*. Of the Diptera, *Phytomyza ranunculi* (Schrank) mines leaves (Dye 1977), and *Geodiplosis ranunculi* (Kieff) forms galls on roots and leaves.

(b) *Microorganisms and viruses — Entyloma microsporum* (Ung.) Schroet. (smut) has been found on *R. repens* in British Columbia, while *Entyloma ficariae* (Cornu & Roze) Fisch. v. Waldh., *Peronospora ficariae* (Nees) Tul. (downy mildew) and *Pseudopeziza* sp. are described as having been found on *Ranunculus* spp. in British Columbia (Toms 1964; Ginns 1986). There are no records of fungal parasites in other Canadian provinces. Harper (1957) documented the following fungi invading *R. repens* in Europe. Of the basidiomycetes, the pycnia and aecia of the Uredinale *Puccinia magnusiana* (Körn) have been found on plants in the vicinity of *Phragmites communis* (Trin.). The pycnia and aecia of *Uromyces dactylidis* (Otth.) are found on plants of *R. repens* living near the alternate hosts: *Poa trivialis* L., and, in Norway, *Dactylis glomerata* L. and *Festuca rubra* L. The smut *Entyloma microsporum* (Ung.) Schroet. is common on leaves from July through October, while *Urocystis anemones* (Pers.) is occasional on leaf blades and petioles. Of the ascomycetes, *Fabraea rununculi* (Fr.) Karst.

is commonly found on leaves in late summer, especially in damp places, and *Erysiphe polygoni* (DC. ex Merat.) is found on leaves both in summer and winter. The phycomycete *Perenospora ficariae* (Nees) Tul. is common on leaves in April and May. *Didymaria didyma* (Ung.) Schroet., of the fungi imperfecti, is commonly found on leaves in summer and autumn, while *Ovularia decipiens* (Sacc.) is said to occur, but this has not been confirmed.

(c) *Higher plant parasites* — no record has been found.

ACKNOWLEDGMENTS

We are indebted to the curators of Canadian Herbaria across the country, who generously loaned their specimens and provided information on the distribution of *Ranunculus repens*. We also thank Paul Cavers, Suzanne Warwick and an anonymous reviewer for helpful comments on an earlier draft.

Alex, J. F., Cayouette, R. and G. A. Mulligan. 1980. Common and botanical names of weeds in Canada. Expert Committee on Weeds, Research Branch, Agriculture Canada, Ottawa, Canada. Publ. no. 1397. pp. 132.

Alex, J. F. and Switzer, C. M. 1976. Ontario weeds: Descriptions, illustrations and keys to their identification. Ontario Ministry of Agriculture and Food. Publ. no. 505. Toronto, Ont. pp. 208.

Auld, B. A. and Medd, R. W. 1987. Weeds. An illustrated botanical guide to the weeds of Australia. Inkata Press. pp. 212.

Bakker, J. P. 1987. Restoration of species-rich grassland after a period of fertilizer application. *In* J. Van. Andel, J. P. Bakker, and R. W. Snaydon, eds. Disturbance in grasslands. Dr. W. Junk. Dordrecht, The Netherlands. pp. 185–200.

Benson, L. 1941. North American Ranunculi. I. Bull. Torrey Bot. Club 68: 157–172.

Benson, L. 1948. A treatise on the North American Ranunculi. Am. Midl. Nat. 40: 1–261.

Benson, L. 1954. Supplement to a treatise on the North American Ranunculi. Am. Midl. Nat. 52(2): 328–369.

Boivin, B. 1967. Enumeration des Plantes du Canada. III. Herbidees, 1er partie: Digitatae: Dimerae, Liberae. Nat. Can. 93: 583–646.

Calder, J. A. and Taylor, R. L. 1968. Flora of the Queen Charlotte Islands. Part 1 Systematics of the Vascular Plants. Queen's Printer, Ottawa, Ont.

Canada Department of Agriculture. 1958. Chemical weed control for the Atlantic Provinces. Experimental Farm Service, Canada Department of Agriculture, Ottawa, Ont.

Chancellor, R. J. 1966. The identification of weed seedlings of farm and garden. Blackwell Scientific Publications; Oxford, U.K. pp. 45.

Chippendale, H. G. and Milton, W. E. J. 1934. On the viable seeds present in the soil beneath pastures. J. Ecol. 22: 508–531.

Clapham, A. R., Tutin, T. G. and Warburg, E. F. 1962. Flora of the British Isles. Cambridge University Press, Cambridge, U.K.

Clegg (Lovett Doust) L. 1978. The morphology of clonal growth and its relevance to the population dynamics of perennials. Ph.D. Thesis, University of Wales, U.K. pp. 150.

Coles, S. M. 1977. *Ranunculus repens* L. in Europe. Watsonia 11: 353–366.

Darlington, A. and Brown, A. L. 1975. One approach to ecology. Longmans London, U.K.

Dolgova, L. P. 1971. Aphids of the genus *Thecabius* (Homoptera, Aphidoidea) in the Altai District. Zoologicheskii Zhurnal 50(8): 1205–1213.

Dye, P. M. 1977. A study of *Phytomyza ranunculi* (Schrank) (Dipt., Agromyzidae) and its insect parasites. Entomologist's Monthly Magazine 112: 122–168.

Edward, P. D. 1971. Potato. Influences of the shoot on tuber formation. Field Crop Abstracts Record no. 0Q027-02435., and Rothamstead Experimental Station Report for 1970. Part 1, 98–99. Harpenden, Herts, U.K.

Federov, A. A. 1974. Chromosome numbers of flowering plants. Otto Koeltz Science Publishers, Koenigstein, Federal Republic of Germany.

Fernald, L. M. 1950. Gray's manual of botany. 8th ed. American Book Co., New York, N.Y.

Ferron, M. and Cayouette, R. 1971. Noms des mauvaise herbes du Quebec. Min. Agric. Quebec. pp. 113.

Frankton, C. and Mulligan, G. A. 1970. Weeds of Canada. Canada Department of Agriculture, Ottawa, Ont. Publ. 948. pp. 217.

Fryer, J. D. and Makepeace, R. J. 1977. Eds. Weed control handbook. Vol. 1: Principles including plant growth regulators. Blackwell Scientific Publications, Oxford, U.K.

Gilkey, H. H. 1957. Weeds of the Pacific Northwest. Oregon State College, Oregon. pp. 185.

Ginns, J. H. 1986. Compendium of plant disease and decay fungi in Canada, 1960–1980. Research Branch, Agriculture Canada, Ottawa, Ont. Publ. no. 1813.

Ginzo, H. D. and Lovell, P. H. 1973a. Aspects of the comparative physiology of *Ranunculus bulbosus* L. and *Ranunculus repens* L. II. Carbon dioxide assimilation and distribution of photosynthates. Ann. Bot. **37**: 765–776.

Ginzo, H. D. and Lovell, P. H. 1973b. Aspects of the comparative physiology of *Ranunculus bulbosus* L. and *Ranunculus repens* L. I. Response to nitrogen. Ann. Bot. **37**: 753–764.

Gleason, H. A. 1952. The New Britton and Brown Illustrated flora of the Northeastern United States and adjacent Canada. Macmillan, New York, N.Y.

Gleason, H. A. and Cronquist, A. 1963. Manual of vascular plants of Northeastern United States and adjacent Canada. Van Nostrand Co. New York, N.Y.

Godwin, H. 1975. The history of the British flora. Cambridge University Press, Cambridge, U.K. pp. 360.

Government of Ontario. 1986. Weed Control Act. Toronto, Ont. Publ. 3M/04/86.

Harper, J. L. 1957. Biological flora of the British Isles: *Ranunculus acris* L., *Ranunculus repens* L., *Ranunculus bulbosus* L. J. Ecol. **45**: 289–342.

Harper, J. L. 1958. Famous plants. 8. The buttercup. New Biology **26**: pp. 1–19.

Harper, J. L. 1977. Population biology of plants. Academic Press, London, U.K. pp. 892.

Harper, J. L. and Sagar, G. R. 1953. Some aspects of the ecology of buttercups in permanent grassland. Proc. Br. Weed Contr. Conf. **1**: 256–263.

Hatfield, A. W. 1970. How to enjoy your weeds. Frederick Muller, London, U.K.

Hickey, M. and King, C. 1988. 100 Families of flowering plants 2nd ed. Cambridge University Press, Cambridge, U.K.

Hill, T. A. 1977. The biology of weeds. The Institute of Biology. Studies in Biology no. 79. Edward Arnold, London, U.K.

Hitchcock, C. L., Cronquist, A., Ownbey, M. and Thompson, J. W. 1964. Vascular plants of the Pacific Northwest. Part 2: Salicaceae to Saxifragaceae. University of Washington Press, Seattle, Wash.

Holmgren, P. K., Keukan, W. and Schofield, E. 1981. Index herbariorum. Part I. The herbaria of the world. 7th ed. (Regnum Veg. 106). Oosthock, Schetema and Holkema, Utrecht, The Netherlands. 452 pp.

Hopkins, A., Wainwright, J., Murray, P. J., Bowling, P. J. and Webb, M. 1988. 1986 survey of upland grassland in England and Wales, U.K. Changes in age structure and botanical composition since 1970–72 in relation to grassland management and physical features. Grass For. Sci. **43**: 185–198.

Hughes, E.C. 1971. Chemical weed control guide 1972–73. British Columbia Department of Agriculture, Victoria, B.C.

Husson, G. P., Vilagines, R. and Delaveau, P. 1986. Research into antiviral properties of a few natural extracts. Annales Pharmaceutiques Francais **44**(1): 41–48.

Kolbe, W. 1987. Influence of various soil management measures on apple yield, fruit quality, and disease incidence in a long-term study at Hofchen (1961–86). Erwerbsobstbau **29**(2): 39–51.

Kuzmanov, B. and Kozuharov, S. 1969. Chromosome numbers of flowering plants in Bulgaria. 2. Izv. Bot. Inst. (Sofia) **19**: 109–115.

Larter, L. N. H. 1932. Chromosome variation and behavior in *Ranunculus* L. J. Genet. **XXVI**: 255–283.

Lavrenko, A. N. and Serditov, N. P. 1986. Chromosome numbers of some species of the *Ranunculaceae* family from the Komi ASSR. Botanicheskii Zhurnal **71**(8): 1143–1144.

Lawson, G. 1884. Revision of the Canadian Ranunculaceae. Proceedings and Transactions of the Royal Society of Canada, **II, Sect. IV**: 15–90.

Levesque, C. A., Rahe, J. E. and Eaves, D. M. 1987. Effects of glycophosphate on *Fusarium* spp.: its influence on root colonization of weeds, propagule density and crop emergence. Can. J. Microbiol. **33**(5): 354–360.

Lovett Doust, L. 1981a. Population dynamics and local specialization in a clonal perennial, *Ranunculus repens*. L. I. The dynamics of ramets in contrasting habitats. J. Ecol. **69**: 743–755.

Lovett Doust, L. 1981b. Population dynamics and local specialization in a clonal perennial, *Ranunculus repens* L. II. The dynamics of leaves and a reciprocal transplant-replant experiment. J. Ecol. **69**: 757–768.

Lovett Doust, L. 1981c. Intraclonal variation and competition in *Ranunculus repens*. New Phytol. **89**: 495–502.

Lovett Doust, L. 1987. Population dynamics and local specialization in a clonal perennial, *Ranunculus repens* L. III. Responses to light and nutrient supply. J. Ecol. **75**: 555–568.

Manitoba Department of Agriculture. 1987. Guide to chemical weed control. Winnipeg, Man. 32 pp.

Marchi, P. 1971. Chromosome numbers of the Italian flora. Plant Breeding Abstracts Record no. 0P043-00730. Inf. Bot. Ital. **3**: 82–94.

Matsuura, H. and Suto, T. 1935. Chromosome numbers. J. Fac. Sci. Hokkaido Univ. **5**(5): 33.

Meichenheimer, R. D. 1979. Relationships between shoot growth and changing phyllotaxy of *Ranunculus*. Am. J. Bot. **66**(5): 557–563.

Montgomery, F. H. 1964. Weeds of the Northern United States and Canada. Frederick Warne and Co. New York, N.Y.

Moore, R. J. 1973. Index to plant chromosome numbers 1967-1971. Oosthoek's Uitgeversmaatschappig B.V., Domstraat 5-13, Utrecht, Netherlands. International Bureau for Plant Taxonomy and Nomenclature. pp. 539.

Moore, R. J. 1977. Index to plant chromosome numbers 1973-1974. Bohn, Scheltema and Holkema, Utrecht, Netherlands. Published by the International Organization of Plant Biosystematists, Committee on Plant Chromosome Numbers. pp. 257.

Muenscher, W. C. 1955. Weeds. Comstock Publishing Association, Ithaca, N.Y.

Ontario Department of Agriculture. 1988. Guide to chemical weed control. Toronto, Ont. Publ. no. 75.

Peabody, D. V. and Swan, D. G. 1976. Washington State University Weed Control Handbook. Washington State University, Pullman, Wash. pp. 185.

Pervova, Yu. A. and Gershunina, L. M. 1976. Intraspecific variability: *Ranunculus repens* L. Byull. Moskova Ispyt. Prir Otd. Biol. **81**(4): 64-74.

Pervova, Yu. A., Vainagy, I. V. and Gershunina, L. M. 1971. On the polyploidy of *Ranunculus repens* L. Ukrainsk Bot. Zurn. **28**: 37-41.

Powell, D. F. 1981. The eradication campaign against the American serpentine leafminer, *Liriomyza trifolii*. Plant Pathol. (Lond.) **30**(4): 195-204.

Rath, N. 1987. Weed control in strawberries. The use of soil-acting residual herbicides. Proc. Meeting E.C. Experts' Group, Dublin, 12-14 June 1985: 107-113. A. A. Balkema, ed. Rotterdam, Netherlands.

Ray, A. 1886. Contribution to American botany. 1. A revision of the North American Ranunculi. Proc. Am. Acad. Arts Sci., **XIII** (New series): 363-379.

Roberts, H. A. and Boddrell, J. E. 1986. Seed survival and seedling emergence in some species of *Geranium, Ranunculus* and *Rumex*. Ann. Appl. Biol. **107**(2): 231-238.

Rousseau, C. 1968. Histoire, habitat et distribution de 220 plantes introduites au Quebec. Nat. Can. **95**: 49-169.

Salisbury, E. J. 1964. Weeds and aliens. Collins, London, U.K.

Sarukhén, J. K. 1971. Studies on plant demography. Ph.D. Thesis, University of Wales.

Sarukhén, J. K. 1974. Studies on plant demography: *Ranunculus repens* L., *R. bulbosus* L., and *R. acris* L. II. Reproductive strategies and seed population dynamics. J. Ecol. **62**: 151-177.

Sarukhén, J. K. and Harper, J. L. 1973. Studies on plant demography: *Ranunculus repens*. L., *R. bulbosus* L., and *R. acris* L. I. Population flux and survivorship. J. Ecol. **61**: 675-716.

Saskatchewan Department of Agriculture. 1966. Chemical weed control in vegetable crops and small fruits for Saskatchewan. Saskatoon, Sask.

Schipstra, K. 1957. Weeds as indicator plants for nutrition diseases. Tijdschr. Pflantzenziekten **63**(1): 15-18.

Schlotter, P., Heimbach, U. and Snel, M. 1986. Fluroxypyr, a new herbicidal compound for the control of economically important dicotyledonous weeds in grassland. Mitteilungen aus der Biologischen Bundesanstalt fur land und Forstwirtschaft, Berlin-Dahlem **232**: 341-342.

Scoggan, H. J. 1978. The flora of Canada. Part 3. Dicotyledoneae (Saururaceae to Violaceae). National Museums of Canada, Ottawa, Ont.

Scott, P. J. 1974. *In* International Organization of Plant Biosystematists chromosome number reports XLIII. Taxon **23**: 193-196.

Shearer, G. D. 1938. Some observations on the poisonous properties of buttercups. Vet. J. **94**: 22-32.

Smith, A. M., Hylton, C. M., Koch, K. and Woolhouse, H. W. 1986. Alcohol dehydrogenase activity in the roots of marsh plants in naturally waterlogged soils. Planta (Berl.) **1168**(1): 130-138.

Smith, K. G. V. and Harper, J. L. 1957. Further notes on insect visitors to *R. bulbosus, R. acris* and *R. repens*. J. Ecol. **45**: 342.

Soane, I. D. and Watkinson, A. R. 1979. Clonal variation in clones of *Ranunculus repens*. New Phytol. **82**: 557-573.

Sparke, C. J. and Williams, G. H. 1986. Sward changes following bracken clearance. *In* R. T. Smith and J. A. Taylor, eds. Bracken ecology, land use, and control technology. Parthenon Publishing Group, Carnforth, U.K. pp. 225-231.

Strykers, J. and van Himme, M. 1971. Red currants. Weed Abstracts Record no. 0W022-00085. Rijksuniversiteit, Ghent, Belgium.

Sutherland, W. J. 1990. The growth pattern of *Ranunculus repens* in patchy environments. J. Ecol. (in press).

Taylor, R. L. and Mulligan, G. A. 1968. Flora of the Queen Charlotte Islands. Part 2: Cytological aspects of the vascular plants. Queen's Printer, Ottawa, Ont.

Toms, H. N. W. 1964. Canadian plant disease survey **44**: 143-225.

Tjon Sie Fat, L. 1979. Contribution to the knowledge of cyanogenisis in angiosperms 14. Cyanogenisis in *Ranunculaceae*. Proc. K. Ned. Akad. Wet. Ser. C Biol. Med. Sci. **82**(2): 197-210.

Triebel, U. 1986. Experiences with Tramat for selective grass weed control in grassland. Bayerisches Landwirtschaftliches Jahrbuch **63**(7): 851–855.

Turner, N. J. 1984. Counter-irritant and other uses of plants in the *Ranunculaceae* by native peoples in British Columbia and neighbouring areas. J. Ethnopharmacol. **11**(2): 181–202.

Tutin, T. G., Heywood, V. H., Burges, N. A., Valentine, D. H., Walters, S. M. and Webb, D. A. 1964. Flora Europaea, Vol. 1. University Press, Cambridge, U.K.

Van den Berg, B. M., Bakker, J. P. and Pegtel, D. M. 1985. Phenotypic responses of *Ranunculus repens* populations in grasslands subjected to different mowing regimes. Acta Botanica Neerlandica **34**(3): 283–292.

Whitehead, D. C., Dibb, H. and Hartley, R. D. 1982. Phenolic compounds in soil as influenced by the growth of different plant species. J. Appl. Ecol. **19**(2): 579–588.

Williams, E. D. 1983. Germinability and enforced dormancy in seeds of species from indigenous grassland. Ann. Appl. Biol. **102**(3): 557–566.

Williams, E. D. 1984. Changes during 3 yr in the size and composition of the seed bank beneath a long-term pasture as influenced by defoliation and fertilizer regime. J. Appl. Ecol. **21**: 603–615.

The biology of Canadian weeds. 96. *Senecio jacobaea* L.

John F. Bain

Department of Biological Sciences, University of Lethbridge, Lethbridge, Alberta, Canada T1K 3M4. Received 11 May 1990, accepted 29 Aug. 1991.

Bain, J. F. 1991. **The biology of Canadian weeds. 96.** *Senecio jacobaea* L. Can. J. Plant Sci. **71**: 127–140. *Senecio jacobaea* L. (tansy ragwort) is a roadside and pasture weed which was introduced into Canada in the 1850s. It is established in cool, wet areas, most commonly on the east and west coasts. The species is important economically because the presence of pyrrolizidine alkaloids in the foliage makes it toxic and the poisoning of livestock has resulted. Individuals produce dimorphic achenes which possess different dormancy and dispersal characters and are therefore able to establish in a wider range of habitats. Vegetative reproduction is common especially after damage to the plant. Control of the weed is achieved either through the application of hormone-like herbicides or by biological means. The establishment of the biological control agent, cinnabar moth (*Tyria jacobaeae* L.), in populations has resulted in defoliation of individuals but has not resulted in effective control of the weed, except in eastern Canada.

Key words: Tansy ragwort, *Senecio jacobaea*, biological control, pyrrolizidine alkaloids

Bain, J. F. 1991. **Biologie des mauvaises herbes du Canada. 96.** *Senecio jacobaea* L. Can. J. Plant Sci. **71**: 127–140. *Senecio jacobaea* L. (séneçon jacobée) est une mauvaise herbe qui pousse le long des routes et dans les pâturages, et qui a été introduite au Canada au cours des années 1850. Elle s'établit dans les régions fraîches et humides, le plus souvent le long des côtes est et ouest. Cette espèce est importante sur le plant économique, car la présence des alcaloïdes de la pyrrolizidine dans son feuillage la rend toxique et a causé l'intoxication du bétail. Les plants individuels produisent des akènes dimorphes dont les caractéristiques de dispersion et de dormance diffèrent; ils peuvent donc s'établir dans un plus vaste éventail d'habitats. La reproduction végétative est fréquente surtout après que la plante a été endommagée. La lutte contre cette mauvaise herbe se fait par l'application d'herbicides de type hormonal ou par des moyens biologiques. L'établissement d'un agent de lutte biologique, le tyria (*Tyria jacobaea* L.), dans les populations a provoqué la défoliation des plants individuels, mais n'a pas permis de lutter efficacement contre la mauvaise herbe, sauf dans l'est du Canada.

Mots clés: Séneçon jacobée, *Senecio jacobaea*, lutte biologique, alcaloïdes de la pyrrolizidine

1. Name

Senecio jacobaea L. — **tansy ragwort**, stinking willy, staggerwort, séneçon jacobée, fleur de St. Jacques, herbe de St. Jacques, jacobée, séneçon. Ferron et Cayouette 1975; Alex et al. 1980; Frankton and Mulligan 1987) Compositae, Asteraceae, composite family, composées.

2. Description and Account of Variation

Senecio jacobaea is a herbaceous biennial, winter annual or short-lived perennial,

Can. J. Plant Sci. 71: 127–140 (Jan. 1991)

2–8(12) dm tall, usually lightly tomentose but glabrate with age, arising from a poorly developed to evident tap root. Stems are strict, erect, arising singly or in clusters from an erect caudex, branching only in the inflorescence. Leaves are alternate, becoming reduced in size upward, broadly ovate to ovate, deeply bi- or tripinnatifid, 7–20 cm long, 2–6 cm wide. Lower leaves are often petiolate and early deciduous, middle and upper leaves subsessile and weakly clasping. Inflorescence (capitulescence) is broadly corymbiform and cymose with 20–60 heads.

Heads are usually radiate, disc 7–10 mm wide; involucral bracts 13, dark tipped, 3–4 mm long. Ray florets are 13, female; ligule yellow, 8–12 mm long. Disc florets numerous, perfect; tube yellow, 5–7 mm long. Achenes of ray florets are glabrous, those of disc florets pubescent along prominent ribs.

Figure 1 illustrates *S. jacobaea* at various stages of growth.

Chromosome numbers of $2n=40$ have been commonly reported from European populations and tetraploids have been detected in Czechoslovakia (Bolkhovshikh et al. 1969; Moore 1973). Bocher and Larsen (1955) reported $2n=32$ from Irish material. Ornduff et al. (1963) reported $2n=40$ from California populations. In Canada, Mulligan (1959) reported $2n=40$ ($n=20$) from Abbotsford, British Columbia. Recent counts from populations of the same area were also $2n=40$ (Bain, unpubl. data).

Senecio jacobaea is easily separable from other *Senecio* species in North America based on its comparatively large size and prominently dissected leaves. It resembles *S. eremophilus* Richards most closely but can be separated by the pattern of leaf dissection; the leaves of *S. eremophilus* taper to a point and are once-parted while those of *S. jacobaea* are rounded and 2–3 parted (Douglas 1982; Frankton and Mulligan 1987). *Senecio jacobaea* also resembles tansy (*Tanacetum vulgare* L.) especially in overall size and leaf characters. The two can be separated easily since tansy has discoid heads, phyllaries with dark margins and is strongly aromatic.

Various infraspecific taxa have been described from Europe (see Kadereit and Sell (1986) for a summary of synonymy), but none was recognized in Flora Europaea (Tutin et al. 1976). Most recently, Kadereit and Sell (1986) recognized the discoid form of *S. jacobaea* as a distinct subspecies, ssp. *dunensis* (Dumort.) Kadereit & Sell and within ssp. *jacobaea* separated those individuals with short internodes and ligules as var. *condensatus* Druce. No infraspecific taxa have been recognized in North America (Fernald 1950; Hitchcock et al. 1969; Scoggan 1979).

3. Economic Importance

(a) *Detrimental* — In North America *Senecio jacobaea* is a problem weed in pastures on both the east and west coasts, particularly in the maritime provinces and in Oregon. In Prince Edward Island, tansy ragwort has been estimated to have reduced pasture yields by as much as 50% (Harris et al. 1971). In Oregon, losses associated with tansy ragwort infestations have been estimated to be $5 million annually (Isaacson and Ehrensing 1977).

Senecio jacobaea contains pyrrolizidine alkaloids which are toxic to cattle, deer, horses and goats (Goeger et al. 1981; Giles 1983; Wardle 1987). Sheep appear to be less affected (Wardle 1987). The alkaloids cause degradation of liver function, usually with lethal results. Species susceptibility has been shown to be correlated with the rate of production by the animal of metabolic pyrroles, a derivative of pyrrolizidine alkaloids (Shull et al. 1976). Certain pyrrolizidine alkaloids have been shown to be carcinogenic, mutagenic and teratogenic (Green and Christie 1961; Bull et al. 1968; White et al. 1983). In rats, high protein diets have been shown to confer some level of protection from ragwort toxicity (Miranda et al. 1982).

In addition to direct toxicity, pyrrolizidine alkaloids have other detrimental effects. Consumption of *Senecio jacobaea* rapidly reduces butterfat production in cattle (Miller 1936). The alkaloids are present in milk produced by cattle that have ingested them but the detrimental effects on sucking calves have not been conclusively demonstrated (reviewed by Watt (1987)). The alkaloids also taint honey produced by bees that have gathered ragwort pollen such that it is usually too bitter and off-colour to market (Deinzer et al. 1977).

Although cattle do not generally graze tansy ragwort directly, the alkaloids are still toxic in silage so the plant's presence in hay often results in the abandonment of the crop. The sublethal effects of the alkaloids are not well documented; however, some reduction in yield from cattle or sheep that have ingested them may be expected (Forbes 1985).

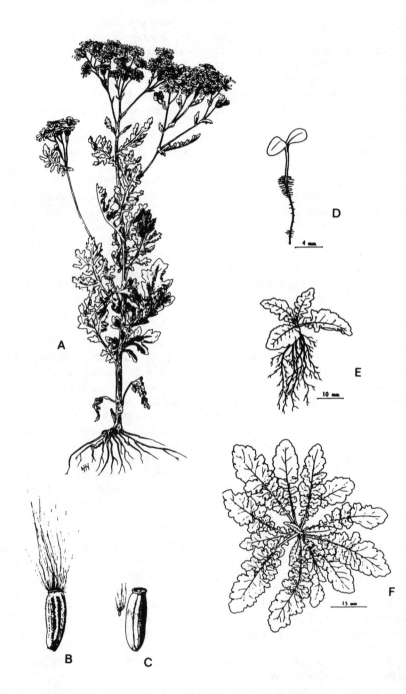

Fig. 1. *Senecio jacobaea.* A, whole plant; B, achene of disc floret; C, achene of ray floret with pappus removed; D, first stage seedling; E, second stage seedling; F, rosette. (A-C from Frankton and Mulligan (1987), D-F from Cameron (1935).)

(b) *Beneficial* — Sharrow and Mosher (1982) suggested that tansy ragwort is a good feed for sheep during summer months and noted that it exceeds 1975 U.S. National Research Council nutrient requirements for sheep for both protein and digestibility.

Ernst and Leloup (1987) in studies conducted in north Holland found that *S. jacobaea* was a good biomonitor of the atmospheric pollutants iron, manganese and zinc and a particularly good monitor of manganese in aerial fallout.

(c) *Legislation* — In the Canada Seeds Act (Anonymous 1986a), *S. jacobaea* is listed as a prohibited noxious weed (Class 1). It is also listed under the Weed Control Act of B.C. (Anonymous 1986b) (regional district of central Fraser Valley, Dewdney-Alouette, Fraser-Cheam, Cowichan Valley, Nanaimo, Alberni-Clayoquot and Comox-Strathcona) as a noxious weed. In Nova Scotia *S. jacobaea* is listed as a Class 1 noxious weed in the regulations to the Weed Control Act (Anonymous 1977).

4. Geographical Distribution

Senecio jacobaea is native to Europe, Asia and Siberia, extending north as far as 62°30′ (Sordmore, Norway) and south into Romania, Hungary and Bulgaria (Harper and Wood 1957). It is considered to be rare in both the extreme north and extreme south of Europe (Tutin et al. 1976). It has been introduced into Australia, New Zealand, South Africa, South America and North America (Harper and Wood 1957; Harris et al. 1971). In North America it occurs on both coasts, in the east from Newfoundland to New England and in the west from southern British Columbia to northern California. It also occurs sporadically across North America (Barkley 1978). In Canada, *S. jacobaea* has been collected in Nova Scotia, New Brunswick, Prince Edward Island, Newfoundland and British Columbia with a few collections from Quebec and Ontario, where repeated collections have been made in the Guelph region (Wellington Co.) (Fig. 2).

5. Habitat

(a) *Climatic requirements* — Although Harper and Wood (1957) describe *S. jacobaea* as

being widely tolerant, and its status as a weed would support this, there appear to be some restrictions, within the broad limits of the temperate regions, on where the plant will grow. In general *S. jacobaea* prefers mesic habitats. In Australia *S. jacobaea* is found in high rainfall areas (Schmidl 1972), while in New Zealand it is found where rainfall exceeds 870 mm yr^{-1} and population density is positively correlated with July-September rainfall (Wardle 1987). In North America, *S. jacobaea* is established in areas with cool, wet, cloudy weather (Barkley 1978).

(b) *Substratum* — *Senecio jacobaea* occurs on many different soil types, but usually on lighter, well-drained soils such as Podzolic grey loams or grey sands. It is generally absent where the water table is high or where the soil is too acidic (Harper and Wood 1957; Harris et al. 1971; Schmidl 1972; Meijden 1974).

(c) *Communities in which the species occurs* — *Sencecio jacobaea* occurs naturally in sand dune communities in Europe (Meijden 1974) as well as both woodland and grassland communities. Harper and Wood (1957) have summarized the community associations in the U.K. In dune communities it is often associated with grasses such as *Agrostis stolonifera* L. and *A. tenuis* Sibith. and forbs including *Galium aparine* L., *G. verum* L. and *Cirsium arvense* (L.) Scop. In woodland communities it is found in both juniper and hawthorne successional stages of beech woods, while in grassland communities *S. jacobaea* is usually associated with *Agrostis tenuis*, *Achillea millefolium* L., *Cirsium vulgare* (Savi) Tenore, *Prunella vulgaris* L., *Ranunculus repens. L.*, *Holcus lanatus* L., and *Cerastium vulgatum* L. (Harper 1958). In Oregon, McEvoy (1984a) lists *Agrostis alba* L., *Festuca arundinacea* Schreb., *Hypericum perforatum* L., and *Cirsium arvense* as associated species. In Canada, *S. jacobaea* is generally found in pastures and wasteplaces so associated species include common weeds such as *Cirsium arvense*, *Taraxacum officinale* Weber, *Leontodon autumnalis* L., *Polygonum* spp., *Hypericum perforatum* L., *Agropyron repens* (L.) Beauv., *Linaria vulgaris* Mill., *Achillea millefolium* L., *Ranunculus* spp.,

Fig. 2. Distribution of *Senecio jacobaea* L. in Canada. (Based on data from herbarium specimens at ACAD, CAN, DAO, NFLD, UBC, UNB, V; abbreviations follow Holmgren et al. (1981).)

Solidago spp., *Plantago* spp., *Equisetum arvense* L., *Tanacetum vulgare* L., *Pteridium aquilinum* (L.) Kuhn, *Poa annua* L., *Rubus* spp. and *Dactylis glomerata* L. (pers. obs. and D. Ralph, K. McCully, J. Thomson, pers. commun.).

6. History
Senecio jacobaea is thought to have been introduced into Canada in the 1850s around Pictou, Nova Scotia (Harris et al. 1971), probably in ship's ballast. In Prince Edward Island the first record is from Tignish in 1888 and by 1900 it was common in Queens and northeast Kings Counties (Catling et al. 1985). In New Brunswick early collections (1891) are from St. John. In Quebec, ragwort was first collected in 1904 in the York region. Collections from Ontario are sporadic but date back to 1861 (Belleville) and 1903 (Niagara Falls). The introduction of *S. jacobaea* to B.C. presumably occurred around 1913 in the Nanaimo region and more recently on the mainland, in the Fraser valley around Abbotsford (Harris et al. 1971).

7. Growth and Development

(a) *Morphology* — In addition to the possession of toxic alkaloids which clearly aid in the plant's success in invading and surviving in pastureland, *S. jacobaea* has reproductive characters which contribute to its success as a weed. These include the high rate of seed production and the possession of two different achene types, each apparently adapted for a different habitat and mode of dispersal (McEvoy 1984b). In addition, the regenerative capacity of both the root and the caudex permits vegetative reproduction to occur, especially in response to disturbance. Cairns (1938) described the root of *S. jacobaea* as lacking a true endodermis and as having a pericyclic phellogen which readily gives rise to buds. Both sexual and vegetative reproduction characteristics are described in detail under separate headings (8b and 8d respectively) below.

(b) *Perennation* — *Senecio jacobaea* is usually considered to be a biennial, overwintering either as seeds or as rosettes, but it is also capable of perennating from the rootstock or caudex and so may behave as a true perennial (Forbes 1977). Such variation in life history has also been reported from Canadian populations (Harris et al. 1978).

(c) *Physiological data* — Harris et al. (1978), based on studies from Prince Edward Island and British Columbia, reported that the accumulation of carbohydrate reserves was important for the winter survival of the rosette. They determined that, after defoliation by cinnabar moth, a minimum of 70 d was required for replenishment of reserves and survival. Cox and McEvoy (1983), based on studies conducted in Oregon, reported that increased water availability was an important factor in promoting recovery after defoliation.

Various secondary metabolites, besides pyrrolizidine alkaloids, have been isolated and identified. Ferry (1977) identified the flavonoid quercetin and three quercetin glycosides from extracts of leaf tissue. Lam and Drake (1973) isolated several polyacetylene compounds, including cosmene, from flower tissue.

(d) *Phenology* — Germination of seed generally occurs in the late summer or autumn with rosettes developing the following spring. Seed possess no innate dormancy so germinate in response to prevailing conditions at time of maturity (see Section 8c below). Germination is normally rapid with maximum germination occurring at 18 and 21 d after flowering for peripheral and central achenes respectively (Baker-Kratz and Maguire 1984). In the Victoria region of Australia, seeds germinating in autumn remain as seedlings or develop to the small rosette stage through the winter and then increase rosette size the following spring (Schmidl 1972). Flowering is controlled, at least in part, by the achievement of a minimum plant or rosette size with the probability of flowering increasing with size (Meigden and Waals-Kooi 1979). Under optimal conditions rosettes may grow up to 30 cm diameter in the first season (Harper 1958). Flowering usually occurs during the second year, from June to mid-November in U.K. (Harper and Wood 1957), and seed dispersal occurs from August through to December. In Canada flowering occurs in late July and August (Frankton and Mulligan (1987) and pers. obs.) with seed dispersal occurring throughout the fall. Some plants may regenerate after flowering, especially in response to disturbance (Schmidl 1972; Islam and Crawley 1983).

(e) *Mycorrhiza* — Vesicular-arbuscular mycorrhizal associations have been reported from both European and U.K. populations (Hawker et al. 1957; Harley and Harley 1987).

8. Reproduction

(a) *Floral biology* — The flowering head opens when the expanding disc florets exert pressure on the involucral bracts. The ray florets emerge secondarily. Expansion and unrolling of ray florets is rapid, taking less than 24 h, and the stigmas of the ray florets separate and are receptive as soon as the flower is fully expanded. Disc florets open subsequently. The flower is visited by numerous kinds of insects (see Table 5 in

Harper and Wood (1957)), mainly members of Hymenoptera and Diptera. The flowers produce both nectar and a faint odour, and pollen presentation occurs throughout the day with a peak (in the U.K.) between 10:00 and 12:00 h (Harper and Wood 1957). Data on the degree of self compatibility are lacking.

(b) *Seed production and dispersal* — Wardle (1987) states that there is much variability among localities with regard to number of capitula and seeds (achenes) produced per plant. Poole and Cairns (1940) reported that, at their study site in New Zealand, an average of 1000–2500 capitula/plant were produced per season and that each capitulum contained 55 seeds (achenes), while in the U.K., Cameron (1935) found that individual plants produced between 68 and 2489 capitula and 70 seeds per capitulum. Thompson (1980) in New Zealand, found that seed production reached 15–25000 seeds m^{-2} in peak years. Meijden and Waals-Kooi (1979) found that a delay in flowering often resulted in increased seed production. Although *S. jacobaea* appears to be well adapted for wind dispersal, Wardle (1987) describes it as a poor wind disperser. Poole and Cairns (1940) estimated that only 0.5% of the seeds produced were actually wind borne. They found that 60% of the seeds released from the head travelled only a few metres downwind. Schmidl (1972) reported that seeds could be dispersed via water or spread by livestock, either through ingestion or by being carried in the mud adhering to the hooves. Salisbury (1961) reported the occurrence of viable seed in bird droppings.

(c) *Viability of seeds and germination* — Viability of *S. jacobaea* seed is high. In Australia, Schmidl (1972) obtained germination rates of between 80 and 90% when seeds were subjected to alternating 12 h day/night periods with day/night temperatures of 30°/25°C. Somewhat lower values (60%) were obtained for seeds produced by late flowering individuals. In Washington, Baker-Kratz and Maguire (1984) obtained similar values overall and found that seeds produced on lower branches were on average heavier

and had higher germination rates. Crawley and Nachapong (1985), based on studies conducted in the U.K., found a slight reduction in germination rate in seeds produced by secondary or regrowth shoots when compared with primary shoots. Wardle and Rahman (1987) found that achenes with the flower parts either abscised or removed were more viable than those where the perianth was still attached.

Seeds of *S. jacobaea* do not show evidence of innate dormancy (Baker-Kratz and Maguire 1984), but germination may be inhibited by vegetation cover in the field and dormancy may be induced by frost or drought (Meijden and Waals-Kooi 1979) or by burial (Thompson and Makepeace 1983). Temperatures between 5 and 30°C were found to be most conducive to germination (Meijden and Waals-Kooi 1979). Sheldon (1974), in the U.K., demonstrated that germination patterns were strongly correlated with variations in humidity at the soil surface, where desiccation of the soil inhibits germination. Dormancy induced by burial may be broken by a disturbance which brings seeds closer to the soil surface. Meijden and Waals-Kooi (1979) and Poole and Cairns (1940) both recorded higher germination rates among seeds buried 1–2 cm below the surface when compared with both those buried deeper and those on the soil surface. Seeds have been shown to have a relatively high viability percentage (24%) after 6 yr of burial (Thompson and Makepeace 1983).

Senecio jacobaea produces dimorphic achenes (Green 1937; McEvoy 1984b) and the adaptive significance of this character has been studied in detail by McEvoy (1984b) and McEvoy and Cox (1987). The central disc achenes retain their pappus, possess trichomes along the angles and are lighter and more numerous than the ligulate or ray achenes which lack any form of appendage or dispersal structure at maturity. In addition McEvoy (1984b) found that, under similar conditions (20°C and 12 h light/dark), ray achenes were slower to germinate than disc achenes and attributed the timing difference to the increased thickness of the pericarp in ray achenes. He suggested that *S. jacobaea* employs two separate strategies for colonization: open disturbed habitats over a wide area, but including the home site, are colonized by disc achenes while nearby, closed habitats may eventually be colonized by ray achenes. McEvoy and Cox (1987) studied dispersal patterns of the achene types on four sites, comparing inland and coastal sites using both a mown and an unmown grid. They found that disc achenes dispersed farther than ray achenes on only one site, the inland, mown site. Disc achenes dispersed earlier than ray achenes on all four sites. On three of the four grids early dispersed disc achenes travelled farther than late dispersed ones. The authors postulated that under conditions of dry summer and wet autumn early dispersal of disc achenes should increase dispersal distances by maximizing the effective functioning of the pappus as a dispersal aid.

(d) *Vegetative reproduction* — Regeneration of shoots can occur from crown buds, excised root fragments and from intact roots (Wardle 1987). Schmidl (1972) reported that over 35% of the plants studied over a 1.5-yr period formed multiple crowns. Disturbance or injury promotes vegetative propagation. Roots of rosettes form buds more readily than those of flowering plants (Poole and Cairns 1940).

9. Hybrids
Four hybrids involving *S. jacobaea* are listed by Benoit et al. (1975) as possibly occurring in the United Kingdom. They are:

Senecio aquaticus Hill × *S. jacobaea* L. (=*S.* × *ostenfeldii* Druce) is partially fertile and sometimes forms intergrading populations with the two parental species. The most morphologically obvious intermediates are also highly sterile. Meijden (1976) reported a probable hybrid of the above species from the island of Terschelling.

Senecio cineraria DC. × *S. jacobaea* (=*S.* × *albescens* Burbidge & Colgan.) is a partially fertile hybrid which resembles *S. jacobaea* in being biennial with erect stems and a leafy inflorescence but has leaves which are both more entire and more tomentose than

S. jacobaea. The level of sterility appears to vary and the existence of stable populations over 70 yr old suggests that interbreeding among hybrids is possible.

Senecio erucifolius L. × *S. jacobaea* (=*S.* × *liechtensteinensis* Murr.), *S. jacobaea* ×*S. squalidus* L., and *S. jacobaea* × *S. vulgaris* L. have been reported but according to Benoit et al. (1975) examination of the voucher specimens does not support the claim that they are hybrids.

A hybrid between *S. jacobaea* and *S. alpinus* (=*S.* × *reisachii*) has also been reported from Tyrol (Harper and Wood 1957). No hybrids have been reported from North America.

10. Population Dynamics
The plants usually function as biennials and therefore produce seed in the second year of growth. However, some variability has been observed in the latter trait. Schmidl (1972) reported, from Australian studies, that out of a sample of 176 plants, 2% were annuals, 45% biennials and 39% perennials. Forbes (1977) reported 8% annuals, 39% biennials and 53% perennials from a study in Aberdeenshire, U.K. Mechanical damage can postpone flowering (Harper and Wood 1957) and in some cases ragwort can continue to grow after flowering (Schmidl 1972; Forbes 1977; Islam and Crawley 1983).

Achene germination and seeding establishment in tansy ragwort populations are both variable. In the Netherlands, Meijden and Waals-Kooi (1979) observed that, during the same season, the percent germination of achenes produced by an individual in the field varied between less than 1 and 10% and that survival of seedlings varied with habitat (from 2.2 to 8% in one season). Establishment was found to be greatly affected by the amount of pasture cover. Cameron (1935), in the United Kingdom, reported seedling numbers of 212 800, 2 152 800 and 5 704 750 per hectare on overgrazed pasture, hard exposed soil and open soil, respectively. No seedlings occurred in continuous pasture plots. Similar results were reported by Meijden and Waals-Kooi (1979) who found that the nature of surrounding vegetation affected seedling survival. Fewer rosettes survived in grassy areas than in cleared or woodland areas. The highest rates of survival and establishment were in cleared areas of grassland. They concluded that open habitats (soil and canopy) were most favourable to establishment.

Although ragwort does not easily become established in closed sward pasture, once established it is an effective competitor at the rosette stage where it is able to cover and suppress neighbouring short plants such as grasses and clover (Harper 1958). The death of the rosette then provides an open site in the pasture where germination of ragwort seeds is favoured. Seedling establishment was found to be 4.3× higher in openings left by recently deceased ragwort plants than in immediately surrounding vegetated areas (McEvoy 1984a). Wardle (1987) speculates that alkaloids such as jacobine may have allelopathic effects but no studies have been conducted demonstrating such properties.

Wardle (1987) cited such characters as small seeds with no innate dormancy, rapid vegetative growth, poor competitive ability, and biennial habit as evidence that ragwort is an early successional species or r-strategist.

Population densities reported by Harris (1974) from grazed pastures in Prince Edward Island were 63.8 plants m^{-2} for grazed pastures and 8.7 plants m^{-2} for ungrazed pastures in 1972 and around 75 plants m^{-2} in British Columbia in 1973. In Prince Edward Island the density levels were reduced by the release of the cinnabar moth as a biological control agent (see Section 13c for greater detail).

11. Response to Herbicides and Other Chemicals

Senecio jacobaea is best controlled by applications of hormone-like herbicides applied during the seedling or early rosette stages. In Canada, Black (1976) found that 2,4-D applied at a rate of 2.2 kg ha^{-1} was more effective than lower rates and that 2,4-D was more effective than 2,4-DB and MCP. Thompson and Saunders (1984) found similar results but Coles (1967) and Thompson (1974,

1977) found picloram to be superior to 2,4-D. Forbes (1978) found 2,4-D, MCPA, and 2,4,5-T to be equally and highly effective. Thompson (1983) stated that glyphosate was superior in controlling flowering plants but Wardle (1987) found that subterranean portions may survive in glyphosate-treated plants. Because the herbicides were not found to be equally effective at all stages of plant growth, repeated treatments (spring and fall) were recommended for optimum control (Black 1976).

Two problems associated with the application of the above herbicides are the damage caused to clover by the herbicide and the increased palatability of the weed to livestock just after spraying. Irvine et al. (1977) reported that water soluble carbohydrate concentration (a measure of palatability) in *S. jacobaea* increased for a period of 14 d after spraying with 2,4-D so that if spring application of 2,4-D is made, then livestock must be excluded from the pasture for a period of at least 3–4 wk. To minimize damage to clover crops Forbes (1985) recommended delaying the autumn application of herbicide until after clover dieback.

12. Response to Other Human Manipulations

Senecio jacobaea does not respond well to mechanical control. Since vegetative reproduction is stimuluated by damage to the plant, mowing generally results in an increase in infestation levels. However flame throwers were found to be very effective in killing reproductive plants and destroying the viability of the attached seed (Wardle 1987).

Management techniques designed to promote a dense continuous sward in pastureland would appear to be an effective method of control as *S. jacobaea* does not readily establish from seed on closed sites and individuals are poor competitors during establishment (Thompson 1980). The addition of superphosphate or urea was found to decrease ragwort densities in pasture (Thompson and Saunders 1986).

13. Response to Parasites
(a) *Insects and other nondomestic animals* — Harris et al. (1971) listed the most common

insects associated with *S. jacobaea* in Canada noting that all are polyphagous and that none should interfere with the establishment of insects with the potential to act as biological control agents.

Of the numerous insects found associated with *S. jacobaea* in its natural habitat, three have been studied and used as biological control agents in attempts to control the weed (Watt 1987). These include the ragwort seed fly (*Pegohylemia seneciaella* Meade), the flea beetle (*Longitarsus jacobaeae* Waterhouse) and the cinnabar moth (*Tyria jacobaeae* L.). The ragwort seed fly was first introduced into New Zealand in 1928 but was not effective. It is now established in California and Oregon where, although it attacks the plants, it does not reduce population sizes. Wardle (1987) lists another seed fly (*Pegohylemia jacobaeae* Hardy), introduced as a biological control agent, as being established in New Zealand.

The flea beetle has become established in British Columbia, California and Australia. During the larval stage the insect damages ragwort by defoliation and during the adult stage either by partially decapitating the plants thus causing floral abortion (Binns 1976) or by attacking the roots of the plants (Frick 1970). When released with the cinnabar moth, a synergistic effect leading to almost complete control has been reported (Hawkes 1981), but high levels of control are not always observed (Watt 1987). The cinnabar moth was introduced in Australia in the 1950s and, once established, was successful in causing defoliation of tansy ragwort plants. Since then numerous successful establishments have been made around the world. The cinnabar moth decreases the number of flowering individuals and so reduces biomass and seed production within a population but in general the total number of plants in a sward is unaffected (Harris 1974; Dempster and Lakhani 1979; Lakhani and Dempster 1981) so that the population persists. Prins et al. (1989) have shown that, in *S. jacobaea*, the regrowth response to defoliation is partly the result of an increase in the net assimilation rate and partly the result of redistribution of dry matter from below ground tissue. In Canada field survival of the cinnabar moth was first achieved in 1963. It is now established in Nova Scotia, New Brunswick, Prince Edward Island and British Columbia. The interactions between ragwort and cinnabar moth populations have been studied extensively, both in the United Kingdom (Dempster 1971; Dempster and Lakhani 1979; Lakhani and Dempster 1981; Crawley and Gillman 1989) and in North America (Myers and Campbell 1976; Myers 1980; Myers and Post 1981). Based on a 4- to 6-yr study of nine North American sites, Myers (1980) concluded that, in the cinnabar moth-ragwort system, the nature of the plant population controlled the nature of the insect population rather than the reverse. Introduction of the cinnabar moth as a biological control agent was observed to have an initial reducing effect upon the ragwort population size but once a new equilibrium density was reached the moth had little subsequent effect. In a related study, Myers and Post (1981) found that food plants (ragwort) with higher nitrogen levels increased larval survival and moth fecundity leading to over exploitation of the food supply and greater population fluctuations. The implication for biological control is that fertilization may lead to better control of ragwort but at present data are incomplete. Crawley and Gillman (1989) found no important differences in the population dynamics of the cinnibar moth living in the more closed habitat of a mesic grassland when compared with the results of the above studies, conducted in more open habitats. With respect to the plant, they found that greater interspecific competition limited seedling recruitment. The plant-insect interaction was most affected by autumn and spring rainfall.

(b) *Microorganisms and viruses* — Harper and Wood (1957) provided a list of fungi associated with *S. jacobaea* and Harper (1958) listed four — *Puccinia expansa* Link, *P. dioicae* Magn., *Bremia lactucae* Regel. and *Sphaerotheca humuli* (DC) Burr. var. *fuliginea* (Schlecht.) Salm. as common pathogens. The suitability of *P. expansa* as a biocontrol agent was investigated by Alber et al.

(1985, 1986) who found, under glasshouse conditions, that *P. expansa* reduced dry weight of *S. jacobaea* by 60% after six innoculations at 2-wk intervals, and that all collections of *S. jacobaea* and another problem weed *S. alpinus* were severely attacked while other related taxa were slightly or not at all affected. They concluded that *P. expansa* was specific enough to be used as a biocontrol agent of the two species. Conners (1967) lists *Septoria senecionis* West. as occurring on ragwort in Nova Scotia and Farr et al. (1989) list *Leptosphaeria ogiliviensis* (Berke. & Broome) Ces & De Not as occurring in Oregon.

ACKNOWLEDGMENTS
The assistance of C. Crompton, K. McCully, D. Ralph, and J. P. Thomson in providing information, including the status of provincial and federal legislation, is gratefully acknowledged. The assistance and cooperation of the curators of ACAD, CAN, DAO, NFLD, UBC, UNB, V in providing loans of or access to herbarium specimens is also gratefully acknowledged.

Alber, G., Defago, G., Kern, H. and Sedler, L. 1984. Damage to *Senecio jacobaea* by the rust fungus *Puccinia expansa*. Proc. 6th Intl. Symp. of Biological control of weeds.

Alber, G., Defago, G., Kern, H. and Sedler, L. 1986. Host range of *Puccinia expansa* Link (=*P. glomerata* Grev.), a possible fungal biocontrol agent against *senecio* weeds. Weed Res. 26: 69–74.

Alex, J. F., Cayouette, R. and Mulligan, G. A. 1980. Common and botanical names of weeds in Canada. Agriculture Canada, Ottawa, ON. Publ. 1397, 132 pp.

Anonymous. 1977. Regulations to the Weed Control Act 1968. Publ. No. 10. Nova Scotia Department of Agriculture and Marketing, Halifax, NS.

Anonymous. 1986a. Canada Seeds Act. Canada Gazette Pt. II Vol. 120 no. 17. p. 3383.

Anonymous 1986b. Regulations to the Weed Control Act of British Columbia. Weed control Regulation 66/85.

Baker-Kratz, A. L. and Maguire, J. D. 1984. Germination and dry-matter accumulation in dimorphic achenes of tansy ragwort (*Senecio jacobaea*). Weed Sci. 32: 539–545.

Barkley, T. M. 1978. *Senecio*. Pages 50–139 in C. T. Rogerson, ed. North American Flora series II pt. 10. New York Botanical Garden, New York, NY.

Benoit, P. M., Crisp, P. C. and Jones, B. M. G. 1975. *Senecio. In* C. A. Stace ed. Hybridization and the flora of the British Isles. Academic Press, London, U.K.

Binns, E. S. 1976. Adults of *Longitarsus jacobaea* (L.) (Col., Chrysomelidae) defoliating ragwort (*Senecio jacobaea* L.; Compositae). Entomol. Month. Mag. 111: 129–130.

Black, W. N. 1976. Effects of herbicide rates and time of application on the control of tansy ragwort in pastures. Can. J. Plant Sci. 56: 605–610.

Bocher, T. W. and Larsen, K. 1955. Chromosome studies on some European flowering plants. Bot. Tidsskr. 52: 125–131.

Bolkhovskikh, Z. V., Grif, U. and Matavejeva, T. 1969. Chromosome numbers of flowering plants. Academy of Sciences of the USSR, V. L. Komarov Botanical Institute. Leningrad, USSR.

Bull, L. B., Culvenor, C. C. J. and Dick, A. T. 1968. The pyrrolizidine alkaloids. Their chemistry, pathogenicity and other biological properties. North Holland, Amsterdam, The Netherlands. 294 pp.

Cairns, D. 1938. Vegetative propagation in ragwort. N.Z.J. Sci. Technol. 20: 137A–138A.

Cameron, E. 1935. A study of the natural control of ragwort (*Senecio jacobaea* L.). J. Ecology 23: 265–322.

Catling, P. M., Erskine, D. S. and MacLaren, R. B. 1985. The plants of Prince Edward Island with new records, nomenclature changes, and corrections and deletions. Agriculture Canada, Ottawa, ON. Publ. 1798, 272 pp.

Coles, P. G. 1967. Ragwort control with picloram. Proc. 20th N.Z. Weed and Pest Control Conf. 32–36.

Conners, I. L. 1967. An annotated index of plant diseases in Canada and fungi recorded on plants in Alaska, Canada and Greenland. Canada Department of Agriculture, Ottawa, ON. Publ. 1251, 381 pp.

Cox, C. S. and McEvoy, P. B. 1983. Effect of summer moisture stress on the capacity of tansy ragwort (*Senecio jacobaea*) to compensate for defoliation by cinnabar moth. (*Tyria jacobaea*). J. Appl. Ecol. 20: 225–234.

Crawley, M. J. and Nachapong, M. 1985. The establishment of seedlings from primary and regrowth seeds of ragwort (*Senecio jacobaea*). J. Ecol. 73: 255–261.

Deinzer, M. L., Thomson, P. A., Burgett, D. M. and Isaacson, D. L. 1977. Pyrrolizidine alakloids: their occurrence in honey of tansy ragwort. (*Senecio jacobaea* L.). Science 195: 497–499.

Dempster, J. P. 1971. The population ecology of the Cinnabar Moth *Tyria jacobaea* L. (Lepidoptera, Arctiidae). Oecologia **7**: 26–27.

Dempster, J. P. and Lakhani, K. H. 1979. A population model for cinnabar moth and its food plant, ragwort. J. Anim. Ecol. **48**: 143–163.

Douglas, G. W. 1982. The sunflower family of British Columbia. Vol. 1. Senecioneae. British Columbia Provincial Museum Occ. Paper no. 23. Vancouver, BC.

Ernst, W. H. O. and Leloup, S. 1987. Perennial herbs as monitor for moderate levels of metal fall-out. Chemosphere **16**: 233–238.

Farr, D. F., Bills, G. S., Chamuras, G. P. and Rossman, A. Y. 1989. Fungi on plants and plant products in United States. A.P.S. Press, St. Paul, MN. 1252 pp.

Fernald, M. L. 1950. Gray's manual of botany. 8th ed. American Book Co., New York, NY.

Ferron, M. and Cayouette, R. 1975. Noms de mauvaises herbes du Quebec. 3rd ed. Agriculture Quebec. Quebec, PQ.

Ferry, S. 1977. Sur les polyphenols (acidesphenols, flavonoides) de quelques senecons indigenes. Plantes medicinales et phytotherapie **11**: 25–39.

Forbes, J. C. 1977. Population flux and mortality in a ragwort (*Senecio jacobaea*) infestation. Weed Res. **17**: 387–391.

Forbes, J. C. 1978. Control of *Senecio jacobaea* L. (ragwort) by autumn or spring herbicide application. Weed Res. **18**: 109–110.

Forbes, J. C. 1985. The impact and control of ragwort (*Senecio jacobaea* and *S. aquaticus*) in grassland. Br. Grassland Soc. Occasional Symp. no. 18. Weeds, pests, diseases of grassland and herbage legumes. Crop Protection Monograph no. 29 pp. 147–154.

Frankton, C. and Mulligan, G. A. 1987. Weeds of Canada. NC Press, Toronto, ON.

Frick, K. E. 1970. Ragwort flea beetle established for biological control of tansy ragwort. Calif. Agric. **24**: 12–13.

Giles, C. J. 1983. Outbreak of ragwort *Senecio jacobaea* poisoning in horses. Equine Vet. J. **15**: 248–250.

Goeger, D. E., Cheeke, P. R., Shmitz, J. A. and Buhler, D. R. 1981. Toxicity of tansy ragwort *Senecio jacobaea* to goats. Am. J. Vet Res. **43**: 252–254.

Green, H. G. 1937. Dispersal of *Senecio jacobaea* J. Ecol. **25**: 569.

Green, C. R. and Christie, G. S. 1961. Malformations in fetal rats induced by the pyrrolizidine alkaloid heliotrine. Br. J. Exp. Pathol. **42**: 369.

Harley, J. L. and Harley, E. L. 1987. A check-list of mycorrhiza in the British flora. New Phytol. **105**: 1–102.

Harper, J. L. 1958. The ecology of ragwort (*Senecio jacobaea*) with especial reference to control. Herb. Abstr. **28**: 151–157.

Harper, J. L. and Wood, W. A. 1957. Biological flora of the British Isles. *Senecio jacobaea*. J. Ecol. **45**: 617–637.

Harris, P. 1974. The impact of the cinnabar moth on ragwort in east and west Canada and its implication for biological control. Proc. 3rd Intl. Symp. on Biological control of weeds. Montpelier, France. 1973, 119–123.

Harris, P., Thompson, L. S., Wilkinson, A. T. S. and Neary, M. E. 1978. Reproductive biology of tansy ragwort, climate and biological control by the cinnabar moth in Canada. Proc. 4th Intl. Congress on Biological Control of Weeds. University of Florida, Gainsville, FL. pp. 163–173.

Harris, P., Wilkinson, A. T. S., Neary, M. E. and Thompson, L. S. 1971. *Senecio jacobaea* L., Tansy ragwort. Technical Communication. Commonwealth Institute of Biological Control **4**: 97–104.

Hawker, L. E., Harrison, R. W., Nicholls, V. O., Ham, A. M. 1957. Studies on vesiculararbuscular endophytes. Trans. Br. Mycol. Soc. **40**: 375–390.

Hawkes, R. B. 1981. Biological control of tansy ragwort in the state of Oregon. Proc. 5th Intl. Symp. on Biological Control of Weeds. pp. 623–626.

Hitchcock, C. L., Cronquist, A., Ownbey, M. and Thompson, J. W. 1969. Vascular plants of the Pacific Northwest. University of Washington Press, Seattle, WA.

Holmgren, P. K., Keuken, W. and Schofield, E. 1981. Index herbariorum. Part 1. The herbaria of the world. 7th ed. (Regnum Veg. 106) Oosthock, Schetema and Holkema, Utrecht, The Netherlands, 452 pp.

Irvine, H. M., Forbes, J. C. and Draper, S. R. 1977. Effects of 2,4-D on the water-soluble carbohydrate content of ragwort (*Senecio jacobaea* L.) leaves. Weed Res. **117**: 169–172.

Isaacson, D. L. and Ehrensing, D. T. 1977. Biological control of tansy ragwort. Weed Control Bulletin. Oregon Dept. Agric. No. 1, 8 pp.

Islam, Z. and Crawley, M. J. 1983. Compensation and regrowth of ragwort (*Senecio jacobaea* L.) attacked by cinnabar moth (*Tyria jacobaeae*). J. Ecol. **71**: 829–843.

Kadereit, J. W. and Sell, P. D. 1986. Variation in *Senecio jacobaea* L. (Asteraceae) in the British Isles. Watsonia **16**: 21–23.

Lakhani, K. H. and Dempster, J. P. 1981. Cinnabar moth and its food plant ragwort: further analysis of a simple interaction model. J. Anim. Ecol. **50**: 231-249.

Lam, J. and Drake, D. 1973. Polyacetylenes of *Senecio jacobaea*. Phytochemistry **12**: 149-151.

McEvoy, P. B. 1984a. Seedling dispersion and the persistence of ragwort *Senecio jacobaea* (Compositae) in a grassland dominated by perennial species. Oikos **42**: 138-143.

McEvoy, P. B. 1984b. Dormancy and dispersal in dimorphic achenes of tansy ragwort, *Senecio jacobaea* L. (Compositae). Oecologia **61**: 160-168.

McEvoy, P. B. and Cox, C. S. 1987. Wind dispersal distances in dimorphic achenes of ragwort, *Senecio jacobaea*. Ecology. **68**: 2006-2015.

Meijden, E. van der. 1974. The distribution of *Senecio jacobaea* L. and *Tyria jacobaeae* L. in relation to soil properties. Acta Bot. Neerlandica **23**: 681-690.

Meijden, E. van der. 1976. Het verspreidingsgebied van *Senecio jacobaea* L. var. *nudus* Weston. Gorteria **8**: 57-61.

Meijden, E. van der and Waals-Kooi, R. E. van der. 1979. The population ecology of *Senecio jacobaea* in a sand dune system. I. Reproductive strategy and the biennial habit. J. Ecol. **67**: 131-153.

Miller, D. 1936. Biological control of noxious weeds. N.Z.J. Sci. Technol. **18**: 581-584.

Miranda, C. L., Buhler, D. R., Ramsdell, H. S., Cheeke, P. R. and Schmitz, J. A. 1982. Modifications of chronic hepatoxicity of pyrrolizidine (*Senecio*) alkaloids by butylated hydroxyanisole and cysteine. Toxicol. Lett. **10**: 177-182.

Moore, R. J. 1973. Index to plant chromosome numbers 1967-71. Regnum Vegetable Vol. 90. Oosthoek's, Utrecht, The Netherlands.

Mulligan, G. A. 1959. Chromosome numbers of Canadian weeds II. Can. J. Bot. **37**: 81-92.

Myers, J. H. 1980. Is the insect or the plant the driving force in the cinnabar moth — tansy ragwort system? Oecologia **47**: 16-21.

Myers, J. H. and Campbell, B. J. 1976. Distribution and dispersal in populations capable of resource depletion. Oecologia **24**: 7-20.

Myers, J. H. and Post, B. J. 1981. Plant nitrogen and fluctuations of insect populations: a test with the cinnabar moth — tansy ragwort system. Oecologia **48**: 151-156.

Ornduff, R., Raven, P. H., Kyhos, D. W. and Kruckeberg, A. R. 1963. Chromosome numbers in Compositae III. Senecioneae. Am. J. Bot. **50**: 131-140.

Poole, A. L. and Cairns, D. 1940. Botanical aspects of ragwort (*Senecio jacobaea* L.) control.

Bull. N.Z. Dep. Sci. Industrial Res. **82**: 1-66.

Prins, A. H., Verkaar, H. J. and Herik, M. van der. 1989. Responses of *Cynoglossum officinale* L. and *Senecio jacobaea* L. to various degrees of defoliation. New Phytol. **111**: 725-731.

Salsibury, E. 1961. Weeds and Aliens. Collins, London, U.K.

Schmidl, L. 1972. Biology and control of ragwort, *Senecio jacobaea* L., in Victoria, Australia. Weed Res. **12**: 37-45.

Scoggan, H. L. 1979. Flora of Canada. National Museums of Canada. Ottawa, ON.

Sharrow, S. H. and Mosher, W. D. 1982. Sheep as a biological control agent for tansy ragwort. J. Range Manage. **35**: 480-482.

Sheldon, J. C. 174. The behaviour of seeds in soil. 3. The influence of seed morphology and the behaviour of seedlings on the establishment of plants from surface lying seeds. J. Ecol. **62**: 47-66.

Shull, L. R., Buckmaster, G. W. and Cheeke, P. R. 1976. Effect of pyrrolizidine alkaloids on liver microsome mixed function oxidase activity in rats. J. Anim. Ecol. **43**: 1024-1027.

Thompson, A. 1974. Herbicide effects on ragwort in pasture. Proc. 27th N.Z. Weed and Pest Control Conf. pp. 90-93.

Thompson, A. 1977. Herbicides for the spot treatment of ragwort in pasture. Proc. 30th N.Z. Weed and Pest Control Conf. pp. 34-37.

Thompson, A. 1980. Ragwort population and control studies. Proc. 33rd N.Z. Weed and Pest Control Conf. pp. 55-62.

Thompson, A. 1983. Pasture weed control by rope wick applicator. Proc. 36th N.Z. Weed and Pest Control Conf. pp. 96-98.

Thompson, A. and Makepeace, W. 1983. Longevity of buried ragwort (*Senecio jacobaea* L.) seed. N.Z.J. Exp. Agric. **11**: 89-90.

Thompson, A. and Saunders, A. E. 1984. A comparison of 2,4-D and MCPA alone and in combination of the control of ragwort. Proc. 37th N.Z. Weed and Pest Control Conf. pp. 33-36.

Thompson, A. and Saunders, A. E. 1986. The effect of fertilizer on ragwort in pasture. Proc. 39th N.Z. Weed and Pest Control Conf. pp. 175-178.

Tutin, T. G., Heywood, V. H., Valentine, D. H., Walters, S. M. and Webb, D. A. 1976. Flora Europaea. Vol. 4. Cambridge University Press, Cambridge, U.K. p. 201.

Wardle, D. A. 1987. The ecology of ragwort (*Senecio jacobaea* L.) — A review. N.Z.J. Ecol. **10**: 67-76.

Wardle, D. A. and Rahman, A. 1987. Influence of capitulum maturity on achene germination of

Senecio jacobaea and *Carduus nutans*. N.Z.J. Agric. Res. **30**: 117–120.

Watt, T. A. 1987. The biology and toxicity of ragwort (*Senecio jacobaea* L.) and its herbicidal and biological control. Herb. Abstr. **57**: 1–16.

White, R. D., Krumperman, P. H., Cheeke, P. R. and Buhler, D. R. 1983. An evaluation of acetone extracts from 6 plants in the Ames mutagenicity test. Toxicol. Lett. **15**: 25–32.

The biology of Canadian weeds. 97. *Barbarea vulgaris* R.Br.

Marilyn A. MacDonald[1] and Paul B. Cavers

Department of Plant Sciences, University of Western Ontario, London, Ontario, Canada N6A 5B7. Received 29 May 1990, accepted 5 Sept. 1990.

MacDonald, M. A. and Cavers, P. B. 1991. **The biology of Canadian weeds. 97.** *Barbarea vulgaris* **R.Br.** Can. J. Plant Sci. **71**: 149–166. *Barbarea vulgaris* R.Br. is an introduced weed of recently disturbed areas, small-seeded grain crops, roadsides and pastures. It is abundant in southern Ontario, Quebec and the northeastern U.S.A.; frequent in the Maritimes, British Columbia and the northwest coastal U.S.A.; and rare south of 33°N, north of 50°N and across the prairies. The weediness of this species largely results from its prolific seed production, enforced and induced seed dormancy, and its rapid growth under favourable conditions.

Key words: *Barbarea vulgaris*, yellow rocket, weed biology

MacDonald, M. A. and Cavers, P. B. 1991. **Biologie des mauvaises herbes du Canada. 97.** *Barbarea vulgaris* **R.Br.** Can. J. Plant Sci. **71**: 149–166. *Barbarea vulgaris* R.Br. est une mauvaise herbe introduite que l'on retrouve dans les endroits récemment perturbés, dans les champs de cultures à petits grains, le long des routes et dans les pâturages. Elle abonde dans le sud de l'Ontario, au Québec et dans le nord-est des États-Unis; elle est fréquente dans les Maritimes, en Colombie-Britannique et dans les régions côtières du nord-ouest des États-Unis. On la trouve rarement au sud du 33′ parallèle nord et au nord du 50′ parallèle nord ou dans les Prairies. Le caractère néfaste de cette espèce est dû principalement à son abondante production de graines, à la dormance forcée et induite de ses graines et à sa croissance rapide dans des conditions favorables.

Mots clés: *Barbarea vulgaris*, barbarée vulgaire, biologie des mauvaises herbes

1. Name

Barbarea vulgaris R.Br. — **Yellow rocket, barbarée vulgaire** (Alex et al. 1980), winter cress, Herb barbara (Frankton and Mulligan 1970), wild mustard, bitter cress, yellow weed (Delorit 1970), barbarée commune, cresson de terre, cresson d'hiver, herbe de Sainte-Barbe, roquette des marais, roquette jaune, velar d'Orient (Ferron et Cayouette 1971). Brassicaceae, mustard family, Crucifères.

The binomial *B. vulgaris* R.Br. has been used by the majority of authors (e.g., Schreiber 1962; Fertig 1963; Tahvanainen 1972b) following the description of Gleason and Cronquist (1963). However, a few Canadian and other herbarium specimens that we examined could not be assigned with certainty to one or another of the possible species; *B. vulgaris, B. orthoceras, B. verna* or *B. stricta* (See Section 2b; Table 1). Also, we found no evidence of breeding experiments on cross-fertility or character validity involving these four species.

2. Description and Account of Variation

(a) The root crown diameter ranges from less than 0.1 cm to 5 cm. The tap roots often exceed 50 cm in depth. An extensive, much-branched, fibrous secondary root system develops.

---

[1]Present address (M.A.MacD.): Unit 0-2965 Richmond Rd., Ottawa, Ontario K2B 6S7, Canada.

Can. J. Plant Sci. 71: 149–166 (Jan. 1991)

Table 1. Floral and vegetative characteristics used to distinguish the North American species of *Barbarea* based on treatments by Clapham et al. (1962), Gleason and Cronquist (1963) and Mulligan (1978)

Pairs of lateral lobes, basal leaves	Cauline leaves (margins)	Length (cm) of silique	Length (mm) of beak
	Characters		
	Barbarea vulgaris		
1–4	Simple to dentate	1.5–5.0	2.0–3.0
	Barbarea stricta		
1–4	Simple to dentate	1.5–5.0	0.5–1.5
	Barbarea verna		
4–10	Divided to cut	4.0–7.0	1.0–2.5
	Barbarea orthoceras		
1–4	Divided to cut	2.0–3.5	0.3–1.0

Generally biennial (infrequently winter annual) or short-lived perennial (reproducing once or repeatedly). It produces a vegetative rosette of up to 60 glabrous leaves, each with a large ovate to rotund terminal lobe, 0–4 pairs of lateral lobes and an elongate petiole (rachis), with the width of the terminal lobe varying from 0.2 to 10 cm across, the width of the lateral lobes up to 1 cm and the length of the petiole (rachis) from 0.5 to 20 cm. Rosette leaves remain green throughout the winter, although the petioles may turn purple.

The flowering plant has one to several, generally branched stems from 0.4 to 80 cm in height which arise from the same root (caudex). These stems have a characteristic eight-strand ridging which continues well up the stem, and marks major vascular bundles (from which siliques and cauline leaves arise). Cauline leaves are green, glabrous, clasping, alternate (in a loose spiral) and decrease in size toward the top of the stem; as well as losing the shallow lobing often seen on lower cauline leaves.

Flowers are regular and hypogynous, about 8 mm wide and crowded. The four sepals are oblong, persistent and ascending, covering about two-thirds of the opened flower; two are somewhat longer than the others and have a prominent keel-shaped ridge. The four petals are yellow, spatulate to obovate and somewhat overlapped. There are four long stamens and two short stamens. The long stamens are offset by two large nectaries; and the short ones partly surrounded at the base by a semicircular nectary (Fig. 1). The anthers are oblong to lanceolate, and the ovary cylindrical with a narrowing style and a truncate stigma. There are 1–12 ovules in each of the two cells of the ovary.

Siliques are 1.0 to 4.0 cm from the base of the valve to the tip of the persistent beak (which ranges from 1.8 to 3 mm) on pedicels from 3 to 6 mm long and 0.5 mm wide. Valves dehisce from the bottom upwards and scatter the 1–20 small, lightly reticulate, grey to reddish brown, flattened, ovoid seeds borne in each silique. In var. *vulgaris*, the siliques are appressed and form a dense raceme; in var. *arcuata* the siliques are spreading and form an open raceme (Fig. 1).

Canadian plants have a chromosome number of $2n = 16$ (Mulligan 1959) as do European specimens (Manton 1932).

(b) The species is most often confused with the native *B. orthoceras* Ledeb. and the introduced *B. verna* (Mill.) Aschers and *B. stricta* Andrz. These species are distinguished in Table 1 (compiled from Clapham et al. (1962); Gleason and Cronquist (1963); and

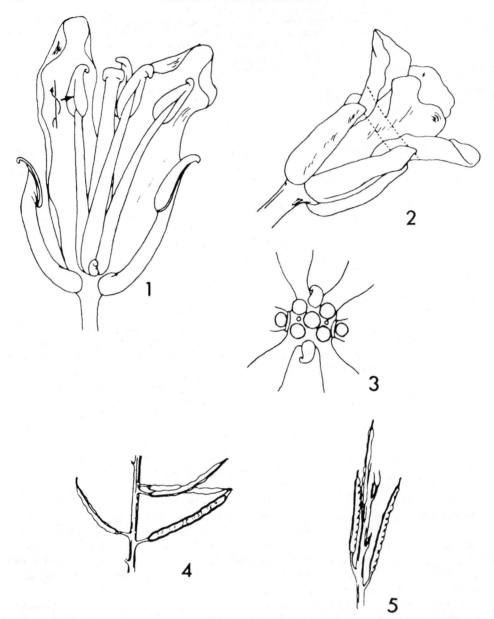

Fig. 1. Details of the floral structure of *Barbarea vulgaris*. 1. Arrangement of short and long stamens (×5.5). The arrow indicates the structure inside the cleft. 2. Actual difference in stamen heights in a closed flower (×3.5). 3. Positions of all six stamens and all four nectaries (×9). Centre circle is pistil; other circles are stamens. 4. Silique arrangement in var. *arcuata* (×0.75). 5. Silique arrangement in var. *vulgaris* (×0.75).

Mulligan (1978)). In addition, *B. vulgaris*, at some life-cycle stages, may be confused with other species of the Cruciferae, but the characteristic shape of its basal leaves and its ridged stalk should permit ready identification.

(c) Intraspecific variation is quite common. Montgomery (1957) recognized four varieties in Ontario; var. *arcuata,* var. *vulgaris,* var. *brachycarpa,* var. *sylvestris* but did not describe them or give their distribution. However, the first two of these are common throughout the species' range in eastern Canada. The type variety, var. *vulgaris*, has strongly appressed siliques and a mean seed weight in southern Ontario of 0.48 mg. It is most common on riverbanks, in woodlands and in other nonagricultural sites. Var. *arcuata* (Opiz) Fries has open siliques, a mean

seed weight in southern Ontario of 0.61 mg and is the common variety in arable fields and other agricultural situations.

(d) Illustrations of the floral structure are given in Fig. 1 and of (i) seed, (ii) seedling, (iii) cauline rosette, and (iv) fruiting adult in Fig. 2.

3. Economic Importance
(a) *Detrimental* — *Barbarea vulgaris* is an important weed of small-seeded grain and hay crops in Ontario (Alex and Switzer 1983).

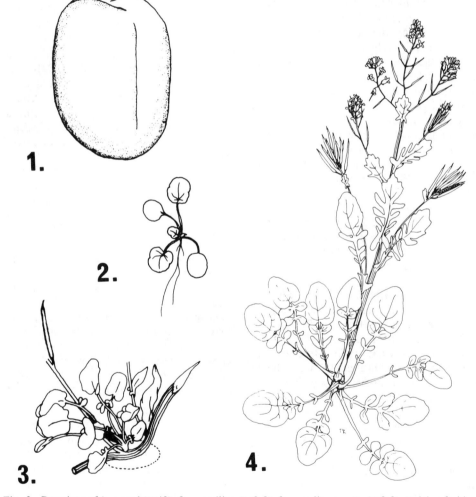

Fig. 2. Drawings of 1, a seed (×40), 2, a seedling (×0.8), 3, a cauline rosette (×0.8), and 4, a fruiting adult (×0.4), of *Barbarea vulgaris.*

Out of seven major weed species in spring wheat in Russia, *Barbarea vulgaris* caused the third greatest reductions in crop yield (Nesterova and Chukanova 1981). This weediness is based on a combination of rapid increase in numbers (Fertig 1968), inedibility of the rachis at maturity (which causes rejection by cows of hay containing the raches) (Fertig 1963; Dutt et al. 1982), long-term seed dormancy and intermittent recruitment. The species is not known to be allergenic. However, some evidence indicates allelochemic (Gressel and Holm 1964) or toxic compounds are produced (erucic acid and goiterin, a haemolytic compound (Appelqvist, pers. commun.)). While the early stages of growth of yellow rocket (prior to silique formation) are relatively high in protein and low in fibre, the later stages are inedible, low in nutritive value and result in the refusal of hay (in which stems of *B. vulgaris* are mixed) by cows and goats (Schreiber and Fertig 1955; Dutt et al. 1982). Ensiling may overcome some of the problem and at least kills the seeds which otherwise pass through the animals and may be spread with manure or refuse hay (Fertig et al. 1963; Andersen 1968; Staniforth 1975).

In New York State, yellow rocket is the most frequent invader of legume-grass meadows (Fertig 1963). It may comprise up to 50% of the total yield of first-cutting hay in first- and second-year legume stands in that state.

Because of its early spring growth, *B. vulgaris* may serve as a temporary host for pests of brassicaceous crops (Root and Tahvanainen 1969; Morgan 1971; Ivanova 1973; Nair et al. 1973; Nowicki 1973; Bruckart and Lorbeer 1976; Shukla et al. 1976; Finch and Ackley 1977). Cucumber mosaic virus overwinters in subterranean structures of *B. vulgaris* (Rist and Lorbeer 1989).

Barbarea vulgaris produces a number of mustard oils, including sinigrin (R: $CH_2 =$ CH CH_s2), glucocapparin (R: CH_3), gluconasturtiin (R: C_6C_5 CH_2 CH_2) and a characteristic, nonvolatile glucobarbarin (R: C_6H_5 CHOH CH_2) (Kjaer and Gmelin 1957). Flea beetles and other insects may rely on the complex of mustard oils to locate their host (Feeny et al. 1970). Mammals which eat large amounts of isothiocyanates may suffer from their toxic (e.g. from nitriles) and sometimes goitrogenic effects (Kjaer 1960).

Barbarea vulgaris is one of the worst weeds in vegetable and small fruit fields in Belgium (Himme et al. 1984, 1985).

(b) *Beneficial* — The retention of green leaves throughout the winter makes this plant a source of fresh greens in the early spring (Palmer 1962); indeed, the generic name is derived from the feast day of St. Barbara (14th century). People collected rosettes of *B. vulgaris* to eat in celebration of this early spring feast day. A 100-g sample of *B. vulgaris* provides more than 60 mg of vitamin C (the daily human recommendation) (Korovka 1976; Zennie and Ogzewalla 1977). The production of noticeable amounts of sinigrin gives its leaves a tangy flavour. The characteristic generic glucoside, glucobarbarin, is a nonvolatile mustard oil and probably relatively tasteless (Kjaer 1960). The species was briefly included in a breeding program in Sweden for brassicaceous species producing seeds for condiments but was abandoned because of the longevity of the seeds in the soil (Appelqvist pers. commun.). In the early stages of growth *B. vulgaris* is high in protein, low in crude fibre and has "relatively fair quality roughage value" (Schreiber and Fertig 1955). Although hay containing a high percentage of yellow rocket is not readily eaten by cows, the first cutting of hay crop silage with a high percentage of yellow rocket is generally consumed (Schreiber and Fertig 1955). The spring-produced flowers may serve as an early source of pollen and nectar for hymenopteran visitors. The fibrous roots may minimize erosion on recently disturbed soil.

(c) *Legislation* — Yellow rocket (*Barbarea* spp.) is listed as a primary noxious weed under the Canada Seeds Act (Agriculture Canada 1967) and as a noxious weed under the Ontario Weed Control Act (Anonymous 1988), the Nova Scotia Weed Control Act (Anonymous 1977a), the Manitoba Noxious

Weeds Act of 1976 (Anonymous 1976) but not 1981 (Anonymous 1981), and the Agricultural Abuses Act of Quebec (Anonymous 1977b).

4. Geographical Distribution

Barbarea vulgaris is probably of Mediterranean origin (J. Vaughan pers. commun.) and is now cosmopolitan in temperate regions. It occurs abundantly in southern Ontario and Quebec, and in limited numbers in the Maritime provinces, British Columbia and the Prairie provinces (considered absent in Saskatchewan) (Frankton and Mulligan 1970). The northern limit to its range is about 51°N. It has been reported from Poste-de-la-Baleine and Fort Chimo in Quebec (Rousseau 1968). Both variety *vulgaris* and variety *arcuata* are found in the Clay Belt of northern Ontario (Baldwin 1958). Variety *arcuata* was collected by Scoggan (1951) from shallow soil at Norway House at the NE end of Lake Winnipeg in Manitoba. The distribution of *B. vulgaris* in Canada is shown in Fig. 3 and is based on herbarium specimens from DAO, UWO, CAN, TRT, HAM, MTMG, QFA, ACAD, WOCB, SASK, ALTA, UBC, WIN, OAC, LKHD, QK, UNB, Mount Allison and on data from Erskine (1960), Rousseau (1968), Boivin (1972), and Thomas and Wise (1982). Varieties are not separated because (a) some specimens were not at a stage where such classification was possible, and (b) most authors (above) did not separate them.

In the United States, it extends south to Arkansas, occurs extensively in the northeast, and is found with limited abundance in distinct patches in the North-central States and in Washington and Oregon (Anonymous 1971).

Kott (1963) reported that *B. vulgaris* was spreading in all the European parts of the USSR (except the steppes and the forest tundra), in the Caucasus, the Urals and in Siberia as far as Lake Baikal. It has been reported throughout Europe, north to 65° in Finland; in N. Africa and in Asia; has been introduced to Australia and New Zealand and

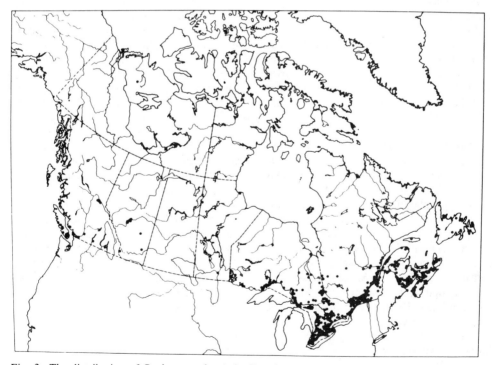

Fig. 3. The distribution of *Barbarea vulgaris* in Canada.

is common in the southern United Kingdom (Clapham et al. 1962). It has been reported in soil taken from glacial deposits in Britain (Godwin 1960).

5. Habitat

(a) *Climatic requirements* — *Barbarea vulgaris* has an obligate requirement for vernalization; its southward spread, in terms of successful reproduction, is limited to areas with several weeks at 5°C or less. Seed dormancy is induced by drying and/or cool temperatures (less than 10°C); thus persistent seed banks (and therefore recurrent populations) of *B. vulgaris* are maintained in areas with periods of low rainfall in late summer and of cool temperatures from late summer to early spring. Schreiber (1962) reported that the elongation of floral stalks occurred after temperatures rose above 10°C for more than one week. The northern limit for the species probably is related to the length of the season available for seed-setting after this temperature has been reached. Rosettes of *B. vulgaris* will grow at or below temperatures of 5°C.

Rosettes of *B. vulgaris* tolerate soil moisture regimes from dry to subhydric; can withstand submersion and silt deposition; and grow in a range of light intensities from 107 640 lx (open, bare ground) to less than 1300 lx (woodland, with a complete canopy (MacDonald 1977)).

(b) *Substratum* — There are no observable specific substrate requirements. *Barbarea vulgaris* grows on sand, gravel, silt, and clay soils of varying fertility and pH (e.g., clay loam high in phosphorus, potassium and magnesium, with a pH of 7.6; silt loam low in phosphorus, high in potassium and magnesium, with a pH of 7.0 (MacDonald 1977); acid soils in central Quebec (data on herbarium specimens)). Moist, rich soils are probably optimal (Rabotnov 1964; Frankton and Mulligan 1970). Germination of *B. vulgaris* seeds decreased substantially within the first month following application of a slurry of semi-liquid manure (Titov and Babakov 1988).

(c) *Communities* — In Table 2, the proportion of cover contributed by different species including *B. vulgaris* is given for a variety of sites in and near London, Ontario. A brief discussion of the history of these sites is provided in MacDonald (1977). The species does best in recently-disturbed areas, can take advantage of openings in older communities but does poorly in grasslands. In some cases, as in the woodland (Table 2), cover by litter in the fall preceded severe grazing damage by slugs to yellow rocket plants.

Throughout its range, yellow rocket is an early spring dominant and is abundant in early successional stages on disturbed sites (Kott 1963; Rabotnov 1964; Werner 1977; Keever 1980). It has had a long history of occupation of disturbed or briefly available habitats (Salisbury 1942).

6. History

Barbarea vulgaris was introduced to North America about 1800 (Nuttall 1818; Rousseau 1968) although specimens were still rare to absent in Ontario as late as 1878 (Macoun and Gibson 1878). It was not listed as one of the 149 common weeds in Canada in 1930 (Anonymous 1930) and was comparatively rare, being restricted to low, wet ground (Montgomery 1955).

By 1948 it was common throughout Ontario and Quebec (Howitt and MacLeod 1948) and had been found as far north as Moosonee (Baldwin 1958). It was known to be spreading and was a common impurity in clover, grass and alfalfa seeds. It had been added to the list of secondary noxious weeds. At that time it was felt that draining of the field, followed by ploughing and fall or spring cultivation, or by grazing by sheep, would eradicate the weed (Howitt and MacLeod 1948).

From the 1950s up to the present, it has increased in numbers in the central region of the continent (Frankton and Mulligan 1970). By 1976 the species was considered to be one of the 117 most common weeds in Canada (Mulligan 1976). It is also one of the three most important broad-leaved perennial weeds in Wisconsin forage crops but its numbers

Table 2. Proportion of total cover contributed by different species at each of five sites near London, Ontario where *B. vulgaris* populations were studied

Species	Site				
	Recently disturbed	Abandoned orchard	Farm	Riverbank	Wood
Bare ground	0.20	0.23	0.25	0.31	0.72
Monocotyledonous species					
Agropyron repens (L.) Beauv.	0.44	0.20	0.04	0.00	0.00
Agrostis stolonifera L.	0.00	0.02	0.11	0.50	0.00
Dactylis glomerata L.	0.00	0.02	0.08	0.00	0.00
Phleum pratense L.	0.01	0.01	0.02	0.00	0.00
Poa compressa L.	0.08	0.01	0.00	0.00	0.00
P. pratensis L.	0.00	0.28	0.00	0.09	0.00
P. trivialis L.	0.10	0.00	0.00	0.00	0.00
Setaria glauca (L.) Beauv.	0.02	0.00	0.01	0.00	0.00
Total grass cover	0.65	0.54	0.27	0.59	0.00
Dicotyledonous species					
Arctium minus Schk.	0.00	0.02	0.00	0.04	0.00
Barbarea vulgaris R.Br.	0.09	0.11	0.01	0.01	0.24
Cirsium arvense (L.) Scop.	0.00	0.00	0.02	0.00	0.00
Daucus carota L.	0.00	0.01	0.01	0.00	0.00
Nepeta cataria L.	0.00	0.07	0.00	0.00	0.00
Plantago rugelii Decne.	0.00	0.00	0.11	0.00	0.00
P. major L.	0.00	0.00	0.07	0.00	0.00
Polygonum persicaria L.	0.00	0.00	0.09	0.00	0.00
Prunella vulgaris L.	0.00	0.00	0.04	0.00	0.00
Rumex crispus L.	0.00	0.00	0.01	0.00	0.00
Solanum dulcamara L.	0.00	0.00	0.00	0.00	0.01
Taraxacum officinale Weber.	0.02	0.00	0.09	0.01	0.00
Trifolium spp.	0.02	0.00	0.01	0.00	0.00
Urtica dioica L.	0.00	0.00	0.00	0.04	0.00
Other	0.02	0.02	0.02	0.00	0.03
Total "dicot" cover	0.15	0.23	0.48	0.10	0.28

have not increased significantly recently (Doll 1980; Doll and Quinones 1983).

7. Growth and Development

(a) *Morphology* — New rosettes can develop from vegetative buds on the root system. Rosettes arise similarly from root fragments exposed to sunlight.

The small smooth seeds of *B. vulgaris* mix readily into the soil, forming seed banks which permit rapid establishment when intermittently available sites recur. Since vegetative spread and competitive ability (especially with grasses) is limited, this seed dispersal and dormancy is a main contributor to the weediness of *B. vulgaris*. A detailed description of the morphology and anatomy of this species is provided by Korsmo (1954).

(b) *Perennation — Barbarea vulgaris* over-winters as seeds and by several vegetative means. Following seed maturation vegetative buds may develop on the root crown (caudex) and on root branches which lie near the surface of the soil. A number of stems arise from these rosettes in the following spring. Further thickening of the root crown, development of vegetative buds and formation of leaves can lead to perennation into a third (or more) growing season (MacDonald 1977). Over-wintering is more likely if the ramet separates from the parent plant (Kott 1963).

If the flowering stalks are removed as they are developing, new stalks are often formed. These new stalks mature at the same time as stalks on control (undisturbed) plants. If the stalks are removed during seed maturation the basal buds remain vegetative and rosettes develop. A larger percentage of plants perennate if the stalks are removed while the seeds are maturing than if they are removed after seed maturation. Since green seeds will mature and remain viable on cut stalks, clipping after seed formation is not recommended as a control measure (MacDonald 1977).

Even after seed production and shattering, removal of the stalks increases the probability of successful perennation (MacDonald 1977). Lindsay and Bassett (1951) suggested that the majority of 2-yr-old plants die from crown rot (*Sclerotinia* spp.). The removal of the stalks may prevent further mechanical damage to the caudex by movement of the stalk (i.e. decrease the possibility of fungal infection).

Besides regenerating as described above, the plant may perennate through cauline rosettes (MacDonald and Cavers 1974). These rosettes develop in the axils of cauline leaves as seed formation ends. If the stalk falls to the ground, the cauline rosette develops a root system. In the next growing season, if it has overwintered successfully, the cauline rosette is likely to flower. However, most of these rosettes fail to overwinter.

Rosettes below the size required for vernalization may overwinter and, if they avoid frost-heaving in early spring (a major cause of mortality), go through another growing season (MacDonald 1977). Rabotnov (1964) suggested that these "juveniles" formed a reservoir from which, if conditions became favourable (e.g. by removal of vegetation cover), adults developed rapidly.

In general, young rosettes that have not flowered have the best chance of surviving the winter, plants that have flowered once are next and cauline rosettes have the least chance. However, conditions in the habitat have a great influence on the possibility of survival.

(c) *Physiology* — The pattern of growth is reflected in the pattern of total nonstructural carbohydrate (TNC) usage in the species (Hastings and Kust 1970a). Rosettes begin aboveground growth in the spring, increase in size throughout the summer, and from September to November accumulate TNC (thereby increasing root size). In the spring, when temperatures exceed 10°C, TNC consumption increases. Very shortly afterwards the plant bolts, and TNC consumption decreases (cauline leaves are contributing photosynthate). Flowering and seed production reduce TNC to the lowest percentage in the plant's life cycle. Upon completion of these activities, root TNC is stored rapidly and rosettes and ramets are formed. Competition, disease and/or herbivory which reduce TNC should decrease the likelihood of perennation. Young plants stored TNC more efficiently than did older plants, but total TNC (g/plant) was greater in older plants (Hastings and Kust 1970a).

(d) *Phenology* — Recruitment of seedlings from the seed bank occurs when there is adequate moisture, light and alternating temperatures. Drought, vegetative cover, burial, or cool temperatures induce seed dormancy (MacDonald 1977). Thus, where favourable conditions for germination occur in the spring, the plant is a biennial or perennial; where they occur in the autumn, a winter annual or perennial. In North America the majority of seedlings emerge in the spring (Lindsay and Bassett 1951; Schreiber 1962; Tahvanainen 1972a; Keever 1980). In England, seedlings emerge throughout the year, with the vast majority appearing in spring and summer (Roberts 1986).

Most vegetative growth occurs in the spring, when the unvernalized rosette (seedling) forms an average of five leaves and develops a tap root. Changes in root nonstructural carbohydrate are discussed in Section 7(c). There is an obligate requirement and a minimum size for vernalization. Vegetative rosettes of less than five leaves and 0.06 g generally fail to bolt, even after an extended cold period of several months. Early spring flowering (April in southern Ontario) is followed by seed development (about 2–3 mo) and seed dispersal in mid to late summer. Perennation, by regeneration of the basal rosette, ramet formation and possibly cauline rosette development, begin in late August.

Rosettes of *B. vulgaris* will grow at or below temperatures of 5°C, thus extending the growing season into the late autumn and winter months. Schreiber (1962) reported that although floral buds were present as early as February in Ithaca, New York no flowering stalks elongated until temperatures rose to 10°C.

(e) *Mycorrhiza* — Not known.

8. Reproduction

(a) *Floral biology* — Recent breeding experiments indicate that the species is primarily an outcrosser. The corolla is a bright yellow, obvious in the infrared region of the spectrum (Mulligan and Kevan 1973) and attractive to hymenopteran pollinators (Tahvanainen 1972a). Mulligan and Kevan (1973) found *B. vulgaris* to be predominantly allogamous.

Ginsberg (1983) described *B. vulgaris* as an attractive flower species for native bees in spring in New York State. However, *Apis mellifera*, an introduced species, appeared to outcompete native bees.

A detailed morphological description of the foliaceous flowers of *B. vulgaris* is given by Rohweder (1959).

(b) *Seed production and dispersal* — Salisbury (1942), in a randon sample of 25 siliques, found that seed number ranged from 3 to 21 per silique with an average of 13 ± 0.56 (SE). The average seed weight in a sample of 172 seeds was 0.0006 g and the average number of seeds for a large plant was 38 000.

Samples of 105 seeds from plants growing in favourable (open, moist) and unfavourable (closed, moist) conditions in London, ON were weighed and did not differ; the average weight per seed was 0.61 mg (± 0.15 mg standard deviation) for var. *arcuata* and 0.47 ± 0.09 mg for var. *vulgaris* (MacDonald unpublished).

Seed production in different habitats near London, ON (MacDonald 1977) ranged from 280 seeds/plant in a grass-covered dry site (5–10 seeds per silique, 10–15 siliques per branch, 3–4 branches per stalk and 1 stalk per plant) to 88 000 seeds/plant in a tilled, weeded site (20 seeds per silique, 50–60 siliques per branch, 7–8 branches per stalk and 8–12 stalks per plant). Estimates of 40 000–116 000 seeds per plant, combined with a high density of plants per unit area, have indicated that an average of 300 million seeds and up to several billion seeds could be deposited per hectare of hayfield (Kott 1963).

Seed dispersal is initiated by the mechanical force generated by dehiscence of the silique valves. Because of the lack of wind-catching devices, most seeds are deposited within a meter of the parent, the actual distance depends on plant height, surrounding vegetation, temperature and humidity (MacDonald unpublished). Seeds are covered with an adhesive mucilage which, when moistened, may either inhibit dispersal, through adherence to soil particles or vegetation, or promote dispersal, through attachment to animals (Fahn and Werker 1973). Plants of *B. vulgaris* have grown in the tops of pollarded willows near Cambridge, UK and must have reached such heights through seed dispersal (Ridley 1930).

Seeds of *B. vulgaris* can pass through a variety of animals such as cattle, horses, pigs (Salisbury 1961; Andersen 1968) and rabbits (Staniforth 1975) and remain viable. Seeds of *B. vulgaris* are also distributed in seed lots of timothy and similar sized grains. If undetected, or sold illegally, such seed lots can form the basis of large infestations (Fertig 1968). Since hay containing stems or stalks of *B. vulgaris* is refused by livestock, the seeds may be dispersed when such hay is mixed with manure and reapplied to the fields.

Little study has been made of the effect of continued submergence on the seeds of *B. vulgaris*. However, seeds are still viable after 54–57 d submergence and seeds remain afloat, even in agitated water, for several hours, long enough to facilitate dispersal (P. B. Cavers pers. obs.).

(c) *Viability of seeds and germination* — Seeds of *B. vulgaris* may remain dormant for at least 10–20 yr in the soil (MacDonald 1977). The viability and germination of these seeds are affected by moisture, degree of soil disturbance and temperature. For example, an estimated 90 000 dormant seeds/m^2 were maintained in dry disturbed soil and 3000/m^2 in wet disturbed soil (based on burial and retrieval experiments by MacDonald (1977)). Loss from the seed bank varied, as shown in Table 3. In a comparable experiment with seeds of var. *vulgaris* there were no significant differences in the proportion germinating but significantly more seeds (ca. 10% more in each treatment) died (MacDonald 1977).

Seeds shed from the parent plant in late August have no innate dormancy. However, drying (with or without an initial wetting) induces dormancy. In southern Ontario, for example, since August is often a dry month with intermittent rainfall, most seeds become dormant.

Even if conditions become favourable, few seeds germinate. Temperatures below 10°C also induce dormancy; cold autumn and winter temperatures therefore ensure little recruitment of seedlings from seeds shed in August. Neither drought nor temperature-induced dormancy are not broken immediately when the seed is returned to conditions suitable for germination. A 3- to 5-d time lag before seeds begin to germinate increases the probability that seeds will germinate when optimum conditions are available for a prolonged period (MacDonald 1977).

Baskin and Baskin (1989) buried fresh seeds of *B. vulgaris* 7 cm deep in soil in nylon mesh bags in an unheated greenhouse in Kentucky. Seed samples were exhumed monthly for over 2 yr. They found that exhumed seeds could germinate in any month of the growing season but would not germinate while buried.

In the United Kingdom, Roberts (1986) conducted a detailed study of seedling emergence in soils stirred three times per year for 5 yr. 6.4% of the seeds of *Barbarea vulgaris* emerged in the 4th and 5th years, the seventh highest percentage out of a total of 70 species.

Optimal conditions for germination of *B. vulgaris* include continuously available moisture, light of at least 14 h duration per day and alternating temperatures (25°C/day, 15°C/night). Under such conditions, all viable seeds from a nondormant sample have germinated within 5 d (MacDonald 1977).

Other researchers have tested germination at a variety of temperatures and found different temperature regimes to be optimal (e.g., 20–35°C (Toole and Toole 1939); 15–30°C (Everson 1949); or 20°–30°C (Steinbauer and Frank 1954)) and different periods needed for germination of all viable seeds (e.g., 10 d (Steinbauer and Frank 1954)). However, *B. vulgaris*, in response to variation in microenvironment (especially near the surface of the soil, exhibited a great fluctuation in dormancy within the same seed lots (Taylorson 1970). This fluctuation is at least in part a phytochrome controlled reaction (Toole 1961), with seeds consistently having more rapid germination in light. Seeds near the surface of the soil and not covered by litter or vegetation obtain sufficient light for phytochrome-mediated germination to occur (Taylorson 1972; Taylorson and Hendricks 1972; Hendricks and Taylorson 1974).

The conditions under which germination is possible are often suitable for seedling establishment (MacDonald 1977).

Table 3. Proportion of seeds of var. *arcuata* which had died or germinated during storage under four contrasting regimes (from MacDonald 1977)

	Length of storage					
	7 mo (overwinter)		12 mo		24 mo	
Storage regime	Dead	Germinated	Dead	Germinated	Dead	Germinated
Disturbed soil, dry	0.08	0.00	0.13	0.01	0.04	0.08
Disturbed soil, wet	0.19	0.38	0.17	0.51	0.34	0.70
Undisturbed soil, dry	0.05	0.00	0.05	0.01	0.04	0.09
Undisturbed soil, wet	0.12	0.10	0.12	0.06	0.14	0.69

(d) *Vegetative spread* — See perennation (Section 7b).

9. Hybrids

Given the taxonomic difficulties with this genus, the possibility of hybridization is difficult to evaluate. The complex of individuals that make up *B. vulgaris* is distinguished by characters which are given in ranges (e.g., 1 to 4 pairs of lateral lobes, persistent style 1.8–3 mm long) which overlap with those of co-occurring, closely related species. The reliance on outcrossing and on pollination by nonspecific Hymenoptera suggests a likelihood of hybridization. Hinds (1986) found that some collections from New Brunswick were intermediate between *Barbarea orthoceras* and *B. vulgaris*, thus they may represent hybridization.

10. Population Dynamics

(Most of the following is taken from Mac-Donald 1977.)

Essentially an opportunist, *B. vulgaris* is found in a wide range of disturbed or intermittently open habitats (e.g., woods, see Section 5).

Individuals of *B. vulgaris* grow most rapidly, live longest and reproduce most prolifically on recently-disturbed, moist, rich soil.

Because of the microclimatic control of germination (see Section 8(c)), most new seedling recruits in London, ON are nearly equal-aged (usually recruited over a 2- to 3-wk period in May). Additional seedlings may arise throughout the remainder of the growing season but have a poorer chance of survival than the spring-recruited ones. For example, seedlings produced in early summer often died from drought, and seedlings produced in September were not able to develop a root system sufficient to avoid frost heaving in the next spring.

On open, moist soil over half of the seedlings grow large enough (bigger than 0.06 g and six leaves) to survive over winter, become vernalized and flower in the next spring. During the growing season feeding damage by flea beetles, although heavy (removing

10–15% of the leaf surface area), did not appear to affect this growth pattern.

In woodlands, most germination occurs in the spring; many seedlings grow rapidly to or beyond the 0.06 g and 6-leaf size. However, after the leaf canopy has formed, rosettes gain little weight. None of the rosettes survive predation by slugs in the autumn after leaf fall.

In the successional sequence between these two extremes, *B. vulgaris* suffers the greatest mortality (at every stage of its life cycle) in those mesic soils dominated by grasses such as *Agropyron repens* and *Poa* spp. Seedlings are recruited as in open habitats, but the majority die before producing even one true leaf. In London, ON only about 5% reached a 6- to 8-leaf size and fewer than 1% of the ones that reached this size overwintered and flowered. Of these flowering plants, about half produced no and half produced a few (under 200) seeds.

On subhydric soils, the competitive stress from grasses is ameliorated. Seedlings are recruited in the spring and in periods following flooding during the growing season. Growth is somewhat slower than that of seedlings on open soil, but the mean weight of the seedlings is 0.06 g by September. Most mortality results from trampling, erosion and predation.

11. Response to Herbicides and Other Chemicals

In established alfalfa in the northeastern United States applications of simazine, atrazine or terbacil on 15 Sept. gave effective control of *Barbarea vulgaris* rosettes (Hastings and Kust 1970b). In Quebec alfalfa fields metribuzin at 0.56 kg ha^{-1} pre-emergence gave fairly good control while 2,4-DB at 1.4–1.68 kg ha^{-1} gave very good control (Ferron 1974). Ferron (1974) also reported that MCPA-amine or -ester and 2,4-D-amine, all at 0.42–0.56 kg ha^{-1} postemergence gave good control but 2,4-D-ester was not effective in oats, herbage legumes and newly established alfalfa. Fawcett and Jennings (1978) state that 2,4-D controls *B. vulgaris* in pastures. In oats, chlorbromuron was satisfactory

(Ferron 1974). Other herbicides which have been used to control *B. vulgaris* include chloroluron and bromoxynil (Fedorushenko 1973), lenacil (Lobanov 1973), chorsulfuron (Smirnov and Zakherenko 1984) and flurochloridone and pyridate (Bayer 1986). Herbicides applied in arable land usually encounter seedlings or young rosettes of *B. vulgaris*.

The removal of annual weeds by the application of bentazone + MCPA, or benazolin and/or bromoxynil + MCPA may create openings for *B. vulgaris* (Aamisepp 1978).

Germination of seeds of *B. vulgaris* in the laboratory was inhibited by 20–200 mg L^{-1} of chlormequat chloride or daminozide (Hintikka 1988). This induced dormancy could be broken by treatment with gibberellic acid.

The Ontario Weed Committee (Anonymous 1987) recommends an application of 2,4-D (LV ester) at 0.84 to 1.1 kg ha^{-1} in September or October, or in early May before flowering of *B. vulgaris*. The Ontario Weed Committee rates yellow rocket as susceptible to 2,4-D, resistant to MCPB and controlled by higher than normal rates or repeated applications of MCPA or 2,4-DB.

12. Response to Other Human Manipulations

Muenscher (1980) suggested disking or harrowing badly infested fields in late summer and early autumn, and mowing low enough to cut off all the flowering stalks. However, rosettes which are clipped and root systems which are fragmented often regenerate. Plants which have produced seeds should not be clipped because the seeds are dispersed (and will be viable even if the inflorescence is still green when clipped) and the basal rosettes regenerate (Schreiber 1962; MacDonald, unpublished). The Ontario Weed Committee recommends mowing rather than herbicide-application when the plants are flowering (Anonymous 1987). In Russia, Kott (1967) found that early autumn ploughing completely destroys the weed in the rosette stage. Kott also reported that mowing down flowering plants 40–60 cm high to 10–15 cm in May killed most plants.

Effective seed cleaning, hand-pulling of initially rare specimens, and, in some places, the use of smother crops or repeated cultivation most effectively exhausts the seed bank of the species.

13. Response to Parasites and Herbivores

A list of diseases of *B. vulgaris* in North America includes: *Albugo candida* (Pers. ex Chev.) Kuntze, white-rust; *Alternaria* sp., leaf spot; *Cercospora barbarea* (Sacc.) Chupp, leaf spot; *Peronospora parasitica* Pers. ex Fr., downy mildew; *Ramularia barbareae* Pk., leaf spot; *Sclerotium rolfsii* Sacc., stem rot; *Xanthomonas barbareae* Burkh., black rot; *Ruga verrucosans*, curly top virus; *Aureogenus vastans*, yellow dwarf virus (all the above from Anonymous (1960)); potato-yellow dwarf virus (King 1966); cucumber mosaic virus (Bruckart and Lorbeer 1976; Rist and Lorbeer 1989); *Plasmodiophora brassicae* Wor. (Conners 1967); *Spiroplasma citri* which causes brittle root disease of horseradish (O'Hayer et al. 1982); *Sclerotinia* spp. (in the seedling stage, or after mechanical damage to rosettes, Morgan (1971)). In Europe it is also a host of *Erysimum* latent virus (Shukla et al. 1976).

In North America *B. vulgaris* is attacked by the southern root-knot nematode, *Meloidogyne incognita* (Davidson and Townshend 1967) and the northern root-knot nematode, *Meloidogyne hapla* ((Townshend and Davidson 1962). In Europe, nematodes attacking *B. vulgaris* include *Heterodera schactii* (Oostenbrink 1955) and *Ditylenchus destructor* (Ivanova 1973).

A list of insect herbivores in North America includes the aphids *Brevicoryne brassicae* (Root and Olson 1969) and *Aphis nasturtii* (Root and Tahvanainen 1969); the black cutworm moth, *Agrotis ipsilon* (Busching and Turpin 1976); the cabbage maggot, *Hylemya brassicae* (Nair et al. 1973); the flea beetles *Phyllotreta bipustulata*, *P. striolata*, *P. zimmermanni* and *P. cruciferae* (Tahvanainen 1972; Hicks and Tahvanainen 1974) and *Psylloides napi*, *P. chrysocephala*, *P. punctulata* and *P. cuprea* (Tahvanainen and Root 1970; Hicks and Tahvanainen 1974); and cabbage white butterflies *Pieris brassicae* and *P. rapae* (R. J. Staniforth pers. commun.). In Vermont, *B. vulgaris* is the main food plant of *Pieris rapae* (Chew 1981). Hicks and

Tahvanainen (1974) reported that the main flea beetles associated with *Barbarea vulgaris* are *Psylloides napi* (the dominant species); *Phyllotreta striolata* and *P. cruciferae*. Root and Tahvanainen (1969) carried out an extensive study of invertebrates associated with *B. vulgaris* near Ithaca, New York.

A list of casual visitors in southern Ontario includes: *Colemeogilla maculata* Lengitimb., ladybug; *Pegomyia affinis* Grp., a dipteran leaf miner; *Coccinella transversoguttata*, ladybug; *Tachyporus nitidulus*, Junebug; and the hymenopterans *Chrysocharis parksi* and *Dacnusa* spp. (P. Cavers, pers. obs.); plus the hymenopterans *Dialictus perpunctatus; Andrena phippotes; Halictus rubicundus;* and *Apis mellifera* (MacDonald unpublished).

In Europe and Asia many of the above insects attack *B. vulgaris*. In northern India the aphids *Brevicoryne barbareae* and *B. brassicae* are important (David and Hameed 1975; Hameed et al. 1977). In Britain, plants of *B. vulgaris* are poor for survival of the pierid butterfly *Anthocharis cardamines* (L.) but many eggs are deposited on the inflorescences because they are large and persistent (Courtney 1982). Shukla et al. (1976) found that flea beetles (*Phyllotreta* spp.) transmitted *Erysimum* latent virus from *B. vulgaris*.

In North America, attacks on *B. vulgaris* are made by slugs, *Deroceras reticulatum* (*Agriolimax reticulatum*) (Pimentel 1961; Tahvanainen and Root 1972) and by the higher plant parasite *Cuscuta gronovis* Willd. (dodder) (Anonymous 1960).

ACKNOWLEDGMENTS

Financial support through an NRC scholarship (M.A.M.) and an NSERC Operating Grant (to P.B.C.) is gratefully acknowledged. We thank Stefani Tichbourne for typing the manuscript and Marguerite Kane for two drawings in Figure 2. G. A. Mulligan, W. Cody, S. Warwick and other staff of the Biosystematics Research Institute provided invaluable assistance and advice. We thank Suzanne Warwick and an anonymous referee for critical reviews of the manuscript and Cathy Major for assistance in checking references.

Aamisepp, A. 1978. Remaining effect of chemical control in a first-year clover-grass ley. Weeds and Weed Control, 19th Swedish Weed Conference, Uppsala, Sweden, D 1-2; 62.

Agriculture Canada. 1967. Seeds Act and Regulations. Queen's Printer, Ottawa, ON. 50 pp.

Alex, J. F., Cayouette, R. and Mulligan, G. A. 1980. Common and botanical names of weeds in Canada. Agriculture Canada, Ottawa, ON. 132 pp.

Alex, J. F. and Switzer, C. M. 1983. Ontario Weeds. Ontario Ministry of Agriculture and Food, Toronto, ON. Publ. no. 505, 200 pp.

Andersen, R. N. 1968. Germination and establishment of weeds for experimental purposes. Weed Sci. Soc Am. 236 pp.

Anonymous 1930. Weeds and weed seeds illustrated and described. Department of Agriculture Bull. 137, Ottawa, ON. 72 pp.

Anonymous 1960. Index of plant diseases in the United States. Agric. Handbook No. 165. Crops Research Division, Agric. Res. Service, USDA, Washington, DC. 531 pp.

Anonymous 1971. Common weeds of the United States. USDA Publ., Dover Pub. Inc., New York, NY. 463 pp.

Anonymous 1976. The noxious weed Act, Manitoba. Chapter N110, Queen's Printer Winnipeg, MB.

Anonymous 1977a. Regulations to the Weed Control Act (Nova Scotia). Publication 10. Queen's Printer, Halifax, NS.

Anonymous 1977b. Agriculture Abuses Act. Division IV, Noxious Weeds, Quebec, Queen's Printer, Quebec, PQ.

Anonymous 1981. Revised Regulation N110-R1, The Noxious Weeds Act, Manitoba, Queen's Printer, Winnipeg, MB.

Anonymous 1987. Guide to chemical weed control. Publication 75. Ontario Ministry of Agriculture and Food, Toronto, ON AGDEX 641.

Anonymous 1988. Weed Control Act, 1988. Statutes of Ontario 1988. Chapter 51 and Regulation 944. Revised Regulations of Ontario, 1980 as amended to O. Reg. 531/88. Queen's Printer for Ontario, Toronto, ON.

Baldwin, W. K. W. 1958. Plants of the Clay Belt of Northern Ontario and Quebec. Bulletin 156, National Museum of Canada, Ottawa, ON.

Baskin, J. M. and Baskin, C. C. 1989. Seasonal changes in the germination responses of buried seeds of *Barbarea vulgaris*. Can. J. Bot. **67:** 2131–2134.

Bayer, G. H. 1986. Weed control in winter wheat. Proc. 40th Annual Meeting of NE Weed Science Society, Ithaca, NY. p. 57.

Boivin, B. 1972. Flora of the Prairie Provinces III. Phytologia **22:** 315–398.

Bruckart, W. L. and Lorbeer, J. W. 1976. Cucumber mosaic virus in weed host near commercial fields of lettuce and celery. Phytopathology **66**: 253–259.

Busching, M. K. and Turpin, F. T. 1976. Oviposition preference of black cutworm moths among various crop plants, weeds and plant debris. Economic Entomol. **69**: 587–590.

Chew, F. S. 1981. Coexistence and local extinction in two Pierid butterflies. Am. Nat. **118**: 655–672.

Clapham, A. R., Tutin, T. G. and Warburg, E. F. 1962. Flora of the British Isles. Cambridge University Press, Cambridge, UK. 1269 pp.

Conners, I. L. 1967. An annotated index of plant diseases in Canada and fungi recorded on plants in Alaska, Canada, and Greenland. Department of Agriculture, Ottawa, ON. Publ. 1251, 381 pp.

Courtney, S. P. 1982. Coevolution of pierid butterflies and their cruciferous foodplants. IV. Crucifer apparency and *Anthocharis cardamines* (L.) oviposition. Oecologia **52**: 258–265.

David, S. K. and Hameed, S. F. 1975., One new species and two new records of aphids (Homoptera: Aphididae) from Lahaul in N.W. Himalaya. Oriental Insects **9**: 213–219.

Davidson, T. R. and Townshend, J. L. 1967. Some weed hosts of the southern root-knot nematode, *Meloidogyne incognita*. Nematologica **13**: 452–458.

Delorit, R. J. 1970. An illustrated taxonomy manual of weed seeds. Agron. Publ., River Falls, WI. 175 pp.

Doll, J. D. 1980. Survey of pasture weeds in Wisconsin. Proc. NC Weed Control Conf. **34**: 96–98.

Doll, J. D. and Quinones, A. 1983. 1983 survey of perennial weeds in Wisconsin. Proc. NC Weed Control Conf. (1983) 53–63.

Dutt, T. E., Harvey, R. G. and Fawcett, R. S. 1982. Feed quality of hay containing perennial broadleaf weeds. Agron. J. **74**: 673–676.

Erskine, D. S. 1960. Plants of Prince Edward Island. Canada Department of Agriculture, Ottawa, ON. Publ. 1088, 270 pp.

Everson, L. E. 1949. Preliminary studies to establish laboratory methods for the germination of weed seeds. Proc. Assoc. Offic. Seed Analysts. N. Am. **39**: 84–89.

Fahn, A. and Werker, E. 1973. Anatomical mechanisms of seed dispersal. Pages 151–221 *in* T. T. Kozlowski, ed. Seed biology, importance, development and germination. Vol. I. Academic Press, New York, NY.

Fawcett, R. S. and Jennings, V. M. 1978. Today's weed: yellow rocket. Weeds Today **9**: 21.

Fedorushenko, V. S. 1973. Application of herbicides to peas. [in Russian]. Zashchita Rastenii **4**: 17.

Feeny, P., Paauwe, K. L. and Demong, N. J. 1970. Flea beetles and mustard oils: Host plant specificity of *Phyllotreta cruciferae* and *P. striolata* adults (Coleoptera: Chrysomelidae). Ann. Entomol. Soc. Am. **63**: 832–841.

Ferron, M. 1974. [Winter cress control trials in 1972]. Division de la Defense des Cultures, Quebec. [in French]. Page 97 *in* Canada, Conseil des Recherches et Services Agricoles du Quebec **18**: 150 pp.

Ferron, M. et Cayouette, R. 1971. Noms des mauvaises herbes du Quebec. 2nd ed. Min. Agric. Colonisation, Quebec, PQ. 113 pp.

Fertig, S. N. 1963. Yellow Rocket, a difficult weed problem. Farm Res. **29**: 4–5.

Fertig, S. N., Huddleston, J. H. and Furrer, A. H. 1963. The effect of stage of maturity and ensiling on the viability of yellow rocket (*Barbarea vulgaris*) seed. Proc. NE Weed Control Conf. **17**: 352–356.

Fertig, S. N. 1968. Broadleaf weed problems of the Northeast Weed Control Conference. Proc. NE Weed Control Conf. **22**: 19–26.

Finch, S. and Ackley, C. M. 1977. Cultivated and wild host plants supporting populations of the cabbage root fly. Ann. Appl. Biol. **85**: 13–22.

Frankton, C. and Mulligan, G. A. 1970. Weeds of Canada. Queen's Printer, Ottawa, ON. Publ. 948, 217 pp.

Ginsberg, H. S. 1983. Foraging ecology of bees in an old field. Ecology **64**: 165–175.

Gleason, H. A. and Cronquist, A. 1963. Manual of vascular plants of Northeastern United States and adjacent Canada. D. van Nostrand, Princeton, NJ. 810 pp.

Godwin, H. 1960. The history of weeds in Britain. Pages 1–10 *in* J. L. Harper, ed. The biology of weeds. Blackwell, Oxford, UK. 256 pp.

Gressell, J. B. and Holm, L. G. 1964. Chemical inhibition of crop germination by weed seeds and the nature of inhibition by *Abutilon theophrasti*. Weed Res. **4**: 44–53.

Hameed, S., Sud, V. and Giamzo, S. 1977. New records of aphids from Kulu and Lahaul valleys (Himachal Pradesh). Indian Entomol. **37**: 203–205.

Hastings, R. E. and Kust, C. A. 1970a. Reserve carbohydrate storage and utilization by yellow rocket, white cockle and hoary alyssum. Weed Sci. **18**: 140–148.

Hastings, R. E. and Kust, C. A. 1970b. Control of yellow rocket and white cockle in established alfalfa. Weed Sci. **18**: 329–333.

Hendricks, S. B. and Taylorson, R. B. 1974. Promotion of seed germination by nitrate, nitrite, hydroxylamine and ammonium salts. Plant Physiol. **54**: 304–309.

Hicks, K. L. and Tahvanainen, J. O. 1974. Niche differentiation by crucifer-feeding flea beetles (Coleoptera: Chrysomelidae). Am. Midl. Nat. **91**: 406–423.

Himme, M. van, Stryckers, J. and Bulcke, R. 1984. [Strawberries] Aardbei. Mededelingen van het Centrum voor Onkruidonderzoek van de Rijksuniversiteit Gent **40**: 107–108. [Nl]

Himme, M. van, Stryckers, J. and Bulcke, R. 1985. [Cucurbits: gherkins; courgettes] Komkommerachtigen: augurk; mergpompoen (''courgette''). Mededeling van het Centrum voor Onkruidonderzoek van de Rijksuniversiteit Gent **42**: 109–112. [Nl]

Hinds, H. R. 1986. The flora of New Brunswick. Primrose Press, Fredericton, NB. 460 pp.

Hintikka, V. 1988. Induction of secondary dormancy in seeds of *Barbarea stricta* and *B. vulgaris* by chlormequat and daminozide, and its termination by gibberellic acid. Weed Res. **28**: 7–11.

Howitt, J. E. and MacLeod, J. D. 1948. The Weeds of Ontario. Ontario Department of Agriculture Bull. 409, Toronto, ON. 129 pp.

Ivanova, I. V. 1973. The infection rate of weeds with the nematode *Ditylenchus destructor*. Byulleten 'Vsesoyuznogo Instituta Gel'mintologii im K. I. Skryabina **11**: 39–42.

Keever, C. 1980. Mechanisms of plant succession on old fields of Lancaster County, Pennsylvania. Bull. Torrey Bot. Club. **106**: 299–308.

King, L. J. 1966. Weeds of the world, biology and control. Interscience Publishers Inc., New York, NY. 526 pp.

Kjaer, A. 1960. Naturally derived isothiocyanates (mustard oils) and their parent glucosides. Fortschr. Chem. Org. Naturstoffe **18**: 122–176.

Kjaer, A. and Gmelin, R. 1957. *iso* Thiocyanates XXVIII. A new *iso*thiocyanate glucoside (glucobarbarin) furnishing (-)-5-phenyl-2-oxazolidinethione upon enzymatic hydrolysis. Acta Chem. Scand. **11**: 906–907.

Korovka, L. S. 1976. Ascorbic acid content of wild-growing edible plants of the Komi-Permiak National Okrug. Vopr. Pitan **6**: 76–77. (In Russian.)

Korsmo, E. 1954. Anatomy of weeds. Kirstes Boktrykkeri, O. Grondahl and Sons, Oslo, Norway. 413 pp.

Kott, S. A. 1963. Biology of the common winter cress (*Barbarea vulgaris*) Bot. Zhur. (Leningrad) **48**: 1648–1652. (In Russian.)

Kott, S. A. 1967. Control of yellow rocket. Zemledelie, Mosk. **29**: 48.

Lindsay, D. R. and Bassett, I. J. 1951. Preliminary report on the life history of yellow rocket (*Barbarea vulgaris* R.Br.) Proc. Nat. Weed Com. Canada, East Sec. **5**: 73–75.

Lobanov, V. E. 1973. The effectiveness of Ro-neet and lenacil in sugar-beet crops. L'gov. opyt-delekts. Khimiya v Sel'skom Khozyaistve **11**: 452–453. (In Russian.)

MacDonald, M. A. 1977. Effects of environmental heterogeneity on the abundance of *Barbarea vulgaris* R.Br. Ph.D. Thesis, University of Western Ontario, London, ON.

MacDonald, M. A. and Cavers, P. B. 1974. Cauline rosettes — an asexual means of reproduction and dispersal occurring after seed formation in *Barbarea vulgaris* (yellow rocket). Can. J. Bot. **52**: 913–918.

Macoun, J. and Gibson, J. 1878. Synopsis of the flora of the valley of the St. Lawrence and Great Lakes. Can. Jour. N.S. **15**: 51 et seq.

Manton, I. 1932. Introduction to the cytology of the Cruciferae. Ann. Bot. **46**: 509–556.

Montgomery, F. H. 1955. Common weeds of Ontario. Ontario Department of Agriculture. Bull. 505, Toronto, ON. 104 pp.

Montgomery, F. H. 1957. The introduced plants of Ontario growing outside of cultivation (Part II). Roy. Can. Inst. Trans., (Toronto) **32**: 3–35.

Morgan, O. D. 1971. A study of four weed hosts of *Sclerotinia* species in alfalfa fields. Plant Dis. Rep. **55**: 1087–1089.

Muenscher, W. C. 1980. Weeds. Cornell University Press, Ithaca, NY. 586 pp.

Mulligan, G. A. 1959. Chromosome numbers of Canadian Weeds II. Can. J. Bot. **37**: 81–92.

Mulligan, G. A. 1976. Common weeds of Canada. Information Canada/Agriculture Canada/McClelland and Stewart Ltd., Toronto, ON. 140 pp.

Mulligan, G. A. 1978. *Barbarea stricta* Andrz., a new introduction to Quebec. Naturaliste Canadien **105**: 297–298.

Mulligan, G. A. and Kevan, P. G. 1973. Color, brightness, and other floral characteristics attracting insects to the blossoms of some Canadian weeds. Can. J. Bot. **51**: 1939–1952.

Nair, K. S., McEwen, F. L. and Alex, J. F. 1973. Oviposition and development of *Hylemya brassicae* (Bouche) (Diptera: Anthomyiidae) on cruciferous weeds. Proc. Entomol. Soc. Ontario **104**: 11–15.

Nesterova, O. A. and Chukanova, O. V. 1981. [The harmfulness of the predominant weed species in wheat]. (In Russian.) Sibirskii Vestnik Sel'skohozyaistvennoi Nauki **5**: 9–13.

Nowicki, B. 1973. Host range of the fungus *Plasmodiophora brassicae* Wor. Acta AGrobot. **26**: 53–61.

Nuttall, T. 1818. The genera of North American plants and a catalogue of the species of the year 1817. D. Hearth, Philadelphia, PA. 254 pp.

O'Hayer, K., Schultz, G., Eastman, C., Fletcher, J. and Goodman, R. 1982. The aster leafhopper *Macrosteles fascifrons:* a newly discovered vector of *Spiroplasma citri*. Phytopathology **72**: 1005.

Oostenbrink, M. 1955. Over da waardplanten van het bietencystenaaltje, *Heterodera schachtii* Schmidt. Versl. Meded Plantenziektenkd **127**: 186–193.

Palmer, E. L. 1962. The mustard plants: Staple foods and nuisance weeds can be found in crucifer family. Nat. Hist. NY. **71**: 33–44.

Pimentel, D. 1961. Species diversity and insect population outbreaks. Ann. Entomol. Soc. Am. **54**: 76–86.

Rabotnov, T. 1964. About the biology of Monocarpic Perennial Meadow Plants. Moscow Soc. Natur. **71**: 47–55. (In Russian.)

Ridley, H. N. 1930. The dispersal of plants throughout the world. L. Reeve & Co., Ashford, UK. 744 pp.

Rist, D. L. and Lorbeer, J. W. 1989. Occurrence and overwintering of cucumber mosaic virus and broad bean wilt virus in weeds growing near commercial lettuce fields in New York. Phytopathology **79**: 65–69.

Rohweder, O. 1959. Uber verlaubte Bluten von *Barbarea vulgaris* RBr and ihre morphologische Bedeutung. Flora oder Allgemeine Botanische Zeitung **148**: 255–282.

Roberts, H. A. 1986. Seed persistence in soil and seasonal emergence in plant species from different habitats. J. Appl. Ecol. **23**: 639–656.

Root, R. B. and Olson, A. M. 1969. Population increase of the cabbage aphid, *Brevicoryne brassicae*, on different host plants. Can. Entomol. **101**: 768–773.

Root, R. B., and Tahvanainen, J. O. 1969. Role of winter cress, *Barbarea vulgaris*, as a temporal host in the seasonal development of the crucifer fauna. Ann. Entomol. Soc. Am. **62**: 852–855.

Rousseau, C. 1968. Histoire, habitat, et distribution de 220 plantes introduites au Québec. Naturaliste Canadien **95**: 49–171.

Salisbury, E. J. 1942. The reproductive capacity of plants. Bell, London, U.K. 244 pp.

Salisbury, E. J. 1961. Weeds and aliens. Collins New Naturalist Series, London, U.K. 384 pp.

Schreiber, M. M. 1962. Growth, development and perennial nature of yellow rocket. Weeds **10**: 91–95.

Schreiber, M. M. and Fertig, S. N. 1955. The chemical composition of yellow rocket (*Barbarea vulgaris*). Agron. J. **47**: 104–105.

Scoggan, H. J. 1951. Botanical investigations along the Hayes River route, northern Manitoba. Annual Report of the National Museum of Canada for the Fiscal Year 1949–1950. Bulletin **123**: 139–161.

Shukla, D. D., Proeseler, G. and Schmelzer, K. 1976. Studies on viruses and virus diseases of cruciferous plants. XVIII. Beetle transmission and some new natural hosts of *Erysimum* latent virus. Acta Phytopathol. Acad. Sci. Hung. **10**: 211–215.

Smirnov, B. A. and Zakharenko, A. V. 1984. [Application of glean to barley.] Zashchita Rastenii **4**: 19. (In Russian.)

Staniforth, R. J. 1975. The comparative ecology of three riverbank annuals, *Polygonum lapathifolium* L., *P. pensylvanicum* L. and *P. persicaria* L. Ph.D. thesis. University of Western Ontario, London, ON.

Steinbauer, G. P. and Frank, P. 1954. Primary dormancy and germination requirements of seeds of certain Cruciferae. Assoc. Offic. Seed Anal. Proc. **44**: 176–181.

Tahvanainen, J. O. 1972a. Phenology and microhabitat selection of some flea beetles (Coleoptera: Chrysomelidae) on wild and cultivated crucifers in central New York. Entomol. Scand. **3**: 120–138.

Tahvanainen, J. O. 1972b. Population biology of crucifer-D feeding flea beetles (Coleoptera: Chrysomelidae). Diss Abstr. Int. **32**: 5234-B.

Tahvanainen, J. O. and Root, R. B. 1970. The invasion and population outbreak of *Psylloides napi* (Coleoptera: Chrysomelidae) on yellow rocket (*Barbarea vulgaris*) in New York. Ann. Entomol. Soc. Am. **63**: 1479–1480.

Tahvanainen, J. O. and Root, R. B. 1972. The influence of vegetational diversity on the population ecology of a specialized herbivore, *Phyllotreta cruciferae* (Coleoptera: Chrysomelidae). Oecologia **10**: 321–346.

Taylorson, R. B. 1970. Changes in dormancy and viability of weed seeds in soils. Weed Sci. **18**: 265–269.

Taylorson, R. B. 1972. Phytochrome controlled changes in dormancy and germination of buried weed seeds. Weed Sci. **20**: 417–422.

Taylorson, R. B. and Hendricks, S. B. 1972. Interactions of light and a temperature shift on seed germination. Plant Physiol. **49**: 127–130.

Thomas, A. G. and Wise, R. 1982. The 1981 weed survey of cultivated land in Manitoba.

Agriculture Canada Weed Survey Series, Regina, SK. Publ. No. 82-1, 124 pp.

Titov, V. S. and Babakov, V. P. 1988. Germination of weed seeds and weediness of crop stands when using organic fertilizers. Agrokhimiya **2**: 37–41. (In Russian.)

Toole, E. H. 1961. The effect of light and other variables on the control of seed germination. Assoc. Offic. Seed Analysts, Fifty Year's Seed Testing 1908–1958: 41–45.

Toole, E. H. and Toole, V. K. 1939. Germination of some *Brassica* types at different temperatures. Proc. Int. Seed Testing Assoc. **11**: 51–56.

Townshend, J. L. and Davidson, T. R. 1962. Some weed hosts of the northern root-knot nematode, *Meloidogyne hapla* Chitwood, 1949, in Ontario. Can. J. Bot. **40**: 543–548.

Werner, P. A. 1977. Colonization success of a biennial plant species: experimental field studies of species cohabitation and replacement. Ecology **58**: 840–849.

Zennie, T. M. and Ogzewalla, C. D. 1977. Ascorbic acid and vitamin A content of edible wild plants of Ohio and Kentucky. Econ. Bot. **31**: 76–79.

The biology of Canadian weeds. 98
Potentilla anserina L.

K. Miyanishi[1], O. Eriksson[2] and R. W. Wein[3]

[1] *Department of Geography, University of Guelph, Guelph, Ontario, Canada N1G 2W1;*
[2] *Department of Botany, University of Stockholm, Stockholm, Sweden; and* [3] *Boreal Institute for Northern Studies and Department of Forest Science, University of Alberta, Edmonton, Alberta, Canada T6G 2E9. Received 22 Aug. 1990, accepted 23 January 1991.*

Miyanishi, K., Eriksson, O. and Wein, R. W. 1991. **The biology of Canadian weeds. 98.** *Potentilla anserina* **L.** Can. J. Plant Sci. **71**: 791–801. *Potentilla anserina* L., silverweed (Rosaceae), occurs in all provinces of Canada as well as in the two territories. Although generally found in wet sandy areas along rivers and on beaches, silverweed also occurs in waste areas, along roadsides, and in lawns. This shade-intolerant stoloniferous plant has recently become dominant in overgrazed sedge meadows of the Peace-Athabasca Delta, resulting in deterioration of portions of the primary range for wood bison in Wood Buffalo National Park in northern Alberta. This contribution presents both a review of the literature and some original data on the biology and ecology of the species.

Key words: Silverweed, disturbance, ecology, herbaceous perennial, demography

Miyanishi, K., Eriksson, O. et Wein, R. W. 1991. **Biologie des adventices canadiennes. 98.** *Potentilla anserina* **L.** Can. J. Plant Sci. **71**: 791–801. L'argentine, *Potentilla anserina* L. (Rosacées), pousse dans toutes les provinces du Canada et les deux territoires. Bien qu'elle affectionne habituellement les sols sablonneux humides, près des rivières et sur les plages, on la trouve aussi dans les dépotoirs, le long des routes et sur les pelouses. Cette plante stonolifère, qui tolère mal l'ombre a récemment envahi des prés de carex surexploités du delta de la Rivière-de-la-Paix et de l'Athabasca, ce qui a entraîné la détérioration d'une partie des parcours où vit le bison des bois du parc national Wood Buffalo, dans le nord de l'Alberta. Le présent document procède à une revue bibliographique de la biologie et de l'écologie de l'argentine et y ajoute quelques données originales.

Mots clés: Argentine, perturbation, écologie, herbacées vivaces, démographie

1. Name
Potentilla anserina L. — **silverweed** (Canada Weed Committee 1969), wild or goose-tansy, silver-feather, argentina, dog's-tansy, goose-grass (Britton and Brown 1913), goose potentil (Panigrahi and Dixit 1980); **potentille ansérine**, argentine, richette, ansérine, argent, argentille, bec d'oie, drisérine, herbe, potentille, herbe à clef, herbe aux oies, iris d'argentine, panne, pied d'oie, quintefeuille (Ferron and Cayouette 1970); Rosaceae, rose family, Rosacées.

Synonyms listed by Britton and Brown (1913) include *Argentina anserina* (L.)

Rydb., *A. vulgaris* Lam., *A. Babcockiana* Rydb., and *A. litoralis* Rydb. Smaller northern plants have been either designated as a subspecies or given species status as *Argentina egedii* (Britton and Brown 1913) or *Potentilla egedii* Wormsk. (Trelawny 1983). *Potentilla egedii* is usually distinguished not only by its smaller size but also by its glabrous stolons and the lack of silvery pubescence of the leaflets (Trelawny 1983). *P. pacifica* J. T. Howell has also been included as a subspecies of *P. anserina* (Rousi 1965).

2. Description and Account of Variation
Potentilla anserina is an herbaceous perennial stoloniferous rosette plant, spreading by

long slender often reddish runners 30–90 cm long with internodes 10–15 cm long and capable of rooting and starting new plants at internodes. Leaves are in basal tufts, are 10–45 cm long, petiolate and pinnately compound with 7–25 paired leaflets that generally increase in size toward the tip (Fig. 1). Leaflets are all sharply serrate, dark green and glabrous above, distinctively silvery-grey and silky-pubescent on the under surface. The solitary flowers, 2–2.5 cm across, grow on leafless stalks 2–10 cm high which develop on basal peduncles from nodes on the runner. The five yellow petals are broadly oval or obovate, entire or emarginate, 7–10 mm long, slightly longer than sepals. Stamens number 20–25; style is filiform and lateral; receptacle is villous; achenes are numerous, more or less corky, and grooved at the upper end.

This species is highly variable with morphological variations involving glabrous or pubescent leaves and stolons, small or large leaves, green or silvery leaves, entire or divided bractlets, distinctly or indistinctly grooved achenes. On the basis of such differences, Hultén (1968) has separated the northern plants into *Potentilla anserina* subsp. *Egedii; P. Egedii* Wormsk. subsp. *Egedii* var. *Egedii* and var. *groenlandica* (Tratt.) Polunin; *P. Egedii* subsp. *grandis* (Torr. & Gray) Hult. and subsp. *yukonensis* (Hult.) Hult. However, Porsild and Cody (1980) could find no distinctions between specimens identified as *P. anserina* and *P. Egedii* spp. *yukonensis* on the basis of achene or bractlet characteristics.

Three different chromosome numbers have been reported by Rousi (1965) from plants in Europe, North America and New Zealand ($2n=4x=28$, $2n=5x=35$ and $2n=6x=42$). Tetraploids ($2n=28$) and hexaploids ($2n=42$) have also been recorded in plants from California (Hughes and Janick 1974) and from England (Goswami and Matfield 1975). Tetraploids appear to be more common than hexaploids (Ockendon and Walters 1970) and no morphological distinctions have been found associated with ploidy level (Cobon and Matfield 1976). No diploids have been found in this species aggregate and no chromosome numbers for Canadian specimens have been reported in the literature.

The common name, silverweed, derives from the distinctive silvery aspect of the lower surface of the leaves and the pinnately compound leaves distinguish this species from all other cinquefoils which have palmate leaves.

3. Economic Importance

(a) *Detrimental* - Although generally a plant of low wet meadows, mudflats and lake and slough margins (Porsild 1974), this species is also listed as a weed of waste areas, roadsides and lawns (Alex and Switzer 1976; McKay and Catling 1979), northern human settlements (Porsild and Cody 1980), and pastures and meadows (Eriksson 1986a) and has been considered an important weed of horticultural crops in England (Clay 1987). It is included in Agriculture Canada's inventory of Canadian weeds (Crompton et al. 1988). Recent observations of important summer feeding grounds of bison in Wood Buffalo National Park in northern Alberta indicate that the drier meadows of the Peace-Athabasca Delta, no longer seasonally flooded since completion of the Bennett dam on the Peace River, are becoming virtual monospecific stands of silverweed following disturbance by bison (Fig. 2). Since this plant is not a forage species for bison, such invasions result in degradation of bison habitat.

(b) *Beneficial* - The fleshy roots of this species are edible raw or cooked (Peterson 1978) and apparently have a taste similar to sweet potatoes or parsnips when harvested in early spring (Fernald and Kinsey 1958). The young shoots can also be eaten as salad (Panigrahi and Dixit 1980). North American Indians as well as northern Europeans have at times relied on silverweed roots as an emergency food (Fernald and Kinsey 1958). It has reportedly been ground and used as fodder for domestic animals such as geese (Ridley 1930). The leaves contain 198 ppm of vitamin E and the whole herb is considered to possess astringent, spasmolytic, tonic and vulnerary properties. As an herbal medicine, it is prescribed in the form of a tea or in wine for diarrhoea, leukorrhea, kidney stones, arthritis and cramps (Panigrahi and Dixit

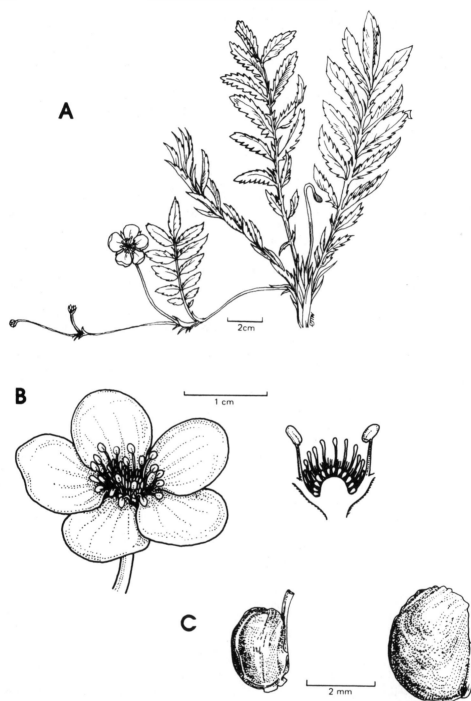

Fig. 1. (a) Mature flowering silverweed (*Potentilla anserina* L.), (b) flower and cross section illustrating the numerous ovaries on the receptacle, and (c) ripe seed.

Fig. 2. Example of the extent of ground cover by silverweed in some meadows in the Peace-Athabasca Delta, Wood Buffalo National Park, Alberta, Canada.

1980). This species is also listed as a rich source (up to 17.5% of root dry weight) of tannins as well as a source of dyes for wool (Chopra et al. 1956). Because of its vegetative reproduction, it may also be used as a ground cover to alleviate erosional problems along river banks and road cuts, particularly in wet areas.

(c) *Legislation* - This species is not currently listed in any Federal or Provincial Weed or Seed Acts.

4. Geographical Distribution

Potentilla is a major genus of the Rosaceae with 305 species and numerous natural hybrids (Wolf 1908). Both the genus *Potentilla* and the species *P. anserina* are widely distributed in cool temperate regions of the whole northern hemisphere (Torrey and Gray 1969). Silverweed has been recorded in North America, Europe, Asia, South America and Australia (Panigrahi and Dixit 1980). In North America silverweed is found along the Atlantic coast to Greenland, north to Alaska, Yukon and the Northwest Territories, west to British Columbia and California, and south to New Mexico (Britton and Brown 1913). Within Canada it occurs in every province as well as in both territories (Fig. 3). The northern limit recorded for this species is Inuvik, NWT (lat. 68°23′N).

5. Habitat

(a) *Climatic requirements* - Given its wide latitudinal range from the Northwest Territories to California, this species appears to have a very wide tolerance for a range of climatic conditions. Although recorded north of the Arctic Circle, silverweed is generally considered to be non-arctic (Porsild and Cody 1980) and non-alpine (Porsild 1974).

(b) *Substratum* - *Potentilla anserina* has been reported on mesic to wet, gravelly or sandy, coarse-textured soils in fresh, alkaline or

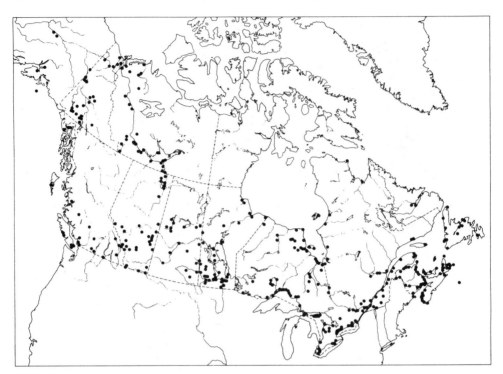

Fig. 3. Distribution of *Potentilla anserina* in Canada from specimens in the following herbaria: ALTA, CAN, DOA, OAC, TRT, UNB (herbarium abbreviations from Holmgren and Keuken (1974)).

saline conditions along rivers and shores of lakes and ponds (Currah et al. 1983), in low meadows, marshy ground, ditches, mudflats, slough margins (Porsild 1974), and often on calcareous or even marly soils (Cormack 1977; Voss 1985) as well as on rock outcrops of sandstones and micaceous rocks (Panigrahi and Dixit 1980).

(c) *Communities in which the species occurs* - In a vegetation survey of a James Bay coastal marsh (Ringius 1980), silverweed was a major component of the community occupying mounds within a salt pan inland from the mean daily high tide line. Other species in the community included *Carex paleacea, Triglochin maritima, Galium labradoricum*, and *Festuca rubra*.

A vegetation survey was also conducted in a meadow in the freshwater Peace-Athabasca Delta along the northern shore of Lake Claire. The density of silverweed ramets was highest in the driest most exposed portion of the meadow which was also the most highly disturbed by bison (Fig. 4). On either side of the bison trails, silverweed formed virtual monocultures. Silverweed declined in abundance with increasing moisture availability as the meadow became dominated by *Carex* spp. Other species associated with silverweed at the drier end of the meadow included *Hordeum jubatum, Sonchus uliginosus, Anemone canadensis, Agropyron trachycaulum* and *Potentilla norvegica*.

In a vegetation survey of footpaths and vehicle tracks in a sand dune ecosystem, silverweed was found to be a major indicator species of disturbance by trampling along with *Bellis perennis, Poa pratensis* and *Juncus articulatus* (Liddle and Greig-Smith 1976).

6. History
Considered native to North America (Scoggan 1978; Crompton et al. 1988), no information

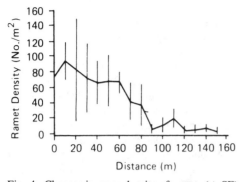

Fig. 4. Changes in mean density of ramets (± SE) of silverweed along transects dissecting a meadow, starting at the permanently exposed driest end (0 m) to the permanently submerged end (240 m).

is available from historical references of any changes in its abundance or distribution.

7. Growth and Development

(a) *Morphology* - Silverweed is a procumbent rosette plant that produces long stolons. A stolon consists of a sympodial chain of elements or modules. Each of them bears two bracts. From one of the axils of the bracts a daughter rosette is formed, and from the other axil the next stolon internode develops. The rosettes are hereafter termed ramets. Silverweed has a considerable capacity for vegetative reproduction, often developing dense mats of ramets up to densities of about 2000 ramets per m² (Eriksson 1986a). Each ramet becomes physiologically independent after the withering of stolon internodes in the autumn. A ramet consists of a short vertical rhizome bearing swollen adventitious roots containing starch (Jessen 1913). Flowers are developed from the mother ramet, and also terminally on stolon internodes. This means that vegetative reproduction and flowering are developmentally linked (Eriksson 1985). Each flower may produce a set of achenes that separate when shed.

(b) *Perennation* - The ramets are perennial and all aboveground tissues wither in the autumn. The plants overwinter as short upright rhizomes and the winter buds develop on the uppermost part of the rhizome.

Silverweed is a hemicryptophyte (Raunkiaer 1937) and seeds are dormant during winter.

(c) *Physiological data* - A study of transpiration and water turnover rates in silverweed growing on a sandy fishpond shore (Kvet 1975) showed that the transpiration rate in silverweed paralleled Piché evaporation rates over two relatively warm summer days. Therefore it was concluded that water relations in the plant are controlled primarily by microclimatic conditions.

(d) *Phenology* - A rosette of leaves is formed from the rhizome in late spring (May). Stolons and flowers are produced concomitantly from June to September. The main flowering period is during June and July, and the main period of stolon growth occurs somewhat later, during the period from July to September. Germination of seed takes place during the whole summer, but mainly in June.

(e) *Mycorrhiza* - This species has been described as actively mycorrhizal (Currah et al. 1983) although no evidence was provided.

8. Reproduction

(a) *Floral biology* - Silverweed is self-incompatible, hermaphroditic and insect-pollinated (Rousi 1965; Ockendon and Walters 1970; Eriksson 1987). The most important pollinators seem to be syrphid flies, but also in some cases bumble bees. Although the flowers are hermaphroditic, the expression of gender in flowers and ramets is variable (Eriksson 1987). The number of ovules per flower was 39.3 in ramets growing under nutrient-rich conditions, while it was significantly lower at 35.3 under nutrient-poor conditions. In contrast, the number of stamens remained almost constant, about 20 per flower. Such an increasing "femaleness" under favourable conditions is an expected outcome according to sex allocation theory (Charnov 1982).

(b) *Seed production and dispersal* - Achenes of silverweed are 1.5–2.3 mm in length and 0.9–1.7 mm in width with 1000 achenes weighing 0.76 g (Kelley 1953). The average number of achenes per achene-producing flower varies between years from 5.4 to 8.1, with an individual maximum of about 60 achenes per flower (Eriksson 1986a). Most ramets in an investigated seashore meadow population produced at least one achene, and the average number of achenes per ramet varied between 9.7 and 13.0. The achene production is often limited by available pollen (Eriksson 1987). Most achenes are deposited in the vicinity of the mother ramet, but achenes have a layer of air-containing cells in the fruit-wall (Jessen 1913), enabling them to float for a considerable time (Rommell 1953). This may be of great importance in the colonization of new localities on shores of lakes, rivers and seas.

(c) *Viability of seeds and germination* - Although Kelley (1953) reported that achenes of this species would not germinate after being stored dry but would germinate well if stored moist at low temperatures, Eriksson (unpublished) found that achenes could be stored in dry places and retain viability for at least 5 yr. The easiest way to germinate them under controlled conditions was to place them on filter paper in petri dishes with distilled water and to expose them to 12 h of darkness at 5°C and 12 h of full light at 25°C. Low germination was reported by Kelley (1953) with a maximum of 13–15% after 6 mo storage in cold wet peat or sand. However, Eriksson (personal observation) obtained well over 50% germination. Rousi (1965) suggested scratching with sandpaper or soaking in concentrated sulphuric acid for a few minutes before chilling for 2 wk as an alternative method of germination.

Under natural conditions, seeds germinate mainly during early summer. Silverweed does not develop a permanent seed bank and showed no significant differences between relative abundance in the existing vegetation and in the seed bank along a transect in a seashore meadow (Jerling 1983). Successful establishment of seedlings occurs even in rather closed swards, but is enhanced by small-scale disturbances.

(d) *Vegetative reproduction* - Silverweed produces daughter ramets from stolons. Stolons may attain a length of about 1 m. In the field only a minority of ramets produce stolons, mostly only one stolon, and with an average of 1.7 to 3.0 daughter ramets depending on the year (Eriksson 1986a). Under favourable conditions, however, a mother ramet may produce up to 10 stolons and about 50 daughter ramets.

A daughter ramet is capable of both flowering and stolon production at the age of 1 yr. In contrast, a seedling in the field takes about 5 yr to produce flowers or stolons (Eriksson 1986a).

Vegetative reproduction greatly dominates the recruitment to natural populations (Ockendon and Walters 1970; Eriksson 1986a). Plants growing in the wild generally flower poorly and flower production appears to be inversely related to plant vigour (Ockendon and Walters 1970). The main ecological advantages gained from vegetative reproduction are threefold. First, it enables daughter ramets to establish in small-scale disturbances in the vegetation; clones are capable of a mobile "foraging" behaviour (Eriksson 1986b). Second, the death risk of the genets becomes reduced as the number of independent ramets, of which the genet consists, increases (Eriksson 1988a). Third, it is a much safer way of producing ramets. Daughter ramets survive much better than seedlings (Eriksson 1986a). Production of seeds is, however, the only way to colonize new localities, and it increases the genetic variability within populations.

9. Hybrids

Although natural intrageneric hybrids between various species within the genus *Potentilla* occur, attempts at crossing *P. anserina* with other species in the genus have not been successful (Goswami and Matfield 1975) and no natural hybrids of *P. anserina* have been recorded.

However, successful intergeneric crosses have been recorded between *P. anserina* and the cultivated strawberry *Fragaria* × *ananassa* Duch. ($2n=56$) (Hughes and Janick

1974). Berry set with *P. anserina* pollen was 67–78% and achene set was 23.8 per berry, compared with 93% and 68.1 for controls.

10. Population Dynamics

The population dynamics of silverweed on a Baltic seashore meadow in Sweden have been subjected to a detailed analysis (Eriksson 1986a, 1988b). The annual growth rate of the population (e^r) varied between years from 0.68 to 1.05 indicating that the population fluctuated considerably between years. The yearly survivorship of established ramets was generally high. Ramets that produced stolons in 1 yr survived less well to the next year (about 70%) than did ramets that did not produce stolons (about 85%). The half-life of established ramets was 3.1 yr. The main period of mortality in the population coincided with the period of stolon formation during late summer. The cause of this pattern was, however, unclear. It was not a result of density effects as has been suggested for similar observations in other species (Cook 1985). The main internal variables determining the growth and dynamics of the silverweed population are survivorship of ramets and the proportion of ramets developing stolons. Under high-density conditions, the values of these variables decrease. Hence, the population is, to some extent, internally regulated.

11. Response to Herbicides and other Chemicals

Pot trials in England (Clay 1987) have shown that glyphosate (Roundup) and triclopyr (Garlon 2) applied at a spray volume rate of 386 L ha^{-1}, fluroxypyr (Starane 2) at 1.5 kg ha^{-1} and MCPB (Tropotox) at 7.5 kg ha^{-1} were all effective in killing silverweed. Amitrole (Weedazol TL) reduced growth severely and killed some plants. Although paraquat (Gramoxone 100) killed foliage, the plants grew back quickly following treatment (Clay 1987). No field trials on this species have been reported for Canada. However, two other species of this genus, the biennial rough cinquefoil (*Potentilla norvegica* L.) and the perennial sulfur cinquefoil (*P. recta* L.) have been classified as intermediate in response to

2,4-D by the Ontario Herbicide Committee (1978).

12. Response to Other Human Manipulations

Since silverweed is sensitive to shading (it is usually outcompeted by tall grasses), it is favoured by grazing and clipping. Under such conditions, it may form very dense monospecific populations of great persistance. Thus, silverweed grows well in disturbed areas and has been found to invade overgrazed and highly disturbed meadows in the Peace-Athabasca Delta within Wood Buffalo National Park, Alberta. A study of the effects on silverweed abundance of protecting disturbed Delta meadows from bison grazing was conducted. Three 10 × 10-m plots were surrounded with wire fencing and three adjacent similar-sized plots were left unprotected. Each of the six plots was sampled with 10 randomly-located 1 × 1-m square quadrats at initiation of the study in 1986 and with 5 randomly-located quadrats in 1988 after 2 yr of grazing protection. Since ramet density was found to be significantly correlated ($r=0.91$, $P<0.0001$, $n=57$) with visual estimates of percent cover in a separate study by the authors within the same area, changes in silverweed abundance were monitored in the exclosure study by using percent cover estimates. This study found that 2 yr of grazing protection resulted in a significant decline in mean percent cover (18 to 7%) by silverweed while there was no significant change in mean cover (16 to 13%) in the grazed plots (Fig. 5), suggesting the importance of disturbance by bison in maintenance of this silverweed population.

On the other hand, silverweed does not appear to respond well to burning. As a possible means of stimulating growth of graminoids and controlling the growth of weedy dicots such as silverweed, experimental summer burns were carried out in another study within the same Delta meadow. Five pairs of 1 × 1-m-square permanent plots were established in 1986. One plot of each pair was assigned to either a burn or control treatment. The burn plots were burned 2 yr in a row,

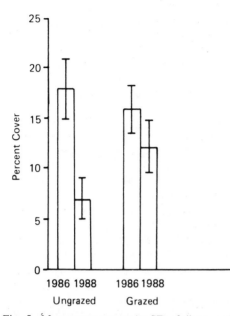

Fig. 5. Mean percent cover (± SE) of silverweed in plots prior to treatment in 1986 (*n*=30) and after 2 yr of grazing protection in the ungrazed treatment and two years of exposure to grazing in the grazed treatment in 1988 (*n*=15).

each time after visual estimates of percent cover by silverweed were recorded. The results indicate that, while a single summer burn had no significant effect on cover by silverweed, two consecutive summer burns resulted in a significant decline in mean cover from 83% to 27% (Fig. 6). The change in mean cover in the control plots from 81% to 66% was not significant. These results may be due either to a direct deleterious effect of fire on silverweed or to an indirect effect through improved growth and vigour of competing grasses and sedges following burning.

These studies suggest that whether disturbance has a positive or negative effect on silverweed populations depends on the type of disturbance and possibly on effects that such disturbances have on competing plants in the community.

13. Responses to Parasites

Although at least 53 species of fungi have been recorded as plant pathogens on various species of the genus *Potentilla,* the only fungi recorded specifically on *P. anserina* are *Ramularia arvensis* Sacc., *R. punctiformis* Sacc. (Conners 1967), *Marssonina potentillae* (Desm.) Magn. and *Phyllosticta anserinae* Tehon (United States Department of Agriculture 1960), all of which cause leaf spot.

ACKNOWLEDGMENTS

Financial assistance from the Natural Sciences and Engineering Research Council of Canada (K.M. and R.W.W.) and logistical support and assistance from Parks Canada and all the staff of Wood Buffalo National Park are gratefully acknowledged.

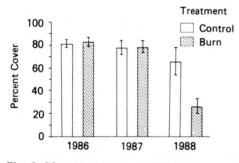

Fig. 6. Mean percent cover (± SE) of silverweed in burn and control plots (*n*=5) before (1986) and after one (1987) and two (1988) consecutive summer burns.

Alex, J. F. and Switzer, C. M. 1976. Ontario weeds. Ontario Ministry of Agriculture and Food, Toronto, ON. Publ. 505, 200 pp.
Britton, N. and Brown, A. 1913. An illustrated flora of the northern United States and Canada. Vol. II. Dover Publications, Inc., New York, NY. 735 pp.
Canada Weed Committee. 1969. Common and botanical names of weeds in Canada. Canada Department of Agriculture, Ottawa, ON. Publ. 1397, 67 pp.
Charnov, E. L. 1982. The theory of sex allocation. Princeton University Press, Princeton, NJ.
Chopra, R. N., Nayar, S. L. and Chopra, I. C. 1956. Glossary of Indian medicinal plants. C.S.I.R., New Delhi, India.
Clay, D. V. 1987. Effects of eight herbicides on *Potentilla anserina* and *Rorippa sylvestris.* Ann. Appl. Biol. 110 (Suppl.): 118–119.
Cobon, A. M. and Matfield, B. 1976. Morphological and cytological studies on a hexaploid clone of *Potentilla anserina* L. Watsonia 11: 125–129.

Conners, I. L. 1967. An annotated index of plant diseases in Canada and fungi recorded on plants in Alaska, Canada and Greenland. Canada Department of Agriculture, Ottawa, ON. Publ. 1251, 381 pp.

Cook, R. E. 1985. Growth and development in clonal plant populations. Pages 259–296 *in* J. B. C. Jackson, L. W. Buss, and R. E. Cook, eds. Population biology and evolution of clonal organisms. Yale University Press, New Haven, CT. 530 pp.

Cormack, R. G. H. 1977. Wildflowers of Alberta. Hurtig Publishers, Edmonton, AB. 415 pp.

Crompton, C. W., McNeill, J., Stahevitch, A. E. and Wojtas, W. A. 1988. Preliminary inventory of Canadian weeds. Technical Bulletin 1988-9E, Agriculture Canada, Ottawa, ON. 292 pp.

Currah, R., Smreciu, A. and Van Dyk, M. 1983. Prairie wildflowers. University of Alberta Devonian Botanic Garden, Edmonton, AB. 300 pp.

Eriksson, O. 1985. Reproduction and clonal growth in *Potentilla anserina* L. (Rosaceae): the relation between growth form and dry weight allocation. Oecologia (Berlin) 66: 378–380.

Eriksson, O. 1986a. Survivorship, reproduction and dynamics of ramets of *Potentilla anserina* on a Baltic seashore meadow. Vegetatio 67: 17–25.

Eriksson, O. 1986b. Mobility and space capture in the stoloniferous plant *Potentilla anserina*. Oikos 46: 82–87.

Eriksson, O. 1987. Regulation of seed-set and gender variation in the hermaphroditic plant *Potentilla anserina*. Oikos 49: 165–171.

Eriksson, O. 1988a. Patterns of ramet survivorship in clonal fragments of the stoloniferous plant *Potentilla anserina*. Ecology 69: 736–740.

Eriksson, O. 1988b. Ramet behaviour and population growth in the clonal herb *Potentilla anserina* J. Ecol. 76: 522–536.

Fernald, M. L. and Kinsey, A. C. 1958. Edible wild plants of eastern North America. (revised by Rollins, R.C.). Harper and Row, Publishers, New York, NY. 452 pp.

Ferron, M. and Cayoutte, R. 1970. Nom des mauvaises herbes du Québec, 3ième éd. Agriculture Québec, QA 38 R4-4, Québec, PQ. 113 pp.

Goswami, D. A. and Matfield, B. 1975. Cytogenetic studies in the genus *Potentilla* L. New Phytol. 75: 135–146.

Holmgren, P. K. and Keuken, W. 1974. Index herbariorum. Part I. The herbaria of the world. 6th ed. (Regnum Veg. 92) Oosthock, Schetema and Holkema, Utrecht. 397 pp.

Hughes, H. G. and Janick, J. 1974. Production of tetrahaploids in the cultivated strawberry. HortScience 9: 442–444.

Hultén, E. 1968. Flora of Alaska and neighboring territories. Stanford University Press, Stanford, CT. 1008 pp.

Jerling, L. 1983. Composition and viability of the seed bank along a successional gradient on a Baltic seashore meadow. Holarct. Ecol. 6: 150–156.

Jessen, K. 1913. The structure and biology of arctic flowering plants. 8. Rosaceae. Meddelelser on Groenland 37, Copenhagen, Denmark.

Kelley, W. R. 1953. Study of seed identification and seed germination of *Potentilla* spp. and *Veronica* spp. Cornell University Agric. Exp. Sta. Mem. 317.

Kvet, J. 1975. Transpiration in seven plant species colonizing a fishpond shore. Biol. Plant. 17: 434–442.

Liddle, M. J. and Greig-Smith, P. 1976. A survey of tracks and paths in a sand dune ecosystem II. Vegetation. J. Appl. Ecol. 12: 909–930.

McKay, S. and Catling, P. 1979. Trees, shrubs and flowers to know in Ontario. J.M. Dent and Sons (Canada) Ltd., Toronto, ON. 208 pp.

Ockendon, D. J. and Walters, S. M. 1970. Studies in *Potentilla anserina* L. Watsonia 8: 135–144.

Ontario Herbicide Committee. 1978. Guide to chemical weed control. Ontario Department of Agriculture and Food, Toronto, ON. Publ. 75, 103 pp.

Panigrahi, G. and Dixit, B. K. 1980. Studies on taxonomy and economic utilization of twelve species of *Potentilla* (Rosaceae) in India. J. Econ. Tax. Bot. 1: 127–134.

Peterson, L. 1978. A field guide to edible wild plants of eastern and central North America. Houghton Mifflin Company, Boston, MA. 330 pp.

Porsild, A. E. 1974. Rocky Mountain wild flowers. National Museums of Canada. Ottawa, ON. 454 pp.

Porsild, A. E. and Cody, W. J. 1980. Vascular plants of continental Northwest Territories, Canada. National Museums of Canada, Ottawa, ON. 200 pp.

Raunkiaer, C. 1937. Plant life forms. Clarendon Press, Oxford, U.K.

Ridley, H. N. 1930. The dispersal of plants throughout the world. London, U.K.

Ringius, G. S. 1980. Vegetation survey of a James Bay coastal marsh. Can. Field Nat. 94: 110–120.

Romell, L. -G. 1953. Växternas spridningsmöjligheter. Pages 30–199 *in* C. Skottsberg, ed. Växternas liv 8. Födagshuset Norden, Malm. 308 pp.

Rousi, A. 1965. Biosystematic studies on the species aggregate *Potentilla anserina* L. Ann. Bot. Fenn. **2**: 47–112.

Scoggan, H. J. 1978. The flora of Canada. Part 3 — Dicotyledonae. National Museum of Natural Sciences Publications in Botany No. 7(3), Ottawa, ON.

Torrey, J. and Gray, A. 1969. A flora of North America. Hafner Publishing Co., London, U.K. 711 pp.

Trelawny, J. G. 1983. Wildflowers of the Yukon and Northwestern Canada including adjacent Alaska. Gray's Publishing Ltd., Sidney, BC. 214 pp.

United States Department of Agriculture. 1960. Index of plant diseases in the United States. Agriculture Handbook No. 165. U.S. Govt. Print Office, Washington, DC. 531 pp.

Voss, E. G. 1985. Michigan flora. Part II. Cranbrook Institute of Science Bulletin 59 and University of Michigan Herbarium, Ann Arbour, MI. 724 pp.

Wolf, T. 1908. Monographie der Gattung *Potentilla*. Bibliotheca Botanica, Stuttgart, Germany.

The biology of Canadian weeds. 99.
Matricaria perforata Mérat (Asteraceae)

S. L. Woo[1], A. G. Thomas[2,4], D. P. Peschken[2], G. G. Bowes[2], D. W. Douglas[2],
V. L. Harms[1], and A. S. McClay[3]

[1]*Department of Crop Science and Plant Ecology, University of Saskatchewan, Saskatoon,
Saskatchewan, Canada S7N 0W0;* [2]*Research Station, Agriculture Canada, Box 440,
Regina, Saskatchewan, Canada S4P 3A2; and* [3]*Alberta Environmental Centre, Bag 4000,
Vegreville, Alberta, Canada T0B 4L0. Received 17 Dec. 1990, accepted 15 May 1991.*

Woo, S. L., Thomas, A. G., Peschken, D. P., Bowes, G. G., Douglas, D. W., Harms, V. L. and
McClay, A. S. 1991. **The biology of Canadian weeds. 99.** *Matricaria perforata* Mérat (Asteraceae).
Can. J. Plant Sci. **71**: 1101–1119. Scentless chamomile, *Matricaria perforata* Mérat, (=*M. maritima*
var. *agrestis* (Knaf) Wilmott), is an introduced weed having an annual to short-lived perennial life cycle.
Two cytotype races are found in Canada with a distinctive geographic distribution. The tetraploid ($2n=36$)
is abundant in agricultural habitats of the Prairie region, whereas the diploid ($2n=18$) is found mainly
in ruderal habitats of the Atlantic region. Infestations are found in many annual and perennial crops,
pastures, wasteland, lawns, gardens, roadsides, fence lines, and ditches. The plant reproduces entirely
by seed, producing up to 1.8 million seeds m^{-2} in dense monospecific stands. A density of 25 annual
plants m^{-2} can result in a 55% reduction in spring wheat yield under cool wet conditions. Shallow
preseeding tillage in late autumn or early spring is an effective method of cultural control. Several
herbicides are recommended for control of the weed in crop and noncrop areas. Scentless chamomile
is considered a suitable candidate for biological control.

Key words: Weed biology, scentless chamomile, *Matricaria perforata*, *Matricaria inodora*, *Matricaria
maritima* var. *agrestis*, *Tripleurosperum inodorum*

Woo, S. L., Thomas, A. G., Peschken, D. P., Bowes, G. G., Douglas, D. W., Harms, V. L. et
McClay, A. S. 1991. **Biologie des mauvaises herbes du Canada. 99.** *Matricaria perforata* Mérat
(Asteracées). Can. J. Plant Sci. **71**: 1101–1119. La matricaire inodore, *Matricaria perforata* Mérat
(=*M. maritima* var. *agrestis* (Knaf) Wilmott), est une plante introduite dont le type de croissance varie
d'annuel à pluriannuel. Deux cytotypes existent au Canada, chacun avec une aire de distribution géographique distincte. La forme tétraploïde ($2n=36$) est abondante dans les habitats agricoles de la région
des Prairies, tandis que le diploïde ($2n=18$) s'observe principalement dans les habitats rudéraux de
la région de l'Atlantique. La mauvaise herbe colonise de nombreuses cultures annuelles et pérennes,
ainsi que les pâturages, les terrains incultivables, les pelouses, les jardins, les bords de routes, les bas
de clôtures et les fossés. La plante se reproduit exclusivement par la graine — il peut y avoir jusqu'à
1,8 million de graines par m^{2} en peuplement pur dense. Un taux d'infestation de 25 plantes par m^{2}
peut abaisser de 55% le rendement du blé de printemps en conditions pluvieuses fraîches. Un travail
superficiel de pré-semis en fin d'automne ou au début du printemps est un moyen efficace de lutte cul-
turale. Plusieurs herbicides sont recommandés, tant pour les terres cultivées que pour les aires non
agricoles. La matricaire inodore semble offrir des possibilités pour la lutte biologique.

Mots clés: biologie des mauvaises herbes, matricaire inodore, *Matricaria perforata*, *M. inodora*, *M.
maritima* var. *agrestis*, *Tripleurospermum inodorum*

[4]Author to whom correspondence should be sent.

Can. J. Plant Sci. **71**: 1101–1119 (Oct. 1991)

1. Name

Matricaria perforata Mérat (Rauschert 1974) - Synonyms: *M. inodora* L., *M. maritima* var. *agrestis* (Knaf) Wilmott, *M. maritima* ssp. *inodora* (L.) Clapham, *Tripleurospermum inodorum* (L.) Schultz-Bip., *Tripleurospermum perforatum* (Mérat) Wagenitz (Wagenitz 1987), *Chamomilla inodora* (L.) Gilib. (Kartesz and Kartesz 1980); **scentless chamomile** (Alex et al. 1980), scentless mayweed, barnyard daisy, corn feverfew, wild chamomile, false chamomile, false mayweed, bachelor's button; **matricaire inodore** (Alex et al. 1980). Asteraceae, composite family, Astéracées; tribe Anthemideae.

The nomenclature of *Matricaria perforata* is historically complex, and for simplicity, the taxonomic treatment by Rauschert (1974) is adopted for use in this review. According to Rauschert, *Matricaria* is the acceptable generic name for scentless chamomile. Nomenclature confusion was initiated by Linnaeus' (1753) original application of the *Matricaria* type to a scentless chamomile specimen, rather than a wild chamomile (*Chamomilla recutita* (L.) Rauschert) specimen as he apparently intended. The subsequent attempts by him and others to revise the typifications have resulted in confusion over the specific epithets. Rauschert (1974) concludes that the only unambiguous and legitimate name that can be applied to scentless chamomile is *Matricaria perforata* Mérat. This revision is accepted by various authors, either fully (Kay 1976; Halliday and Beadle 1983; Hanf 1983) or in part (Kartesz and Kartesz 1980; Moss 1983; Weed Science Society of America 1989). However, the nomenclature of this taxon is still questionable and further investigations are required to clarify the problem.

2. Description and Account of Variation

Annual to short-lived perennial, glabrous, 15–100 cm tall, prostrate-erect, ascending cymose branches, often with spreading basal stems under conditions of minimal competition; stem colour dark green, occasionally red or red-streaked with the presence of anthocyanins. Roots dense and fibrous; leaves alternate, finely tripinnately dissected; ultimate leaf segments linear to filiform, thin not fleshy, with acute tips.

Capitula conspicuous, numerous up to 3200 per plant, 20–45 mm in diameter, with 18–35 white pistillate ray florets on the periphery, measuring 12–16 mm by 2.5–3.5 mm, with three terminal lobes; disk contains 275–550 protandrous, yellow bisexual disk florets, five-lobed corolla measuring 2.0–2.5 mm by 0.34–0.40 mm, five fused anthers around the style; receptacle solid, convex becoming hemispheric to slightly conical with maturity, 4.8–5.9 mm high by 5.7–7.2 mm wide, lacking scales; phyllaries glabrous, oblong to narrowly triangular, blunt-tipped with narrow (to 0.3 mm) hyaline to light-brown, scarious margins. Achenes inverted-pyramidal in shape, dark-brown to black-brown, 1.3–2.2 mm long by 0.5–1.1 mm wide, three well separated light-brown wing-like ventral ribs that are solid or dense in texture, areas between ribs and dorsal surface transversely rugose, two circular to broadly orbicular resin glands on dorsal surface, pappus very short and truncate. Fig. 1 shows details of the morphology of *M. perforata*.

Canadian populations of *M. perforata* are polyploid: diploid, $2n = 18$; tetraploid, $2n = 36$ (Mulligan 1959; Woo 1989); with some individuals in local populations revealing extra chromosomes, $2n = 18 + 1-3$. A single population at St. John's, Newfoundland has chromosome counts of $2n = 27, 36, 37$ (Woo 1989). Chromosome counts on European material also indicate diploid and tetraploid cytotypes (Rottgardt 1956; Kay 1965, 1969, 1972; Lankosz-Mroz 1976).

Matricaria perforata may be confused with other daisy-like Asteraceae genera such as *Anthemis, Chrysanthemum* and *Chamomilla*. *Anthemis* is readily differentiated by the presence of chaffy scales on the receptacle surface and *A. cotula* L., by a pungent unpleasant odor when crushed (Tutin et al. 1976; Scoggan 1979). *Matricaria* has finely dissected leaves in comparison to the leaves of *Chrysanthemum*, which are oblanceolate with dentate to coarsely lobed margins (Boivin 1972; Moss 1983). The receptacle of

Fig. 1. *Matricaria perforata* Mérat (a) lateral, dorsal, and ventral view of achene (10×), (b) seedlings with oblanceolate cotyledons and pinnately divided true leaves (2×), (c) rosette stage with bipinnately to tripinnately divided leaves (0.5×), (d) upper portion of central flowering stem of mature plant (0.3×).

Chamomilla is hollow and conically shaped with an acute tip at the time of anthesis, whereas the receptacle of *Matricaria* is larger, solid-centered and hemispheric or rounded with an obtuse apex. The capitula of *Chamomilla* are small (12–22 mm) and exhibit reflexed ray florets at anthesis. In comparison, the capitula of *Matricaria* are larger (20–45 mm) and exhibit ray florets which remain spread during anthesis, then reflex later in maturity (Fernald 1950; Clapham et al. 1962; Scoggan 1979; Moss 1983).

Three taxa of *Matricaria* may be recognized in Canada: *M. maritima* spp. *phaeocephala* (Rupr.) Rauschert, *M. maritima* spp. *maritima* L., and *M. perforata* Mérat. Under the present taxonomic treatment, the wild chamomile and pineappleweed, usually referred to in the North American literature as *Matricaria chamomilla* L. and *M. matricarioides* (Less.) Porter, respectively, are now recognized by Rauschert (1974) as *Chamomilla recutita* (L.) Rauschert and *C. suaveolens* (Pursh.) Rydb. *Matricaria maritima* spp. *phaeocephala* has distinctive phyllary margins that are 0.4–1 mm wide and dark-brown to black in colour in comparison to the other taxa which have narrow (up to 0.3 mm), hyaline to light-brown phyllary margins (Clapham et al. 1962; Hultén 1968; Porsild and Cody 1980). The growth habit of *M. maritima* spp. *maritima* is depressed to prostrate and the ultimate leaf segments are short and broad with blunt tips, to 5 mm long, thick and succulent (Fernald 1950; Néhou 1954). The achenes have three slightly inflated corky ribs with little separation between the ribs, and oval resin glands, which are longer than broad (Kay 1972). In comparison, *M. perforata* grows erect and the ultimate leaf segments are linear with acute tips, to 12 mm long, and thin, not fleshy (Néhou 1954; Clapham et al. 1962). The achenes have three well separated noninflated ribs and oval resin glands that are broader than long (Néhou 1954; Hamet-Ahti 1967; Kay 1972).

3. Economic Importance

(a) *Detrimental* — In Saskatchewan, a 3-yr competition experiment in small plots was conducted on Black Chernozemic soils between fall and spring-emerging *M. perforata* and spring wheat grown in a reduced tillage system. With spring-emerging *M. perforata*, yield was reduced by 55% in a cool, wet year at a density of 25 plants m^{-2} but yield was not significantly reduced by similar densities in a drought year (Douglas 1989). Fall-emerging winter annual *M. perforata* at the same density reduced spring wheat yield approximately 20% in a drought year and 60% in a moderately moist year. In winter wheat, the same density of spring emerging *M. perforata* caused a slight reduction of yield only in a cool, moist year (Douglas 1989). Winter annuals reduced yield in winter wheat by 6% in a moderately moist year and 3% in a drought year, indicating that *M. perforata* may be stressed more than winter wheat by drought. Yield losses in infested farm fields seeded to spring wheat ranged between 30 and 80% at 25 plants m^{-2} (Douglas 1989).

Hoag et al. (1980) reported that winter annuals at a density of 1.6 plants m^{-2} reduced spring wheat yield by more than 40% in North Dakota. Losses due to summer annuals were considerably less.

In greenhouse tests in England, Mann and Barnes (1945) reported reduction of barley yield by *M. perforata* as great as 45%, while Welbank (1963) ranked *M. perforata* among the least competitive species in kale and wheat. Wilson and Wright (1990) studied the effect of various weed species on yield of winter wheat in field tests in England and rated the competitive ability of *M. perforata* as second to *Avena fatua* L. at low densities (i.e., with little intraspecific interference). In each of these English experiments, weeds and crop emerged concurrently. It is likely that the *M. perforata* was diploid because that is the common chromosome race in Great Britain (Kay 1965).

Matricaria perforata is not palatable to livestock and nutrient analysis indicated its feed value to be poor (Stahlman and Hoag 1974).

As part of a biological control project, the insect fauna and disease organisms occurring on *M. perforata* were investigated by a survey of the European literature, except that of the USSR (Peschken, unpublished data), and by field surveys in Canada (Peschken and McClay, unpublished data). Those organisms which are major and minor pests of cultivated crops are described in this section. If a European species also occurs in North America, it is mentioned: HEMIPTERA: *Adelphocoris lineolatus* (Goeze) and *Calocoris norvegicus* (Gemlin) (Miridae) have been introduced to North America and are minor pests of several crops, especially alfalfa and strawberries in North America as well as Europe (Beirne 1972; Hill 1987). *Lygus rugulipennis* Poppius (Miridae) is a polyphagous pest of many crops and a major pest of sugar beets (Varis 1972). Among weeds, *M. perforata* is one of its favoured hosts. HOMOPTERA: The meadow spittlebug, *Philaenus spumarius* (L.) (Cercopidae), is polyphagous and a minor pest on strawberries in Europe, Asia and the United States, and on sugar beets in Europe (Hill 1987). The aphids (Aphididae) *Aphis fabae* Scopoli and *Myzus persicae* Sulzer are polyphagous pests in Europe and North America (Hill 1987). *Aphis fabae* is an especially serious pest of field beans and sugar beets. It transmits about 30 plant virus diseases. *Myzus persicae* is completely cosmopolitan and is a major pest of tobacco, beet, cereals, and especially solanaceous vegetables in the field and in greenhouses. It transmits over 100 virus diseases in more than 30 plant families. *Brachycaudus cardui* (L.) can become a pest on *Prunus* spp. (Börner 1952) and has been reported from British Columbia (Forbes and Chan 1989). *Dysaulacorthum vincae* Walk. (= *Aulacorthum solani* (Kaltenbach)) is an important vector of virus diseases, especially of many leafy vegetable crops (Minks and Harrewijn 1989). COLEOPTERA: *Subcoccinella vigintiquattuor-punctata* (L.) (Coleoptera: Coccinellidae) is a pest of several crops including alfalfa, clover, peas and potatoes in Europe (Richards et al. 1976). LEPIDOPTERA: *Cnephasia stephensiana* (Doubleday), *C. interjectana* (Haworth) and *C. incertana* (Treitschke) (Tortricidae) are occasional pests, especially of beans and peas (Bradley et al. 1973). *Cnephasia interjectana*

has been introduced to Canada where it is a minor pest of *Chrysanthemum* spp. (Hill 1987). DIPTERA: *Napomyza lateralis* (Fallén) (Agromyzidae) is an occasional pest on several crops and ornamental plants (Spencer 1969). TYLENCHIDA: the nematodes *Meloidogyne hapla* Chitw. (Meloidogynidae) and *Ditylenchus dipsaci* (Kuhn) (Tylenchidae) are polyphagous pests on many crops in Europe and North America (Buhr 1964; Martens et al. 1988).

Ten insect species, which were found feeding on *M. perforata* in Canada, are occasional pests of cultivated crops. It is not known, however, whether *M. perforata* serves as an important reservoir for these pests. ORTHOPTERA: The grasshoppers *Melanoplus sanguinipes* (F.) and *M. bivittatus* (Say) (Acrididae) feed on the leaves and are widely distributed in Canada. They periodically reach damaging densities on crops (Beirne 1972). THYSANOPTERA: *Thrips vulgatissima* Haliday (= *Taeniothrips vulgatissimus* (Haliday)) (Thripidae) feeds in the shoot tips. In one location, it was observed to be numerous and caused some necrosis of the tips of *M. perforata* shoots. It occurs widely in Europe and North America. The principal host plant is *Heracleum* (Stannard 1968), but it also becomes numerous in greenhouses (Morison 1957). *Haplothrips leucanthemi* (Schrank) (Phlaeothripdae) is a Palaearctic species and has been introduced to North America (Stannard 1968). Although its preferred diet is pollen of many plant species according to Lewis (1972), it has been reported as a pest of red clover, sweet clover, alfalfa, and sometimes alsike clover in the prairie provinces of Canada (Beirne 1972; Philip 1975; Hill 1987). HEMIPTERA: *Lygus unctuosus* (Kelton) is occasionally a pest of alfalfa and clover (Beirne 1972). *Nysius niger* Baker (Lygaeidae) is a holarctic species and occurs in Canada from New Brunswick to British Columbia (Barber 1947). It is usually only a minor pest of many crops (Beirne 1972). It has been confused with *Nysius ericae* (Schilling) which does not occur in North America (Ashlock 1977; M. D. Schwartz, personal communication).

HOMOPTERA: Two leafhoppers (Cicadellidae) suck on the leaves and stems of *M. perforata*. *Macrosteles quadrilineatus* (Forbes) occasionally becomes so abundant that it damages crop plants, but it is of economic importance primarily as a vector of several viruses including aster yellows (Beirne 1956). *Cuerna septentrionalis* (Walker) is common on the grasslands of Alberta and Manitoba (Beirne 1956). LEPIDOPTERA: The larvae of two cutworms *Autographa californica* (Speyer) and *Anagrapha falcifera* Kirby (Phalaenidae) feed on the leaves of *M. perforata*. *Autographa californica*, the cabbage looper or alfalfa looper, can become a pest on several crops, especially alfalfa and canola (Philip 1975), and it is a minor pest of lettuce in Europe and North America (Hill 1987). The larvae of *Anagrapha falcifera*, commonly called the celery looper, occasionally damages celery and tobacco in Ontario (Rockburne and Lafontaine 1976).

(b) *Beneficial* — The flowers of *M. perforata* are frequented by many insects in the superfamily Apoidea, the bees, which are important pollinators (Ruppert 1987). *Matricaria perforata* is favoured as a source of nectar and pollen by many species of beneficial predators and parasites such as hoverflies (Diptera: Syrphidae), the tachinid flies (Diptera: Tachinidae) and the parasitic Hymenoptera.

Crude and semipurified whole plant extracts from *M. perforata* growing in France inhibited the growth of polio and herpes virus (Suganda et al. 1983). The antiviral substance was isolated and purified and identified as glycosyl-7-0-luteolin (Suganda et al. 1984).

(c) *Legislation* — *Matricaria perforata* is legislated as a noxious weed in the provincial Noxious Weeds Acts of Manitoba (Manitoba 1970), Alberta (Alberta 1980), Saskatchewan (Saskatchewan 1977) and the Peace River-Liard district of British Columbia (British Columbia 1976). *Matricaria perforata* is classified as a "secondary noxious weed seed" in class 3 of the Canada Seeds Act (Anonymous 1986).

4. Geographical Distribution

Matricaria perforata is distributed throughout Canada (Fig. 2a), from the southern region of Vancouver Island to the eastern shores of Newfoundland (Scoggan 1979). The most northerly locations include the upper Peace River region of Alberta/British Columbia and The Pas, Manitoba. Sightings of *M. perforata* from more northerly Arctic locations have likely been confused with the circumpolar *M. maritima* ssp. *phaeocephala*. *Matricaria perforata* is most abundant in the Prairies and in the Atlantic region. This geographic distribution corresponds to the range centres of the two cytotype races (Fig. 2b). The tetraploid cytotype is associated with agriculture in Alberta, Saskatchewan, Manitoba and southern Ontario, and the diploid cytotype is associated with ruderal habitats in New Brunswick, Nova Scotia, and Prince Edward Island (Mulligan 1959; Woo 1989). Both cytotypes have been noted in southeastern Quebec along the St. Lawrence River and both cytotypes may be present in Newfoundland since triploid chromosome counts were obtained (Woo 1989).

In the United States, *M. perforata* is distributed in the Northwestern, Great Plains, North Central and Northeastern regions, with the most southerly locations being in Kansas and Missouri (Great Plains Flora Association 1977; Shetler and Skog 1978). Hultén (1968) indicates a locality for *M. perforata* in central Alaska.

In Europe, *M. perforata* is found in the northern regions of Scandinavia and the British Isles, south to Spain and eastward to the USSR, where its native origins are thought to be in the Caucasus Mountain region (Pobedimova 1961; Kay 1965, 1969, 1972; Hamet-Ahti 1967). The species is also noted in India and Japan, as well as New Zealand (Tahara 1921 in Kay 1969; Koul 1964; Matthews 1982; Rahman 1982).

5. Habitat

(a) *Climatic requirements* — Site characters (degree days, precipitation, minimum and maximum daily temperature) were obtained for 14 sites in Manitoba, Saskatchewan, and

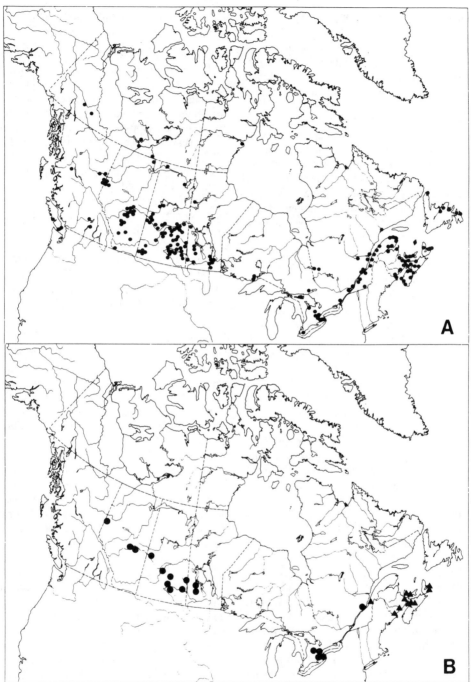

Fig. 2. (a) Distribution of *Matricaria perforata* Mérat in Canada based on specimens in the following herbaria: ALTA, CAN, DAO, MMMN, MT, MTJB, MTMG, NDA, SASK, UAC, USAS, UVIC, UWPGM, V, WIN (abbreviations as in Holmgren et al. (1981). (b) Distribution of *Matricaria perforata* Mérat diploid $2n=18$ (▲) and tetraploid $2n=36$ (●) cytotypes across Canada.

Alberta (ranging from 50°12′N 96°30′W to 55°14′N 118°22′W) where *M. perforata* was collected for a morphometric study. No clinal correlation was found between the morphological variation and these environmental characters (Woo 1989). In addition, results utilizing site data for the current year or the 30-yr average did not differ. This suggested that *M. perforata* was influenced by climatic conditions during the year of growth but not adapted to the long-term environmental conditions. Since *M. perforata* is a relatively recent introduction to the Prairie region and it occupies a variety of weedy habitats, it may not yet be adapted to the specific geographical climatic conditions (Woo 1989).

(b) *Substratum* — In the Prairie region, *M. perforata* is predominantly found on Black Chernozemic, Dark Grey Chernozemic, and Grey Luvisolic soils, with the occasional occurrence on Dark Brown Chernozemic soils (Kessler 1989b). It is associated with low-lying areas that are poorly drained and difficult to cultivate in the spring (Kessler 1989a). The soil textures of 20 sites with *M. perforata* in Manitoba, Saskatchewan, and Alberta are variable; clay, clay loam, silty clay loam, loam and fine sandy loam (Woo 1989, unpublished data). The characteristics of other soil properties are equally variable: organic matter 2.7–35.4%, pH 5.5–7.9, conductivity 0.1–3.2 mS cm^{-1}, and the lime content is very low or absent.

In England, diploid *M. perforata* is common in cereal fields on both light- and heavy-textured acid soils, both light- and heavy-textured chalk soils, and light calcareous soils but infrequent on heavy calcareous soils (Kay 1965). The diploid cytotype is also prevalent on acidic soil (pH 5.4–5.6) after the addition of mineral and farmyard manures (Mann 1939; Warington 1958). The European tetraploid cytotype has been reported on solonchak (saline) soils of the Lower Volga and the Caucasus Mountains (Kay 1969). Kay (1976) reported *M. perforata* on saline steppes in Europe. In Poland, the weed occurs on black soils developed on varves and heavy morainic clays, on morainic

loams and sandy morainic loams, as well as calcareous varves (Wójcik 1973).

(c) *Communities in which the species occurs* — The communities in which *M. perforata* is found are not specific. Urban, roadside and drainage ditches, fence lines, various croplands, hayland, pastures, farmyards, and wasteland can support infestations (Stahlman and Hoag 1974; Anonymous 1982; Kessler 1989a). It is particularly prevalent on roadsides disturbed by construction or maintenance (Kay 1965). *Matricaria perforata* may be found growing in association with many common agricultural weed species, usually as a minor species in the field (Thomas and Wise 1987, 1988). If it is the predominant weed species, *M. perforata* may be found scattered throughout the habitat, or growing in low, moderate, or high density stands (Woo, unpublished data).

6. History

The earliest herbarium record of *M. perforata* in Canada is from Campbellton, New Brunswick in 1876. First collections from the other Atlantic Provinces were: Pictou, Nova Scotia (1883); Brackley Point, Prince Edward Island (1888); and St. John's Newfoundland (1908). In Quebec, *M. perforata* was first found in 1880 on the Magdalen Islands. The oldest Ontario record is from Port Arthur (Thunder Bay) in 1909. On the west coast of Canada, *M. perforata* was first collected at Victoria, British Columbia in 1893. In the Prairie Provinces, it was collected at Rhein, Saskatchewan (1928), at Lacombe and Sylvan Lake, Alberta (1933) and at Scandinavia, Manitoba (1941). In the Northwest Territories, a collection was made in 1938 at Chesterfield Inlet on Hudson's Bay. Kay (1969) proposed that the diploid *M. perforata* was introduced to eastern Canada by settlers from western Europe where the diploid cytotype predominates. Mulligan (1959) felt that the weed was introduced to the Atlantic coast of Canada in ships' ballast. This is supported by a sighting of *M. perforata* on 10-yr-old landfill, containing former ballast, in New York Bay, New York (Brown 1878), as well as at old ballast dump sites along the Willamette River near Linnton, Oregon in 1916 (Nelson 1917). The tetraploid may have been introduced to western Canada as a contaminant in crop seed from northern and eastern Europe (Kay 1969), or it may have been an escaped garden ornamental (Mulligan 1959).

7. Growth and Development

(a) *Morphology* — *Matricaria perforata* has a dense, extensively branched fibrous root system which anchors the plant firmly in the ground. Occasionally, basal shoots lying along the ground surface will develop adventitious roots along the contact region (Néhou 1954). *Matricaria perforata* is phenotypically plastic. The plants become more branched and spreading, appearing bushy and globose, with decreased plant competition. Plants in dense stands exhibit little to no basal branching, appearing erect and slender, with sharply ascending upper lateral branches. The tetraploid plants are larger, more erect and more spreading than the diploid plants. Measurements of the central stem height and basal shoot length, as well as the volume of the pollen grains are larger for the Canadian tetraploid plants than for the diploid (Mulligan 1959; Woo 1989).

(b) *Perennation* — *Matricaria perforata* is noted as an annual, biennial, and short-lived perennial in the literature. A common garden study conducted at Regina, Saskatchewan found that plants could survive mean daily temperatures around −10°C (November, December, January and February), mean monthly temperatures ranging from −1.1°C to −25.6°C, and snowfall between 10 and 15 mm (water equivalent) over the study period. The plants are hemicryptophytes, dying back to the caudex for perennation (Ellenberg and Mueller-Dombois 1967). The tetraploid populations have a greater overwintering ability than the diploid populations; consequently they exhibit more biennial and perennial growth forms. The maximum life duration observed in the common garden study was two growing seasons (Woo 1989).

In a concurrent study, it was found that the overwintering ability of plants increased with monthly transplant dates from May to July, then declined with subsequent transplant dates (Woo 1989). Seedlings grown for a month in the greenhouse and then transplanted to the field in May and early June developed as annuals, which only survived the initial year, or as perennials, which flowered the first year and survived to the following year. Seedlings transplanted in June and July developed as annuals, biennials, or perennials. However, transplants to the field from late July to early September developed as biennials, having remained vegetative for the initial season. No seedlings survived to the following year if transplanted in October.

(c) *Physiological data* — Tissue culture of *M. perforata* explants from disk florets, receptacle, and stem resulted in callus formation when grown on nutrient medium supplemented with 0.5 mg L^{-1} NAA and 0.5 mg L^{-1} kinetin. Whole plant regeneration occurred after transplanting the callus to a nutrient medium supplemented with 0.1 mg L^{-1} kinetin (Cellarova et al. 1982). Explants of ray florets did not form a callus and the callus formed from leaf explants could not be induced to regenerate whole plants. Histological examination of the leaf explant callus indicated that root and shoot apical meristems were formed initially, but later, shoot meristematic tissue degenerated and only root-like organs were produced (Rychlova et al. 1984).

Dock Gustavsson (1989) compared the growth of several annual dicotyledonous weeds at different light intensities, nutrient levels, and densities in the greenhouse and growth chamber. After 12 d of growth *M. perforata* had the lowest aerial shoot weights (0.1–6.0 mg $plant^{-1}$) and a low relative growth rate (RGR) of 0.94–1.96 g g^{-1} wk^{-1} in comparison to other species. The RGR decreased when plant density increased or light intensity decreased. Based on the product of aerial shoot weight and RGR, the growth ability of *M. perforata* was similar to that of *Chenopodium album* L. and *Capsella bursa-pastoris* (L.) Med. but less than that of

Sinapis arvensis L., *Stellaria media* (L.) Vill., *Lapsana communis* L., *Polygonum lapathifolium* L., and *Thlaspi arvense* L.

(d) *Phenology* — In Saskatchewan, achenes of *M. perforata* germinate soon after snow melt, during April. Under appropriate autumn conditions, with adequate moisture and warmth, achenes will also germinate but these seedlings will rarely survive the winter in Saskatchewan. Seedlings initiated in late summer may survive as winter annual forms. In Ontario wheat fields, the largest number of seedlings emerged during October. Smaller but significant numbers of seedlings emerged during April, May, or August, with few seedlings emerging during June and July (Westfall 1987). Mann (1939) observed that achenes of *M. perforata* in the U.K. germinated throughout the growing season, after 25 Apr.

Seedlings have oblanceolate cotyledons (Fig. 1). The first true leaves are pinnately to slightly bipinnatifidly dissected, whereas subsequent leaves are bipinnately to tripinnately divided. A rosette is formed that may persist and overwinter if development is vegetative during the initial growing season. Bolting commences with elongation of the central stem; however, axillary or basal shoots may bolt first and a central stem may never develop. Flower buds form at the apices of numerous determinate, cymose branches. *Matricaria perforata* seedlings transplanted to a common garden in Regina took 39.6–84.8 d from germination to bolting, with tetraploid populations taking 15–23 d longer than the diploid populations (Woo 1989).

Matricaria perforata requires a long-day photoperiod to initiate a flowering response (Roberts and Feast 1974). When overwintered rosettes and spring germinated seedlings were collected during April from fields in Ontario and grown under an 8-h photoperiod at an alternating temperature of 20/15°C, no plants flowered. When grown under a 15-h photoperiod at 20/15°C, overwintered rosettes flowered after 62 d and spring seedlings after 72 d (Westfall 1987). When autumn germinated seedlings had been vernalized at 5°C for 2–8 wk, 20% of the seedlings flowered

under an 8-h photoperiod (Westfall 1987). Plants in a common garden study at Regina flowered in 58–108 d after germination, with tetraploid populations taking 22–27 d longer than the diploids (Woo 1989). This is intermediate to observations of 110–135 d from germination to flowering made by Kay (1965) and of about 50 d by Roberts and Feast (1974). In Saskatchewan fields, flowering is initiated by June and is terminated near the end of October after a killing frost.

Overwintering plants at Regina, Saskatchewan resumed growth in early April, from new basal shoots at the caudex or from the rosette base, if the previous season's growth had been vegetative (Woo 1989). The plant in the second season is more extensively branched and lacks a single prominent central stem, which makes the plant appear bushier and more globose than the growth form observed in the first season. Overwintering plants flower in mid-May and flower production is more prolific than in the previous season. Differences in time to flower between the two cytotypes are less apparent the second season than in the first. Senescence occurs by early September (Woo 1989).

(e) *Mycorrhiza* — No reports for this species.

8. Reproduction

(a) *Floral biology* — The capitula of *M. perforata* are composed of pistillate ray florets on the periphery, and protandrous, bisexual disk florets in the centre. A reproductive biology experiment conducted among Canadian populations indicated that the flowers were obligate allogamous (Woo 1989). Kay (1965) found that *M. perforata* had a sporophytic self-incompatibility system that may be controlled by two dominant alleles of a multi-allelic system. The pollen is heavy, sticky, and not readily dispersed by wind, suggesting that the mode of pollination is entomophilous. Kay (1969) noted in Great Britain that flowers were cross-pollinated by flies which were always numerous on the plants.

(b) *Seed production and dispersal* — Achene production among 13 Canadian populations of *M. perforata* ranged from 345 to 533 achenes per capitulum (Woo 1989). However, this apparently high achene production was not indicative of fertility since achene viability was variable. Counts of up to 3200 capitula per plant have been noted, and potential achene production in a dense stand of *M. perforata* has been estimated between 0.3 and 1.8 million achenes m^{-2}, which is equivalent to the production of a single *M. perforata* plant under appropriate growing conditions (Kay 1965; Kessler 1989d; Woo 1989). Capitula usually shatter at maturity, or the entire capitulum may break off the plant, thus dispersing the achenes on the ground where they are further spread by wind. The achenes are buoyant for 12 h in water (Ridley 1930). Kay (1965) found that although 88% of the achenes had sunk after 96 h, 4% remained afloat after 220 d in seawater. These reports suggest that achenes can be transported by runoff (Mitich 1976). Domestic animals may play a role in dispersal (Ridley 1930) since, for example, 26% of the achenes fed to cattle remained viable in dung (Dorph-Peterson 1925). A significant number of achenes were found in lentil, mustard, and wheat grain samples in Saskatchewan, suggesting that contaminated grain may be an important dispersal mechanism (Kessler 1989d).

(c) *Viability of seeds and germination* — The early European work on germination requirements and dormancy of *M. perforata* (Kolk 1962) indicated that light was essential for the germination of freshly harvested achenes but this requirement decreased with increasing age of achenes stored in the laboratory. A variable proportion of the freshly harvested achenes is dormant. For example, from 62 to 87% of the achenes less than 2 mo old were reported to germinate in light and from 0 to 9% in darkness, but after storage in the laboratory for 8–12 mo from 92 to 98% of the achenes germinated in light and from 19 to 43% in darkness. After 3 yr of laboratory storage, the germination in darkness of eight different collections varied from 5 to 80% (Kolk 1962). From 0 to 15% of the viable achenes in these collections were considered dormant because they did not germinate in

light at alternating temperatures of 30/10°C. Alternating temperatures could not substitute for the effect of light on achenes germinated in the dark. Gibberellic acid had no effect on germination but removal of the achene coat increased germination (Kolk 1962). Scarification may increase the percentage germination of freshly-harvested achenes. Westfall (1987) scarified achenes from tetraploid plants with liquid nitrogen, sulphuric acid, or sandpaper and found small but significant increases in some seed collections. Fresh achenes from diploid plants germinated at a slower rate than achenes from tetraploid plants, which were not dormant (Kay 1965).

The effect of low water potentials on germination has been investigated using polyethylene glycol solutions (Lonchamp and Barralis 1983). A few achenes germinated in water (−1 bar) in the dark but no germination occurred at low water potentials of −10, −20, or −30 bars. These low osmotic treatments influenced the amount of subsequent germination when the achenes were transferred back to water (−1 bar) and tested at three temperatures in the dark. Very little germination occurred at temperatures of 15/10°C and 20/15°C but at 30/20°C approximately 80% of the achenes germinated in the dark. The remaining achenes at 15/10°C and 20/15°C only germinated when transferred to water in the light. These results indicate that a drought stress as a pretreatment changes the subsequent germination response to temperature and light.

Germination in light was not enhanced by nitrate, but in darkness nitrate can to some extent replace the requirement for light (Espeby 1989). Concentrations above 2430 mg L^{-1} N significantly slowed the rate of germination in light but did not affect the final germination percentage. Exposure to chilling temperatures of 5°C decreased the percentage germination and this induction of dormancy can be prevented if nitrate is present.

Viability of achenes stored dry indoors is generally maintained for 4 yr near the maximum but declines to nearly zero after 10–12 yr (Dorph-Peterson 1925; Kjær 1939,

1948; Kolk 1962; Lewis 1973). In Denmark, Kjær (1939) reported that 1% of the achenes buried at 25-cm depth in pots in the field were still viable after 10 yr and Dorph-Peterson (1925) found 8% viable at 20 cm after 6 yr. In England from 11 to 47% of achenes buried in bags at 13- to 39-cm depths were viable after 4 yr (Lewis 1973). Under North Dakota conditions, 6–10% of achenes buried at depths from 2.5 to 30 cm remained viable after 6 yr (Hoag et al. 1980). Depth of burial was not correlated with greater viability of the achenes. The viability of achenes mixed with soil and buried in earthenware cylinders to a depth of 15 cm was 27% after 5 yr (Roberts and Feast 1972) and 23% after 6 yr (Roberts and Feast 1973). In contrast, when the soil in the cylinders was disturbed periodically each year to simulate a cultivation, from 3 to 11% of the achenes remained viable after 5–6 yr (Roberts 1964; Roberts and Feast 1972; Roberts and Feast 1973). In monocultures of winter wheat or spring barley in France the mean annual rate of decline in the seed bank was 88% the first year, 71% of the remaining seed the second year, and 56% of the remaining seed the third year (Barralis et al. 1988).

Buried achenes exhibited no annual dormancy cycle. Freshly-harvested achenes that were buried during the autumn at 10- and 25-cm depths in soil in France, exhumed at 3-wk intervals over the next 28 mo, and then tested at 15/10°C in light, germinated at nearly 100% at all recovery times (Lonchamp et al. 1984). Only 10% of the achenes germinated in the dark when first exhumed but the germination percentage rose to 90% after 1 yr and then was the same as that of the achenes germinated in the light for the rest of the experiment. Comparable results were obtained in a burial experiment conducted at the Regina Research Station (Kessler 1989d).

(d) *Vegetative reproduction* — No means of vegetative reproduction exists.

9. Hybrids

Naturally occurring hybrids between *Anthemis* species and *M. perforata* are noted,

and artificial hybrids of *Anthemis cotula* ($2n=18$) × *M. perforata* ($2n=36$) have chromosome counts of $2n=27$, low pollen viability (4.8%) and are sterile (Kay 1965; Mitsuoka and Ehrendorfer 1972). Attempts to artificially cross *M. perforata* with *Chamomilla* species were not successful, suggesting that these two genera are not as closely related as *Anthemis* and *Matricaria* (Kay 1965; Mitsuoka and Ehrendorfer 1972; Heywood and Humphries 1977).

Artificial crosses between diploid and tetraploid populations are possible, indicating genome homologies between the cytotypes. Crosses between populations from Borden, Prince Edward Island ($2\times$) and Vegreville, Alberta ($4\times$) and Dauphin, Manitoba ($4\times$) and St. Andrews, New Brunswick ($2\times$) yielded sterile triploid progeny (Woo 1989). Occasional floral abnormalities such as a few sporadic ray florets on the periphery of a small, unexpanded disk floret region and shrunken, empty, greenish-colored anthers are apparent in these hybrids (Woo 1989).

10. Population Dynamics

A single *M. perforata* plant, growing without competition, may cover an area in excess of 1 m². Spring-emerged seedlings will form a very dense carpet in low-lying areas and limit growth of seedlings of other species (Woo, unpublished data). Populations of *M. perforata* monitored at Rothamsted, U.K. were found to increase when there was no spring cultivation and there was heavy rainfall between March and July (Warington 1958). Emergence peaked during May in Sweden but some seedlings also emerged throughout the growing season (Håkansson 1983). Mann (1939) observed that *M. perforata* at Woburn, England prospered under high light conditions amongst growing crops, and minimal tillage conditions.

11. Response to Herbicides and other Chemicals

Matricaria perforata can be controlled in field crops grown in Canada by several commercial products which contain or are mixtures that contain bromoxynil or clopyralid

(Anonymous 1990). Only spring seedlings are susceptible to bromoxynil. In winter wheat, winter and spring annual *M. perforata* seedlings were susceptible to chlorsulfuron, clopyralid, and metsulfuron methyl (Reekie and Bowes 1988). Brown and Uprichard (1976) summarized the results from 50 research trials located in several countries and found that 0.05–0.1 kg ha^{-1} of picloram controlled the weed in field crops growing in Europe.

In general, herbicide rates higher than those used on cropland are required to control large *M. perforata* plants that grow in pastures and along roadsides. In a native blue grass pasture, picloram applied at 0.14 kg ha^{-1} or dicamba applied at 1.1 kg ha^{-1} effectively controlled *M. perforata* the year after an autumn application (Webster 1971). In another report, Webster (1970) found that 0.28 kg ha^{-1} of picloram effectively controlled plants that were 25 cm tall, which are typical plants of roadsides in western Canada. In tree rows and waste areas located in North Dakota, glyphosate or paraquat applied at 0.8 kg ha^{-1} or amitrole applied at 2.2 kg ha^{-1} adequately controlled the weed. Carder (1969) reviewed the control of *M. perforata* following the application of 27 herbicides applied between 1955 and 1969 and found that only picloram applied at 0.21 kg ha^{-1} was effective in the Peace River region of northwest Canada. This rate could be reduced to 0.14 kg ha^{-1} when crop competition was present and further reduced when there was competition from a perennial grass.

A British study found that there were regional and genetic differences among diploid *M. perforata* populations in their susceptibility to MCPA, ioxynil, and simazine (Ellis and Kay 1975a, b, c). Herbicide susceptibility was not related to spray retention and plant morphology, but had some relationship to rate of growth. It was concluded that the differences in resistance may be due to physiological rather than physical characteristics of the populations (Ellis and Kay 1975b). Resistance to ioxynil, MCPA, and simazine could be increased in a susceptible population after one generation of selection.

It was concluded that the population variation in herbicide resistance was partly due to the use of these herbicides (Ellis and Kay 1975a, c).

Matricaria perforata is susceptible to the hydroxybenzonitrile herbicides, ioxynil and bromoxynil, because they effectively inhibit chloroplast electron transport (Sanders and Pallett 1982). Treatments of ioxynil and bromoxynil to plants resulted in complete inhibition of CO_2 uptake and net photosynthesis after 4 d (Sanders et al. 1984). Although ioxynil caused greater inhibition of electron transport, bromoxynil had a greater phytotoxic effect on *M. perforata* over the 28 d of treatment (Sanders and Pallett 1985). These physiological changes were accompanied by chloroplast swelling, a decrease in starch grains and thylakoid disruption prior to cellular destruction (Sanders and Pallett 1986). The susceptibility of *M. perforata* to the hydroxybenzonitrile herbicides, especially bromoxynil, is due to the translocation of the herbicides to the apex and developing leaves causing cessation of growth (Sanders and Pallett 1987).

12. Response to Other Human Manipulations

Late autumn and early spring tillage are recommended for the control of *M. perforata* before seeding a crop (Lobay 1964; Lobay and Carder 1965; Stahlman and Hoag 1974). Shallow tillage is most effective on hot dry days since *M. perforata* can re-establish if a portion of the root system remains in moist soil (Stahlman and Hoag 1974; Kessler 1989c). A zero tillage (direct-drilled), tine-cultivated, or ploughed cultivation regime produced no differences in either the number of *M. perforata* seedlings emerging or the number of seeds found in the soil in a winter crop sequence in England (Froud-Williams et al. 1983a,b,).

Disturbed and waste nonagricultural areas that have *M. perforata* should be seeded to bromegrass (Lobay and Carder 1965) since bromegrass is a strong competitor. However, *M. perforata* will invade bromegrass stands which are severely tramped by cattle (Lobay 1964).

Mowing can be used as a control method. Viable achenes are produced 12 d after anthesis of the first ray florets (Hoag et al. 1980), when anthesis is completed in all but the central disk florets (D. Cole, personal communication), or 2 d after completion of capitulum anthesis (J. O'Donovan, personal communication). In order to prevent the formation of viable achenes, plants should be mowed in a vegetative stage or prior to anthesis.

13. Responses to Parasites
In the surveys of the insect fauna and disease organisms on *M. perforata* mentioned in section 3(a), a total of 68 insect species, 12 fungal and two nematode species were found in the European literature. In the Canadian field surveys, 14 insect species were for the first time observed feeding on *M. perforata* in Canada.

Those insect species and disease organisms recorded from Europe which appear to be restricted stenophagous and monophagous feeders could be further investigated in regard to their value as biocontrol agents for Canada. The genus *Matricaria* is centered in the Caucasus and Western Asia (Kay 1969). Thus, a field survey of those regions and of the USSR literature would very likely reveal many additional insects. Only one of the insects found feeding on *M. perforata* in Canada is specific and none are numerous enough on this weed to effect control.

(a) *Insects* — Of the 68 insects occurring in Europe on *M. perforata*, 3 were in the order Thysanoptera, 10 Hemiptera, 6 Homoptera, 21 Coleoptera, 15 Lepidoptera, and 13 in the Diptera. Six of the insects were endophytic in the stem, 7 in the leaves, 6 on or in the roots and/or root crown, 19 endo- or exophytic in the flowers and seed heads, 25 fed externally on the stems, leaves, flowers and buds, and 4 species developed in the stems, and/or leaves or flowers. There were 37 polyphagous insects, 16 stenophagous insects, and 13 restricted stenophagous insects. Two monophagous insects specialized on species in the genus

Matricaria. *Apion hookeri* Kirby (Coleoptera: Curculionidae) probably breeds only on *M. perforata* (Dieckmann 1977). The larvae feed on the receptacle, tubular flowers and seeds, and destroy 35% of the seeds in attacked flower heads (Freese 1987). The weevil *Ceutorhynchus edentulus* Schultze is reported from *M. perforata* and *Chamomilla suaveolens* Rydb. (=*Matricaria matricarioides* (Less.) Porter) (Smreczyński 1974). The larvae mine the stem (D. Schroeder, unpublished data).

Field surveys in Saskatchewan, Alberta, and Nova Scotia produced 14 insect species feeding on *M. perforata* (Peschken and McClay, unpublished data). Two species each were in the orders Orthoptera, Thysanoptera, Hemiptera, Homoptera, Lepidoptera, three species in the Coleoptera, and one species in the Diptera. All but two were polyphagous. The Coleoptera *Epicauta ferruginea* (Say) (Meloidae) was found feeding on the ray florets of *M. perforata*, and *Orsodacne atra childreni* (Kirby) (Chrysomelidae) on the pollen. *Epicauta ferruginea* has been collected primarily from Asteraceae and it is found in the three Canadian prairie provinces (J. D. Pinto, personal communication). The weevil *Apion hookeri*, not previously reported from North America, was discovered at two localities in Nova Scotia in August 1990 (Peschken, unpublished data). It is the only monophagous insect found on *M. perforata* in Canada. The larvae of the one Diptera, *Phytomyza matricariae* Hendel (Agromyzidae) mine even the most finely divided leaves of *M. perforata* and this fly also breeds on species in the genera *Achillea* and *Tanacetum*. It is the only restricted stenophagous insect found on *M. perforata* in Canada and it has a holarctic distribution (Spencer 1969). Insect populations and damage on scentless chamomile in Canada are in general low. The higher number of specialized insects on scentless chamomile in Europe is assumed to be the reason that this weed is rapidly replaced by grasses and herbs in the course of succession, unless frequently disturbed (Günther 1988). Ten insects are occasional pests in Canada and have been mentioned in section 3a.

(b) *Fungi* — Three European fungi were host specific: *Protomyces matricariae* (Syd.) (Taphrinales: Protomycetaceae) (Buhr 1964) and *Entyloma matricariae* Rostr. (Ustilaginales) (Lindeberg 1959) have been reported only from *M. perforata*, and *Peronospora leptosperma* de Bary has been reported from *M. perforata* and *Chamomilla recutita* L. (Docters van Leeuwen 1957; Buhr 1964). Eight additional species were not host specific. None of these fungi were of economic importance.

ACKNOWLEDGMENTS

This research was supported in part by a grant to V.L. Harms from the Hooke Research Trust Account, University of Saskatchewan and by funding from the Canada/Saskatchewan Subsidiary Agreement on Agriculture Development — an initiative under the Canada/Saskatchewan Economic and Regional Development Agreement (ERDA). We thank J. Arnott, D. Harron, D. Kessler, B. Kishchuk, and D. Potter for their contributions under short-term ERDA contracts. We particularly thank M. G. Maw (retired) for valuable discussions and advice during the initial years of this research project.

Alberta. 1980. The Weed Control Act. Weed Designation Regulation. Alberta Regulation 138/80. Queen's Printer, Edmonton, AB. 2 pp.

Alex, J. F., Cayouette, R. and Mulligan, G. A. 1980. Common and botanical names of weeds in Canada. Agriculture Canada, Ottawa, ON. Publ. 1397. 132 pp.

Anonymous. 1982. Scentless chamomile: a problem weed. Alberta Agriculture, Edmonton, AB. Agdex 640-6. 3 pp.

Anonymous. 1986. Canada Seeds Act. Weed Seed Order. Canada Gazette Pt. II Vol. 120 No. 17. pp. 3382–3385.

Anonymous. 1990. Chemical weed control in cereal, oilseed, pulse and forage crops. Saskatchewan Agriculture and Food, Regina, SK. Agdex 641. 112 pp.

Ashlock, P. D. 1977. New records and name changes of North American Lygaeidae (Hemiptera Heteroptera: Lygaeidae). Proc. Entomol. Soc. Wash. **79**: 575–582.

Barber, H. G. 1947. Revision of the genus Nysius in the United States and Canada (Hemiptera Heteroptera: Lygaeidae). J. Wash. Acad. Sci. **37**: 354–366.

Barralis, G., Chadoeuf, R. and Lonchamp, J. -P. 1988. Longevité des semences de mauvaises herbes annuelles dans un sol cultivé. Weed Res. **28**: 407–418.

Beirne, B. P. 1956. Leafhoppers (Homoptera: Cicadellidae) of Canada and Alaska. Can. Entomol. (Suppl. 2) **88**: 1–180.

Beirne, B. P. 1972. Pest insects of annual crops in Canada. IV. Hemiptera-Homoptera. V. Orthoptera. VI. Other groups. Mem. Entomol. Soc. Can. No. 85. 73 pp.

Boivin, B. 1972. Flora of the Prairie Provinces. Part III. Phytologia **23**: 84–85.

Börner, C. 1952. Europae centralis Aphides. Die Blattläuse Mitteleuropas. Schriften der Thüringischen Landesarbeitsgemeinschaft für Heilpflanzenkunde und Heilpflanzenbeschaffung in Weimar. Heft 4 und Mitteilungern der Thüringischen Botanischen Gesellschaft. Weimar. Beiheft 3.1. Lieferung pp. 1–259. 2. Lieferung. pp. 260–488.

Bradley, J. D., Tremewan, W. G. and Smith, A. 1973. British tortricoid moths. Cochylidae and Tortricidae: Tortricinae. I. The Ray Society, London, U.K. 251 pp.

British Columbia. 1976. Weed control act. The British Columbia Gazette - Part II, Order in Council 1548: 315.

Brown, A. 1878. Plants introduced with ballast and on made land. Bull. Torrey Bot. Club. **6**: 255–258.

Brown, J. G. and Uprichard, S. D. 1976. Control of problem weeds in cereals with 3,6-dichloropicolinic acid and mixtures with phenoxy herbicides. Proc. Br. Crop Prot. Conf. Weeds. **1**: 118–225.

Buhr, H. 1964. Bestimmungstabellen der Gallen (Zoo- und Phytocecidien) an Pflanzen Mittel- und Nordeuropas. I. Fisher, Jena. 761 pp.

Carder, A. C. 1969. Control of scentless chamomile by herbicides. Res. Rep. Can. Weed. Comm. (West. Sect.) p. 315.

Cellarova, E., Grelakova, K., Repcak, M. and Honcariv, R. 1982. Morphogenesis in callus tissue cultures of some *Matricaria* and *Achillea* species. Biol. Plant. (Praha) **24**: 430–433.

Clapham, A. R., Tutin, T. G. and Warburg, E. F. 1962. Flora of the British Isles, 2nd ed. Cambridge University Press, Cambridge, U.K. pp. 852–854.

Dieckmann, L. 1977. Beiträge zur Insektenfauna der DDR: Coleoptera - Curculionidae (Apioninae). Beitr. Entomol. **27**: 7–143.

Dock Gustavsson, A. -M. 1989. Growth of annual dicotyledonous weeds. Analysis using relative growth rate (RGR) and unit production ratio (UPR). Crop Prod. Sci. **5**: 1–106.

Docters van Leeuwen, W. M. 1957. Gallenboek. Nederlandse door dieren en planten veroorzaakte Gallen. 2nd. ed. Thieme, Zutphen. 332 pp.

Dorph-Petersen, K. 1925. Examinations of the occurrence and vitality of various weed seed species under different conditions made at the Danish State Seed Testing Station during the years 1896-1923. Rep. IV. Int. Seed Test Congr. pp. 124-131.

Douglas, D. 1989. Scentless chamomile — crop yield losses. ERDA Information Sheet no. 4, Agriculture Canada, Regina, SK. 2 pp.

Ellenberg, H. and Mueller-Dombois, D. 1967. A key to Raunkiaer plant life forms with revised subdivisions. Pages 449-465 *in* Mueller-Dombois, D. and Ellenberg, H. (1974). Aims and methods of vegetation ecology. Appendix A. John Wiley and Sons, New York, NY.

Ellis, M. and Kay, Q. O. N. 1975a. Genetic variation in herbicide resistance in scentless mayweed (*Tripleurospermum inodorum* (L.) Schultz Bip.). I. Differences between populations in response to MCPA. Weed Res. **15**: 307-315.

Ellis, M. and Kay, Q. O. N. 1975b. Genetic variation in herbicide resistance in scentless mayweed (*Tripleurospermum inodorum* (L.) Schultz Bip.) II. Intraspecific variation in response to ioxynil and MCPA, and the role of spray retention characteristics. Weed Res. **15**: 317-326.

Ellis, M. and Kay, Q. O. N. 1975c. Genetic variation in herbicide resistance in scentless mayweed (*Tripleurospermum inodorum* (L.) Schultz Bip.) III. Selection for increased resistance to ioxynil, MCPA and simazine. Weed Res. **15**: 327-333.

Espeby, L. 1989. Germination of weed seeds and competition in stands of weeds and barley. Influences of mineral nutrients. Crop Prot. Sci. **6**: 1-156.

Fernald, M. L. 1950. Gray's manual of botany. 8th ed. American Book Company, New York, NY. pp. 1516-1517.

Forbes, A. R. and Chan, C. K. 1989. Aphids of British Columbia. Technical Bull. 1989-1E. Research Branch, Agriculture Canada. Ottawa, ON. 260 pp.

Freese, A. 1987. On the possibility of biological control of *Matricaria perforata* Mérat. Report. CAB International Institute of Biological Control. European Station, Delémont, Switzerland. 50 pp.

Froud-Williams, R. J., Chancellor, R. J. and Drennan, D. S. H. 1983b. Influence of cultivation regime upon buried weed seeds in arable cropping systems. J. Appl. Ecol. **20**: 199-208.

Froud-Williams, R. J., Drennan, D. S. H. and Chancellor, R. J. 1983a. Influence of cultivation regime on weed floras of arable cropping systems. J. Appl. Ecol. **20**: 187-197.

Great Plains Flora Association. 1977. Atlas of the flora of the Great Plains. The Iowa State University Press, Ames, IA. pp. 392.

Günther, W. 1988. Ökologische Untersuchungen zur Phytophagen- und Entomophagen-Fauna der geruchlosen Kamille (*Matricaria inodora* L.). Diplomarbeit. Zoologisches Institut, Christian-Albrechts-Universität, Kiel, Federal Republic of Germany. 89 pp.

Håkansson, S. 1983. Seasonal variation in the emergence of annual weeds — an introductory investigation in Sweden. Weed Res. **23**: 313-324.

Halliday, G. and Beadle, M. 1983. Consolidated index to Flora Europaea. Cambridge University Press, Cambridge, U.K. 210 pp.

Hamet-Ahti, L. 1967. *Tripleurospermum* (Compositae) in the northern parts of Scandinavia, Finland and Russia. Acta Bot. Fenn. **75**: 3-19.

Hanf, M. 1983. The arable weeds of Europe with their seedlings and seeds. BASF, Federal Republic of Germany. 494 pp.

Heywood, V. H. and Humphries, C. J. 1977. Anthemideae, systematic review. Pages 851-898 *in* V. H. Heywood, J. B. Harbone and B. L. Turner, eds. The biology and chemistry of the Compositae. Vol. 2. Academic Press, London, U.K.

Hill, D. S. 1987. Agricultural insect pests of temperate regions and their control. Cambridge University Press, Cambridge, U.K. 659 pp.

Hoag, B. K., Lukach, J. R., Fisher, J. J. and Miller, S. D. 1980. False chamomile control in north central North Dakota. Proc. North Cent. Weed Control Conf. **35**: 86-87.

Holmgren, P. K., Keuken, W. and Schofield, E. K. 1981. Index herbariorum. Part 1. The herbaria of the world. 7th ed. Dr. W. Junk Publ., The Hague, The Netherlands. 452 pp.

Hultén, E. 1968. Flora of Alaska and neighbouring territories. Stanford University Press, Stanford, CA. 1008 pp.

Kartesz, J. T. and Kartesz, R. 1980. A synonymized checklist of the vascular flora of the United States, Canada, and Greenland. Vol. II. The biota of North America. The University of North Carolina Press, Chapel Hill, NC. 498 pp.

Kay, Q. O. N. 1965. Experimental and comparative ecological studies of selected weeds. Ph.D. Thesis, University of Oxford, Oxford, U.K. 221 pp.

Kay, Q. O. N. 1969. The origin and distribution of diploid and tetraploid *Tripleurospermum inodorum* (L.) Schultz Bip. Watsonia. **7**: 130-141.

Kay, Q. O. N. 1972. Variation in sea mayweed (*T. maritimum* (L.) Koch.) in the British Isles. Watsonia **9**: 81–107.

Kay, Q. O. N. 1976. *Matricaria* L. Pages 165–167 *in* T. G. Tutin, V. H. Heywood, N. A. Burges, D. M. Moore, D. H. Valentine, S. M. Walters, and D. A. Webb, eds. Flora Europaea. Vol. 4. Plantaginaceae to Compositae. Cambridge University Press, Cambridge, U.K.

Kessler, D. 1989a. Scentless chamomile — habitats. ERDA Information Sheet no. 2, Agriculture Canada, Regina, SK. 2 pp.

Kessler, D. 1989b. Scentless chamomile — distribution. ERDA Information Sheet no. 3, Agriculture Canada, Regina, SK. 2 pp.

Kessler, D. 1989c. Scentless chamomile — weed management. ERDA Information Sheet no. 5, Agriculture Canada, Regina, SK. 2 pp.

Kessler, D. 1989d. Scentless chamomile — seed production and germination. ERDA Information Sheet no. 6, Agriculture Canada, Regina, SK. 2 pp.

Kjær, A. 1939. Germination of buried and dry stored seeds. I. 1934–1939. Proc. Int. Seed Test. Assoc. **12**: 167–190.

Kjær, A. 1948. Germination of buried and dry stored seeds. II. 1934–1944. Proc. Int. Seed Test. Assoc. **14**: 19–26.

Kolk, H. 1962. Viability and dormancy of dry stored weed seeds. Växtodling **18**: 1–192.

Koul, M. L. H. 1964. Cytology of some composites. J. Sci. Res. Banaras Hindu University **14**: 20–22.

Lankosz-Mroz, M. 1976. Karyological investigations on *Tripleurospermum maritimum* (L.) Koch. ssp. *inodorum* (L.) Hyl. ex Vaarama from Poland. Acta Biol. Cracov. Ser. Bot. **19**: 93–105.

Lewis, J. 1973. Longevity of crop and weed seeds: survival after 20 years in soil. Weed Res. **13**: 179–191.

Lewis, T. 1972. Thrips, their biology, ecology and economic importance. Academic Press, London, UK. 349 pp.

Lindeberg, B. 1959. Ustilaginales of Sweden (exclusive of the Cintractias on Caricoideae). Symb. Bot. Ups. **16**: 175.

Linnaeus, C. 1753. Species plantarum. 1st ed. Holmiae: 891.

Lobay, W. 1964. Scentless chamomile. Proc. North Central Weed Control Conf. **20**: 60–61.

Lobay, W. and Carder, A. C. 1965. Scentless mayweed control in Alberta. Publ. No. 153. Agricultural Extension Service, Department of Agriculture, Edmonton, AB.

Lonchamp, J. -P. and Barralis, G. 1983. Effets de faibles potentiels hydriques sur les possibilités de germination des semences d'*Alopecurus myosuroides* Huds. et de *Matricaria perforata* Mérat. Agronomie **3**: 435–441.

Lonchamp, J. -P., Chadoeuf, R. and Barralis, G. 1984. Evolution de la capacité de germination des semences de mauvaises herbes enfouies dans le sol. Agronomie **4**: 671–682.

Manitoba. 1970. The Noxious Weeds Act. Chapter N110 in Vol. III of the revised Statutes of Manitoba. Queen's Printer, Winnipeg, MB. 20 pp.

Mann, H. H. 1939. The weed herbage of a slightly acid arable soil. J. Ecol. **27**: 89–113.

Mann, H. H. and Barnes, T. W. 1945. The competition between barley and certain weeds under controlled conditions. Ann. Appl. Biol. **32**: 15–22.

Martens, J. W., Seaman, W. L. and Atkinson, T. G. 1988. Diseases of field crops in Canada. Can. Phytopathol. Society, Harrow, ON. 160 pp.

Matthews, L. J. 1982. Pasture weeds of New Zealand. Pages 387–394 *in* W. Holzner and M. Numata, eds. Biology and ecology of weeds. Dr. W. Junk Publishers, The Hague, The Netherlands.

Minks, A. K. and Harrewijn, P., ed. 1989. World crop pests. Vol. 2c. Aphids, their biology, natural enemies, and control. Elsevier, Amsterdam, The Netherlands. 310 pp.

Mitich, L. W. 1976. Weed watch. Weeds Today (Spring). p. 26.

Mitsuoka, S. and Ehrendorfer, F. 1972. Cytogenetics and evolution of *Matricaria* and related genera (Asteraceae-Anthemideae). Österr. Bot. Zeitschr. Wien. **120**: 155–200.

Morison, G. D. 1957. A review of British glasshouse Thysanoptera. Trans. R. Entomol. Soc. Lond. **109**: 467–534.

Moss, E. H. 1983. Flora of Alberta. 2nd ed. Revised by J. G. Packer. University of Toronto Press, Toronto, ON. 687 pp.

Mulligan, G. A. 1959. Chromosome numbers of Canadian weeds. II. Can. J. Bot. **37**: 81–92.

Néhou, J. 1954. Étude comparative de *Matricaria inodora* L. et de *M. maritima* L. (Composées, Radiées). Bull. Soc. Sci. Brétagne **28**: 133–153.

Nelson, J. C. 1917. The introduction of foreign weeds in ballast as illustrated by ballast-plants at Linnton, Oregon. Torreya **17**: 151–160.

Philip, H. G. 1975. Insect pests of Alberta. Agdex 612-1. Edmonton, AB. 77 pp.

Pobedimova, E. G. 1961. *Tripleurospermum* Sch. Bip. (translated to English). Pages 157–184 *in* B. K. Shishkin and E. G. Bobrov, eds. Flora

S.S.S.R. Botanical Institute of the U.S.S.R. Academy of Science, Moscow, U.S.S.R.

Porsild, A. E. and Cody, W. J. 1980. Vascular plants of continental Northwest Territories, Canada. National Museum of Natural Sciences, National Museums of Canada, Ottawa, ON. pp. 588–589.

Rahman, A. 1982. New Zealand. Pages 229–308 *in* W. Holzner and M. Numata, eds. Biology and ecology of weeds. Dr. W. Junk Publishers, The Hague, The Netherlands.

Rauschert, S. 1974. Nomenklatorische Probleme in der Gattung *Matricaria* L. Folia Geobot. Phytotaxonomy **9**: 249–260.

Reekie, G. and Bowes, G. 1988. Scentless chamomile control in winter wheat. Winter Wheat Final Rep. 1985–88. University of Saskatchewan, Saskatoon, SK. pp. 1053–1054.

Richards, A. M., Pope, R. D. and Eastop, V. F. 1976. Observations on the biology of *Subcoccinella vigintiquattuor-punctata* (L.) in southern England. Ecol. Entomol. **1**: 201–207.

Ridley, H. N. 1930. The dispersal of plants throughout the world. L. Reeve and Company Ltd., Ashford, U.K.

Roberts, H. A. 1964. Emergence and longevity in cultivated soil of seeds of some annual weeds. Weed Res. **4**: 296–307.

Roberts, H. A. and Feast, P. 1972. Fate of seeds of some annual weeds in different depths of cultivated and undisturbed soil. Weed Res. **12**: 316–324.

Roberts, H. A. and Feast, P. M. 1973. Emergence and longevity of seeds of annual weeds in cultivated and undisturbed soil. J. Appl. Ecol. **10**: 133–143.

Roberts, H. A. and Feast, P. M. 1974. Observations on the time of flowering of mayweeds. J. Appl. Ecol. **11**: 223–229.

Rockburne, E. W. and Lafontaine, J. 1976. The cutworm moths of Ontario and Quebec. Agriculture Canada, Ottawa, ON. 164 pp.

Rottgardt, K. 1956. Morphologische, cytologische und physiologische Untersuchungen von Ökotypen in Schleswig-Holstein. Beitr. Biol. Pflanz. **32**: 225–278.

Ruppert, V. 1987. Blüten für Nutzinsekten. TASPO Magazin. **14**: 36–37.

Rychlova, M., Cellarova, E. and Honcariv, R. 1984. The study of morphological and histological changes in tissue cultures of *Matricaria inodora* L. Biol. Plant. (Praha) **26**: 197–201.

Sanders, G. E., Cobb, A. H. and Pallett, K. 1984. Physiological changes in *Matricaria inodora*

following ioxynil and bromoxynil treatment. Naturforsch. Sect. C. Biosci. **39**: 505–509.

Sanders, G. E. and Pallett, K. E. 1982. Studies into the different response of three weed species to the hydroxybenzonitriles. Proc. Br. Crop Prot. Conf. Weeds **1**: 325–333.

Sanders, G. E. and Pallett, K. E. 1985. In vitro activity and binding characteristics of the hydroxybenzonitriles in chloroplasts isolated from *Matricaria inodora* and *Viola arvensis*. Pestic. Biochem. Physiol. **24**: 317–325.

Sanders, G. E. and Pallett, K. E. 1986. Studies into differential activity of the hydroxybenzonitrile herbicides. I. Photosynthetic inhibition, system development, and ultrastructural changes in two contrasting species. Pestic. Biochem. Physiol. **26**: 116–127.

Sanders, G. E. and Pallett, K. E. 1987. Studies into differential activity of the hydroxybenzonitrile herbicides. II. Uptake, movement and metabolism in two contrasting species. Pestic. Biochem. Physiol. **28**: 163–171.

Saskatchewan. 1977. The Noxious Weeds Act, R.R.S. 1965 — Section 2 (i). The Saskatchewan Gazette, Volume 73, Number 36, Part II: 519.

Scoggan, H. G. 1979. The flora of Canada. Part 4. Dicotyledoneae. National Museum of Natural Sciences. Publication in Botany 7. National Museum of Canada, Ottawa, ON. pp. 1580–1582.

Shetler, S. G. and Skog, L. E. eds. 1978. A provisional checklist of species for flora North America. Missouri Botanical Garden, St. Louis, MO. 199 pp.

Smreczyński, S. 1974. Cześć XIX. Chrzaszcze — Coleoptera. Zeszyt 98 e. Ryjkowce — Curculionidae. Podrodzina curculioninae. Pleminona: Barini, Coryssomerini, Ceutorhynchini. Klucze do Oznaczania Owadów Polski. Pol. Tow. Entomol. Nr. 83 serii kluczy. pp. 1–180.

Spencer, K. A. 1969. The Agromyzidae of Canada and Alaska. Mem. Entomol. Soc. Can. **64**: 1–311.

Stahlman, P. W. and Hoag, B. K. 1974. Observations on false chamomile in North Dakota. Proc. North Central Weed Control Conf. **29**: 41–42.

Stannard, L. J. 1968. The thrips or Thysanoptera of Illinois. Ill. Nat. Hist. Surv. Bull. **29**: 215–552.

Suganda, A. G., Amoros, M., Fauconnier, B. and Girre, L. 1984. Actions antiherpétique et antipoliomyélitique du *Matricaria inodora* L. Plant. Med. Phytother. **18**: 215–225.

Suganda, A. G., Amoros, M., Girre, L. and Fauconnier, B. 1983. Effets inhibiteurs de quelques extraits bruts et semi purifiés de plantes indigènes françaises sur la multiplication de l'herpesvirus humain 1 et du poliovirus humain 2 en culture cellulaire. Nat. Prod. (Lloydia) **46**: 626–632.

Thomas, A. G. and Wise, R. F. 1987. Weed survey of Saskatchewan cereal and oilseed crops 1986. Weed Survey Series Publ. 87-1. Agriculture Canada, Regina, SK. 251 pp.

Thomas, A. G. and Wise, R. F. 1988. Weed survey of Manitoba cereal and oilseed crops 1986. Weed Survey Series Publ. 88-1. Agriculture Canada, Regina, SK. 201 pp.

Tutin, T. G., Heywood, V. H., Burges, N. A., Moore, D. M., Valentine, D. H., Walters, S. M. and Webb, D. A. 1976. eds. Flora Europaea. Vol. 4. Plantaginaceae to Compositae. Cambridge University Press, Cambridge, U.K.

Varis, A. L. 1972. The biology of *Lygus rugulipennis* Popp. (Het., Miridae) and the damage caused by this species to sugar beet. Ann. Agric. Fenn. **11**: 1–56.

Wagenitz, G. 1987. Nachträge, Berichtigungen und Ergänzungen zum Nachdruck der 1. Auflage von Band VI/2 (1928/9). Pages 1353–1357 *in* Hegi. G. 1928/29. Illustrierte Flora von Mittel-Europa. Verlag Paul Parey, Berlin.

Warington, K. 1958. Changes in the weed flora on Broadbalk permanent wheat field during the period 1930–55. J. Ecol. **46**: 101–113.

Webster, G. D. 1970. Control of scentless chamomile in advanced stages of growth. Res. Rep. Canada Weed Comm. (West. Sect.) pp. 200–201.

Webster, G. D. 1971. Control of scentless chamomile in forage (fall treatments). Res. Rep. Canada Weed Comm. (West. Can. Sect.) p. 148.

Welbank, P. J. 1963. A comparison of competitive effects of some common weed species. Ann. Appl. Biol. **51**: 107–125.

Weed Science Society of America. 1989. Composite list of weeds. Weed Sci. Soc. Amer., Champaign, IL. 112 p.

Westfall, B. 1987. Biology and control of scentless chamomile (*Matricaria maritima* L. var. *agrestis* (Knaf) Wilmott) in cereals. M.Sc. thesis, Department of Environmental Biology, University of Guelph, Guelph, ON. 89 pp.

Wilson, B. J. and Wright, K. J. 1990. Predicting the growth and competitive effects of annual weeds in wheat. Weed Res. **30**: 201–211.

Wójcik, Z. 1973. The plant communities of root-crop fields in lowlands and highlands of Poland: floristic, ecologic and regional differentiation. Feddes Repert. **84**: 573–588.

Woo, S. L. 1989. Biosystematics and life history strategies of scentless chamomile (*Matricaria perforata* Mérat) in Canada. M.Sc. thesis, Department of Crop Science and Plant Ecology, University of Saskatchewan, Saskatoon, SK. 194 pp.

The biology of Canadian weeds. 99.
Viola arvensis Murr.

Douglas J. Doohan and Thomas J. Monaco[1]

[1] *Department of Horticultural Science, North Carolina State University, Raleigh, NC 27606-7609, U.S.A. Received 7 Jan. 1991, accepted 25 July 1991.*

Doohan, D. J. and Monaco, T. J. 1992. **The biology of Canadian weeds. 99.** *Viola arvensis* **Murr.** Can. J. Plant Sci. **72**: 187–201. *Viola arvensis* Murr., field violet, is distributed in all Canadian provinces and most of the continental United States. It is one of the most common weeds associated with grain production in Europe. *Viola arvensis* tolerates most herbicides used in production of grains and many other crops. Selective pressure from increased herbicide use and long grain rotations appears to be responsible for increased frequency and density of *V. arvensis* in a number of important crops. The objective of this article is to summarize biological data known for this species.

Key words: *Viola arvensis* Murr., weed biology, germination, response to herbicides

Doohan, D. J. et Monaco, T. J. 1992. **La biologie des mauvaises herbes du Canada. 99.** *Viola arvensis* **Murr.** Can. J. Plant Sci. **72**: 187–201. *Viola arvensis* Murr., violette des champs, se rencontre dans toutes les provinces canadiennes et dans la plus grande partie du territoire continental des Etats-Unis. C'est aussi une des adventices les plus communes des céréales en Europe. *Viola arvensis* résiste à la plupart des herbicides employés en céréaliculture et dans de nombreuses autres productions végétales. La pression sélective résultant de l'usage accru des désherbants et de la pratique de longues rotations céréalières semble expliquer cette recrudescence de *V. arvensis*, tant en fréquence qu'en densité, dans plusieurs cultures importantes. La communication récapitule les données connues sur la biologie de l'espèce.

Mots clés: *Viola arvensis* Murr., biologie des mauvaises herbes, germination, réaction à l'égard des herbicides

1. Name

Viola arvensis Murr. — **field violet** (Alex et al. 1980); field pansy, wild pansy, hearts ease (Muenscher 1955); **violette des champs,** pensee des champs, petite pensee, (Ferron and Cayouette 1971). Violaceae, violet family, Violacee.

2. Description and Account of Variation

(a) *Morphology and cytology* — *Viola arvensis* is a diffusely branched, winter or summer annual herb. Roots (Figs. 1 and 2) are fine and fibrous with a wintergreen odor when crushed (Radford et al. 1968). Juvenile stems are acaulescent, bearing a rosette of leaves. Stems are angular-terete, becoming elongated with age (Fig. 3). Mature stems may be pubescent throughout or only on the angles. Leaves are dimorphic, often ciliate at the base and pubescent on the abaxial veins. Basal, acaulescent leaves (Figs. 1, 2 and 4) are petiolate, alternate, orbicular-ovate and dentate. The blades are 1–1.5 cm long, 1–1.5 cm wide and are borne on petioles 1–2 cm long. Upper, cauline leaves (Fig. 3) are alternate, petiolate, stipulate, oblong/cuneate to lanceolate, dentate/crenate, 2–8 cm long and 1–1.75 cm broad. Stipules are enlarged, conspicuous, leaf-like, pectinate with an enlarged terminal lobe. Chasmogamous, perfect

Present address (D.J.D) and address for reprints: Plant Industry Branch, Nova Scotia Department of Agriculture and Marketing, P.O. Box 550, Truro, Nova Scotia, Canada B2N 5E3.

Due to an error in the original printing this account was incorrectly numbered.

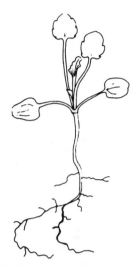

Fig. 1. *Viola arvensis* seedling.

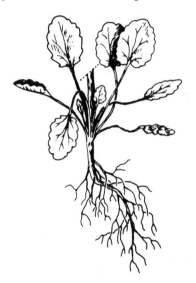

Fig. 2. *Viola arvensis* basal leaves.

flowers (Figs. 3 and 5), 0.5–1 cm broad, consist of a persistent calyx, auricled at the base, with five lanceolate, acute sepals, and a corolla of five petals, which are shorter than or equal in length to the sepals. The lower petal is spurred at the base and consistently white with a small, conspicuous yellow spot at the throat. Upper petals are usually white, occasionally tinged with pink or mauve. The two laterals are similar in color but are

distinctly bearded at the throat. Flowers arise in the leaf axils, and are borne singly on slender, 2- to 4-cm-long pedicels (Fig. 3). Fruit are tan, globose, capsules, 0.3- to 0.7-mm diameter, with 1 cell and 3 valves, bearing 3–4 parietal placentae. Fruit dehisce upon drying with each valve folding together lengthwise to violently expel the seed. Seed are tan, reniform and 1–1.7 mm long. Germination is epigean. Cotyledons are petiolate, ovate, 3–5 mm long and 3–4 mm wide when fully expanded.

The chromosome number for Canadian specimens of *V. arvensis* is $2N=24$ (Moss 1983). Tutin et al. (1968) and Radford et al. (1968) reported identical chromosome numbers for specimens from Europe and the southeastern United States, respectively.

(b) *Similar species* — Thirty-nine annual species of *Viola* are native to, or naturalized in Canada (Scoggan 1978). *Viola tricolor* L. and *V. rafinesquii* Greene (*V. kitaibeliana* Schultes ssp. *rafinesquii*) are often confused with *V. arvensis*. All three are pansies, characterized from other *Viola* species by broad, leaf-like, deeply divided stipules and lateral petals projecting upward. Table 1 contrasts morphological characters of each. *Viola arvensis* and *V. tricolor* were introduced from Europe (Fernald 1950); whereas, *V. rafinesquii* is considered native to North America (Shinners 1961).

Viola tricolor is frequently found growing in association with *V. arvensis* in eastern Canada. *Viola tricolor* is distinguished easily from *V. arvensis* by much larger petals, which are two to three times the length of the sepals. Petals are variously yellow, violet, purple and white. Upper, cauline leaves of *V. tricolor* are cordate.

Viola rafinesquii has been reported from dry fields and waste places in Saskatchewan and southwestern Ontario. This annual is most abundant on the Great Plains of the United States; however, it also occurs in several eastern states (Shinners 1961). It is a common weed of lawns in the piedmont region of North Carolina. *Viola rafinesquii* is more delicate and slender stemmed than *V. arvensis*. It is distinguished (Table 1) by obovate to

Fig. 3. *Viola arvensis* mature plant with stem, cauline leaves, stipules and flowers.

linear-oblanceolate, entire cauline leaves, and by producing chasmogamous flowers in early spring and cleistogamous flowers in late spring. The bluish white to creamy petals are nearly twice as long as the sepals.

Viola lanceolata L. has been reported as a perennial weed in blueberry (*Vaccinium corymbosum* L.) fields in coastal British Columbia (Scoggan 1978). This stoloniferous perennial bears white, purple-veined, chasmogamous flowers. Cleistogamous flowers are also produced. *Viola lanceolata* is also found in Ontario, Quebec, New Brunswick and Nova Scotia.

Fig. 4. *Viola arvensis* rosette.

Fig. 5. *Viola arvensis* flower.

(c) *Intraspecific variation* — Kakes (1982) reported great phenotypic plasticity in response to environmental conditions. *Viola arvensis* growing in spring or winter cereals has an upright habit of growth. Individuals are usually small, producing few seed capsules. Under full sunlight, high fertility and abundant soil moisture, large, fecund, spreading, decumbent plants develop.

Seeds were obtained from North Carolina, Michigan, Vermont, Connecticut and Nova Scotia and sown outdoors on 25 Sept. 1988 at Truro, Nova Scotia. All seed germinated more or less simultaneously, about 10 Oct. Seedlings were transplanted to pots and transferred to a greenhouse with a natural late fall/early winter photoperiod and a day/night temperature regime of 24/18°C. Plant development was monitored until flowering. Plants from all locations were consistent in morphology and development. Development of flower buds occurred simultaneously on all plants in about 110 d.

3. Economic Importance

(a) *Detrimental* — Data on the effect of *V. arvensis* on crop yield and quality are scarce. In Canada and the United States, it is most frequently found in fields with histories of long grain rotations.

Recently, reports of heavy infestations in strawberry (*Fragaria* × *ananassa* Deuchesne) fields have been made from several locations in eastern Canada and the United States (Chase and Putnam 1984; Monaco 1987; Doohan and Monaco 1988; Ahrens 1989). Infestations were frequently associated with land rotated from grain production or use of grain straw, infested with *V. arvensis*, for mulch.

Viola arvensis forms dense mats of tough twining stems that interfere with row crop establishment, cultural practices and harvest. Severe infestations have necessitated the premature abandonment of strawberry fields in Connecticut (Ahrens 1989). In Nova Scotia, we have observed infestations in soybeans (*Glycine max* L.) and cucurbits (*Cucurbita* spp.) that were grown in rotation with spring or winter cereals. Ahrens (personal communication) reported infestations in Christmas tree plantations where other weeds had been controlled with pre-emergence herbicides. He did not consider the species to be competitive with Christmas trees.

Viola arvensis is widespread and common in Europe, occurring in many crops. It is one of the three most serious weeds in Finland

Table 1. Useful characters to distinguish *V. arvensis, V. tricolor* and *V. rafinesquii*

	V. arvensis	*V. tricolor*	*V. rafinesquii*
Stems			
Pubescence	Entirely or only on angles	Entirely	Angles only or glabrous
Leaves (cauline)			
Shape	Lanceolate to oblong/ cuneate	Ovate to ovate/ lanceolate	Spatulate to oblanceolate
Base	Cuneate	Round or cordate	Cuneate
Margin	Dentate/crenate	Crenate	Entire or a single pair of teeth near apex
Length	2–5 cm	1.5–6 cm	0.5–3 cm
Pubescence	Entirely or only veins below	Glabrous, ciliate or eciliate	Glabrous or eciliate
Stipules	Pubescent, lanceolate terminal lobe	Ciliate, crenate, elliptic terminal lobe	Ciliate, pectinate/ palmate at base, elongated terminal lobe
Flowers			
Diameter	1–2 cm	1.5–2.5 cm	Up to 2 cm
Length of sepals	Petals shorter than sepals	Petals 3× length of sepals	Petals 2× length of sepals
Color	White to pale yellow, tips purple tinged	White, bright yellow and purple	Bluish white to creamy, purple veined
Sepal length	5–10 mm	6–12 mm	2–3 mm
Spur length	1–2 mm	2–3 mm	1–1.5 mm
Cleistogomy	No	No	Yes
Seed length	1–1.7 mm	1.6–2 mm	1.1–1.3 mm
Chromosome no.	$2N=34$	$2N=26$	$2N=34$

(Holm et al. 1979) where its proportion in the top 20 cm of soil in cereal fields ranged from 1 to 13% of the seed bank (Paatela and Ervio 1971). *Viola arvensis* is widespread in the Soviet Union, Portugal and England, where constant effort is required to maintain its control in a number of crops (Holm et al. 1979). It was the most frequent dicotyledonous weed in grain fields in south England (Froud-Williams et al. 1983). *Viola arvensis, Stellaria media* L. and *Galium aparine* L. were the most important species interfering with operation of grain harvesting machinery in Germany. Stems and leaves of *V. arvensis* were ground by harvesting machinery, blocking sieve holes of grain combines and increasing the moisture level of the harvested crop (Bachthaler et al. 1986). It is also common in root crops such as sugar-beet (*Beta vulgaris* L.) and sweet turnip (*Brassica rapa* L.) when these are grown in rotation with cereal grains. *Viola arvensis* was considered the most serious weed in rape (*Brassica napus* L.), in West Germany, making up 22% of the weed biomass. It was the eighth most prevalent dicotyledonous species in herbicide evaluation experiments in maize (*Zea maize* L.) conducted in Bavaria between 1962 and 1979 (Bachthaler et al. 1986). Infestations of *V. arvensis* have also been reported in forage grasses, alfalfa (*Medicago sativa* L.) and vegetable crops

(Roberts and Neilson 1982; Bachthaler et al. 1986).

(b) *Beneficial* — All species of *Viola* are edible (MacLeod and MacDonald 1976). *Viola* were used in cooking, as sources of herbal remedies and condiment ingredients during rennaisance and colonial times (Harris 1961; le Strange 1977). Leaves and flowers are high in vitamin A and vitamin C. Leaves can be used in salads and, because of their mucilagenous properties, as a thickner in soups. Flowers have been used in cough remedies and are purportedly beneficial to the digestive system.

Viola arvensis is an attractive plant, and provides ground cover; thereby contributing to erosion control. We are not aware of any current commercial uses.

(c) *Legislation* — *Viola arvensis* is not noxious under any provincial or federal weed control legislation.

4. Geographical Distribution

Viola arvensis occurs in all 10 Canadian provinces (Fig. 6); however, it is most common in Ontario, Quebec, New Brunswick, Nova Scotia, Newfoundland and British Columbia. Its northern range reported for Canada is 54° in Alberta (Fig. 6).

Viola arvensis occurs throughout most of New England and at least as far south as the piedmont of Georgia (Gleason 1952) (Fig. 7). It is reported in very few of the published floras of midwestern and western states; however, it is widely grown in gardens in Utah and is a naturalized garden escape in Cache County in the northern panhandle (Welsh et al. 1987). The species can be found in all Pacific states, particularly along the coast (Peck 1961; Munz 1974; Cresco 1984).

Viola arvensis occurs throughout continental Europe. Hilgondorff (1948) described the species as occurring in most agricultural districts of New Zealand.

5. Habitat

(a) *Climatic requirements* — Geographical distribution implies adaptation to a wide range of cool and warm temperate climatic conditions. Its greater prevalence in eastern North America and on the west coast may be due to greater rainfall in those regions; however, other factors such as moderate winter temperatures and varied crop rotation may also be involved.

The soil moisture requirement of *Viola arvensis* is unclear. Drought tolerance may give the species a competitive advantage over many other annual weeds during dry weather (Bachthaler et al. 1986). *Viola arvensis* density increased when growth of other species was curtailed during dry weather. Frequency increased the year following a growing season of normal precipitation (Bachthaler et al. 1986). The density of *V. arvensis* in grain and root crop fields with varying soil moisture conditions averaged 55 m^{-2} under dry conditions, 42 m^{-2} under moderate soil moisture and 25 m^{-2} under high soil moisture conditions (Mukula et al. 1969). The density of *V. arvensis* was inversely related to the total number of weeds. Density increased with irrigation, provided there was no competition from other weeds (Bachthaler et al. 1986). The species is more tolerant of continuous flooding than *G. aparine* or *S. media* (Bachthaler et al. 1986).

Temperature requirements of *V. arvensis* have not been reported and therefore can only be deduced from geographical distribution and seasonality. In Nova Scotia, germination occurs in the fall or spring when overnight frosts are common. Vegetative and reproductive growth occurs in spring, summer and fall. Flowering and seed production may continue into December when freezing occurs for part of most diurnal cycles. In the piedmont of North Carolina, the entire life cycle is completed during fall, winter and spring. Germination commences early in October and may continue throughout winter. Plants set seed and die by early summer. Freezing at night is common during late fall, winter and early spring, but rare during the day.

(b) *Substratum* — Although *V. arvensis* grows on most agricultural soils, extensive data from the Federal Republic of Germany indicates a preference for light-textured, sandy soils.

Fig. 6. Canadian distribution of *V. arvensis*, based on herbaria samples from DAO, QUE, NFLD, NSAC, UNB and V. (Abbreviations as in Holmgren and Keuken (1974).)

Fig. 7. United States distribution of *V. arvensis*, based on herbaria samples from; A, CH, CM, DAO, DAV, F, MICH, MO, UC and US. (Abbreviations as in Holmgren and Keuken (1974).)

Extensive colonization of heavier-textured soils can occur during periods of drought or when other weeds are controlled by herbicides (Bachthaler et al. 1986). A neutral to alkaline soil environment may be preferred; however, supporting data are equivocal (Clausen 1922; Bachthaler et al. 1986). Clear relationships between distribution of *V. arvensis* and mineral nutrients have not been established (Bachthaler et al. 1986).

(c) *Communities in which the species occurs* — *Viola arvensis* inhabits annually disturbed environments such as arable fields, roadsides, ditch banks and curb edges. Annual recruitment of seedlings and successful reproduction requires soil disturbance and suppression of competing species (Bachthaler et al. 1986).

Fourbet et al. (1979) classified *V. arvensis* as a characteristic species of grain monoculture. The grain field environment provides favorable conditions for germination, vegetative development, seed ripening and dispersal (Bachthaler et al. 1986). *Viola arvensis* was observed in 19% of spring cereal fields in New Brunswick in 1985 (Doohan 1985). It had a frequency of 10% in cereal fields and strawberry fields in L'Assomption and Richelieu regions of Quebec, respectively (Doyon et al. 1986a, b).

6. History
Viola arvensis originated in Eurasia and is now naturalized throughout much of Canada and the United States (Fernald 1950; Scoggan 1978). European settlers may have introduced the species deliberately for its culinary and medicinal virtues. Nondeliberate introductions probably occurred as well. *Viola arvensis* was naturalized on Long Island, New York by the first half of the 19th century (Torrey 1843). Brainerd (1921) referred to it "as a naturalized and sometimes troublesome weed in the south" (southern U.S.). Muenscher (1955) included *V. arvensis* in his classic handbook, but only as a garden escape and weed of roadsides and waste places. This species was first mentioned in North American weed science literature by Turner and Ingram (1975) in a list of several weeds

occurring in a herbicide evaluation test in winter wheat (*Triticum aestivum* L.) in Quebec. The recent increase in frequency and density of *V. arvensis* in Canada and the United States seems to parallel the European experience where its increased occurrence has been attributed to longer crop rotations and increased reliance on herbicides for weed control.

7. Growth and Development
(a) *Morphology* — Seed dispersal begins about 1 mo before winter cereal harvest and continues beyond the harvest period. Up to 55% of the seed remains on the plants at the time of cereal harvest and may be harvested with the grain. Circumstantial evidence indicates that *V. arvensis* spreads in contaminated grain straw used for crop mulching and livestock bedding.

(b) *Perennation* — *Viola arvensis* persists as seed through extended periods unfavorable for vegetative growth. Autumn-germinating plants overwinter as seedlings or vegetative rosettes. Alex and Switzer (1976) indicated that *V. arvensis* persisted for 1 or possibly 2 yr in Ontario. Clausen (1922) reported formation of adventitous roots on stems covered by organic litter or sand resulting in phenotypic perennation of individual plants.

(c) *Physiological data* — *Viola arvensis* is partially shade-tolerant. Main shoot length is related to shading intensity of surrounding vegetation. Average length of main shoots were 20 cm in winter rye (*Secale cereale* L.) and 26 cm in oats (*Avena sativa* L.). Winter rye intercepted more light than oats (Bachthaler et al. 1986).

(d) *Phenology* — Seedling emergence occurs during April through June but is greatly reduced or arrested during July and August. At Paradise, Nova Scotia in 1987, seedling emergence was considerable in May with about 400 seedlings per square meter (Fig. 8). Emergence declined in June and July, totally ceasing during August. A second period of emergence commenced during late September with considerable seedlings recorded at counts during October. Emergence continued but was low during November. Plots were tilled after each count, except in August.

Plants that overwinter as rosettes begin to flower in spring when favorable growing conditions resume. Spring-germinating plants flower by late spring or early summer in cool temperate climates. Vegetative and reproductive growth may continue until late autumn, depending on initial date of germination and subsequent growing conditions. *Viola arvensis* is indeterminant; therefore, it is common to see new flowers on senescing plants.

We observed growth and development of *V. arvensis* in a greenhouse at Truro, Nova Scotia, operated with a 24/18°C thermoperiod and a natural June/July photoperiod. Initial seedling growth was slow. Approximately 1 mo after germination, at about the six-leaf stage, the growth rate accelerated. The main stem and axillary buds began to elongate. New leaves became increasingly lanceolate, in contrast to the oval seedling leaves. This transition was followed shortly by development of flower buds. Mature seed were released initially about 70 d after germination. We have not observed any vegetative or reproductive response to photoperiod.

(e) *Mycorrhiza* — No reports on mycorrhizal relationships have been found.

8. Reproduction

(a) *Floral biology* — *Viola arvensis* is self-fertile and largely autogamous (Salisbury 1961). Cross-pollination does occur, as evidenced by reports of hybridization with other species of *Viola* (Clausen 1920, 1922; Tutin et al. 1968; Kakes 1982). Anthers and style are enclosed completely by the corolla tube. The style is broadly clavate. Anthers are inferior in position to the stigma. A small drop of nectar is found at the base of the spur of the lower petal. These characteristics suggest a role for insect vectors in cross-pollination; however, we have never observed insect foraging.

(b) *Seed production and dispersal* — Average seed production of 75 seeds per capsule has

been reported (Bachthaler et al. 1986). We observed 45–50 seeds per capsule in material collected at Truro, Nova Scotia in late November 1988. Estimates of seed production per plant ranged from 1410 (Fogelfors 1977) to 2500 (Bachthaler et al. 1986). We believe these estimates are reasonable for individuals growing in competition with other plants. Plants grown at Truro, Nova Scotia in well-fertilized soil covered with black plastic mulch to prevent growth of other plants and to facilitate seed collection produced from 20 000 to 46 000 seeds per plant between July and December 1988. An average of 87% of seed collected on two occasions in August 1988 and stored for 9 mo germinated in controlled environment chambers.

Dehiscent seed capsules of *V. arvensis* propell seed up to 2.1 m from the mother plant (Salisbury 1961). Secondary seed dispersal is by surface water, wind and animal foraging.

(c) *Viability of seed and germination* — Viability of exhumed seed of *V. arvensis* confirmed as 300 yr old (Harrington 1972) and 400 yr old (Odum 1965) has been reported.

Bachthaler et al. (1986) reported that 80% of planted seed germinated in 11 yr. Fifty-five percent of seed germinated in 6 yr in cultivated soil and 7% of those that did not germinate were still viable (Roberts and Feast 1973). In uncultivated soil, 20% of seed germinated in 6 yr and 38% were still viable.

Seed germinated at a higher rate in the second year following planting than in the first, with the number of seedlings emerging each subsequent year declining exponentially (Roberts and Feast 1973). One percent or less of seed harvested at the end of summer germinated in controlled environment chambers (Haakansson 1979). Haakansson (1983) transferred seed of *V. arvensis* from burial in the field to controlled environment chambers on a regular basis throughout the year, and monitored germination 3 wk after each transfer. Germination was maximum in December, declining to a minimum by May and then slowly increasing over the course of summer and fall.

Chancellor (1964a) found that *V. arvensis* germinated in both spring and fall. He classified it as an arable weed, meaning that cultivation stimulated germination. Studies conducted at Paradise, Nova Scotia (Fig. 8) corroborate these observations. Seedling emergence was significantly higher in tilled plots than in untilled plots. Chancellor, (1964b) reported average depth of germination of *V. arvensis* as 12 mm.

High soil temperatures have been implicated in reduction or absence of germination of *V. arvensis* during summer (Haakansson 1983). Rate of germination early in spring was correlated positively to the sum of daily maximum temperatures above 0°C, 14 d prior to emergence (Ervio 1981). Germination was favored by high rainfall and large diurnal fluctuations in temperature during a second emergence cycle in late June and early July. Germination declined during middle and late summer. Induction of dormancy by high soil temperatures was suggested. Lauer (1953) obtained maximum germination with a regime of 15/5°C and reported a general stimulatory effect of diurnally fluctuating temperature. Krug (1929) reported that frost increased rate of germination. Germination (Table 2) was almost completely inhibited by continuous fluorescent light (100 μM m^{-2} s^{-1}) (Doohan et al. 1990). Germination in continuous darkness was 90% at 15/5°C (8/16 h thermoperiod), 78% at 5°C, 55% at 15°C and 3% at 25°C.

Forty-two percent germination of a mixture of *V. arvensis* and *V. tricolor* seed was obtained in constant darkness, with an alternating 12-h thermoperiod of 15/10°C (Lonchamp and Gora 1979). Dark-imbibed seed germinated at oxygen partial pressures of 8 and 21% but not lower oxygen tensions. However, when seed subjected to oxygen partial pressures of 0% (obtained through the use of pure nitrogen gas), 2 and 4%, for 5 d were subsequently transferred to chambers with atmospheric oxygen levels, final germination was higher than with seed that had been continuously exposed to atmospheric oxygen tensions. The stimulatory effect of reduced oxygen partial pressure on subsequent germination declined as duration of exposure increased. Seed exposed to 0 and 2% oxygen for 25 d germinated at the same rate as seed kept continuously at atmospheric oxygen levels. Seed exposed to 4 and 8% oxygen for 25 d germinated at a lower rate than those kept continuously at atmospheric oxygen levels or 0 and 2% oxygen. Seed that did not germinate during this treatment regime entered a state of secondary dormancy that

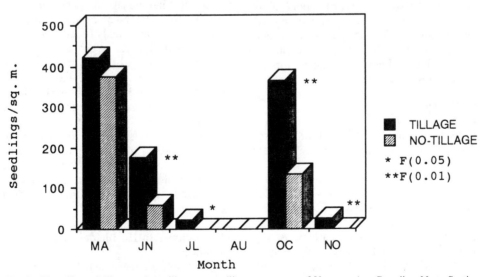

Fig. 8. The effect of tillage and no-tillage on seedling emergence of *V. arvensis* at Paradise, Nova Scotia.

Table 2. Germination of *V. arvensis* at four temperature regimes and two photoperiods (adapted from Doohan et al. (1990))

Temperature (°C)	% germination	
	Light	Dark
5	0	78
15	1	55
25	0	3
15/5	1	90
LSD (0.05)	1	1

could not be broken by 1 mo of stratification at 4°C. Imbibition in a solution of 0.1 g L^{-1} of gibberellic acid (GA$_3$) in illuminated chambers resulted in an additional 15–20% germination of seed that had been exposed to various oxygen partial pressures for 5 d but had little effect on seed that had been exposed for longer periods.

We evaluated the following treatments for stimulation of *V. arvensis* germination: seed imbibition in tap water (control), concentrated sulfuric acid for 2 min/imbibition in tap water, imbibition in 10^{-4} M kinetin, concentrated sulfuric acid for 2 min/imbibition in 10^{-4} M kinetin, imbibition in 10^{-7} M GA$_3$ and concentrated sulfuric acid for 2 min/imbibition in 10^{-7} M GA$_3$. Seed were washed in tap water for 1 h following acid scarification. Germination was 90% with acid scarification/imbibition in 10^{-7} M GA$_3$ and essentially nil with other treatments. Subsequently, we have found that imbibition in 10^{-3} M GA$_3$, without acid scarification, will provide a high germination rate of most seed stocks.

9. Hybrids

Frequently *V. arvensis* and *V. tricolor* grow in the same field. Tutin et al. (1968) reported that hybridization between the two species was common.

Hybridization occurs between *V. arvensis* and the stoloniferous perennial, *V. calaminaria* ssp. *westfalica* (Kakes 1982). F$_1$ hybrids were fertile, combining many morphological and reproductive traits of both parents. A large proportion of F$_1$ individuals were perennial. F$_1$ hybrids reproduced mainly by self-fertilization. F$_2$ hybrids had reduced fertility.

10. Population Dynamics

Kakes (1982) classified *V. arvensis* as typical of **r** selection. Traits of **r** selection as characterized by Pianka (1970) are occupation of the earliest stages of succession, density independent mortality, a life span of usually less than 1 yr and high allocation of resources to reproduction.

Viola arvensis cannot persist in undisturbed environments (Bachthaler et al. 1986). Twenty-one percent of cereal fields cleared from forest for 1–5 yr were infested with *V. arvensis*. Sixty-three percent of fields cleared and in cultivation for 31–50 yr were infested, with a mean density of 34 plants m^{-2} (Raatikainen and Raatikainen 1972). Plants at Truro, Nova Scotia continued to grow and produce seed for at least 6 mo; however, under typical agricultural conditions life-span is in the order of 2–4 mo. Fogelfors (1977) found that plant density in spring barley was only reduced by 4% in comparison to a pure stand of *V. arvensis*.

The increasing frequency of *V. arvensis* throughout Europe has been attributed to herbicide resistance and a reduction in the use of rotational crops in cereal grain production (Gummesson 1983; Makepeace 1978). Grain fields treated with 2,4-D or MCPA had a frequency of 41% infestation and an average density of 2 individuals m^{-2} compared to a frequency of 34% and an average density of 1 m^{-2} in untreated fields (Bachthaler et al. 1986). *Viola arvensis* is consistently more competitive in winter cereals than in spring varieties (Raatikainen et al. 1978; Froud-Williams et al. 1983). This may be due to its ability to grow during cold weather, after the crop has entered dormancy.

New infestations, of *V. arvensis* form enlarging patches of several individuals due to the dispersal pattern of the dehiscent seed capsules. Cultivation and other cultural practices readily spread seed within individual fields and beyond.

11. Response to Herbicides and Other Chemicals

Viola arvensis tolerates many herbicides used on cereals and other crops. It is generally tolerant of growth regulator herbicides. Combinations of growth regulator herbicides and combinations of growth regulator herbicides with hydroxy benzonitrile herbicides have been recommended for control of many hard-to-kill weeds in cereals; however, control of *V. arvensis* has been inconsistent (Turner and Ingram 1975; Horsnail and Wilson 1978). The Ontario Weed Committee (1988) classified *V. arvensis* as resistant to 2,4-D and mecoprop. Information on susceptibility to other growth regulator herbicides was not provided. We observed tolerance of established plants to dicamba at 0.2 and 0.4 kg ha^{-1} and to clopyralid at 0.2 kg ha^{-1}. Increasing frequency of *V. arvensis* in Great Britain has been attributed to tolerance of urea herbicides used widely in cereal production (Makepeace 1978). Applications of napropamide, diphenamid, chlorthal dimethyl and chloroxuron to established overwintering rosettes were ineffective (Chase and Putnam 1984). Control with chlorotriazine herbicides is not well documented. However, correlation between *V. arvensis* infestation and corn production in Federal Republic of Germany suggests tolerance may be a problem (Bachthaler et al. 1986). Tolerance to pre-emergence applications of the chloroacetanilide, metozachlor, has been reported (Bachthaler et al. 1986). *Viola arvensis* can be controlled in strawberries with pre-emergence applications of terbacil or simazine; however, these herbicides are not effective as postemergence applications (Doohan and Monaco 1988).

The species is moderately tolerant of fluoroxypyr. Sanders and Pallet (1987) found that *V. arvensis* metabolized fluoroxypyr more quickly than susceptible *S. media*. Additionally, translocation from the treated leaf was much lower in *V. arvensis* than in *S. media*. Electron transport in chloroplasts of *V. arvensis* was highly sensitive to ioxynil and bromoxynil (Sanders and Pallet 1982). The authors concluded that *V. arvensis* tolerance to these herbicides was based on factors other than resistance at the chloroplast level.

Viola arvensis control in cereals has depended upon use of herbicide mixtures. Combinations of bifenox and linuron (Lake 1974) or mecoprop and tribunil (Jenneus 1983) have provided good control in winter cereals. Pendimethalin controls *V. arvensis* in winter barley. *Viola arvensis* may be susceptible to sprays of calcium nitrate, up to the four-leaf stage (Bachthaler et al. 1986). Susceptibility to sulfonylurea and imidazolinone herbicides has been reported (Roberts and Bond 1983, 1984). These herbicides may have the greatest potential for effective management of *V. arvensis* in cereals and other tolerant crops.

Control in sugar-beet can be obtained with a mixture of propham, chlorpropham, fenuron and metamitron (Elliot and Jung 1980). A mixture of chlormethoxynil with a formulation of benazolin plus clopyralid controlled *V. arvensis* in winter rape, when applied at the two-leaf stage of the crop. Trifluralin, preplant incorporated, plus metozachlor, pre-emergence, gave moderate control in winter rape (Gummesson 1983).

Pyridate has potential for controlling *V. arvensis* in tolerant vegetable crops and corn. Postemergence applications of 2.0 kg ha^{-1} killed most plants of *V. arvensis* and severely stunted survivors (Roberts and Bond 1983). Lipinski et al. (1979) reported effective control in carrots (*Daucus carota* L.) with linuron. Handley and King (1976) reported fair control in green peas (*Pisum sativum* L.) with pre-emergence applications of chlorthal dimethyl plus methazole. Pre-emergence cyanazine and postemergence dinoseb both provided moderate control of *V. arvensis* in green peas. Postemergence applications of bentazon were ineffective (Gummesson 1977).

Excellent control of established *V. arvensis* in strawberries has been demonstrated with oxyfluorfen and acifluorfen (Chase and Putnam 1984; Monaco 1987; Ahrens 1988; Doohan and Monaco 1988). Strawberries tolerated these herbicides when applied during late fall or winter or at crop renovation. We obtained good control with early postemergence (cotyledon stage) applications of terbacil, simazine and chlorthal dimethyl (Doohan and Monaco 1988). Ahrens (1989) reported similar results with early postemergence applications of terbacil, napropamide or chlorthal dimethyl.

12. Response to Other Human Manipulations

Culture of a competitive crop has been effective in reducing growth of *V. arvensis*. Ervio (1972) reported a linear reduction in growth as sowing rates of grain increased over a range of 25–200 kg ha^{-1}. Spring barley planted at 180 kg ha^{-1} reduced *V. arvensis* foliage dry weight by 83% and seed production by 96%, compared to a pure stand of the species (Fogelfors 1977). *Viola arvensis* responded positively to irrigation when other weeds were controlled (Bachthaler et al. 1986).

Control by cultivation is possible when plants are small, but is limited by the stimulatory effect of tillage on germination. This is supported by Nielsen and Pinnerup (1982) who reported lower incidence of *V. arvensis* under reduced cultivation.

13. Response to Parasites

We observed leaf spot symptoms on fully developed leaves of potted plants growing under conditions of excessive moisture or nutrient deficiencies. Symptoms similar to damping-off have been observed occasionally on seedling plants in the greenhouse. We have not observed disease symptoms on field-grown plants. *Bremiella megasperma*, which causes a downy mildew, is the only documented pathogen on *V. arvensis* (Farr et al. 1989).

ACKNOWLEDGMENTS

Illustrations were adapted from *Weeds of Ontario* by Alex and Switzer (1976). Thanks to Professor Paul Fantz for his review of the manuscript and helpful suggestions. This work was supported, in part, by the Nova Scotia Department of Agriculture and Marketing, the North Carolina Agricultural Research Service and by a Postgraduate Scholarship from the Natural Science and Engineering Research Council (Canada).

Ahrens, J. F. 1988. Control of field violet in strawberries with acifluorfen and oxyfluorfen. Proc. Northeast Weed Sci. Soc. **42**: 233–234.

Ahrens, J. F. 1989. Control of field violet in strawberry plantings. Proc. Northeast Weed Sci. Soc. **43**: 149.

Alex, J. F., Cayouette, R. and Mulligan, G. A. 1980. Common and botanical names of weeds in Canada. Agriculture Canada, Ottawa, ON. Publ. 1397. 132 pp.

Alex, J. and Switzer, C. M. 1976. Weeds of Ontario. Ontario Ministry of Agriculture and Food, Toronto, ON. Publ. 505. 200 pp.

Bachthaler, V. G., Neuner, F. and Kees, H. 1986. Development of the field pansy (*Viola arvensis* Murr.) in dependence of soil conditions and agricultural management. Nachrichtenbl. Deut. Pflanzenschutzd. **38** (3): 33–41 [English translation.].

Brainerd, E. 1921. The violets of North America. Bulletin 224. Vermont Agricultural Experimental Station. Free Press Printing Company, Burlington, VT. 164 pp.

Chancellor, R. J. 1964a. Emergence of weed seedlings in the field and the effects of different frequencies of cultivation. Proc. 7th Br. Weed Control Conf. pp. 599–606.

Chancellor, R. J. 1964b. The depth of weed seed germination in the field. Proc. 7th Br. Weed Control Conf. pp. 607–613.

Chase, W. R. and Putnam, A. R. 1984. Biology and control of field violet in strawberries. Proc. North Cent. Weed Control Conf. **39**: 147.

Clausen, J. 1920. Studies on the collective species *Viola tricolor* L. I. Botanisk Tidsskrift. **37**: 205–221.

Clausen, J. 1922. Studies on the collective species *Viola tricolor* L. II. Botanisk Tidsskrift. **37**: 363–411.

Creso, I. 1984. Vascular plants of western Washington. Irene Creso/Johnson Cox Printers, Tacoma, WA. 532 pp.

Doohan, D. J. 1985. Cereal weed survey. Adaptive Research Reports, Plant Industry Branch, New Brunswick Department of Agriculture, Fredericton, NB. **7**: 76–77.

Doohan, D. J. and Monaco, T. J. 1988. Studies on the biology and control of field violet. Abstr. WSSA. **28**: 76.

Doohan, D. J., Monaco, T. J. and Sheets, T. J. 1990. The physiological ecology of field violet (*Viola arvensis* Murr.) germination. Proc. South. Weed Sci. Soc. **43**: 328.

Doyon, D., Bouchard, C. J. and Neron, R. 1986a. Inventaire des mauvaises herbes dans les cultures du Québec (1980–1984). Principales données des relevés floristiques et agronomiques. MAPAQ. Service de Recherche en phytotochemie de Quebec. Vol. 5. 131 pp.

Doyon, D., Bouchard, C. J. and Neron, R. 1986b. Inventaire des mauvaises herbes dans les cultures du Québec (1980–1984). Principales données des relevés floristiques et agronomiques. MAPAQ. Service de Recherche en phytotochemie de Quebec. Vol. 3. 93 pp.

Elliot, R. A. and Jung, K. U. 1980. The control of annual weeds pre-emergence in sugar-beet, with a mixture of propham, chlorpropham, fenuron and metamituron, 1977–1980. Proc. Br. Weed Control Conf., 523.

Ervio, Leila-Riitta. 1972. Growth of weeds in cereal populations. J. Sci. Agric. Soc. Finl. **44**: 19–28.

Ervio, Leila-Riitta. 1981. The emergence of weeds in the field. Ann. Agric. Fenn. **20**: 292–303.

Farr, D. L., Bills, G. F., Chamuris, G. P. and Rossman, A. Y. 1989. Fungi on plants and plant products in the United States. American Phytopathological Society, St. Paul, MN. 1252 pp.

Fernald, M. L. 1950. Gray's manual of botany. 8th ed. American Book Co., New York, NY. 1632 pp.

Ferron, M. and Cayouette, R. 1971. Noms de mauvaises herbes du Quebec. ed. 2. Ministere de l'Agriculture et de la colonization du Quebec. Publ. 288-71. 113 pp.

Fogelfors, H. 1977. The competition between barley and five weed species as influenced by MCPA treatment. Swed. J. Agric. Res. **7**: 147–151.

Fourbet, J. F., Huet, Ph. and Jan, P. 1979. Problems poses par la simplification des systemes de culture dans la lutte contre les mauvaises herbes. Proc. Eur. Weed Res. Soc. Symp. 123–133.

Froud-Williams, R. J., Drennan, D. S. H. and Chancellor, R. J. 1983. Influence of cultivation regime on weed floras of arable cropping systems. J. Appl. Ecol. **20**: 187–197.

Gleason, H. A. 1952. The new Britton and Brown illustrated flora of the United States and adjacent Canada. Vol. 2. The New York Botanical Garden, New York, NY. 655 pp.

Gummesson, G. 1977. Weed control in peas. Weeds and Weed Control, 18th Swedish Weed Conference. p. 58.

Gummesson, G. 1983. Chemical and non-chemical control-changes in weed stand following different control measures. 24th Swedish Weed Conf. **1**: 239.

Haakansson, S. 1979. Seasonal influence on germination of weed seeds. 1979 Eur. Weed Res. Soc. Symp., Mainz, Germany. pp. '/2-80.

Haakansson, S. 1983. Seasonal variation in the emergence of annual weeds — an introductory investigation in Sweden. Weed Res. **23**: 313–324.

Handley, R. P. and King, J. M. 1976. Experiments in peas with a mixture of chlorthal-dimethyl and methazole for residual weed control on sandy soils. Proc. 1976 Br. Crop Protect. Conf. — Weeds. pp. 433–439.

Harrington, J. F. 1972. Seed storage and longevity. Pages 145–245 *in* T. T. Kozlowski, ed. Seed biology. Academic Press, New York, NY.

Harris, B. C. 1961. Eat the weeds. Barre Publishing, Barre, MA. 223 pp.

Hilgondorf, F. W. 1948. Weeds of New Zealand – and how to eradicate them. 4th ed. Revised by J. W. Calder. Whitcombe & Tombs Ltd., Christchurch, New Zealand. 149 pp.

Holm, L., Pancho, J. V., Herberger, J. P. and Plucknett, D. L. 1979. A geographical atlas of world weeds. John Wiley & Sons, New York, NY. P. 384.

Holmgren, P. K. and Keuken, W. 1974. Index herbarorium. Part 1. The herbaria of the world. 6th ed. (Regnum Veg. 92). Oosthoek, Scheltema & Holkema, Utrecht, The Netherlands. 397 pp.

Horsnail, G. B. and Wilson, C. W. 1978. The flexibility in use of an hydroxybenzonitrile: mecoprop estermixture for broad-leaved weed control in cereals. Proc. 1978 Br. Crop Protect. Conf. — Weeds. pp. 137–142.

Jenneus, B. 1983. Dicot weeds in winter wheat, autumn spraying — comparisons between mecoprop and different herbicide mixtures. 25th Swedish Weed Conf. pp. 15–19.

Kakes, P. 1982. Genecological investigations on zinc plants. V. Barriers to gene flow limiting the introgression of *Viola arvensis* (Murr.) into *Viola calaminaria* Lej. spp. *westfalica* (Lej.). Ernst. Acta. Bot. Neerl. **31**: 371–378.

Krug, H. 1929. Bettrage zur keimunsphysiologie und Bekampfung von samenkrautern. Bot. Arch. 27: 420–518.

Lake, R. L. 1974. Nortron improved weed control in sugar beet. Agtec, Fisons Agricultural Technical Information, Harston, Cambridge, UK. pp. 4–28.

Lauer, E. 1953. Über die Keimtemperatur bei Ackerunkrautern und deren Einflub auf die Zusammensetzung von Unkrautgesellschaften. Flora **140**: 551–595.

le Strange, R. 1977. A history of herbal plants. Arco Publishing Co. Inc., New York, NY. 304 pp.

Lipinski, Z., Skapski, H. and Gawronski, St. 1979. Evaluation of annual herbicide application on yield and quality of vegetable crops, weed populations and herbicide residues in soil. Proc. West. Soc. Weed Sci. **32**: 98–99.

Lonchamp, J. P. and Gora, M. 1979. Influence d'anoxies partielles sur la germination de semences de mauvaises herbes. Oecologia Plantarum. **14**: 121–128.

MacLeod, H. and Macdonald, B. 1976. Edible wild plants of Nova Scotia. Nova Scotia Museum, Halifax, NS. 135 pp.

Makepeace, F. J. 1978. Herbicide developments in a changing husbandry era and the new weeds emerging from it. Proc. Bri. Assoc. Adv. Sci. pp. 62–70.

Monaco, T. J. 1987. Control of field pansy (*Viola rafinesquii* Green) in strawberries. WSSA Abstr. **27**: 51.

Moss, E. H. 1983. Flora of Alberta. 2nd ed. Revised by J. G. Packer. University of Toronto Press, Toronto, ON. 687 pp.

Muenscher, W. C. 1955. Weeds 2nd ed. The Macmillan Company, New York, NY. 579 pp.

Mukula, J., Raatikainin, M., Lallukka, R. and Raatikainen, T. 1969. Composition of weed flora in spring cereals in Finland. Ann. Agric. Fenn. **8**: 59–110.

Munz, P. A. 1974. A flora of southern California. University of California Press, Berkley and Los Angeles, CA. 1086 pp.

Nielsen, H. J. and Pinnerup, S. P. 1982. Reduced cultivation and weeds. Weeds and Weed Control. 23rd Swedish Weed Conference. pp. 370–384.

Odum, E. P. 1965. Germination of ancient seeds: floristical observations and experiments with archaeologically dated soil samples. Dansk Bot. Ark. **24**: 2.

Ontario Weed Committee. 1988. Guide to weed control. Publication 75. Ontario Ministry of Agriculture and Food, Toronto, ON. 200 pp.

Paatela, J. and Ervio, Leila-Riitta. 1971. Weed seeds in cultivated soils in Finland. Ann. Agric. Fenn. **10**: 144–152.

Peck, M. E. 1961. A manual of the higher plants of Oregon 2nd ed. Oregon State University Press, Corvallis, OR. 936 pp.

Pianka, E. R. 1970. On r and K selection. Am. Nat. **104**: 592–597.

Raatikainen, M. and Raatikainen, T. 1972. Weed colonization of cultivated fields in Finland. Ann. Agric. Fenn. **11**: 100–110.

Raatikainen, M., Raatikainen, T. and Mukula, J. 1978. Weed species, frequencies and densities in winter cereals in Finland. Ann. Agric. Fenn. **17**: 115–142.

Radford, A. E., Ahles, H. E. and Bell, C. R. 1968. Manual of the vascular flora of the Carolinas. University of North Carolina, Press; Chapel Hill, NC. 1183 pp.

Roberts, H. A. and Bond, W. 1983. Evaluation of pyridate for weed control in drilled vegetable crops. Ann. Appl. Biol. **102**: 110–111.

Roberts, H. A. and Bond, W. 1984. Evaluation of DPX-T6376 for weed control in drilled vegetables. Ann. Appl. Biol. **104**: 82–83.

Roberts, H. A. and Feast, P. M. 1973. Emergence and longevity of seeds of annual weeds in cultivated and undisturbed soil. J. Appl. Biol. **10**: 133–143.

Roberts, H. A. and Neilson, J. E. 1982. Seed banks of soils under vegetable cropping in England. Weed Res. **22**: 13–16.

Salisbury, E. J. 1961. Weeds and aliens. Collins, London, U.K. 384 pp.

Sanders, G. E. and Pallet, K. E. 1982. Studies into the different response of three weed species to the hydroxybenzonitriles. Proc. 1982 Br. Crop Prot. Conf. — Weeds. pp. 324–331.

Sanders, G. E. and Pallet, K. E. 1987. Comparison of the uptake, movement and metabolism of fluroxypyr in *Stellaria media* and *Viola arvensis*. Weed Res. **27**: 159–166.

Scoggan, H. J. 1978. The flora of Canada. Part 3. National Museums of Canada, Ottawa, ON. 1115 pp.

Shinners, L. H. 1961. *Viola rafinesquii:* nomenclature and native status. Rhodora **63**: 327.

Torrey, J. 1843. A flora of the state of New York. People of the State of New York, Albany, NY. 484 pp.

Turner, M. and Ingram, G. H. 1975. Bromoxynil/MCPA mixtures for weed control in winter wheat. Canada Weed Committee. Research Report. Eastern Section. p. 21.

Tutin, T. G., Heywood, V. H., Burges, N. A., Moore, D. M., Valentine, D. H., Walters, S. M. and Webb, D. A. 1968. Flora Europaea. Volume 2. Cambridge At The University Press, Cambridge, U.K. 455 pp.

Welsh, S. C., Atwood, N. D., Goodrich, S. and Higgins, L. C. (Ed.). 1987. A Utah Flora. Great Basin Naturalist Memoirs no. 9. Brigham Young University, Provo, UT. 894 pp.

The biology of Canadian weeds. 100.
Lythrum salicaria

Tarun K. Mal[1], Jon Lovett-Doust[1], Lesley Lovett-Doust[1], and G. A. Mulligan[2]

[1] *Biological Sciences, University of Windsor, Windsor, Ontario, Canada N9B 3P4; and* [2] *Agriculture Canada, Research Branch, Centre for Land and Biological Resources Research, Wm. Saunders Bldg., Ottawa, Ontario, Canada K1A 0C6. Received 15 October 1991, accepted 13 April 1992.*

Mal, T. K., Lovett-Doust, J., Lovett-Doust, L. and Mulligan, G. A. 1992. **The biology of Canadian weeds. 100.** *Lythrum salicaria.* Can. J. Plant Sci. **72**: 1305–1330. *Lythrum salicaria* is a serious weed of wetlands in Canada, particularly in Ontario and Quebec. Indeed some assessments suggest that this exotic is now responsible for the conversion of more wetland habitat than is current human development pressure! *Lythrum* is a heterostylous species and clones by means of root buds. Despite its tristylous breeding system, *Lythrum* is a successful colonizer, and can produce prodigious numbers of seeds. It is likely that control can be achieved by hand-pulling in low-density populations, but once the species is established it generally becomes abundant and often approaches a monoculture. This species is particularly difficult to control because of its strong competitive ability, the extreme sensitivity of wetland habitats, and the likelihood of serious repercussions for wetland wildlife and fisheries if herbicides are used to control it. We see better possibilities for control through cultural techniques (e.g., manipulation of water levels to favour native species), enhancement of North American herbivores, and, possibly, the introduction of biological control agents from Europe and Asia.

Key words: Purple loosestrife, *Lythrum salicaria*, wetlands, introduced weed

Mal, T. K., Lovett-Doust, J., Lovett-Doust, L. et Mulligan, G. A. 1992. **Biologie des mauvaises herbes canadiennes. 100.** *Lythrum salicaria.* Can. J. Plant Sci. **72**: 1305–1330. *Lythrum salicaria* est une dangereuse mauvaise herbe des zones humides du Canada, particulièrement au Québec et en Ontario. On attribue en effet à cette plante introduite la perturbation de plus de zones humides que n'en causent les activités humaines d'aménagement courantes. C'est une espèce hétérostylée qui forme ses clones à partir de bourgeons racinaires. Malgré son mode de reproduction trimorphe, *Lythrum* est un excellent colonisateur et produit d'innombrables quantités de graines. On peut encore le maîtriser en l'arrachant à la main quand le peuplement n'est pas trop dense, mais une fois qu'elle est bien installée, l'espèce prolifère et souvent évolue vers la monoculture. Elle est particulièrement difficile à combattre à cause de sa forte compétitivité, de l'extrême vulnérabilité des habitats humides et des risques que comportent les herbicides pour la faune terrestre et aquatique qu'ils abritent. D'autres méthodes offrent, selon nous, de meilleures possibilités de lutte, notamment les méthodes culturales, comme la manipulation du plan d'eau pour favoriser les espèces indigènes, l'encouragement des populations herbivores nord-américaines et, éventuellement, l'introduction d'agents de lutte biologique d'Europe et d'Asie.

Mots clés: La salicaire, *Lythrum salicaria*

1. Names

Lythrum salicaria L. — **purple loosestrife, la salicaire** (Alex et al. 1980). Section *Mesolythrum*, subgenus *Salicaria* (Koehne 1903; Ornduff 1978), Lythraceae, loosestrife

Can. J. Plant Sci. 72: 1305–1330 (Oct. 1992)

family. For discussion of cultivars and hybrids see Section 2c, Intraspecific variation, and Section 9, Hybrids.

2. Description and Account of Variation

(a) *Description* — Perennial herb 0.5–2.7 m tall with up to 30–50 herbaceous stems rising from a persistent perennial tap root and spreading rootstock (up to 0.5-m diameter, Fig. 1). It forms a wide-topped crown, diameter up to 1.5 m (Thompson et al. 1987). Adventitious roots have not been noted (Shamsi and Whitehead 1974a). Annual, erect squarish stems have evenly-spaced nodes and short slender branches. Stem and foliage glabrous to pubescent, or sub-tomentose above and in the inflorescence (Gleason 1952). Leaves 3–10 cm long, sessile, lanceolate to ovate, acute ± cordate at base. Lower leaves

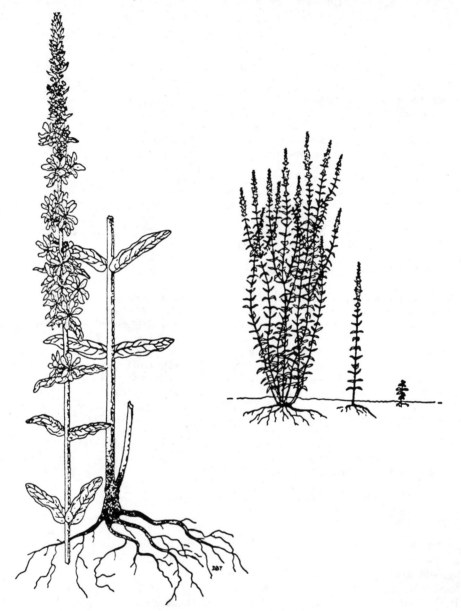

Fig. 1. Structure, growth forms, field identification characters of *L. salicaria* (from Thompson et al. (1987)).

opposite, decussate or in whorls of three, but upper leaves and floral bracts are alternate (Clapham et al. 1962). Inflorescence a dense terminal spike of numerous small whorl-like cymes arising from the axils of small leafy bracts (Hickey and King 1981). These axillary inflorescences are arranged spirally on the main inflorescence axis. Spike length from a few cm − >1 m (Balogh 1986a).

Flowers actinomorphic – slightly zygomorphic (Richards et al. 1989), hermaphroditic, hypogynous (perigynous according to Cheung and Sattler (1967)), 10–15 mm long; bracteoles caducous (Fig. 2). It has six alternating whorls of appendages (K(6) C6 A6+6 G(2): one whorl of outer sepals (epicalyx, or calyx *sensu lato*, homologous to bracts) (Cadet 1954), one whorl of inner sepals (calyx *sensu stricto*), one whorl of petals, two whorls of stamens, and one whorl of carpels (Cheung and Sattler 1967). The species is heterostylous (tristylous), with three distinct arrangements of pistils and stamens, although semi-homomorphic flowers have also been reported (Stout 1925). Calyx pubescent, persistent, forms tube 3.5–9.0 mm long with 5–7 ribbed valvate sepals and corresponding numbers of bracts. Petals 5–7 free, pink-purple, 5–12.5 mm long, obovate, inserted near the top of the calyx tube, alternate with sepals. In any flower, the number of sepals and petals is equal, with twice as many stamens (stamens 10–14, varying with the number of petals/sepals, arranged in two whorls); flowers with six sepals and petals and 12 stamens are typical. Anthers (1.25 × 1 mm) introrse, two-celled, dorsifixed and longitudinally dehiscent. Ovary superior, comprising two fused carpels, style simple, stigma capitate, two loculi contain numerous anatropous ovules, placentation axile.

Flowers are categorized according to stylar morphs as short-, medium- and long-styled. Short-styled flowers, for example, have long and medium filaments. Long filaments originate opposite sepals and medium filaments are opposite petals. Medium-styled flowers have long and short filaments. The long filaments originate opposite the sepals and short filaments are opposite to petals. Long-styled flowers have medium and short filaments. The medium filaments originate opposite the sepals and short filaments are opposite the petals.

Measurements of various floral parts (+ standard error, and range) are presented in Table 1. Thus the outer, episepalous stamens are always longer than the inner, epipetalous ones

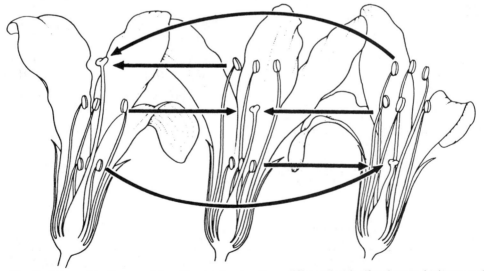

Fig. 2. Trimorphic flowers of *L. salicaria* showing three different levels of anthers and stigmas and "legitimate" pollen flow among them (from Meeuse and Morris (1984)).

(Stirling 1933, 1936). Long-styled flowers have a globular stigma larger than that of the other two forms, with longer surface papillae. The filaments of the longest stamens are generally bright pink in colour with purple anthers. Those of mid-length stamens are uncoloured, while the short set of stamens have greenish filaments with greenish anthers. The anthers of the mid-length set are larger than the others (Darwin 1877; East 1927).

The size and colour of pollen grains depends on whether they come from long, mid-sized or short stamens. They are 30–38 μm long $\times$ 20–26 μm broad; 23–26 μm long $\times$ 13–16 μm broad; and 20–25 μm long $\times$ 11–13 μm broad, respectively (Schoch-Bodmer 1938–1939). Pollen grains from long stamens are green, whereas those from medium and short stamens are yellow (Kerner 1902; Barlow 1923; Schoch-Bodmer 1938–1939). Mulcahy and Caporello (1970) also measured pollen size and abundance on the short, mid-sized, and long stamens (Fig. 2) and agreed that long stamens bore significantly larger pollen. Green pollen

grains tend to be more starchy and need higher stigmatic sugar concentrations to germinate than do the more lipid-rich yellow pollen grains (McLean and Ivimey-Cook 1960). Pollen is heterocolpate, with three true apertures (tricolporate) and three additional furrows (pseudocolpi). They also lack germinal pores (Huynh 1972; Graham et al. 1987). However Sohma (1979) reported one pseudocolpus and a germinal pore at the equator with pollen grains radially symmetrical, isopolar, and tectate.

Fruit is an oblong-ovoid capsule (3–4 mm long, 2 mm broad) with two valves, enclosed in the calyx. It dehisces septicidally, and bears an average of 93, 130, and 83.5 seeds per capsule in long-, mid- and short-styled forms respectively (Darwin 1877). Nicholls (1987) repeated Darwin's studies and concluded that there exists gender specialisation where mid-style morphs are more successful as female parents than as pollen parents. Seeds (0.5–0.6 mg in mass, 400 μm long, 200 μm wide) are nonendospermic, light, flat, and thin-walled with two cotyledons (Thompson et al. 1987).

Table 1. Measurements of floral parts in each of the three sex morphs. Lengths expressed in mm ($\pm$ SE), and range is stated in square brackets [   ]

Floral part	Floral morph		
	Long	Mid	Short
Ovary	2.07 (0.019) [1.4 – 2.7]	2.12 (0.022) [1.4 – 2.8]	2.15 (0.023) [1.3 – 2.9]
Pistil	10.71 (0.082) [7.7 – 13.4]	6.95 (0.060) [5.6 – 8.8]	3.28 (0.031) [2.4 – 4.4]
Long stamen	—	9.76 (0.091) [5.7 – 12.6]	9.76 (0.082) [6.8 – 13.6]
Medium stamen	6.15 (0.060) [3.8 – 8.2]	—	6.12 (0.062) [4.3 – 8.6]
Short stamen	2.97 (0.046) [1.1 – 4.6]	3.12 (0.061) [1.9 – 5.7]	—
Perianth	14.66 (0.153)	14.76 (0.177)	14.80 (0.176)
Index of heterostyly[z]	0.422 (0.005) [0.262 – 0.58]	0.283 (0.006) [0.050 – 0.435]	0.288 (0.005) [0.062 – 0.446]

[z] The index of heterostyly, shown in the last row is calculated as

$$I = \frac{\text{distance between stigma and nearest set of anthers,}}{\text{height of longest sporophyll}}$$ according to Eiten (1963).

Base chromosome number in the genus *Lythrum* is 5, with haploid numbers of 5, 10, 15, 25, and 30. In *L. salicaria*, *n* is either 15, 25, or 30 (Tobe et al. 1986; Graham et al. 1987). Buttler and Schippmann (1984) reported variation in chromosome number in the species. $2n=60$ was found in plants from Norway, Sweden, Denmark, Holland, Poland, Slovakia and North America. $2n=50$ was found in northern Germany, north-east Poland and Scandinavia. $2n=30$ was found in Israel (Dulberger 1968, 1970) and Japan, and $2n=58$ has been reported rarely in Europe. Aneuploids have also been recorded as $2n=45$ and $2n=59$. C. G. Eckert and S. C. H. Barrett (pers. commun.) have made preliminary chromosome counts of *L. salicaria* from Ontario populations and found $2n=50$–60, and Mulligan (1957) reported $2n=60$ for plants from Ottawa, Ontario. Dollon and Hamel (1967) reported the chromosome number of $2n=60$ for material from France. They concluded, on surveying the literature, that the number usually reported was $2n=60$ and that other numbers were suspect.

(b) *Morphological characters* — The only other species of *Lythrum* growing wild in Canada is the native *L. alatum* Pursh, winged loosestrife. It is found in the extreme south of Ontario. Winged loosestrife has small solitary flowers in the axils of alternate upper leaves, whereas purple loosestrife has showy flowers in pairs or clusters in the axils of opposite or whorled upper leaves. Wand lythrum, *Lythrum virgatum* L. is naturalized further south and is sometimes cultivated in Canada. Purple loosestrife has leaf bases rounded or cordate and calyx lobes much shorter than the awl-shaped calyx appendages, whereas wand lythrum has narrowed leaf bases and the calyx-lobes and appendages are more or less equal. In addition, the flowers of purple loosestrife are much larger than those of wand lythrum. Purple loosestrife is commonly confused with the widespread native fireweed, *Epilobium angustifolium* L.; however, purple loosestrife has a squarish stem, opposite leaves and flowers with five

to seven narrow, wrinkled deep magenta petals whereas fireweed petals has a rounded stem, alternate leaves, and flowers with four broad, pale magenta petals (Broderick 1990). From a distance, the flowering spikes of purple loosestrife are more compact and narrower than those of fireweed and are a deeper magenta in colour (Mann 1991).

(c) *Intraspecific variation* — The pubescence of purple loosestrife varies from sparse to dense. A few taxonomists have accorded various densities of pubescence taxonomic status at the varietal or form level. We do not think that their designation is taxonomically useful because populations are variable. Many large-flowered cultivars have been selected from wild purple loosestrife (Table 2). "Dropmore Purple" appears to be mostly *L. salicaria* with perhaps some genetic input from *L. virgatum* (see Section 9, Hybrids).

(d) *Illustrations* — The morphology of seedlings, young and mature *L. salicaria*, flowers and fruits are shown in Fig. 1. Figure 2 shows the trimorphic flowers.

3. Economic Importance

(a) *Detrimental* — *Lythrum salicaria* is an invasive weed of wetlands, and tends to form monocultures, crowding out native species in areas flooded in the spring. Fernald (1940) reported loss of endemic flora of the St. Lawrence floodplain below Montreal following invasion by *Butomus umbellatus* L., and *L. salicaria*. As *Lythrum* invades, species diversity declines and rare species become extinct (Moore and Keddy 1989). For example, growth of 44 native wetland species declined following the establishment of *L. salicaria* (Gaudet and Keddy 1988). Johansson and Keddy (1991) assessed the relative competitive ability of *L. salicaria* and five other species in a controlled experiment. The competitive hierarchy was *Lythrum > Cyperus > Juncus > Eleocharis > Mimulus > Verbena*. In field plots in the Montezuma National Wildlife Refuge, a negative relationship was seen between the abundance of purple loosestrife and cattail over a 3-yr study

Table 2. Specimens of named cultivars of *Lythrum* in the Agriculture Canada Herbarium, Ottawa

Cultivar	Source of material	Type of style	Our identification
Morden Pink	Morden Research Station, Morden, MB	Mid	*L. salicaria*
Morden Pink	McConnell Nursery Co., Port Burwell, ON	Mid	*L. salicaria*
Morden Gleam	Morden Research Station, Morden, MB	Mid	*L. salicaria*
Morden Rose	Morden Research Station, Morden, MB	Mid	*L. salicaria*
Brightness	Morden Research Station, Morden, MB	Mid	*L. salicaria*
Brightness	Hillier & Sons, Manchester, U.K.	Long	*L. salicaria*
Lady Sackville	Morden Research Station, Morden, MB	Mid	*L. salicaria*
Mr. Robert	Morden Research Station, Morden, MB	Mid	*L. salicaria*
Dropmore Purple	Morden Research Station, Morden, MB	Long	*L. salicaria* (the relatively short calyx appendages on this specimen suggest that this cultivar may have some genes of *L. virgatum*)
Dropmore Purple	The Manitoba Hardy Plant	Long	*L. salicaria* (the relatively short calyx appendages on this specimen suggest that this cultivar may have some genes of *L. virgatum*)
Rose Queen	Arboretum, Wageningen, The Netherlands	Mid	*L. virgatum*
Rose Queen	Hillier & Sons, Winchester, U.K.	Mid	*L. virgatum*

(Rawinski and Malecki 1984). In the Hamilton Marshes adjacent to the Delaware River near New Jersey, USA, the annual aboveground production of *L. salicaria* was 21 t ha^{-1}, far exceeding all other plant species' production, while in the nearby Tinicum Marsh, aboveground net annual production was 1749 g m^{-2} yr^{-1} (Whigham and Simpson 1976). Moore and Keddy (1989) surveyed 25 wetlands in eastern Canada and determined that "infertile" wetlands had higher species richness and more nationally rare species present. Infertile wetlands were also more vulnerable to invasion of *L. salicaria*, eutrophication, and human disturbance than more fertile wetlands.

Lythrum salicaria provides little of food value and offers relatively poor cover and nesting materials (Mann 1991). In Ontario, nesting of waterfowl becomes difficult as dense clumps of purple loosestrife restrict access to open water and offer undetected passage to predatory foxes and raccoons (Reschke 1990). Non-game species also suffer, e.g., black terns and marsh wrens are losing their nesting sites. Only red-wing blackbirds appear able to cope with this changed wetland habitat. Balogh and Bookhout (1989a) also reported that dense stands of *L. salicaria* provided poor waterfowl and muskrat habitat and displaced more than 50% of the plant biomass in some wetland communities in the USA.

In many areas where purple loosestrife is on the increase, wildlife species are in decline. In many cases this is interpreted as being due to consequent changes in physical and trophic structure and reduction of habitat diversity. Black tern (*Chlidonias niger*) particularly in the glacial basins of North central USA, Canvasback (*Athya vallisneria*) in the prairie pothole region, sandhill crane (*Grus canadensis*), long-billed marsh wren, muskrat and bog turtle (*Clemmys muhlenbergi*) in northern New York State have shown serious declines (Rawinski and Malecki 1984; Thompson et al. 1987; Keddy 1988). Thus the introduction or invasion of *L. salicaria* can severely impact wildlife conservation areas, as illustrated in Illinois (Harty 1986). Thompson et al. (1987) attributed an annual loss of 190 000 ha of wetland in the USA to the invasion of *L. salicaria*. Purple loosestrife stands in spring-flooded pastures of la Baie du Fevre had already invaded the pasture, and rendered the large infested areas effectively inaccessible and unpalatable to dairy cattle by the 1940s (Louis-Marie 1944).

However, Cusick (1986) concluded the species had not become a serious pest in the Ohio River Valley, despite its presence there for over a century. Further investigation of sites where *L. salicaria* has *not* taken over may provide some clues on strategies for control.

In the above reports there is no proof of "cause-and-effect" although they certainly provide good circumstantial evidence that *Lythrum* invasion and spread is responsible for major changes in wetland plant communities. On the other hand it is possible that the environmental conditions which favour *Lythrum* are at the same time the very conditions which are detrimental to rare wetland species and important forage plants. Our current investigations test these alternative explanations of *Lythrum*'s ascendancy.

(b) *Beneficial* — *Lythrum salicaria* was used in the past as a medicinal herb. Pulverized leaves and tannin-rich decoctions from roots were used for treatment of chronic diarrhoea, dysentery, bleeding, leucorrhea, bloodspitting, wounds, ulcers and sores (Grieve 1959; Stevens 1961). Recently the species has aroused renewed interest from pharmacologists because stem and flower extracts produce significant hypoglycemia in hyper- and normo-glycemic rats. The extracts reduced blood sugar in rats by increasing blood insulin (Lamela et al. 1985, 1986). This has potential implications for weight control medication and possibly for the treatment of some forms of diabetes.

The nectar and pollen and the attractiveness of the flowers to bees as a "honey plant", and the colourful showy inflorescences have long interested beekeepers and gardeners. References to the usefulness of purple loosestrife is common in bee industry journals along with instructions for planting and dispersal (van't Haaff 1968). However, the honey produced by bees gathering from *Lythrum* is apparently of marginal quality (Feller-Demalsy and Parent 1989).

Cultivars are considered very desirable as perennial ornamentals and reportedly never become weedy in a garden environment (although this may be due to having plants of a single morph, which will not be able to cross-pollinate and set seed). There is no evidence of the introgression of genes from cultivars into wild populations, despite the fact that many people have transplanted *Lythrum* from wetlands to their gardens, and nurseries often collect stock from the wild to sell. According to Mann (1991), the many insects that pollinate loosestrife find it an important food source and some of these insects in turn are prey for insectivorous birds.

The superior competitive ability of *Lythrum* was interpreted as beneficial in Europe! Bodrogkozy and Horvath (1979) found that the spread of weedy *Alopecurus pratensis* in the floodplain of the Tisza in Europe could be controlled by the flood-spread of *L. salicaria* seeds.

Bush et al. (1986) studied the feasibility of using *L. salicaria* as an environmental biomonitor and recorded greater accumulation of polychlorobiphenyl (PCB) congeners in the older leaves of the plants collected from the banks of the Hudson river, suggesting the accumulation of PCBs with time. The major transport of PCBs in the plant was systemic, via roots from the soil. PCBs were also absorbed from the air by purple loosestrife plants when the PCBs were present at high ambient concentrations (140 ng m^{-3}). Mudroch and Capobianco (1978) observed uptake of metals in sediment and marshwater by *L. salicaria* and other aquatic and emergent plant species from Lake St. Clair, Ontario. Metal concentrations (Zn, Pb, Cu, Cr, Ni, Co, and Cd) were found to be higher in the roots of *L. salicaria* than in the aboveground parts.

(c) *Legislation — Lythrum salicaria* has been declared a noxious weed under the weed control acts of various provincial or state governments of Canada and the United States (Manitoba, California, Idaho, Minnesota, Ohio and Wisconsin), although it is not listed in the 1988 Weed Control Act for Ontario (Government of Ontario 1988). In Minnesota, even *L. virgatum* and any hybrids of *L. salicaria* and *L. virgatum* are considered to be noxious weeds (Minnesota Department of Natural Resources 1990). Legislation of comparable weedy status for *L. salicaria* in Illinois and by the Federal Government of Canada is also being considered (Thompson et al. 1987; Keddy 1988). However, since purple loosestrife (1) is virtually impossible to eradicate when it becomes firmly established, and (2) is not a direct threat to man in the sense, for example, of being toxic, designation of it as a primary noxious weed, with penalties for its presence on a site, are neither practical nor likely to be proposed.

4. Geographic Distribution

Lythrum salicaria is cosmopolitan and circumpolar in distribution in the northern hemisphere (Hulten 1971; Shamsi and Whitehead 1974a; Thompson et al. 1987). It occurs extensively in Europe from Great Britain to central Russia. Its northern distribution in Europe extends up to the southern coast of Norway, southern Sweden and Finland near the 65th parallel. It is absent from north-west Finland, Denmark and Iceland (Tutin et al. 1968). Palhinha (1939) and Polunin (1969) reported it in central and southern Europe and Thompson et al. (1987) reported it from Italy. It also occurs in north Africa (e.g., northern Morocco, coastal Algeria, Ethiopia), Syria, Lebanon, Iran and Mediterranean islands. From the main islands of Japan, the native range of the species in Asia, it extends to Manchuria, China, Korea to south-east Asia to the Himalayan region in North India and Pakistan (Hulten 1971; Bokhari 1982). In the southern hemisphere, it has been introduced to Australia, Tasmania and New Zealand (Hulten 1958, 1971; Holm et al. 1979; Hulten and Fries 1986).

Lythrum salicaria is extremely abundant in the north-eastern states of the United States and gradually declines towards the west and south, with an area of high abundance in the southernmost part of Texas. Stuckey (1980) compiled a distribution map for the adjacent USA based on herbarium records as well as information from the literature. He presented data and hypotheses on the pattern of establishment and proliferation of *L. salicaria* in North America, over time, although he did not address the distribution or spread of the species in Canada.

This species has been reported from all Canadian provinces (except Saskatchewan, but later Cody (1978) indicated that it had been collected there too) (Boivin 1966; Cody 1978). Our map (Fig. 3), based on a 1991 review of Canadian herbarium specimens, shows that *Lythrum salicaria* has been collected from all the provinces in Canada, but not the Yukon and North-West Territories. It is most prevalent in the provinces of Ontario and Quebec, and to a lesser extent in New Brunswick and Nova Scotia. It appears that primary colonization of *L. salicaria* in Canada began in the eastern maritime provinces. From there, migration through rivers, canals and waterways ultimately has led to the present distribution. In Ontario and Quebec, infestation of *L. salicaria* is particularly severe along the St. Lawrence and

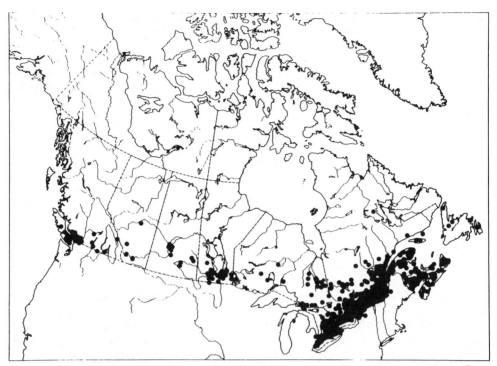

Fig. 3. The distribution of *L. salicaria* in Canada. This map is based on herbarium specimens from the following herbaria (see Holmgren et al. (1981) for detailed addresses): ACAD, A. E. Ronald Herbarium, Alberta Environmental Centre, ALTA, APM, CAFB, DAO, Government of Quebec, Laurentian University, Manitoba Natural Research – Wildlife Branch, MDNR, MMMN, MT, MTMG, National Museum of Canada, New Brunswick Museum, NFLD, OAC, OTT, PFES, QFA, QFB, QUE, Royal British Columbia Museum, Royal Ontario Museum, SASK, SCFQ, UBC, UNB, Université Laval, Université de Sherbrook, University of Manitoba, UPEI, USAS, UVIC, UWO, WAT, WLU, WOCB.

Great Lakes basin (see too Rousseau (1968)). Although its northern distribution in North America is presently limited to about 51°N latitude, scattered occurrence has been reported up to 56°20′N (it reaches the 65th parallel in Russia). The origin of populations on Canada's west coast is presently unknown.

According to recent estimates, approximately 14% of Canada, or 1.27 million km², is covered by wetlands (Table 3). Sixty-three percent of Canada's wetlands are concentrated in Manitoba, Ontario and the Northwest Territories (Lands Directorate 1986; National Wetlands Working Group 1988). Most of this wetland is north of 51°N, the present northern limit of the species in Canada. However, *L. salicaria* may well be capable of further range expansion provided suitable pollinators

are available. As a result, *L. salicaria* has very high potential to spread and dominate new wetland areas. Balogh and Bookhout (1989a,b) developed a method of remote detection of *L. salicaria* stands and identified 213 sites in Ohio; their approach may well be useful in tracking future spread of this species in sparsely populated areas of Canada.

5. Habitat

(a) *Climatic Requirements — Lythrum salicaria* usually occurs in low-lying coastal areas, wet, marshy places, stream banks and ditches at altitudes below 600 m. Temperature is the factor limiting growth and distribution of the species in the northern part of North America (Shamsi and Whitehead 1974a; Thompson et al. 1987). In terms of zones corresponding

Table 3. Distribution of wetlands in Canada (from Lands Directorate (1986))

Province/Territory	Total area of wetlands (000's of ha)	% of total area	% of total Canadian wetlands
British Columbia	3 120	3	2
Alberta	13 740	21	11
Saskatchewan	9 687	17	8
Manitoba	22 470	41	18
Ontario	29 241	33	23
Quebec	12 151	9	10
New Brunswick	544	8	<1
Nova Scotia	177	3	<1
Prince Edward Island	4	<1	<1
Newfoundland-Labrador	6 792	18	5
Yukon	1 510	3	1
Northwest Territories	27 794	9	22
Canada	127 230	14	100

to the average annual minimum temperature, the colonizing rate of *L. salicaria* was found to be lower in the $-34.5°$ to $-29°C$ zone than in $-29°$ to $-23°C$ zone (Bailey and Bailey 1976). The species is somewhat shade tolerant, and can survive in 50% of full sun (Thompson et al. 1987). However, a drop in illumination to 40% of full sun can cause a significant reduction in mean seed dry mass. No growth responses were noted under experimental manipulations of photoperiod, except at a 13-h treatment, the threshold for induction of flowering (Shamsi and Whitehead 1974b).

(b) *Substratum — Lythrum salicaria* grows both in calcareous and slightly acid soils (Perring and Walters 1962) and, in North America, in a wide range of soil textures from sand, clay, gravel, and organic soils to crushed-rock ballast. It typically occurs in the floodplains of freshwater streams, rivers, lakes and ponds and in other habitats temporarily flooded in the spring such as roadside wetlands. Shamsi and Whitehead (1974a) found better germination of *L. salicaria* seeds in sand than in garden soil. It grows better in the hydric portion of a soil moisture gradient (Thompson et al. 1987) and is tolerant of poor mineral nutrition (Shamsi and Whitehead 1974a). Keddy and Constabel

(1986) observed the germination potential of *L. salicaria* along with other shoreline plants in relation to seed size, soil particle size and water level. *Lythrum salicaria* also showed maximum recruitment at the wetter and fine end of the gradient of soil particle size. It showed a comparatively sharp increase in recruitment where the water level was low, but the substratum was made of coarse particles. Keddy and Constabel (1986) attributed this to the small seeds falling into the moist pores between soil particles, and concluded that the response of seeds to the particle-size gradient diminished when water was more readily available. In another set of experiments, Keddy and Ellis (1985) observed no significant response of *L. salicaria* seeds to a water level gradient maintained from 10 cm above to 5 cm below the substrate surface. Toivonen and Back (1989) observed significant increases in the abundance of *L. salicaria* populations as the water level of Lake Taivallampi in southern Finland decreased and eutrophication increased, from 1947–1975. However, by 1985 the relative abundance of *L. salicaria* had declined, and *Typha latifolia*, and *T.* × *glauca* had become dominant. This finding suggests that *L. salicaria* may go through a phase of natural decline after peaking in wetland habitats in Canada.

(c) *Communities in which the species occurs* — Approximately 29 species were found to grow in association with *L. salicaria* in the north-eastern and north-central USA and adjacent provinces in Canada (Thompson et al. 1987; Table 4). In order of average abundance, these associated species include *Typha* spp., *Phalaris* (reed canary grass), *Carex* and *Scirpus, Salix* spp., *Phragmites australis* (Cav.) Steudel (long known as *P. communis* Trin.), and *Equisetum fluviatile* L. (Thompson et al. 1987).

6. History

Lythrum salicaria is native to Eurasia (Shamsi and Whitehead 1974a). Pollen of *L. salicaria* was reported from Pleistocene deposits in eastern Macedonia (Wymstra 1969; Graham and Graham 1971). The origin of the generic name was from the Greek "Lytron", meaning blood, and indicating the red-purple flower colour (Teale 1982). The specific epithet derives from the similarity of *Lythrum* leaves to those of willows (*Salix* spp.), (Balogh 1986a). In North America, *Lythrum salicaria* was recorded in wet meadows of Canada and New England as far back as 1814 (Pursh 1814) and became a significant weed in Quebec during the 1930s (Balogh 1986a). The first herbarium specimen of *L. salicaria* collected in Canada was obtained at Lotbiniere, Quebec, by Thomas Bedard between 1850 and 1874 (Louis-Marie 1944). Louis-Marie (1944) and Rousseau (1968) reviewed the species' introduction and establishment in the St. Lawrence River valley and concluded, on the basis of Pursh (1814) and Hooker's (1829–33) reports, that *L. salicaria* arrived from France sometime during the early nineteenth century. Torrey and Gray (1840) also described the

Table 4. Percent frequency of occurrence of wetland species associated with *L. salicaria* at 45 sites in the Northeast, Midwest, and Northwest United States and southern Canada (from Thompson et al. (1987))

Species	Northeast (*N* = 15)	Midwest (*N* = 15)	Northwest (*N* = 15)	Mean (*N* = 45)
Typha latifolia, broad-leaved cattail	53	40	47	47
Phalaris arundinacea, reed canarygrass	27	47	60	45
Carex spp., sedge	20	27	13	20
Scirpus spp., bulrush	13	7	27	16
Salix spp., willow	0	13	20	11
Equisetum fluviatile, horsetail	0	0	27	9
Typha angustifolia, narrow-leaved cattail	13	13	0	9
Phragmites australis, reed grass	13	13	0	9
Cyperus sp., flatsedge	0	0	20	7
Alisma plantago-aquatica, water-plantain	7	7	0	5
Urtica dioica, stinging nettle	0	7	7	5
Sparganium eurycarpum, bur-reed	7	0	0	2
Agrostis gigantea (alba), redtop bentgrass	7	0	0	2
Acorus calamus, sweetflag	7	0	0	2
Populus deltoides, cottonwood	7	0	0	2
Chenopodium album, pigweed	0	7	0	2
Rubus spp., bramble	0	0	7	2
Euphorbia spp., spurge	0	0	7	2
Impatiens capensis, touch-me-not	0	7	0	2
Cornus stolonifera, red-osier dogwood	0	7	0	2
Convolvulus arvensis, field-bindweed	0	7	0	2
Verbena hastata, blue vervain	0	7	0	2
Solanum dulcamara, bitter nightshade	0	0	7	2
Eupatorium perfoliatum, boneset	7	0	0	2
Solidago sp., goldenrod	0	7	0	2
Aster sp., aster	0	7	0	2
Cirsium arvense, Canada thistle	0	0	7	2
Lactuca scariola, prickly lettuce	0	7	0	2
Unknown grass	0	0	7	2

plant as "well-established" in the flora of North America by 1830.

Purple loosestrife first appeared in the 1800s in ballast heaps of eastern North American harbours (Stuckey 1980). The most likely explanation of its appearance is that loosestrife was probably brought in as seeds, carried in the ballast of sailing ships trading between various European countries and the eastern seaboard. These ships would often take moist sand from tidal flats (a possible source of seeds) as ballast, and unload it on North American shores or shoals upon arrival. Alternatively, the rate of human immigration from Europe was very high around 1815 (Jones 1976) and the seeds may have been deliberately introduced by immigrants who used the plant as a medicinal herb. *Lythrum salicaria* seeds may also have arrived attached to raw wool or on sheep imported from Europe as the New England wool industry expanded from 1812 onwards (Cole 1926; Thompson et al. 1987). Finally, the plant may have been introduced to the United States and Canada by beekeepers, as a source of nectar and pollen (Hayes 1979; Mann 1991).

It is interesting that botanists and agronomists replying to inquiries by Louis-Marie (1944) stated that *L. salicaria* was absent or not a significant weed in Nova Scotia, New Brunswick, Alberta, Saskatchewan, Manitoba, Ontario, Connecticut, New Jersey, Rhode Island, New Hampshire, New York, Indiana, Minnesota, Pennsylvania, Missouri, Florida and California. This is testimony to its very recent explosive spread and establishment in North America.

Early spread of the species can be attributed to the habitat disturbance caused by agricultural settlement, military activities, and construction of canals, highways and railway networks. Thompson et al. (1987), and Stuckey (1980) have mapped the changing distribution of this species from 1880 onwards. Transport routes, intended to improve human access, also facilitated the dispersal and migration of *Lythrum salicaria* (Thompson et al. 1987; Wilcox 1989). It is likely that the drainage of wetlands for agricultural purposes and nutrient loadings to inland waters have also contributed significantly to the colonization and spread of this species.

7. Growth and Development
In an attempt to develop a functional classification of wetland vegetation, Shipley et al. (1989) and Keddy (1990) studied 7 juvenile and 13 adult traits of 25 wetland plant species. According to their analysis, *L. salicaria* proved to have juvenile traits that reflected a "fugitive" strategy (small seedlings, high relative growth rate, rapid and abundant germination), whereas adult traits of the species were more characteristic of a "competitive" strategy (greater height, longer generation time, significant vegetative spread).

(a) *Morphology* — As the individual stem is terminated by an inflorescence, flowering shoots in *L. salicaria* are annual. The maximum height we have recorded is 2.7 m; Thompson et al. (1987) recorded a maximum height of 2.5 m. Malecki (1990) describes rates of shoot extension of 1 cm d^{-1}. On germination of the seed, a strong tap-root system develops from the deep-penetrating primary root system and the shoot grows erect with proportional development of all parts (Shamsi and Whitehead 1974a). Purple loosestrife allocates at least half of its assimilate to the development of roots (Shamsi and Whitehead 1974b). Wood anatomy of the Lythraceae has been described by Baas and Zweypfenning (1979).

(b) *Perennation* — The species has been described as a facultative annual because it can set seed in one growing season (Shipley and Parent 1991; Johansson and Keddy 1991); however, this description is misleading because the species is not semelparous. *Lythrum salicaria* is a perennial, with annual stems arising from a perennating rootstock. There are no reports in the literature concerning the longevity of single genets.

(c) *Physiology* — A series of studies by Shamsi, and Shamsi and Whitehead addresses the comparative physiology of *Lythrum salicaria* and *Epilobium hirsutum*. They showed that *L. salicaria* can grow and thrive in moderate shade by increasing its leaf area with a slight reduction in unit leaf rate (relative increase in mass per unit area, measured as mg cm^{-2} wk^{-1}). It grows better in habitats covered by water temporarily in the spring and that are moist but not covered by water during its active growing period. A 13-h photoperiod is the threshold for extension growth and flowering (Shamsi and Whitehead 1974b), whereas a continuous 9-h photoperiod leads to dwarfism (Shamsi 1976a). A light interruption in the middle of a long dark period, in a short-day photoperiod treatment is known to cause stem elongation and flowering in many long-day plants. *Lythrum* plants were placed in an "8+1 h light-break treatment" where lights were on for 8 h, from 09.00–17.00 h, then off until 24.00 h when they were on for 1 h from 24.00–01.00 h, then off again from 01.00–09.00 h. Under these circumstances purple loosestrife responded by making a developmental shift from a short-day form to a long-day form (i.e., it flowered). This indicates that flowering in *Lythrum* is controlled by photoperiod rather than cumulative assimilation of light energy. However, the plants did not succeed in producing capsules or seeds in the experimental treatment.

Lythrum salicaria showed reduced growth in dilute nutrient solutions. Mineral deficiencies in N, P and K lead to an increased root:shoot ratio and a reduction in flowering and fruiting. The impact of N deficiency was greater than that of P or K deficiency (Shamsi and Whitehead 1977a). In experiments with *Epilobium hirsutum* L., *L. salicaria* showed superior competitive ability at 25°C; however, its relative growth was severely reduced at 8°C (Shamsi and Whitehead 1977b). Survival and growth of *L. salicaria* was greatly improved by fertilizer treatment and greater spacing between plants (7.6 cm; Shamsi 1976b). It is possible that the success of *Lythrum* has been enhanced in the Great Lakes region by nutrient enrichment resulting from the excessive use of fertilizers and release of phosphates, nitrates and ammonia in the basin. Generally the plant grows more vigorously at higher temperatures.

(d) *Phenology* — Seed germination occurs in late spring or early summer. After germination the plant generally takes 8–10 wk to flower; flowering begins in early July and continues until September-October. Basal capsules mature first, and their seeds disperse while the distal part of the inflorescence is still flowering, and the plant is green and leafy. Aboveground parts of the plant then die back in late autumn. The following year, new shoots arise from buds at the top of the rootstock; usually there are significantly more shoots each year.

(e) *Mycorrhizae* — None has been reported. Samples collected from two sites in southern Ontario did not show evidence of mycorrhizae in root tissue.

8. Reproduction

(a) *Floral biology* — Floral development of *L. salicaria* was described by Cheung and Sattler (1967). The maturation of the main inflorescence axis follows an acropetal (centripetal) sequence and that of the axillary lateral inflorescences a basipetalous (centrifugal) one. The sequence of initiation of floral primordia in *L. salicaria* was unique and had not been reported in any other species. The sequence is as follows: (1) inner sepals, (2) outer sepals (epicalyx), (3) outer stamens, (4) gynoecium, (5) inner stamens, and (6) petals.

The species is tristylous and herkogamous; that is it shows spatial separation of stigmas and anthers (see Fig. 2). The three morphs (short-, mid-, and long-styled) of *L. salicaria* are remarkably constant in their floral morphology (Table 1), which is associated with the maintenance of its heteromorphic self-incompatibility system. Darwin (1877), Barlow (1913, 1923) and Nicholls (1987) conducted pollination experiments involving both "legitimate" pollen (from a stamen of a length corresponding to that of the stigma) and "illegitimate" pollen (from a stamen of a length different from that of the stigma). These studies demonstrated a dramatic reduction in seed production from illegitimate matings. Stout (1923) recorded the effect of self-pollination and found that mids were the most self-compatible followed by longs, while shorts were the least. This confirmed Darwin's (1877) classic observations on self-pollination.

Pollination in *L. salicaria* is entomophilous. The major pollinators in nature are honey bees (Apinae), leaf cutter bees (Megachilinae), carpenter bees (Xilopinae), bumble bees (Bombinae), European cabbage white butterflies (*Pieris rapae* L.), common sulphur (*Colias philodice* Latreille), and wood nymph (*Cercyonis pegala* Fabricius) butterflies (Lazri and Barrows 1984; Levin 1970). However, Levin (1970) suggested that pollination may be effected by any insect visitor having a proboscis > 6 mm. Assortative pollination occurs for both floral morphology and plant stature (Darwin 1877; Levin and Kerster 1973). Levin (1970) and Levin et al. (1971) observed foraging behavior of bee and butterfly pollinators at a mixed assemblage of *L. salicaria* and *L. alatum*, and a pure *L. salicaria* population, respectively. *Lythrum salicaria* was preferred by both groups of pollinators. Bee fidelity to *L. salicaria* was greater than to *L. alatum*, while butterfly fidelity was greater to the latter. Both pollinators showed a strong tendency to move in the same general direction as the previous move, which ultimately could increase pollen flow. Interspecific pollinations can take place between the above two species since the floral mechanisms of both do not impose any mechanical barrier. Mulcahy and Caporello (1970) noted that a significant amount of self-pollination occurs within flowers, but that between flowers or plants, pollinations are predominantly legitimate.

In a study of pollen-tube growth following legitimate and illegitimate pollination, Kostoff (1927) found that pollen grains of *L. salicaria* germinated in both type of pollinations, but pollen-tube growth in the latter case was much slower. Eighteen hours following a legitimate pollination, a three-celled embryo had formed, with at least three nuclear divisions in the endosperm in all three morphs (Stevens 1912).

A classic series of papers has been published on the genetics of tristyly in *L. salicaria* (e.g., Fisher and Martin 1947; Fyfe 1953).

Tristyly is of interest because this mating system is broadly an outbreeding one, and successful colonizing weeds are more often self-pollinating. Tristyly is controlled by two unlinked loci with two alleles at each locus (*S,s* and *M,m*) where long is homozygous recessive at both loci (*ssmm*); mid (*M-ss*) is dominant to long, and short (*S---*) is epistatic to mid (Fisher and Mather 1943; Leach 1983). The expected frequency of three style lengths (1:1:1) in a population can be explained by disomic or polysomic genetic models of tristyly (Fisher 1941). Dulberger (1970) showed that tristyly could arise at the diploid level as well as at higher ploidy levels. Disomic inheritance has been reported in Australasia, and tetrasomic in Eurasia (Gilbert and Lee 1980) and North America (C. G. Eckert and S. C. H. Barrett, pers. commun.). Double meiotic reduction occurs at the *S* locus with a probability estimated at 2.5% (Fisher 1949), and at the *M* locus with a probability of about 10% (Fyfe 1953).

(b) *Seed production and dispersal* — Halka and Halka (1974) described the overwhelming importance of sexual reproduction in the propagation and spread of *L. salicaria*. Seed production is dependent on the age, size and vigour of the plant. A single stem can generally produce 900–1000 capsules (Shamsi and Whitehead 1974a; Thompson et al. 1987) and the number of seeds in each capsule varies from 83 to 130 depending on the floral morph (Darwin 1877). Bearing in mind the fact that many plants comprise a number of stems arising from root buds, Thompson et al. (1987) estimated the average seed production per plant to be in the order of 2 700 000.

The small light seeds are readily dispersed by both wind and water (Cutright 1986; Thompson et al. 1987). Woehler and Henderson (1986) and Thompson et al. (1987) suggested there was a limited role for wind dispersal, and proposed that aquatic wildlife such as waterfowl and snapping turtles, domestic livestock, vehicles, boats and even hunters' boots may play a part in seed dispersal, by adhesion.

Malecki (1990) has described high viability for seeds of *L. salicaria*; 100% germination for fresh seeds, 80% after 2–3 years' submergence. In infested sites seeding density can be high (10 000–20 000 m^{-2}).

(c) *Viability of seeds and germination* — Welling and Becker (1990) studied the dynamics of the seed bank of purple loosestrife in three emergent wetlands in Minnesota. They noted a mean density of 410 000 seeds m^{-2} in the top 5 cm of soil — this amounted to more seeds than for all other species combined. Isabelle et al. (1987) reported the germination ability of seeds of *L. salicaria* in roadside snowmelt and suggested its possible effects on plant community structure in wetlands. Welling and Becker (1990) observed a decreased rate of seedling emergence with depth of seed burial. They found negligible seedling emergence from seeds buried at 2 cm. As a result, small disturbances in the soil surface may lead to further recruitment from a dormant seed bank. Shipley and Parent (1991) conducted a germination study of 64 wetland species including *L. salicaria*. They observed a 3-d lag time (number of days taken for germination of the first seed), a maximum germination rate of 0.27% (proportion of germinable seeds that germinate in a day), 92% germination (by the end of 30-d period), and a seedling relative growth rate of 0.26 gg^{-1} d^{-1}.

Seed germination is negligible below 20°C and no germination occurs below 14°C (Shamsi 1974). The critical temperature for emergence of this species appears to lie between 15 and 20°C. A decrease in germination temperature below 20°C depresses subsequent seedling growth. Seed can germinate in a wide range of pH from pH 4 upwards. Seeds survived for several years following storage in a refrigerator for 3 yr, and germination was not statistically different from that of freshly collected seeds (Shamsi and Whitehead 1974a). Nicholls (1987) observed that seeds of the mid-style morph had a greater germination rate than those of the long-style morph, and seeds of the short-style morph showed very low levels of germination. Lehmann (1918), and Lehmann and Lakshmana (1924) found that as little as

one minute of light could stimulate seed germination.

(d) *Vegetative reproduction* — Pearsall (1918) and Ohwi (1965) described *L. salicaria* as "rhizomatous", but Shamsi and Whitehead (1974a) and Thompson et al. (1987) did not find significant clonal growth by means of rhizomes. There *is* localized clonal growth, however, as annual shoots are produced each spring from overwintering, spreading root buds (Shamsi and Whitehead 1974a). The tightly tufted nature of this mode of clonal growth produces a "phalanx" growth form, *sensu* Lovett Doust (1981).

(e) *Artificial propagation* — Heuser (1983) was successful in tissue culture of *L. virgatum* from shoot tips, using a modified MS medium. Tatebe (1961) observed pollen germination and gametophyte growth of *L. salicaria* var. *roseum superbum* (commercial cultivar) on a medium composed of 1% agar and 25% sucrose.

9. Hybrids

Because of its conspicuous showy purple flowers, cultivars of purple loosestrife have been developed and are widely cultivated in Canada (Table 2). According to Harp (1975), the *Lythrum* cultivar "Morden Pink" is a mutant form of *Lythrum virgatum* L. (wand lythrum) obtained in 1934 from plants grown at the Agricultural Research Station at Morden, Manitoba. He also stated that "Morden Pink" crosses with the North American native *Lythrum alatum* Pursh (winged loosestrife) producing the two cultivars "Morden Gleam" and "Morden Rose". However, specimens of named cultivars of *Lythrum* in the Agriculture Canada Herbarium, Ottawa, labelled "Morden Pink", "Morden Gleam" and "Morden Rose", all from material received from the Morden Research Station, are all clearly selections of *L. salicaria* (Table 2), and show none of the characters of either *L. virgatum* or *L. alatum*. Furthermore, it seems unlikely that the smaller flowers of the latter two species and the solitary flowers of *L. alatum* would contribute much to the showy spikes of *Lythrum* cultivars.

Nearly all of the cultivars listed in Table 2 appear to be selections from *L. salicaria*. Exceptions are "Dropmore Purple" that appears to be *L. salicaria* with perhaps some genetic input from *L. virgatum* and "Rose Queen" a selection from *L. virgatum*.

There is some morphological evidence that "Dropmore Purple" has resulted from hybridization between *L. salicaria* and *L. virgatum*. Since *L. salicaria* has a larger flower than *L. virgatum*, it is not surprising that breeding selection was towards *L. salicaria* and that there is now little evidence of traits inherited from *L. virgatum*. It was suggested by Minnesota Department of Natural Resources (1990) that breeders used *L. alatum* in the ornamental breeding program; however, this seems unlikely, in view of its small solitary flowers. There is not yet any evidence of introgression from cultivars of *Lythrum* into naturalized populations of *L. salicaria*. For several reasons, including the usual significant distance between infested wetlands and private gardens, this may remain unlikely.

10. Population Dynamics

Lythrum salicaria is a strong competitor, and tends to displace its neighbours, for several reasons. The species is tolerant of a wide range of ecological conditions, and is able to make direct developmental responses such as producing aerenchyma in submerged stems and changing leaf morphology in response to changes in illumination (Thompson et al. 1987). Seed production is prolific (once all three sex morphs are present), and seeds are readily dispersed. The average time period between initial invasion and subsequent domination by *L. salicaria* in a site varies, depending on the severity of disturbance of the habitat. Initial establishment of a population, followed by accumulation of a large seed bank and early disturbance, can accelerate the formation of a monospecific stand of *L. salicaria* in 1–2 yr (Thompson et al. 1987; Keddy 1988). In a study in Vancouver, Gilbert and Lee (1980) recorded population doubling over 10 yr. A monospecific stand of *L. salicaria* is potentially long-lived, and can maintain itself for more than 20 yr (Thompson et al. 1987). In Europe,

however, monospecific stands tend to become mixed-species stands within a few years (Shamsi and Whitehead 1974a). The greater persistence of monospecific stands in North America than in Europe is probably due to the relative absence here of its European parasites, predators and competing plant species.

One curious aspect of the distribution and abundance of *L. salicaria* is the apparent latency period between its introduction and its recognition as a serious weed. One possible explanation is that it may take some time for all three sex morphs to disperse to (or arise through genetic recombination in) a new population. As a result the species may be present as a few isolated perennating clumps for some time, and flowers may not be able to set seed until compatible plants are also present (they would therefore *appear* to be sterile). The dynamics and relative proportions of long-, mid-, and short-styled plants is, therefore, of particular interest.

Heuch (1979b) showed that the frequencies of the three morphs should ideally be isoplethic (equal) in a large population if no selective factors are operating, and disassortative mating and legitimate fertilization are occurring. In general, the frequencies of the three morphs are 1:1:1. Louis-Marie (1944) examined the flowers of 1000 plants at Baie-du-Fevre, Quebec, and found 34.7% of the styles short, 33.7% medium and 31.6% long. However, locally, in Essex County, Ontario, we have noted some underrepresentation of shorts and/or mids. Schoch-Bodmer (1936), summarizing data collected from 16 populations in North America and Europe, and Gilbert and Lee (1980) in Vancouver, Canada, also found under-representation of shorts. Haldane (1936) and Hoeg (1944) studied and modelled morph ratios in English and Finnish populations respectively and found patterns similar to those noted by Schoch-Bodmer (1936).

Eckert and Barrett (1989) found that all three morphs occurred in 86% of the 51 populations they surveyed in eastern Ontario. Eckert and Barrett (1992) also noted an absence of the short morph and to a lesser extent the mid morph, in 23 out of 102

Ontario populations. They contrasted this with reports from Europe where there is no record of a morph loss, and attributed this phenomenon to population size as well as rates of disassortative mating, perenniality, clonal growth, and self-fertilization. They developed a computer model showing the stochastic loss of style morphs and concluded that a population > 50 should become resistant to losing morphs over 100 yr. Heuch (1979a,b) modelled the effect of a small amount of self-fertilization and different fitness values for the three morphs on their population dynamics. Observed differences between the frequencies of morphs were too large to be accounted for by unequal probabilities of self-fertilization. Heuch (1980) suggested that isolated populations with 20 or more individuals are generally quite stable.

In a colonizing species, with distinct sex morphs, founder effects and drift may greatly influence population genetic structure and dictate the fitness of different morphs. Halka and Halka (1974), concluded that gene flow in *L. salicaria* is high. Darwin (1877) had pointed out that the mid-styled morph is likely to be more successful as a seed producer,

and less efficient as a pollen parent, as it produces more seeds than the other morphs. Nicholls (1987), from his study of the germination of seeds produced by the different morphs, has corroborated Darwin's inference of gender specialisation.

11. Response to Herbicides and Other Chemicals

Keddy (1988) tabulated detailed descriptions of degrees of infestation for purple loosestrife (infestation classes) and has recommended control measures for each (Table 5). She suggests that herbicides *could* be used to control small, or to contain large populations. The main challenge is the species' capacity to resprout from the perennial rootstock (Louis-Marie 1944; Gilbert and Lee 1980). In addition, purple loosestrife shows summer dormancy, which reduces the effectiveness of herbicides.

Gagnon (1953) reduced density by 50% and 73.7%, using an amine salt and a butyl ester of 2,4-D, respectively. McKeon (1959) tried various herbicides (Weedazol at 4.5 and 9.0 kg ha^{-1}, 2,4-Dow at 4.5 kg ha^{-1}, and 2,4-D and 2,4,5-T at 6.7 and 13.5 kg ha^{-1})

Table 5. General guideline for *L. salicaria* control, proposed by Keddy (1988)

Site characteristics	Level of infestation		
	Primary (1–200/ha)	Secondary (200–2000/ha)	Tertiary (2000/ha; 75% cover)
Access by land	Handpull and destroy Selectively spray with Roundup or aquatically approved herbicide	Selectively spray with Roundup or aquatically approved herbicide	Broadcast spray with selective herbicides
Access by water	Handpull and destroy Selectively spray with aquatically approved herbicide	Selectively spray with aquatically approved herbicide	Broadcast spray with selective herbicides
Sensitive site (e.g., rare plants present)	Handpull and destroy Wick application of Roundup or aquatically approved herbicide	Handpull and destroy	Cut, remove and destroy all flower stalks
Herbicide use prohibited	Handpull and destroy	Cut, remove and destroy all flower stalks	Cut, remove and destroy all flower stalks

in the purple loosestrife-infested marshes of the Hudson district of New York. He obtained 100% top kill with three rounds of spraying, but shoots resprouted from the rootstocks, so the effect was short-lived.

The results of field trials suggest that, once it becomes firmly established, purple loosestrife is virtually impossible to control by herbicides. Smith (1959) controlled purple loosestrife in impoundments of the Montezuma National Wildlife Refuge by spraying ammonium sulfamate at 36–45 kg AEH (acid equivalent/ha). However recolonization from the centre of the ponds, where plants had been beyond the reach of spray, caused rapid reinfestation of the impoundments. Thompson et al. (1987) reported modest success with Dicamba, and a mixture of Dicamba and 2,4-D. 2,4-D is generally effective against broad-leaved species, is biodegradable, short-lived and inactivated following contact with moist soil. It is approved for use in the aquatic environment in the United States and is being used in Minnesota for controlling purple loosestrife. However, it is not approved in Canada because its use is associated with toxic effects in the food chain.

Rawinski (1982) and Malecki and Rawinski (1985) applied glyphosate at Howland Island Wildlife Management Area in New York at three different concentrations (1.7, 3.4 and 6.7 kg ha^{-1}) and at three different phenological stages (when plants were vegetative, 13 June; at early flowering, 13 July; and late flowering, 12 Aug.). They achieved 100% control when glyphosate was applied at a rate of 1.7 kg ha^{-1} in mid-August, and found the time of application rather than concentration was the crucial factor. Glyphosate is a systemic herbicide that is absorbed by leaf surfaces and translocated to the entire plant. Its efficacy at low concentration, low potential for bioaccumulation and fairly short half-life (2 mo biological activity in soil and water) makes it an attractive potential control agent for purple loosestrife (Rueppel et al. 1977; Thompson et al. 1987.) It is relatively less toxic to birds (Batt et al. 1980), mammals (Monsanto Co. 1973) and aquatic invertebrates and fishes (Folmar et al. 1979) than are other candidates for loosestrife control.

However, since glyphosate is a broad-spectrum, non-selective herbicide, it may affect the endemic vegetation of the marshland as well as the target weed. Hence targeted spot-spraying and direct application to loosestrife by means of wicks has been suggested. Glyphosate is marketed in two different formulations, Roundup and Rodeo, which contain the same active ingredient. Rodeo includes a new surfactant approved for use over water in the United States, whereas Roundup is only licensed in Canada (Keddy 1988). At present glyphosate is used in Minnesota and Wisconsin in the United States and in Ottawa in Canada (Balogh 1986a; Keddy 1988). However, Christy et al. (1981) and Rawinski (1982) caution against widespread use of this herbicide without thorough assessment of its possible deleterious effects in aquatic ecosystems.

12. Response to Other Human Manipulation

Keddy et al. (1989) proposed that control of unwanted species in wetland areas could best be achieved by manipulating regeneration processes such as seedling recruitment and by controlling the nature and frequency of disturbance, to encourage re establishment of desired species. The best form of control for a new infestation is hand-weeding, with care being taken to remove all plants before they set seed. This is especially effective and highly recommended when only one or a few plants invade a habitat (Keddy 1988).

(a) *Handpulling* — In the primary infestation period, handpulling is an effective measure in control of purple loosestrife. Care must be taken to remove the perennial rootstock as well as the plant. It is easiest to remove young (1–2 yr-old) plants from moist soil. Handpulling operation should be conducted carefully to minimize soil disturbance, otherwise seedling establishment will be stimulated (Keddy 1988). Louis-Marie (1944) first used this technique in the flood-plain pastures north and east of Pierreville, Quebec. Balogh (1986a) reported that handpulling is carried out at present in some areas of the United States. However, as it is labour-intensive, it is unlikely to be feasible for controlling well-established infestations. Perhaps a mixed strategy of chemical control, ecological and management manipulations, followed by hand-pulling of surviving plants will provide an effective control strategy.

(b) *Burning* — As the root-buds lie well below the soil surface (*c*. 2 cm), and the surrounding soil is generally moist, burning is probably not a viable control measure (Thompson et al. 1987; Keddy 1988). Louis-Marie (1944) applied a flame torch to burn the green plants in the growing season. Thompson et al. (1987) also tried this technique, but observed very low mortality of the root crowns in the succeeding year. This does not seem to be a particularly cost-effective method.

(c) *Cutting* — Malecki and Rawinski (1985) showed a significant reduction in number of shoots and seed production following late-summer cutting. However, vegetative regeneration and clonal spread can take place from the cut stems, so the authors proposed the additional treatment of flooding or burning. They also found that cutting alone failed to give reliable control, but when cutting was combined with subsequent flooding, growth of purple loosestrife could be held in check for several years. Seedling establishment and vegetative sprouting can be controlled by clipping 21-d-old plants. However, clipping after day 42 did not prevent establishment, but rather compounded infestation problems by increasing the number of aboveground first-year stems capable of producing seeds (Gabor and Murkin 1990).

(d) *Flooding* — The results of attempts at control of purple loosestrife by flooding are mixed, and appear to depend on the change in water depth, and the duration and timing, site, and nature of loosestrife growth in the flooded area (Malecki and Rawinski 1985; Thompson et al. 1987; Keddy 1988). McKeon (1959) and Smith (1964) did not manage to control the weed by changing water levels, even by 0.6–0.9 m. In contrast, Malecki and Rawinski (1985) reduced the number of plants by completely flooding populations for two or more growing seasons,

but they did not find any effect on stature or reproductive output in surviving plants subjected to manipulations of water level from 0 to 0.5 m. Clay (1986) reported that a reduction in density was achieved by increasing water level by 0.3 m for 2 consecutive years, and that seedlings could be eliminated by raising the water level by 10 cm. Balogh (1986b) also obtained 100% seedling mortality by the 8th week of flooding at all depths. Duration of flooding, rather than the depth of water determined *seedling* mortality.

Complete mortality of mature plants was achieved after 5 wk of raising the water level by 0.3-1 m (Balogh 1986a). Thompson et al. (1987) observed that an increase of water level by 0.4 m for 3 yr could reduce purple loosestrife density and stimulated a threefold increase in cattail density.

Although it is less likely to aggravate problems of chemical pollution, flooding may alter community composition in the wetland, and some desirable or endemic species may be threatened (Keddy 1988). Malecki and Rawinski (1985) also suggested that flooding may have a detrimental effect on the emergent vegetation of the wetland. However, one could argue that fluctuations in water level are much lower today than they were in the past, before the residential development of shorelines. Periodic flooding was a natural aspect of wetland ecosystems, so wetland plants are likely to have evolved to tolerate such conditions, and irreversible negative impacts of flooding would be unlikely. Since purple loosestrife cannot survive being submerged in water during its active growth period, under some circumstances, flooding could effectively control or even eradicate very serious infestations. Care must, however, be taken to protect desired vegetation and wildlife.

(e) *Replacement control* — Growth of purple loosestrife in highly infested areas may be suppressed by planting another, less-detrimental but more competitive wetland species. Balogh (1986a,b) reported that smartweed (*Polygonum lapathifolium* L.) could outcompete loosestrife during the first year of growth. Novak (1968) reported the control of loosestrife in the highly infested Great Meadows NWR near Concord, Massachusetts through a policy of repeated mowing, plowing and subsequent seeding with reed canary grass (*Phalaris arundinacea* L.). Unfortunately, although reed canary grass can outcompete loosestrife, heavy herbivory on the reed canary grass (by meadow voles, *Microtus pennsylvanicus*) may prevent competitive replacement. Indeed, the reed canary grass itself may not be a particularly desirable substitute for the local wetland flora.

Malecki and Rawinski (1985) found that Japanese millet (*Echinochloa frumentacea* (Roxb.) Link) was most successful in outcompeting loosestrife. The millet plants grow rapidly, and are more tolerant of periodic flooding. Control of loosestrife was achieved by sowing Japanese millet on exposed moist soil sites at 34 kg ha^{-1} following a drawdown, before loosestrife seedlings had begun to grow. Seeds of Japanese millet can be used by waterfowl and the species was considered to be unlikely to become a weed in future. However Thompson et al. (1987) expressed concern about this strategy, suggesting that the replacement species might also turn out to be a nuisance. Keddy (1988) also felt that the technique might not be feasible in natural wetland communities.

13. Response to Parasites

(a) *Insects and biological control* — It has generally been stated that purple loosestrife has left behind its natural enemies in Europe (Batra et al. 1986), and therefore is escaping herbivory in Canada. However our preliminary field studies and observations from Michigan Department of Natural Resources suggest a caterpillar of the *Eudryas unio* (pearly wood-nymph) moth is grazing the species. The leaves appear to be palatable to the caterpillar and although caterpillar densities at our field sites were low (on average, two per plant), it is possible that this caterpillar may become a part of strategies to control *L. salicaria*. So far, no other North American organisms have been reported as grazers of *L. salicaria*.

European surveys identified 120 species associated with loosestrife (Batra et al. 1986;

Malecki 1990). Of these, 14 are host-specific for purple loosestrife and are therefore potentially promising as biological control agents.

A cost-benefit analysis for the biological control of *L. salicaria* has been made for 12 northeastern states and 7 northern midwest states in the US where wetlands have been invaded (Thompson et al. 1987). The benefit amounts to $45.9 m compared to a cost of $1.7 m. Benefits were calculated in terms of the realty value of threatened wetlands, wild hay and pasture, fur harvest, migratory bird hunting expenditures, wildlife observation and photography. Costs were measured in terms of combined costs of biological control, 10% of annual honey sales in 19 states, and 5% of annual sales of herbaceous ornamentals.

Detailed life histories of five insects currently considered potential biological control agents are presented in Blossey and Schroeder (1988). The species are:

1. *Hylobius transversovittatus* (Goeze) (root-mining weevil). This species oviposits and develops *exclusively* on *L. salicaria*. Developing larvae feed on the vascular tissues in the root, while adults forage on the shoots of *L. salicaria*, although limited adult feeding can take place on a few other plants. All stages of the weevil are well adapted to withstand prolonged flooding. Hibernation takes place for all life history stages, and different generations of the weevil may co-occur on the same plant. A serious infestation of weevils may cause complete destruction of mature plants.

2. & 3. *Galerucella pusilla* and *G. calmariensis* (leaf-eating beetles): Blossey and Schroeder (1988) and Malecki (1990) observed no significant difference in the appearance and life histories of these species. Adults come out of hibernation and feed on loosestrife in late April–early May. Adults leave host plants after limited foraging; this may serve to reduce competition with, and food shortage among the larvae. Adults and larvae forage on the shoots, leaves and flowers. They completely defoliate the plant and may destroy it, preventing seed production particularly if the density of adults and larvae reaches 200 per plant. Restricted adult

feeding and ovipositing can take place on a few other species, viz. *Lythrum californicum* Torr. & Gray, *L. hyssopifolia* L., *L. lineare* L., *Epilobium angustifolium* L., and *Decodon verticillatus* (L.)Ell.

4. *Nanophyes marmoratus* (Goeze) (flower-feeding beetle): These may reduce seed production since females lay their eggs on the petals of flower buds, and larvae subsequently feed on them.

5. *Bayeria salicaria* (gall gnat): These reduce growth and seed production due to the formation of galls on shoots and flower parts.

Purple loosestrife is now common in many of the wetlands and meadows of Canada and the northern United States. In the opinion of the research groups who are developing biological controls, even if a program costing billions of dollars were implemented, it would be impossible to eradicate or even control loosestrife using herbicides. In addition, such an effort would likely do considerable environmental damage. It may be more economical and environmentally sound to reduce the dominance of purple loosestrife over native vegetation by some form or combinations of strategies of biological control. One (preferable) strategy would be to augment populations of local herbivores that graze *L. salicaria*. If this fails it may be necessary to introduce some of its natural enemies from Europe and Asia. It is not likely that any biological control agents would seriously affect ornamental *Lythrum* growing in cultivated situations. However the potential impact of such control agents on the native flora is presently unknown and since *Lythrum alatum* is regarded as rare and potentially endangered in some regions it is important that these control agents be strongly associated with the target species.

(b) *Microorganisms and viruses* — Leaf spot, a fungal disease caused by *Septoria lythrina* Pk., has been reported by Conners (1967).

(c) *Higher plant parasites* — No record has been found.

ACKNOWLEDGMENTS

We are indebted to the curators of Canadian herbaria who generously loaned their specimens and provided information on the distribution of *Lythrum salicaria*. We also thank Gerry Lee and the Canadian Wildlife Service for their interest in this project. Christopher Eckert and Spencer Barrett kindly provided early access to their paper on style morphs. The Natural Sciences and Engineering Research Council of Canada, through Operating Grants to JLD and LLD, and the Ontario Ministry of Natural Resources, through the Environmental Youth Corps program, provided research support. We are grateful to the anonymous reviewers for their suggestions on improvements to this manuscript.

Alex, J. F., Cayouette, R. and Mulligan, G. A. 1980. Common and botanical names of weeds in Canada. Expert Committee on Weeds, Research Branch, Agriculture Canada, Ottawa, ON. Publ. no. 1397. pp. 132.

Baas, P. and Zweypfenning, R. C. V. J. 1979. Wood anatomy of the Lythraceae. Acta Bot. Neerl. **28**(2/3): 117–155.

Bailey, L. H. and Bailey, E. Z. 1976. Hortus third. Macmillan Publishing Co., Inc., New York, NY. 1290 pp.

Balogh, G. R. 1986a. Ecology, distribution, and control of purple loosestrife (*Lythrum salicaria*) in northwest Ohio. M.S. thesis, The Ohio State University, Columbus, OH. xiv + 107 pp.

Balogh, G. R. 1986b. Distribution and seedling ecology of purple loosestrife in Ohio's Lake Erie marshes. Ohio J. Sci. **86**(2): 51.

Balogh, G. R. and Bookhout, T. A. 1989a. Purple loosestrife (*Lythrum salicaria*) in Ohio's Lake Erie Marshes. Ohio J. Sci. **89**(3): 62–64.

Balogh, G. R. and Bookhout, T. A. 1989b. Remote detection and measurement of purple loosestrife stands. Wildl. Soc. Bull. **17**: 66–67.

Barlow, N. 1913. Preliminary note on heterostylism in *Oxalis* and *Lythrum*. J. Genetics **3**: 53–65.

Barlow, N. 1923. Inheritance of the three forms in trimorphic species. J. Genetics **13**(2): 133–145.

Batra, S. W. T., Schroeder, D., Boldt, P. E. and Mendl, W. 1986. Insects associated with purple loosestrife (*Lythrum salicaria* L.) in Europe. Proc. Entomol. Soc. Wash. **88**: 748–759.

Batt, B. D. J., Black, A. and Cowan, W. F. 1980. The effects of glyphosphate herbicide on chicken egg hatchability. Can. J. Zool. **58**: 1940–1942.

Blossey, B. and Schroeder, D. 1988. Study and screening of potential biological control agents of purple loosestrife (*Lythrum salicaria* L.). First Annual Report of C.A.B. International Institute of Biological Control, European Station, Switzerland. 27 pp.

Bodrogkozy, G. and Horvath, I. 1979. Effect of lasting floods on the species composition and organic-matter production of the marshy meadow-lands in the floodplains of the tisza. Tiscia **14**: 81–88.

Boivin, B. 1966. Enumeration des plantes du Canada. III — Herbicidées, I° Partie: Digitatae: Dimerae, Liberae. Naturaliste Canadien (Canadian Naturalist) **93**: 583–646.

Bokhari, M. H. 1982. Aquatic plants of Iran and Pakistan. III. Lythraceae. Biologia **28**(2): 179–188.

Broderick, D. H. 1990. The biology of Canadian weeds 93. *Epilobium angustifolium* L. (Onagraceae). Can. J. Pl. Sci. **70**: 247–259.

Bush, B. Shane, L. A., Wilson, L. R., Barnard, E. L. and Barnes, D. 1986. Uptake of polychlorobiphenyl congeners by purple loosestrife (*Lythrum salicaria*) on the banks of the Hudson River. Arch. Environ. Contam. Toxicol. **15**: 285–290.

Buttler, K. P. and Schippmann, U. 1984. Chromosomenzahlen von Gefabpflanzen aus Hessen (und dem angrenzenden Bayern), 2. Folge. Hess. Florist. Briefe **33**(3): 46–48.

Cadet, C. 1954. Recherches sur la valeur morphologique du calicule chez les Lythracees. Bull. Sci. Bourgogne **15**: 53–83.

Cheung, M. and Sattler, R. 1967. Early floral development of *Lythrum salicaria*. Can. J. Bot. **45**: 1609–1618.

Christy, S. L., Karlander, E. P. and Parochetti, J. V. 1981. Effects of glyphosate on the growth rate of *Chlorella*. Weed Sci. **29**: 5–7.

Clapham, A. R., Tutin, T. G. and Warburg, E. F. 1962. Flora of the British Isles. 2nd ed. Cambridge University Press, Cambridge, U.K.

Clay, R. T. 1986. Purple loosestrife: a literature review and management recommendations. Ducks Unlimited, Winnipeg, MB. 29 pp. mimeo.

Cody, W. J. 1978. The status of *Lythrum alatum* (Lythraceae) in Canada. Canad. Field-Nat. **92**: 74–75.

Cole, A. H. 1926. The american wool manufacture. Vol. 1. Harvard University Press, Cambridge, MA.

Conners, I. L. 1967. An annotated index of plant diseases in Canada and fungi recorded on plants in Alaska, Canada and Greenland. Research Branch, Canada Department of Agriculture, Ottawa, On. Publ. 1251.

Cusick, A. W. 1986. Distributional and taxonomic notes on the vascular flora of West Virginia. Castanea **51**(1): 56–65.

Cutright, N. J. 1986. Regulation of purple loose-strife by states in the Midwest. Proc. North Central Weed Control Conf. **41**: 123–125.

Darwin, C. 1877. The different forms of flowers on plants of the same species. John Murray, London, U.K.

Dollon, T and Hamel, J. L. 1967. Contribution a l'etude caryo-taxonomique des Lythracees et des Punicacees. Bull. Mus. Nat. Hist. Nat. **39**: 793–818.

Dulberger, R. 1968. Chromosome numbers in *Lythrum* in Israel. Israel J. Bot. **17**: 179–183.

Dulberger, R. 1970. Tristyly in *Lythrum junceum*. New Phytol. **69**: 751–759.

East, E. M. 1927. The inheritance of heterostyly in *Lythrum salicaria*. Genetics **12**: 393–414.

Eckert, C. G. and Barrett, S. C. H. 1989. The effect of population dynamics and life-history traits on genetic drift at style morph loci in tristylous populations. Am. J. Bot. **76**(6 Suppl.): 146.

Eckert, C. G. and Barrett, S. C. H. 1991. Stochastic loss of style morphs from populations of tristylous *Lythrum salicaria* and *Decodon verticillatus* (Lythraceae). Evolution **46**: 1014–1029.

Eiten, G. 1963. Taxonomy and regional variation of *Oxalis* section Corniculatae. I. Introduction, keys and synopsis of the species. Am. Midl. Nat. **69**: 257–309.

Feller-Demalsy, M. J. and Parent, J. 1989. Analyse pollinique des miels de l'Ontario, Canada. Apidologie **20**: 127–138.

Fernald, M. L. 1940. The problem of conserving rare native plants. Ann. Rept. Smithsonian Institution (1939): 375–391.

Fisher, R. A. 1941. The theoretical consequences of polyploid inheritance for the mid-styled form of *Lythrum salicaria*. Ann. Eugen. **11**: 31–38.

Fisher, R. A. 1949. The linkage problem in a tetra-somic wild plant, *Lythrum salicaria*. Proc. 8th Internat. Cong. Genet. Hereditas (Suppl. Vol.) pp. 225–233.

Fisher, R. A. and Mather, K. 1943. The inheritance of style length in *Lythrum salicaria*. Ann. Eugen. **12**: 1–23.

Fisher, R. A. and Martin, V. C. 1947. Spontaneous occurrence in *Lythrum salicaria* of plants duplex for the short style gene. Nature **160**: 541.

Folmar, L. C., Sanders, H. O. and Julin, A. M. 1979. Toxicity of the herbicide glyphosate and several of its formulations to fish and aquatic invertebrates. Arch. Environ. Contam. Toxicol. **8**: 269–278.

Fyfe, V. C. 1953. Double reduction at the mid locus in *Lythrum salicaria*. Heredity **7**: 285–292.

Gabor, T. S. and Murkin, H. R. 1990. Effects of clipping purple loosestrife seedlings during a simulated wetland drawdown. J. Aquat. Plant Managet. **28**: 98–100.

Gagnon, L. P. 1953. The control of purple loose-strife in La Commune at Baie du Febvre-1952. Proc. East. Sect. Natl. Weed Comm. Can. 6: 135–136.

Gaudet, C. L. and Keddy, P. A. 1988. A comparative approach to predicting competitive ability from plant traits. Nature 334: 242–243.

Gilbert, N. and Lee, S. B. 1980. Two perils of plant population dynamics. Oecologia (Berl.) 46: 283–284.

Gleason, H. A. 1952. Illustrated flora of the northeastern United States and adjacent Canada. Vol. 2. New York Botanical Garden, Hafner Publishing Company, Inc., New York, NY.

Government of Ontario. 1988. Weed Control Act. Ministry of the Attorney General, Toronto, ON. 29 pp.

Graham, A. and Graham, S. A. 1971. The geologic history of the Lythraceae. Brittonia 23: 335–346.

Graham, A., Nowicke, J. W., Skvarla, J. J., Graham, S. A., Patel, V. and Lee, S. 1987. Palynology and systematics of the Lythraceae. II. Genera Haitia through Peplis. Amer. J. Bot. 74(6): 829–850.

Grieve, M. 1959. A modern herbal. Vol. 2. Hafner Publishing Co., New York, NY. pp. 431–888.

Haldane, J. B. S. 1936. Some natural populations of *Lythrum salicaria*. J. Genet. 32: 393–397.

Halka, O. and Halka, L. 1974. Polymorphic balance in small island populations of *Lythrum salicaria*. Ann. Bot. Fennici 11: 267–270.

Harp, H. F. 1975. Lythrums for home gardens. Agriculture Canada, Ottawa, ON.

Harty, F. M. 1986. Exotics and their ecological ramifications. Natural Areas J. 6: 20–23.

Hayes, B. 1979. Purple loosestrife — the wetlands honey plant. Am. Bee J. 119: 382–383.

Heuch, I. 1979a. The effect of partial self-fertilization on type frequencies in heterostylous plants. Ann. Bot. 44: 611–616.

Heuch, I. 1979b. Equilibrium populations of heterostylous plants. Theor. Pop. Biol. 15: 43–57.

Heuch, I. 1980. Loss of incompatibility types in finite populations of the heterostylous plant *Lythrum salicaria*. Hereditas 92: 53–57.

Heuser, C. W. 1983. In vitro propagation of *Lythrum virgatum*. HortScience 18(3): 303.

Hickey, M. and King, C. 1981. 100 families of flowering plants. Cambridge University Press, New York, NY.

Hoeg, O. A. 1944. Om forholdstallene for de tre slags blomster av *Lythrum salicaria* i Norge. [The ratio of different forms of flowers in *Lythrum salicaria* L. in Norway.] Blyttia 2: 71–74.

Holm, L., Pancho, J. V., Herberger, J. P. and Plucknett, D. L. 1979. A geographical atlas of world weeds. John Wiley & Sons, Inc., New York, NY xlix + 391 pp.

Holmgren, P. K., Keukan, W. and Schofield, E. 1981. Index herbarium. Part 1. The herbaria of the world. 7th ed. (Regnum Veg. 106). Oosthock,. Schetema and Holkema, Utrecht, The Netherlands. 452 pp.

Hooker, W. J. 1829–1833. Flora Boreali-Americana; or, the botany of the northern parts of British America....London. Vol. I. vi, 335 pp. (Reprinted, Weinheim. 1960).

Hulten, E. 1958. The amphi-Atlantic plants. Almqvist & Wiksell, Stockholm, Sweden. 340 pp.

Hulten, E. 1971. The circumpolar plants. 2. Almqvist & Wiksell, Stockholm, Sweden. 463 pp.

Hulten, E. and Fries, M. 1986. Atlas of North European vascular plants north of the Tropic of Cancer: II. Taxonomic index to the maps 997–1936. Koeltz Scientific, Koenigstein. pp. 674–675.

Huynh, K. L. 1972. Study of pollen arrangement in the tetrad of angiosperms based on cytological data. VI. Lythraceae and Bombacaceae. [*Lythrum salicaria*, *Ammannia latifolia*, *Bombax ceiba*]. Sociedade Broteriana. Boletin de Sociedade Broteriana. 46(2): 171–180.

Isabelle, P. S., Fooks, L. J., Keddy, P. A. and Wilson, S. D. 1987. Effects of roadside snowmelt on wetland vegetation: an experimental study. J. Env. Manage. 25: 57–60.

Johansson, M. E. and Keddy, P. A. 1991. Intensity and asymmetry of competition between plant pairs of different degrees of similarity: an experimental study on two guilds of wetland plants. Oikos 60: 27–34.

Jones, M. A. 1976. Destination America. Holt, Rinehart & Winston, New York, NY.

Keddy, C. 1988. A review of *Lythrum salicaria* (purple loosestrife) ecology and management: The urgency for management in Ontario. Natural Heritage League, Ottawa, ON. 34 pp.

Keddy, P. A. 1990. The use of functional as opposed to phylogenetic systematics: a first step in predictive community ecology. In S. Kawano, ed. Biological approaches and evolutionary trends in plants. Academic Press, London, U.K.

Keddy, P. A. and Constabel, P. 1986. Germination of ten shoreline plants in relation to seed size, soil particle size and water level: an experimental study. J. Ecol. 74: 133–141.

Keddy, P. A. and Ellis, T. H. 1985. Seedling recruitment of 11 wetland plant species along a water level gradient: shared or distinct responses? Can. J. Bot. 63: 1876–1879.

Kerner von Marilaun, A. 1902. The natural history of plants. Trans. F. W. Oliver; 2 vols. Blackie and Sons, London, U.K.

Koehne, E. 1903. Lythraceae. *In* A. Engler, ed. Das Pflanzenreich. W. Engelmann, Leipzig, Germany. Vol. IV, Heft 17, pp. 1–78.

Kostoff, D. 1927. Pollen-tube growth in *Lythrum salicaria*. Genetics **13**: 253–255.

Lamela, M., Cadavid, I., Gato, A. and Callieja, J. M. 1985. Effects of *Lythrum salicaria* in normoglycemic rats. J. Ethnopharmaco. **14**: 83–91.

Lamela, M., Cadavid, I. and Callieja, J. M. 1986. Effects of *Lythrum salicaria* extracts on hyperglycemic rats and mice. J. Ethnopharmacol. **15**: 153–160.

Lands Directorate. 1986. Land use change in Canada. Wetlands in Canada: a valuable resource. Environment Canada, Ottawa, ON. Fact Sheet 86–4. 8 pp.

Lazri, B. and Barrows, E. M. 1984. Flower visiting and pollen transport by the imported cabbage butterfly [*Pieris rapae*] (Lepidoptera: Pieridae) in a highly disturbed urban habitat. Environ. Entomol. **13**(2): 574–578.

Leach, C. R. 1983. Fluctuations in heteromorphic self-incompatibility systems. Theor. Appl. Genet. **66**: 307–312.

Lehmann, E. 1918. Ueber die minimale Belichtungszeit, welche die Keimung der Samen von *Lythrum salicaria* ausloest. Berichte der Deutschen Botanische Gesellschaft **36**: 157–163.

Lehmann, E. and Lakshmana, R. 1924. Ueber die Gueltigkeit des Produktgesetzes bei der Lichtleimung von *Lythrum salicaria*. Berichte der Deutschen Botanische Gesellschaft **42**: 5–54.

Levin, D. A. 1970. Assortative pollination in *Lythrum*. Am. J. Bot. **57**: 1–5.

Levin, D. A. and Kerster, H. W. 1973. Assortative pollination for stature in *Lythrum salicaria*. Evolution **27**: 144–152.

Levin, D. A., Kerster, H. W. and Niedzlek, M. 1971. Pollinator flight directionality and its effect on pollen flow. Evolution **25**: 113–118.

Louis-Marie, Pere. 1944. La Salicaire dans le Quebec. Institut Agricole d'Oka. Province de Quebec, Ministere de l'Agriculture. 46 pp.

Lovett Doust, L. 1981. Population dynamics and local specialization in a clonal perennial, *Ranunculus repens* L.I. The dynamics of ramets in contrasting habitats. J. Ecol. **69**: 743–755.

Malecki, R. 1990. Research update — biological control of purple loosestrife. Report of N.Y. Cooperative Fish and Wildlife Research Unit, Cornell University, Ithaca, NY. 4 pp + 2 figs.

Malecki, R. A. and Rawinski, T. J. 1985. New methods for controlling purple loosestrife. NY Fish Game J. **32**: 9–19.

Mann, H. 1991. Purple loosestrife: A botanical dilemma. The Osprey **22**: 67–77.

McKeon, W. H. 1959. A preliminary report on the use of chemical herbicides to control purple loosestrife (*Lythrum salicaria*) on a small marsh. Proc. Northeast. Weed Control Conf. **13**: 329–332.

McLean, R. C. and Ivimey-Cook, W. R. 1960. Textbook of theoretical botany. John Wiley & Sons Inc., New York, NY.

Meeuse, B. and Morris, S. 1984. The sex life of flowers. Facts on file, New York, NY.

Minnesota Department of Natural Resources. 1990. On the Loose, The newsletter of the DNR's Purple Loosestrife Program. **4**: 1–6.

Monsanto Co. 1973. Roundup herbicide: formulation of isopropylamine salt of glyphosate post-emergence herbicide. Tech. Bull. MON-0573-2-73:7.

Moore, D. R. J. and Keddy, P. A. 1989. Conservation of infertile wetlands: priorities and management. *In* M. J. Bardecki and N. Patterson, eds. Wetlands: Inertia or momentum. Proceedings of conference, Ryerson Polytechnical Institute, Toronto, ON. Oct. 21–22, 1988. Federation of Ontario Naturalists, Don Mills, ON.

Mudoch, A. and Capobianco, J. 1978. Study of selected metals in marshes on Lake St. Clair, Ontario. Arch. Hydrobiol. **84**(1): 87–108.

Mulcahy, D. L. and Caporello, D. 1970. Pollen flow within a tristylous species: *Lythrum salicaria*. Am. J. Bot. **57**(9): 1027–1030.

Mulligan, G. A. 1957. Chromosomes of Canadian weeds. Can. J. Bot. **35**: 779–789.

National Wetlands Working Group. 1988. Wetlands of Canada. Ecological land classification series. No. 24. Sustainable Development Branch, Environment Canada, Ottawa, ON and Polyscience Publications Inc., Montreal, PQ. 452 pp.

Nicholls, M. S. 1987. Pollen flow, self-pollination and gender specialization: factors affecting seed-set in the tristylous species *Lythrum salicaria* (Lythraceae). Plant Syst. Evol. **156**: 151–157.

Novak, L. C. 1968. Mechanical control of purple loosestrife. Prog. Rep. 1, Div. Refuges, Region 5, U.S. Fish and Wildl. Serv., Washington, DC.

Ohwi, J. 1965. Flora of Japan. F. G. Meyer and E. H. Walker, eds. Smithsonian Institution, Washington, DC. ix + 1067 pp.

Ornduff, R. 1978. Features of pollen flow in dimorphic species of Lythrum section Euhyssopifolia. Am. J. Bot. **65**(10): 1077–1083.

Palhinha, R. T. 1939. Flora de Portugal. 2nd ed. Bertrand (Ir-aos), Ltd., Lisbon, Portugal.

Pearsall, W. H. 1918. The aquatic and marsh vegetation of Esthwaite Water. J. Ecol. **6**: 53–74.

Perring, F. H. and Walters, S. M. 1962. Atlas of the British flora. Botanical Society of the British Isles, London, U.K.

Polunin, O. 1969. Field guide: flowers of Europe. Oxford University Press, London, U.K.

Pursh, F. 1814. Flora Americae Septentrionalis; or, a systematic arrangement and description of the plants of North America. 2 vols. White, Cochrane and Co., London, U.K.

Rawinski, T. J. 1982. The ecology and management of purple loosestrife (*Lythrum salicaria* L.) in central New York. M.S. thesis, Cornell University, Ithaca, NY. ix + 88 pp.

Rawinski, T. J. and Malecki, R. A. 1984. Ecological relationships among purple loosestrife, cattail and wildlife at the Montezuma National Wildlife Refuge. NY Fish and Game J. **31**: 81–87.

Reschke, P. 1990. The invader. Angler & Hunter Apr. pp. 16–18.

Richards, J. H., Diggle, P. K. and Barrett, S. C. H. 1989. A comparison of floral development among tristylous taxa of *Lythrum*, *Oxalis*, and the Pontederiaceae. Am. J. Bot. **76**(Suppl. 6): 53.

Rousseau, C. 1968. Histoire, habitat et distribution de 220 plantes introduites au Quebec. Naturaliste Canad. **95**: 49–169. Ludoviciana No. 5.

Rueppel, M. L., Brightwell, B. B., Schaefer, J. and Marvel, J. T. 1977. Metabolism and degradation of glyphosate in soil and water. J. Agric. Food Chem. **25**: 517–528.

Schoch-Bodmer, H. 1936. The proportion of long-, mid-, and short-styled plants in natural populations of *Lythrum salicaria* L. J. Genet. **36**: 39–43.

Schoch-Bodmer, H. 1938–1939. Die Veranderlichkeit der Pollengroke bei *Lythrum salicaria*. In Flora oder allgemeine botanische zeitung. O. Renner, ed. Jena, Verlag Von Gustav Fischer, Germany. pp. 69–110.

Shamsi, S. R. A. 1974. An interpretation of the distribution of *Epilobium hirsutum* and *Lythrum salicaria* in relation to their physiological ecology. Pak. J. Bot. **6**(2): 123–140.

Shamsi, S. R. A. 1976a. Effect of a light-break on the growth and development of *Epilobium hirsutum* and *Lythrum salicaria* in short photoperiod. Ann. Bot. **40**: 153–162.

Shamsi, S. R. A. 1976b. Some effects of density and fertilizer on the growth and competition of *Epilobium hirsutum* and *Lythrum salicaria*. Pak. J. Bot. **8**(2): 213–220.

Shamsi, S. R. A. and Whitehead, F. H. 1974a. Comparative eco-physiology of *Epilobium hirsutum* L. and *Lythrum salicaria* L. 1. General biology, distribution and germination. J. Ecol. **62**: 279–290.

Shamsi, S. R. A. and Whitehead, F. H. 1974b. Comparative eco-physiology of *Epilobium hirsutum* L. and *Lythrum salicaria* L. 2. Growth and development in relation to light. J. Ecol. **62**: 631–645.

Shamsi, S. R. A. and Whitehead, F. H. 1977a. Comparative eco-physiology of *Epilobium hirsutum* L. and *Lythrum salicaria* L. 3. Mineral nutrition. J. Ecol. **65**: 55–70.

Shamsi, S. R. A. and Whitehead, F. H. 1977b. Comparative eco-physiology of *Epilobium hirusutum* L. and *Lythrum salicaria* L. 4. Effects of temperature and inter-specific competition and concluding discussion. J. Ecol. **65**: 71–84.

Shipley, B., Keddy, P. A., Moore, D. R. J. and Lemky, K. 1989. Regeneration and establishment strategies of emergent macrophytes. J. Ecol. **77**: 1093–1110.

Shipley, B. and Parent, M. 1991. Germination responses of 64 wetland species in relation to seed size, minimum time to reproduction and seedling relative growth rate. Functional Ecol. **5**: 111–118.

Smith, L. S. 1959. Some experiences with control of purple loosestrife at the Montezuma National Wildlife Refuge. Proc. Northeast. Weed Control Conf. **13**: 333–336.

Smith. L. S. 1964. Experimental control of purple loosestrife (*Lythrum salicaria*). NY Fish Game J. **11**: 35–46.

Sohma, K. 1979. A study of the pollen grains of *Lythrum salicaria* and *L. anceps*. J. Jpn. Bot. **54**(2): 33–38.

Stevens, N. E. 1912. Observations on heterostylous plants. Bot. Gaz. **53**: 277–308.

Stevens, W. C. 1961. Kansas wild flowers. University of Kansas Press, Lawrence, KS. 461 pp.

Stirling, J. 1933. Studies of flowering in heterostyled and allied species. II. The Lythraceae: *Lythrum salicaria* Linn. Publications of the Hartley Botanical Laboratory **10**: 1–24.

Stirling, J. 1936. Studies of flowering in heterostyled and allied species. III. Gentianaceae, Lythraceae, Oxalidaceae. Publications of the Hartley Botanical Laboratory **15**: 1–24.

Stout, A. B. 1923. Studies of *Lythrum salicaria* — I. The efficiency of self-pollination. Am. J. Bot. **10**: 440–449.

Stout, A. B. 1925. Studies of *Lythrum salicaria* — II. A new form of flower in this species. Bull. Torrey Bot. Club **52**: 81–85.

Stuckey, R. L. 1980. Distributional history of *Lythrum salicaria* (purple loosestrife) in North America. Bartonia **47**: 3–20.

Tatebe, T. 1961. Physiological studies on the fertilization in *Lythrum salicaria* Linn. I. Presence of pollen-germination inhibitors in the ovary. Bot. Magazine (Tokyo) **74**: 291–296.

Teale, E. W. 1982. Stems beyond counting, flowers unnumbered. Audubon **84**: 38–43.

Thompson, D. Q., Stuckey, R. L. and Thompson, E. B. 1987. Spread, impact, and control of purple loosestrife (*Lythrum salicaria*) in North American wetlands. Fish and Wildlife Research 2. U.S. Department of the Interior, Fish and Wildlife Service, Washington, DC. 55 pp.

Tobe, H., Raven, P. H. and Graham, S. A. 1986. Chromosome counts for some Lythraceae sens. str. (Myrtales), and the base number of the family. Taxon **35**: 13–20.

Toivonen, H. and Back, S. 1989. Changes in aquatic vegetation of a small eutrophicated and lowered lake (southern Finland). Ann. Bot. Fennici **26**: 27–38.

Torrey, J. and Gray, A. 1840. A flora of North America. Vol. 1. Wiley and Putnam, New York, NY.

Tutin, T. G., Heywood, V. H., Burges, N. A., Moore, D. M., Valentine, D. H., Walters, S. M. and Webb, D. A. (editors). 1968. Flora Europea. Vol. 2. Cambridge University Press, Cambridge, U.K.

van't Haaff, G. 1968. My experience with purple loosestrife. Am. Bee J. **108**: 244.

Welling, C. H. and Becker, R. L. 1990. Seed bank dynamics of *Lythrum salicaria* L.: implications for control of this species in North America. Aquat. Bot. **38**: 303–309.

Whigham, D. F. and Simpson, R. L. 1976. The potential use of freshwater tidal marshes in the management of water quality in the Delaware River. Procedings of a Symposium on Biological Control of Water Pollution. J. Tourbier and R. W. Pierson, Jr., eds. University of Pennsylvania Press, Philadelphia, PA. pp. 173–186.

Wilcox, D. A. 1989. Migration and control of purple loosestrife (*Lythrum salicaria* L.) along highway corridors. Env. Manag. **13**(3): 365–370.

Woehler, E. E. and Henderson, R. A. 1986. Distribution of purple loosestrife in the Midwest. Proc. North central Weed Control Conf. **41**: 129.

Wymstra, T. A. 1969. Palynology of the first 30 meters of a 120 m deep section in northern Greece. Acta Bot. Neerl. **18**: 511–527.

The biology of Canadian weeds. 101. *Helianthus tuberosus* L.

C. J. Swanton[1], P. B. Cavers[2], D. R. Clements[1], and M. J. Moore[1]

[1]*Department of Crop Science, University of Guelph, Guelph, Ontario, Canada N1G 2W1; and* [2]*Department of Plant Sciences, University of Western Ontario, London, Ontario, Canada N6A 5B7. Received 23 March 1992, accepted 24 June 1992.*

Swanton, C. J., Cavers, P. B., Clements, D. R. and Moore, M. J. 1992. **The biology of Canadian weeds. 101.** *Helianthus tuberosus* **L.** Can. J. Plant Sci. 72: 1367–1382. *Helianthus tuberosus* L., Jerusalem artichoke, is a native perennial tuber-producing weed. In Canada, its range extends from the Maritimes to the Pacific coast, but it is primarily found in southern Ontario and Manitoba. A cultivated form has been grown commercially in Ontario and western Canada for use as a human food source, for livestock feed and for the production of a variety of chemical products such as ethanol. As a weed, *H. tuberosus* competes vigorously with grain and field crops, but does not readily invade arable land except as a volunteer crop. The high carbohydrate content of *H. tuberosus* tubers, coupled with multiple regenerative strategies featuring seeds and tuber-bearing rhizomes, can lead to rapid population increases under favorable conditions.

Key words: *Helianthus tuberosus*, Jerusalem artichoke, weed biology

Swanton, C. J., Cavers, P. B., Clements, D. R. et Moore, M. J. 1992. **Biologie des mauvaises herbes canadiennes. 101.** *Helianthus tuberosus* **L.** Can. J. Plant Sci. 72: 1367–1382. Le topinambour, *Helianthus tuberosus* L. est une plante vivace indigène au Canada. Son aire de répartition s'étend des provinces Maritimes à la côte du Pacifique bien qu'on le retrouve surtout dans le sud de l'Ontario et du Manitoba. Une forme cultivée est produite à l'échelle commerciale en Ontario et dans l'ouest du Canada pour l'alimentation de l'homme et des animaux ainsi que pour la fabrication de divers produits chimiques dont l'éthanol. À l'état sauvage, *Helianthus tuberosus* fait une vive concurrence aux céréales et aux autres grandes cultures mais elle n'envahit pas facilement les terres cultivées sauf comme repousse spontanée. La haute teneur en hydrates de carbone de ses tubercules, alliée à la multiplicité de ces mécanismes de régénération, semis et tubercules souterrains, peut, lorsque les conditions sont favorables, provoquer un accroissement rapide des peuplements.

Mots clés: *Helianthus tuberosus*, topinambour, biologie des mauvaises herbes

1. Name

Helianthus tuberosus L. — **Jerusalem artichoke; topinambour** (Alex et al. 1980); **earth apple; girasole; Canada potato; fusichoke; sunroot** (Wyse and Wilfahrt 1982). Kosaric et al. (1984) reported that there are about 102 common names associated with *H. tuberosus*. Asteraceae, Compositae, composite family, composeés.

2. Description and Account of Variation

(a) Jerusalem artichoke is a perennial, reproducing from seeds and spreading primarily by well-developed fleshy, tuber-bearing rhizomes. Clones of this species often appear in fields and at woodland edges with up to several hundred individual stems separated from each other by 10–12 cm or more. The plants are erect, often reaching heights of more than 2 m, varying from non-branching to branching growth forms (Stauffer et al. 1975). Among cultivated varieties, there is a large amount of variation, ranging from tall plants (over 2 m) with a single stalk, to bushy plants about 1.5 m in height with a lower above-ground biomass (Chubey and Dorrell 1982; Kiehn and Chubey

Can. J. Plant Sci. 72: 1367–1382 (Oct. 1992)

1985). The stems range in diameter from 1.6–3 cm, are often densely hairy and become woody with age. The leaves are simple, oval to lance shaped, with coarsely toothed edges on well-developed 2–8 cm petioles. The flower heads are bright yellow and resemble those of the cultivated sunflower, but are only 3–5 cm in diameter with a 1.5–2.3 cm disk (Wilkinson and Jaques 1979; Wyse and Wilfahrt 1982; Gleason and Cronquist 1991). They are produced at the ends of the main stems and axillary branches. Heads may be solitary or in corymbs. Very few (often <5) seeds are produced per flower head. The seeds (achenes) are grey or brown and often mottled with black, flattened, wedge-shaped and smooth (Alex and Switzer 1976) and are 6–8 mm long (Muenscher 1980) and about 2 mm wide.

Kulshreshtha and Gupta (1979) reported the chromosome number (*n*) of *H. tuberosus* to be 51.

(b) *Helianthus tuberosus* is distinguished by its tall erect stems, medium to large leaves (10–25 cm long and 4–12 cm wide) which are broad near the base and scabrous on the upper surface, its fleshy tuberous roots that generally resemble slender potatoes, and its bright yellow ray florets, typical of sunflowers (Muenscher 1980). The disk florets are also yellow. The disk flowers are not as crowded as those in the flowers of *Rudbeckia serotina* Nutt. (black-eyed Susan), and the 12–20 ray flowers are longer and more upright than in black-eyed Susan (Alex and Switzer 1976; Muenscher 1980). There are a number of closely related perennial sunflower species which may be confused with *H. tuberosus*. However, the leaves of *H. tuberosus* are generally larger than other *Helianthus* species, abruptly contracted or somewhat tapering to a winged petiole and quite thick. Also, the dark (dark green to purple-gray) phyllaries of *H. tuberosus* are 11–18 mm in length and loosely arranged about the disk (Clevenger and Heiser 1963; Gleason and Cronquist 1991). By comparison to *H. tuberosus*, *H. pauciflorus* Nutt. has broader phyllaries, *H. occidentalis* Riddell. and *H. decapetalus* L. have leaves more sharply set

off from the petiole and *H. giganteus* L. has much narrower leaves (Gleason and Cronquist 1991). It is advisable to check for tubers, which are a unique characteristic of *H. tuberosus*, in order to corroborate identifications based on other characteristics.

(c) Individual tubers are produced on the ends of rhizomes which may be more than 50 cm long (Swanton 1986). As many as 75 tubers may be produced per plant (Swanton 1986) but under some conditions plants are unable to produce tubers. Tubers vary in size and shape from round, knobby clusters 10 cm in diameter to slender, smooth swellings 15–20 cm long with a diameter of only a few centimetres occurring at the tips of the rhizome (Alex and Switzer 1976; Wyse and Wilfahrt 1982; Kiehn and Chubey 1985; Swanton 1986). The tubers may also vary in colour from white through pink to red (Wyse and Wilfahrt 1982). Cultivated varieties yield large tubers clustered near the main stem, whereas wild types produce smaller tubers at the ends of long rhizomes (Wyse and Wilfahrt 1982). Swanton and Cavers (1989) described a weedy population occurring in a soybean field with tubers intermediate between those of cultivated varieties and those typical of native Jerusalem artichoke from riverbank populations. The latter may produce no tubers at all in the southern part of the range (Gleason and Cronquist 1963).

Gleason and Cronquist (1963) reported that the variety *subcanescens* Gray (*Helianthus subcanescens*) is frequently found from Manitoba and Wisconsin to Montana and westward. This variety is shorter, approximately 1 m compared to over 2 m for *H. tuberosus* var. *tuberosus*. In variety *subcanescens* the uppermost leaves are opposite (Gleason and Cronquist 1991), but in variety *tuberosus* the lower leaves are opposite, the uppermost leaves alternate.

(d) The aboveground morphology of *Helianthus tuberosus* is illustrated in Fig. 1, featuring (i) a seed, (ii) a sprouting tuber, and (iii) a flowering adult. Figure 2 illustrates differences among tubers from four different biotypes of Jerusalem artichoke.

Fig. 1. Drawings of 1, a seed (×3.5), 2, a sprouting tuber (×1), and 3, a flowering adult of *Helianthus tuberosus* (×0.35).

3. Economic Importance

(a) *Detrimental* — Uncontrolled populations of Jerusalem artichoke can be a serious threat to successful crop production. According to Wyse et al. (1986) "Soybean producers in southern Canada and the midwestern United States are reporting that Jerusalem artichoke infestations are increasing in many fields". Jerusalem artichoke was listed as the 38th most abundant weed in two southern Ontario counties (Hamill et al. 1983). While it causes some weed problems in Ontario, Jerusalem artichoke is not generally of serious concern in other areas of Canada. However, the availability of high-yielding varieties has recently promoted increased cultivation in western Canada (Wall and Friesen 1989) and there is concern over its potential as a volunteer weed in rotations with grain crops.

Wyse and Young (1979) found that densities of 4 tubers/m of row of *H. tuberosus* reduced corn seed yields by 16–25%. They suggested that the lower corn seed yield was caused by a decrease in "fill length and the number of kernels per row of corn". Wyse et al. (1986) found that Jerusalem artichoke

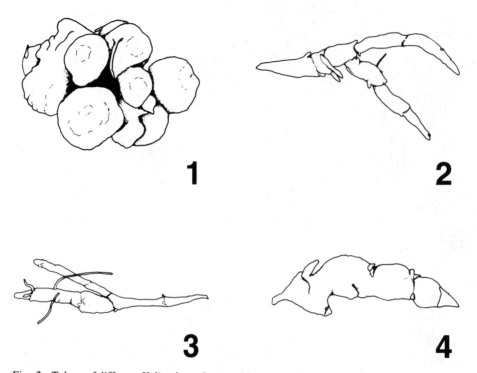

Fig. 2. Tubers of different *Helianthus tuberosus* biotypes collected in different habitats. 1, University (cultivated) (×0.4), 2, Parker (river bank) (×0.3), 3, Basteen (river bank) (×0.3), 4, Breschetti (soybean field) (×0.3).

densities of 1, 2 and 4 tubers per metre of row reduced soybean seed yield by 31, 59 and 71%, respectively. Soybean height, branches per plant, pods per plant and total seed weight were all reduced by the presence of Jerusalem artichoke (Wyse et al. 1986). Soybean leaf area and relative growth rate were reduced by densities of 2 and 4 artichoke tubers per metre of crop row and net assimilation rate was reduced by 4 tubers per metre of crop row (Wyse et al. 1986). Wall and Friesen (1989) found that 4–6 surviving Jerusalem artichoke shoots per square metre could reduce seed yield in barley by 20%. Jerusalem artichoke may also occur in pastures, but its high nutritional quality may render its presence desirable (Seiler 1988).

(b) *Beneficial* — High biomass yields, coupled with a reasonable nutrient value and a substantial level of carbohydrates, give Jerusalem artichoke a number of important applications. New varieties are being developed for high yields and nutrient content (Kiehn and Chubey 1985; Seiler 1988). The original use of this plant was as a food for humans and livestock. Its popularity in this role has fluctuated throughout the years.

Human Food Source. North American Indians appreciated Jerusalem artichoke as a readily available source of food. Early European colonists learned to value it as well (Shoemaker 1927).

Jerusalem artichoke tubers contain a polysaccharide known as inulin. Inulin was first isolated from tubers of Jerusalem artichoke in 1804 (Kosaric et al. 1984). Of all inulin-producing plant species (i.e., chicory, dahlia, dandelion and Canada thistle) Jerusalem artichoke is one of the highest yielding (Stauffer et al. 1981; Ernst 1989). Inulin has been recommended for inclusion in the diets of individuals suffering from diabetes

(Mayfield 1974; Wyse and Wilfahrt 1982) or obesity (Kosaric et al. 1985). It is thought that long-chain carbohydrates such as inulin are not readily metabolized by humans. The consumption of Jerusalem artichoke tubers would reduce the caloric intake, yet satisfy the necessary requirements for protein and minerals (Shoemaker 1927; Mayfield 1974; Kosaric et al. 1985). It is not certain whether inulin can be broken down within the human gastrointestinal system; however, if injected, inulin is excreted in large quantities by the kidneys in a short time (Cantarow and Shepartz 1957).

Seiler (1990) described Jerusalm artichoke tubers as containing "adequate protein and minerals to contribute significantly towards a nutritionally balanced diet". The tubers are a good source of B vitamins, pantothenic acid, potassium, phosphorus, vitamin A, iron and calcium (Kosaric et al. 1984). The mineral and trace element content of Jerusalem artichoke is comparable to or higher than that of other root crops (Seiler 1990). Total amounts of protein are approximately 5% wt wt^{-1} of the tuber on a dry weight basis (Kosaric et al. 1985). For human diets, the limiting essential amino acid in artichoke is methionine. Jerusalem artichoke contains 58% of the methionine found in eggs, while most other amino acids are present in excess of those found in eggs (Kosaric et al. 1985). In comparison, the protein content of the tubers is greater than or equivalent to that of most traditional crops such as soybeans, corn and wheat (Kosaric et al. 1985) and root crops such as potato, turnip and water chestnut (Seiler 1990).

Tubers of Jerusalem artichoke have been utilized in the manufacture of bread sticks, cookies, macaroni and noodles (Kosaric et al. 1985). The organoleptic properties of Jerusalem artichoke tubers are quite different from those of potatoes, even though artichokes are often considered as a substitute (Dallimonti 1979; Kosaric et al. 1985). Inulins do not swell like starch, and cooked tubers remain watery (Kosaric et al. 1985). The taste of raw tubers has been described as being similar to that of Chinese water chestnuts. Tubers are often eaten raw in salads

(Mayfield 1974; Wyse and Wilfahrt 1982). They may also be baked, and can be mashed and seasoned according to taste (Shoemaker 1927).

Livestock Feed. Jerusalem artichoke is nutritionally adequate for ruminants, but contains suboptimal levels of phosphorus (Seiler 1988). Cultivated genotypes are generally superior to wild genotypes in terms of nutrition. Little is reported on its palatability as forage, although Marten et al. (1987) found it was generally rejected by grazing lambs. There has been considerable interest in the use of the aerial plant parts as silage, with farmers reporting favorable results (Rawate and Hill 1985). Kosaric et al. (1984) reported silage yields of Jerusalem artichoke to range from 9 to 30 t ha^{-1}. These calculations were based on a 50–80% moisture content at harvest time. Wyse and Wilfahrt (1982) suggested that maximum silage yields could be obtained by harvesting at or just before flowering. The quality of silage has been described as inferior to that of corn (Boswell 1959; Kosaric et al. 1985), the composition of aboveground parts changing with advancing plant maturity. Generally, as the plant matures, increasing lignin and decreasing protein content lower the silage value (Kosaric et al. 1985) and decrease palatability (Wyse and Wilfahrt 1982; Kosaric et al. 1985). The "stillage" (tuber pulp) obtained after processing of the whole tuber mash for alcohol distillation contains residual sugars, mineral salts and proteins, making it of high nutritive value as an animal feed (Kosaric et al. 1985).

Ethanol Alcohol Production. The interest in Jerusalem artichoke for ethanol production stems primarily from the high potential yield of tubers per hectare and their relatively high carbohydrate content. Aerial plant parts may also provide a good source of fermentable sugars (Leible and Kahnt 1988). Fresh weight yields of tubers have been reported to range from 6.41 to 45.89 t ha^{-1} (Stauffer et al. 1975; Kosaric et al. 1984). Carbohydrate content in the tubers has reached as much as 27.7% of the fresh weight (Chubey and Dorrell 1974) or 80% of the dry weight (Kiehn and Chubey 1985). Tubers of Jerusalem artichoke can serve as a good source of fermentable sugars for the production of alcohol (Stauffer et al. 1975). At 80–90% conversion efficiency, it has been suggested that ethanol yields of 3900–4500 L ha^{-1} are attainable (Hayes 1981). Tubers of Jerusalem artichoke yielded 1.7, 2.0 and 3.7 times more alcohol per hectare than sugar beets, corn and wheat, respectively (Stauffer et al. 1975). During processing of the tubers for ethanol, proteins can also be extracted (Chabbert et al. 1985). *High-fructose Syrup Production.* If the fructose polymers of Jerusalem artichoke are not fermented to produce ethanol, they may be hydrolysed to form fructose (Malmberg and Theander 1986). Jerusalem artichoke tubers could provide a good source of fructose, since as much as 60% of the dry matter of Jerusalem artichoke is composed of fructose (Chubey and Dorrell 1974; Kierstan 1978; Kosaric et al. 1985). High-fructose syrups are important to the food industry. Fructose has a greater sweetening capacity than sucrose or D-glucose on an equivalent weight basis (Pawan 1973). Syrups with high fructose concentrations may be stored without danger of crystallization (Fleming and Grootwassink 1979). High-fructose syrups are not as susceptible to microbial contamination at equal concentrations, because of higher osmotic pressures than sucrose syrups (Kosaric et al. 1985). However, growing Jerusalem artichoke in southern Ontario for fructose production was not economically feasible, according to a study done in the 1980s (R. Roy pers. comm.).

Other Uses. In addition to these major uses, Jerusalem artichoke has also been studied as a substrate for the production of acetone and butanol, "fodder yeast", beer, lactic acid, propionic acid, mannitol and pectic substances (Kosaric et al. 1985).

(c) *Legislation* — Jerusalem artichoke is listed as a noxious weed, schedule A, Class number one, under the Nova Scotia Weed Control Act (Anonymous 1977b). It is also in a Schedule of weeds which may be declared noxious by the Lieutenant Governor in Council in the Manitoba Noxious Weeds Act (Anonymous 1977a). Sunflower (*Helianthus* spp. other than cultivated) presumably includes Jerusalem artichoke and is listed under Class 5 — other weed seeds in the Canada Seeds Act and Regulations of 1956 (Agriculture Canada 1967).

4. Geographical Distribution

Helianthus tuberosus is native to North America (Shoemaker 1972) and is thought to have originated in the Great Lakes area (Simmonds 1976) or possibly in the Ohio and Mississippi River valleys (Cockerell (1918) in Wyse et al. (1986)). It grows wild in many areas of the United States (Seiler 1990) and central Canada, while it may persist as a garden-escape or as a relic of old plantings in areas where it has been introduced such as southeastern Saskatchewan (Scoggan 1979). Jerusalem artichoke has also become naturalized in Nova Scotia (Roland 1946), Prince Edward Island (Erskine 1960), Quebec (Marie-Victorin 1964) and British Columbia, where it was introduced in the 1920s (Munro 1928). Its range extends throughout southeastern Canada and the eastern United States, westward to the Rocky Mountains (Gleason and Cronquist 1991) and southward to Georgia and Arkansas (Shoemaker 1927). It is also cultivated and becoming established on the Pacific coast (Muenscher 1980). Laberge and Sackston (1987a) reported that two cultivated varieties produced lower yields in Montreal, Quebec than in Morden, Manitoba, due to differences in latitude, climate, soils or agronomic practices. The geographic range, based on herbarium specimens from DAO, MT, TRT, OAC, UWO, LKHD, SASK, CAN, MTMG, ALTA and UBC, collections referred to in Clevenger and Heiser (1963) and Scoggan (1979) and data from Wilkinson and Jaques (1979), is shown in Fig. 3.

5. Habitat

(a) *Climatic requirements* — *H. tuberosus* is well adapted to grow in many geoclimatic regions, including Europe and most of North America (Kosaric et al. 1984). When *H. tuberosus* is cultivated, the growing season

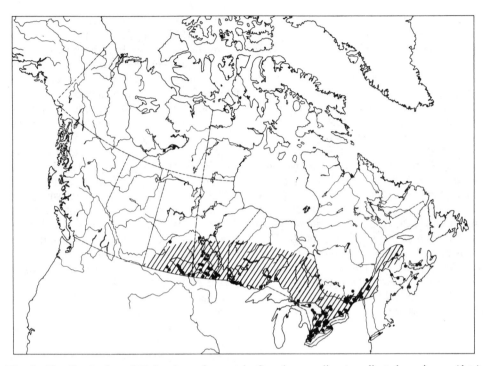

Fig. 3. The distribution of *Helianthus tuberosus* in Canada according to collected specimens (dots) and Wilkinson and Jaques (1979) (hatched area).

extends beyond that of conventional crops, owing to moderate frost tolerance (Stauffer et al. 1975). Frost may even improve tuber flavor (Mayfield 1974). Plants grown from seeds, rhizomes or tubers produce mature tubers in about 130 d. Boswell (1959) recommended growing Jerusalem artichoke only in areas with a growing season of 125 d or more. However, Jerusalem artichoke grows better in the northern United States than in the far south (Boswell 1959) and has been successfully grown in Alaska and the northern countries of Europe (Munro 1928). Jerusalem artichoke grows best in areas with ample rainfall, and irrigation of cultivated plants may be beneficial, particularly during tuber formation (Boswell 1959; Stauffer et al. 1981). Jerusalem artichoke seems less tolerant of dry conditions than other hexaploid wild sunflowers (Clevenger and Heiser 1963) although Mayfield (1974) reported that Jerusalem artichoke grew comparatively well in Kansas during a season featuring dry weather in July and August. Breaking of dormancy in the rhizomatous tubers is facilitated by temperatures of 5°C or less (Sueldo et al. 1991). Overwintering may be hindered in areas where tubers would tend to become dehydrated.

(b) *Substratum* — Jerusalem artichoke is able to grow on most soil types, and has minimal requirements for fertilizer (Dorrell and Chubey 1977; Kosaric et al. 1984). However, for commercial production, maximum yields require better soils and fertility levels. Growth of all biotypes is best on rich sandy loams, light loams, and well-drained river bottom or alluvial soils. Areas featuring these conditions provide the primary habitat for wild populations in the arid prairies (Budd and Best 1964).

(c) *Communities* — Jerusalem artichoke is frequently found in moist habitats such as river and stream banks, meadows and waste areas (Alex and Switzer 1976; Gleason and Cronquist 1991), as well as in cultivated fields (Wyse et al. 1986; Wall and Friesen 1989) and orchards (Roland 1946). Species commonly associated with Jerusalem artichoke in two grassland populations, mown once per year, in London Ontario are: *Saponaria officinalis* L., *Daucus carota* L. *Elytrigia repens* (L.) Nevski., *Asclepias syriaca* L., *Dactylis glomerata* L., *Achillea millefolium* L., *Trifolium pratense* L., *Plantago lanceolata* L., *Glechoma hederacea* L., *Taraxacum officinale* Weber, *Poa* sp. *Vicia* sp. and *Galium* sp. Weed populations of Jerusalem artichoke in southern Ontario have been found in corn, soybean and small grain fields. They are associated with other common weeds such as *Chenopodium album* L., *Amaranthus retroflexus* L., *Amaranthus powellii* Wats., *Abutilon theophrasti* Medic., *Setaria viridis* (L.) Beauv., *Ambrosia artemisiifolia* L. and *Sonchus* spp.

6. History

The first written record of Jerusalem artichoke (*Helianthus tuberosus*) was made by Samuel de Champlain in 1605, when he found it growing in Indian gardens near Cape Cod, Massachusetts (Shoemaker 1927). The Indians had domesticated this species, often cultivating the tubers along with corn and beans (Shoemaker 1927; Mayfield 1974). Tubers were consumed either raw, boiled or roasted (Mayfield 1974). Champlain, having tasted the tubers, described the flavour as being similar to that of globe artichoke, *Cynara scolymus* L. (Shoemaker 1927; Wyse and Wilfahrt 1982).

Lesearbot, a companion of Champlain during his early explorations of North America, has been credited with introducing Jerusalem artichoke into France (Shoemaker 1927). At that time potatoes were not grown outside South America. In fact they were not even known in Europe until after the Seven Year's War from 1756 to 1763 (Mayfield 1974). Artichoke tubers quickly gained in popularity and were soon being cultivated both for the table and as a food for livestock (Mayfield 1974) possibly under the name of "topinambour" (Shoemaker 1927). Shoemaker (1927) suggested that the name "topinambour" may have been used at that time by French merchants, in order to capitalize on the advertising value of six natives from a Brazilian Indian tribe known as "Tupinambas", who came to Paris in the early 1600s and had become popular with the French aristocracy.

From France, the tubers spread throughout the Mediterranean Region. In Italy they were grown in the famous Farnese gardens and called "girasole articiocco", or sunflower artichoke (Shoemaker 1927; Mayfield 1974; Wyse and Wilfahrt 1982). Girasole derives from "girare", to turn, and "sole", the sun (Wyse and Wilfahrt 1982). "Articiocco" means edible, which is true of the tubers (Wyse and Wilfahrt 1982).

Tubers of "girasole articiocco", as they were now known, reached England in 1616 or 1617 (Shoemaker 1927) and were at first considered a rare delicacy, "dainties for a queen" (Mayfield 1974). It is believed that at that time the tubers became known as Jerusalem artichokes (Shoemaker 1927). The name Jerusalem artichoke, as mentioned by Shoemaker (1927) has been a source of confusion, since it is neither descriptive nor true. The name Jerusalem most likely came from an English mispronunciation of the Italian "girasole" (Mayfield 1974). Jerusalem artichokes were soon grown extensively in England. However, the ease with which they were grown and propagated soon made them too common, and they became despised (Mayfield 1974).

7. Growth and Development

(a) *Morphology* — Although Jerusalem artichoke grows either from seeds or from underground parts such as tubers or rhizomes, it is usually grown commercially from tubers (Chubey and Dorrell 1982; Kiehn and Chubey 1985). Mazza (1985) noted that the tuber skin is relatively thin and that moisture content decreases towards the tuber's periphery.

Once established, Jerusalem artichoke plants exhibit a rapid increase in plant height, number of leaves and tubers through one life cycle (Swanton and Cavers 1989). This robust growth habit enables *H. tuberosus* to outcompete most other plant species in arable land. Munro (1928) reported that "The artichoke-crop has been suggested as a weed-eradicator, for it makes such a dense shade that it practically smothers out most competing plants".

(b) *Perennation* — New ramets may arise continuously over several years from tubers, although some varieties overwinter better than others (Kiehn and Chubey 1985). Tubers are susceptible to dehydration at the soil surface (Swanton and Cavers 1988), and thus are likely sensitive to cool, dry winter conditions even when buried. Carbohydrates are stored in the tubers and rhizomes to maintain the clone throughout the winter and provide a ready energy source for rapid spring growth which provides a competitive advantage for Jerusalem artichoke. Dormant seeds provide a further means of perennation.

(c) *Physiology* — Researchers have found that the total reducing sugar content of Jerusalem artichoke tubers increases as they enlarge and mature in the fall (Bacon and Loxley 1952; Chubey and Dorrell 1983), which implies that substances of high molecular weight are formed during the period of carbohydrate storage. Both storage proteins and carbohydrates are primarily accumulated in tubers, to sustain them through the winter (Mussigman and Ledoigt 1989). Swanton and Cavers (1989) demonstrated that allocation to clonal growth takes precedence over sexual reproduction (49% versus 2.6%) in a normal year in southwestern Ontario.

The reducing sugar concentration of tubers can be lowered significantly through the use of supplemental irrigation throughout tuber formation (Dorrell and Chubey 1977). The reducing sugar content also decreases with the initiation and growth of tuber sprouts in the spring (Chubey and Dorrell 1983). In a study of the changes in tuber composition associated with the development of daughter plants, Jefford and Edelman (1960) discovered that the fructosan of the tuber contributed markedly to the growth of the new plants. During the first seven weeks after planting,

80% of the tuber dry weight disappeared and most of this material was translocated to the growing plant. Approximately 85% of the loss in dry weight was accounted for by a parallel disappearance of polymerized fructose.

The main type of carbohydrate found in Jerusalem artichoke is a homologous series of polyfructofuranose units, consisting of linear chains of D-fructose molecules terminated by a D-glucose molecule (Kosaric et al. 1984). The terminology used to identify these carbohydrates has not always been consistent (Kosaric et al. 1984). The name inulin is often used to describe all such polysaccharides consisting largely of fructose units. Stauffer et al. (1981) reported inulin to be those carbohydrates with a degree of polymerization from 9 to 35 fructose molecules. Fleming and Grootwassink (1979) considered inulin to be only those polyfructans of 30 or more moieties in length.

Wright and Raison (1981) found that the development of hardiness and a lower transition temperature of mitochondrial membranes were initiated under conditions which inhibited growth. This occurred in situations of low temperature for nondormant tubers, the onset of tuber rest in the field, and the induction of dormancy by abscisic acid. Their findings suggested that senescence of the aboveground plant parts and the onset of tuber rest could be more important than low temperatures in altering the mitochondrial membranes and inducing hardening in Jerusalem artichoke, and that once initiated, membrane changes appeared to be under genetic control. Plasma membranes also undergo changes which are probably related to acclimation to lower temperatures (Ishikawa and Yoshida 1985).

Hogetsu et al. (1960) observed that the respiration rate was highest in the young apical leaf and decreased as leaf age increased. The respiration rate of the older leaves appeared to converge towards some constant value between 0.7 and 1.0 mg CO_2 g^{-1} h^{-1}. The higher the population density, the sooner the maximum growth rate of each plant was attained. Maximum growth rates (ratio of the increase in dry weight to the total dry weight) of approximately 0.075 g g^{-1} d^{-1} were observed for Jerusalem artichoke. (d) *Phenology* — Growth begins from tubers or seeds in April or May. A period of rapid vegetative growth follows. Flower buds appear from early July to late September depending upon the strain and location. The stolons enlarge at the onset of flowering and tubers are initiated (Kosaric et al. 1984). In Southwestern Ontario, Swanton (1982) reported that rhizomes and tubers began to form by 13 July. The stem is the major sink for assimilates when the leaves are photosynthetically active (Incoll and Neales 1970). In the late summer leaf senescence begins and there is a shift in sucrose translocation to the tubers, which rapidly enlarge until frost stops any further growth. Jerusalem artichoke is a short day plant with respect to tuberization (Hamner and Long 1939).

(e) *Mycorrhiza* — No mycorrhizal associations have been reported.

8. Reproduction

(a) *Floral biology* — Jerusalem artichoke is pollinated by insects and is an outcrosser that requires pollination from distinctly different populations to set seeds (Wyse and Wilfahrt 1982; J.F. Alex pers. comm.). Cool temperatures at the time of full bloom can decrease the potential for successful fertilization and seed development, and any major detriment to growth that delays reproduction may prevent seed formation (Swanton and Cavers 1989). Because it flowers so late, Jerusalem artichoke is regarded as a good late-season source of pollen and nectar (Cirnu 1988).

(b) *Seed production and dispersal* — Very few Jerusalem artichoke florets develop into seeds (Mayfield 1974). Reports on seed production range from 3 to 50 seeds per inflorescence (Russell 1979; Wyse and Wilfahrt 1982). Jerusalem artichoke biotypes differ in terms of tuber size, regenerative capacity and seed production (Swanton and Cavers 1988, 1989). Swanton (1986) found that two cultivated biotypes produced 8 and 66 seeds/100 inflorescences, two weed biotypes 126 and 197 seeds/100 inflorescences and two naturally occurring riverbank biotypes

493 and 536 seeds/100 inflorescences. All of these were grown in field plots in London, Ontario. Inflorescences per plant were 6 and 36 for the cultivated biotypes, 37 and 78 for the weed biotypes and 16 and 30 for the riverbank biotypes. Seed production per plant was calculated as 0.4 and 24 for the cultivated biotypes, 47 and 154 for the weed biotypes and 79 and 163 for the riverbank biotypes. Mean weight per seed in the cultivated and weedy biotypes was between 4.76 and 4.81 mg, which was higher than the 3.45 and 4.41 mg seed weights from the two riverbank populations.

(c) *Viability of seeds and germination* — The seeds of *H. tuberosus* are dormant after maturity; however, Wyse and Wilfahrt (1982) reported that the dormancy could be broken by a cold treatment of 1.7°C for a period of 7 d. The seeds are largely infertile (Lukens 1982). Although few plants would generally originate from seed, seed production is important for maintaining genetic diversity. Seed production may be more important among naturally occurring riverbank populations (see 8b above).

(d) *Vegetative reproduction* — The regeneration of buried rhizome fragments and tubers is an important contribution to rapid Jerusalem artichoke population increases. Methods of regeneration include: vegetative expansion by an extensive rhizome system, vegetative propagation from tubers, pieces of tubers, and pieces of rhizomes (Swanton and Cavers 1988). Gaspar et al. (cited in Russell 1979) reported that the tubers exhibit a postharvest dormancy that could be broken by adding gibberellic acid or a cold treatment of 0°C for 2–3 mo. Swanton and Cavers (1988) suggested that neither rhizomes nor tubers could survive more than 1 yr in the soil in southern Ontario. Cultivation that splits up a rootstock before new tubers have been formed stimulates regeneration from rhizomes (Swanton and Cavers 1988). However, Swanton and Cavers (1988) observed a higher frequency of regeneration from tubers than from rhizomes, particularly from deeper planting depths. The percentage of rhizomes and tubers regenerating also depended on planting date. Regeneration from both tubers and rhizomes was lower for rhizomes and tubers taken from the plant and planted at the time of rapid flower development (1 September) than for rhizomes and tubers planted later (15 October).

9. Hybrids

H. tuberosus is a hexaploid that can be crossed with *H. annuus* L. This cross produces plants with shorter stolons and larger tubers, thus enabling easier commercial harvesting (Kosaric et al. 1984). Kostoff (1939) theorized that part of the *H. tuberosus* hexaploid genome was synonymous with the genome of the diploid *H. annuus*. Jerusalem artichoke also produces fertile crosses with *H. laetiflorus* Pers., *H. subrhomboideus* Rydb. and *H. rigidus* (Cass.) Desf. (Clevenger and Heiser 1963; Dorrell and Whelan 1978). Clevenger and Heiser (1963) speculated that *H. rigidus* and particularly *H. laetiflorus* are hybrids descended from *H. tuberosus* and *H. subrhomboideus*. *H. giganteus* and *H. maximiliani* Schrad. are other species that may provide useful genetic crosses (Kosaric et al. 1984). Analysis of these species and the hybrids that are possible can provide useful variability in characteristics for both sunflower and Jerusalem artichoke breeding programs.

10. Population Dynamics

Biological factors accounting for the success of Jerusalem artichoke within diverse habitats include: (i) a high expenditure of energy on initial growth of stem, branches and leaves; (ii) a large amount of energy allocated to the production of rhizomes and tubers; (iii) a phalanx-like growth morphology, facilitating capture of both above- and below-ground resources; (iv) mobility of nutrients within the plant; (v) seed production; (vi) the ability to regenerate even if severely defoliated; and (vii) the constancy of nutrient allocation to clonal structures (Swanton and Cavers 1989). These factors are complemented by resistance to most diseases and pests, and tolerance of poor soils (Kosaric et al. 1984). However, these characteristics primarily favour the

maintenance of clonal populations already established, rather than colonization of new habitats. Since seed production is low and seeds are not highly dispersive, *H. tuberosus* is not often seen invading disturbed areas. Thus, it is likely to manifest its weediness more as a volunteer crop (Wall and Friesen 1989).

H. tuberosus becomes self-limiting at high densities (Hogetsu et al. 1960), having an optimal planting density of about 30 000 ha^{-1} (Kosaric et al. 1984). Fewer tubers per plant are produced under crowded conditions (Russell 1979). *H. tuberosus* grows well in the presence of competitors. Crop yields of these species did not differ significantly between hand-weeded and weedy check plots monitored by Wall et al. (1987). Weed control is only necessary in the early stages of growth, until the plants are about 0.5 m in height (Kosaric et al. 1985). Conversely, as a weed, Jerusalem artichoke must be controlled early. Wyse et al. (1986) recommended that in soybeans, Jerusalem artichoke growth be controlled within 6 wk of planting because of its strong competitive ability. Both rhizomes and tubers can overwinter in the soil and produce shoots the following year (Vanstone and Chubey 1978). However, excavations in November in London, Ontario revealed largely decaying rhizomes attached to healthy tubers. New shoots may arise throughout the growing season whenever rhizomes and tubers are fragmented and dispersed as a result of tillage.

11. Response to Herbicides and other Chemicals

Long-term control of shoot growth from rhizomes and tubers is essential for successful crop production in fields containing populations of *H. tuberosus*. Commercially acceptable control of top growth was achieved following applications of glyphosate at ≥ 1.0 kg active ingredient (a.i.) per hectare, or dicamba plus 2,4-D plus mecoprop at 0.6 and 1.2 kg a.i. ha^{-1} (Vanstone and Chubey 1978). Atrazine applied preplant or postemergence with oil at rates ≥ 4.5 kg a.i. ha^{-1} as well as postemergence applications of glyphosate or 2,4-D ester at rates of ≥ 2.2 kg a.i. ha^{-1} or 0.56 kg a.i. ha^{-1}, respectively, also gave good control (Russell and Stroube 1979). Swanton (1982) suggested that greater than 90% control of both top growth and regrowth of new shoots could be achieved in corn using split applications of dicamba at 0.28 kg a.i. ha^{-1} or dicamba plus 2,4-D plus mecoprop at 0.55 kg a.i. ha^{-1}, provided that the split application was separated by a period of 10–14 d. Wall et al. (1986) found that Jerusalem artichoke was controlled in barley by a postemergence application of clopyralid at 1.0 kg a.i. ha^{-1}, or clopyralid at 0.5 kg ha^{-1} if combined with 0.5 kg a.i. ha^{-1} of 2,4-D, or dicamba at 0.2 kg a.i. ha^{-1} plus 2,4-D at 0.4 kg ha^{-1}. The combination of clopyralid and 2,4-D was the most effective (Wall and Friesen 1989). Chemical control is most effective at the pre-bloom stage of growth, both top growth and tuber regrowth are controlled and further infestation is reduced (Swanton 1982).

In a study to determine the tolerance of Jerusalem artichoke to selective herbicides, Wall et al. (1987) found that Jerusalem artichoke exhibited good tolerance to preplant incorporated applications of trifluralin, ethalfluralin, pendimethalin, chloramben and EPTC but was not tolerant to metribuzin applications.

12. Response to other Human Manipulations

Eliminating *H. tuberosus* by cultural and/or chemical means is difficult because of the underground rhizomes and tubers. Crop rotations that include small grain crops, such as wheat, barley and oats, may reduce the reproductive capabilities of Jerusalem artichoke. Studies conducted in Minnesota have shown that a single Jerusalem artichoke plant growing in a stand of hard red spring wheat, produced only 1–2 tubers during a growing season, while a single Jerusalem artichoke plant growing in a stand of corn or soybeans, produced 50–60 tubers (Wyse and Wilfahrt (1982).

Wyse and Wilfahrt (1982) suggested that repeated mowings or tillage may reduce populations of Jerusalem artichoke over a period of 1–2 yr, provided they were timed prior to the formation of new rhizomes and tubers. Russell (1979) studied the effects of multiple mowings on *H. tuberosus* and found that stand populations could be reduced by 80% within a year.

Waters et al. (1981) found that increased fertilizer (nitrogen and potassium) increased yields of *H. tuberosus* primarily by increasing tuber size, while higher population densities limited individual tuber growth.

13. Response to Parasites and Herbivores

(a) *Insects* — Larvae of the sunflower stem maggot, *Strauzia longipennis* (Wied.) were reported to cause wilting, chlorosis, and necrosis of leaves of Jerusalem artichoke plants in a disease nursery at Macdonald College of McGill University where sunflowers had been grown continuously for over 20 yr (Laberge and Sackston 1987b). The following insects have been collected from Jerusalem artichoke: northern corn rootworm [*Diabrotica longicornis* (Say)], ladybird beetle (*Adalia bipunctata* L.), potato leafhopper [*Empoasca fabae* (Harris)], granary weevil (*Sitophilus granarius* L.), and honey bee (*Apis mellifera* L.) (Swanton, unpubl. data). Sunflower beetles tend to reject Jerusalem artichoke (Stauffer et al. 1975). Jerusalem artichoke also acts as a host to the weevil *Cosmobaris americana* Casey which attacks sugar beets (Landis et al. 1970) and the treehopper, *Publilia concava* (Say) (Quisenberry et al. 1978).

(b) *Microorganisms* — Conners (1967) lists the following fungi on Jerusalem artichoke in Canada: *Erysiphe cichoracrarum* DC ex Mérat, *Puccinia helianthi* Schw., and *Sclerotinia sclerotiorum* (Lib.) de Bary. Other fungi identified from leaf samples include *Alternaria alternata* (Fr.) Keissler and *Alternaria tenuissima* (Kunze: Pers.) Wiltshire (Swanton, unpubl. data). Johnson (1931) reported *Botrytis cinerea* Pers., *Rhizopus nigricans* Ehr. and *Fusarium* and *Penicillium* spp. were most frequently associated with tubers stored under refrigeration in Minnesota.

McCarter and Kays (1984) identified a southern blight caused by *Sclerotium rolfsii* Sacc. and tuber rots caused by either *S. rolfsii* during the growing season, or by *Fusarium* and *Pseudomonas* spp. during refrigerated or field storage and *Puccinia helianthi* and *Erysiphe cichoraciearum* to be the most important diseases of Jerusalem artichoke in Georgia from 1980 to 1982. Shane and Baumer (1984) identified an apical chlorosis and leaf spot of Jerusalem artichoke incited by *Pseudomonas syringae* pv. *tagetis* Hellmers in Minnesota. Sprouts of Jerusalem artichoke that emerged through the soil, often did not survive if severely infected with this disease. Infections occurring after the plants were well established in the field generally caused only slight stunting. Laberge and Sackston (1987a) also identified apical chlorosis caused by *P. syringae* pv. *tagetis* in Quebec, but yield losses were much lower.

(c) *Mammals* — The suitability of aboveground parts of Jerusalem artichoke for livestock grazing was discussed previously (see 3b). Aboveground parts are also a potential source of browse for other mammalian herbivores, and additionally the tubers may provide a good source of carbohydrates for wildlife. Fairly extensive disturbance of the soil within populations of Jerusalem artichoke was observed at two sites in London, Ontario in November and December.

ACKNOWLEDGMENTS

We gratefully acknowledge the financial support of the Ontario Ministry of Agriculture and Food and the Natural Sciences and Engineering Research Council of Canada. We are most thankful to Marguerite Kane for producing the drawings. We thank Kevin Chandler for his assistance and Beth Livingstone for typing the manuscript. Assistance of participating herbariums is appreciated, especially that of Carole Anne Lacroix of the Ontario Agricultural College herbarium.

Agriculture Canada. 1967. Seeds Act and Regulations. Queen's Printer Ottawa, ON. 50 pp.

Alex, J. F., Cayouette, R. and Mulligan, G. A. 1980. Common and botanical names of weeds in Canada. Research Branch, Agriculture Canada, Ottawa, ON. Publ. 1397, 132 pp.

Alex, J. F. and Switzer, C. M. 1976. Ontario weeds. Ontario Ministry of Agriculture and Food, Publ. 505, p. 154.

Anonymous. 1977a. The Noxious Weed Act, Manitoba. Schedule of weeds which may be declared noxious by the Lieutenant Governor in Council. Chapter N110. Queen's Printer, Winnipeg, MB.

Anonymous. 1977b. Regulations to the Weed Control Act (Nova Scotia). Publication 10. Queen's Printer, Halifax, NS.

Bacon, J. S. D. and Loxley, R. 1952. Seasonal changes in the carbohydrates of the Jerusalem artichoke tuber. Biochem. J. **51:** 208–213.

Boswell, V. R. 1959. Growing the Jerusalem artichoke. USDA Leaflet No. 116, Washington, DC.

Budd, A. C. and Best, K. F. 1964. Wild plants of the Canadian Prairies. Queen's Printer, Ottawa, ON.

Cantarow, A. and Schepartz, B. 1957. Biochemistry. Saunders, Philadelphia, PA.

Chabbert, N., Guiraud, J. P. and Galzy, P. 1985. Protein production potential in the ethanol production process from Jerusalem artichoke. Biotech-lett. **7:** 443–446.

Chubey, B. B. and Dorrell, D. G. 1974. Jerusalem artichoke, a potential fructose crop for the prairies. Can. Inst. Food Sci. Technol. J. **7:** 98–100.

Chubey, B. B. and Dorrell, D. G. 1982. Columbia Jerusalem artichoke. Can. J. Plant Sci. **62:** 537–539.

Chubey, B. B. and Dorrell, D. G. 1983. The effect of fall and spring harvesting on the sugar content of Jerusalem artichoke tubers. Can. J. Plant Sci. **63:** 1111–1113.

Cirnu, I. 1988. Artichoke and Jerusalem artichoke: Two valuable late sources of nectar and pollen. Apicultura-in Romania **63**(7): 7–8.

Clevenger, S. and Heiser, C. B., Jr. 1963. *Helianthus laetiflorus* and *Helianthus rigidus* — Hybrids or species? Rhodora **65:** 121–133.

Conners, I. L. 1967. Annotated index of plant diseases in Canada and fungi recorded on plants in Alaska, Canada and Greenland. Agriculture Canada, Ottawa, ON. Publ. 1251, 381 pp.

Dallimonti, L. 1979. The alternative potato. Org. Gard. Farm. **26**(6): 34–36.

Dorrell, D. G. and Chubey, B. B. 1977. Irrigation, fertilizer, harvest dates and storage effects on the reducing sugar and fructose concentrations of Jerusalem artichoke tubers. Can. J. Plant Sci. **57:** 591–596.

Dorrell, D. G. and Whelan, E. D. P. 1978. Chemical and morphological characteristics of seeds of some sunflower species. Crop Sci. **18:** 969–971.

Ernst, M. 1989. Inulin in vegetable plants of the Compositae family. Gartenbauwissenschaft **54:** 249–252.

Erskine, D. S. 1960. The plants of Prince Edward Island. Canada Department of Agriculture, Ottawa, ON. Publ. 1088, 270 pp.

Fleming, S. E. and Grootwassink, J. W. D. 1979. Preparation of high fructose syrup from the tubers of the Jerusalem artichoke (*Helianthus tuberosus*). CRC Crit. Rev. Food Sci. Nutr. **12:** 1.

Gleason, H. A. and Cronquist, A. 1963. Manual of vascular plants of northeastern United States and adjacent Canada. van Nostrand, Princeton, NJ. 810 pp.

Gleason, H. A. and Cronquist, A. 1991. Manual of vascular plants of northeastern United States and Adjacent Canada. The New York Botanical Garden, Bronx, NY.

Hamill, A. S., Wise, R. F. and Thomas, A. G. 1983. Weed survey of Essex and Kent counties 1978 and 1979. Agriculture Canada Weed Survey Series, Regina, SK. Publ. No. 83-1, 134 pp.

Hamner, K. C. and Long, E. M. 1939. Localization of photoperiodic perception in *Helianthus tuberosus*. Bot. Gaz. (Chicago) **101:** 81–90.

Hayes, R. D. 1981. Energy crops — what little we know. Proceedings of the 3rd Bioenergy R and D Seminar. March 24-25, Ottawa, ON.

Hogetsu, K. J., Oshima, Y., Midorikawa, B., Tezuka, Y., Sakamoto, M., Mototani, I. and Kimura, M. 1960. Growth analystical studies on the artificial communities of *Helianthus tuberosus* with different densities. Japan. J. Bot. **17:** 278–305.

Incoll, L. D. and Neales, T. F. 1970. The stem as a temporary sink before tuberization in *Helianthus tuberosus* L. J. Exp. Bot. **21:** 469–476.

Ishikawa, M. and Yoshida, S. 1985. Seasonal changes in plasma membranes and mitochondria isolated from Jerusalem artichoke tubers. Possible relationship to cold hardiness. Plant Cell Physiol. **26:** 1331–1334.

Jefford, T. G. and Edelman, J. 1960. Changes in content and composition of the fructose polymers in tubers of *Helianthus tuberosus* L. during growth of daughter plants. J. Exp. Bot. **12:** 177–187.

Johnson, H. W. 1931. Storage roots of the Jerusalem artichoke. J. Agric. Res. **43:** 337–352.

Kiehn, F. A. and Chubey, B. B. 1985. Challenger Jerusalem artichoke. Can. J. Plant Sci. **65:** 803–805.

Kierstan, M. P. J. 1978. Production of fructose syrups from inulin-containing plants. Biotech. Bioeng. **20:** 447–450.

Kosaric, N., Cosentino, G. P., Wieczorek, A. and Duvnjak, Z. 1984. The Jerusalem artichoke as an agricultural crop. Biomass **5:** 1–36.

Kosaric, N., Wieczorek, A., Cosentin, G. P. and Duvnjak, Z. 1985. Industrial processing and products from the Jerusalem artichoke. Adv. Biochem. Eng. Biotech. **32:** 1–24.

Kostoff, D. 1939. Autosyndesis and structural hybridity in F_1 hybrid *Helianthus tuberosus* L. × *Helianthus annuus* L. and their sequences. Genetics **21:** 285–300.

Kulshreshtha, V. B. and Gupta, P. K. 1979. Cytogenetic studies in the genus *Helianthus* L. Cytologia **44:** 325–334.

Laberge, C. and Sackston, W. E. 1987a. Adaptability and diseases of Jerusalem artichoke (*Helianthus tuberosus*) in Quebec. Can. J. Plant Sci. **67:** 349–352.

Laberge, C. and Sackston, W. E. 1987b. Diseases of Jerusalem artichoke in Quebec in 1984. Phytoprotection **66:** 173.

Landis, B. J., Peay, W. E. and Fox, L. 1970. Biology of *Cosmobaris americana* Casey, a weevil attacking sugar beets. J. Econ. Entomol. **63:** 38–41.

Leible, L. and Kahnt, G. 1988. Effect of location, nitrogen fertilization and harvest date on the yield of fermentable sugars of Jerusalem artichoke tops and tubers. J. Agron. Crop Sci. **161:** 339–352.

Lukens, T. 1982. Jerusalem artichoke for ethanol production. Northern Agricultural Energy Center, Peoria, IL.

Malmberg, A. and Theander, O. 1986. Differences in chemical composition of leaves and stem in Jerusalem artichoke and changes in low-molecular sugar and fructan content with time of harvest. Swedish J. Agric. Res. **16:** 7–12.

Marie-Victorin, Fr. 1964. Flore Laurentienne, 2nd Edition. Presses de l'Université de Montréal, Montréal, PQ. 924 pp.

Marten, G. C., Sheaffer, C. C. and Wyse, D. L. 1987. Forage nutritive value and palatability of perennial weeds. Agron. J. **79:** 980–986.

Mayfield, L. 1974. The Jerusalem artichoke. Horticulture **52:** 53–54.

Mazza, G. 1985. Distribution of sugars, dry matter and protein in Jerusalem artichoke tubers. Can. Inst. Food Sci. Technol. J. **18:** 263–265.

McCarter, S. M. and Kays, S. J. 1984. Diseases limiting production of Jerusalem artichokes in Georgia. Plant Dis. **68:** 299–302.

Muenscher, W. C. 1980. Weeds. Second Edition with a new forward and three new appendixes by P.A. Hyypio. Cornell University Press, Ithaca, NY.

Munro, J. B. 1928. The Jerusalem artichoke (*Helianthus tuberosus*). Province of British Columbia Field Crop Circular No. 6. Queen's Printer, Victoria, BC. 8 pp.

Mussigmann, C. and Ledoigt, G. 1989. Major storage proteins in Jerusalem artichoke tubers. Plant Physiol. Biochem. **27:** 81–86.

Pawan, G. L. S. 1973. Molecular structure and function of food carbohydrates. G. G. Birch and L.F. Green, eds. Applied Science Publishers, London, U.K. 65 pp.

Quisenberry, S. S., Yonke, T. R. and Lopp, D. D. 1978. Key to the genera of certain immature treehoppers of Missouri with notes on their host plants (Homoptera: Membracidae). J. Kansas Entomol. Soc. **51:** 109–122.

Rawate, P. D. and Hill, R. M. 1985. Extraction of a high-protein isolate from Jerusalem artichoke (*Helianthus tuberosus*) tops and evaluation of its nutrition potential. J. Agric. Food Chem. **33:** 29–31.

Roland, A. E. 1946. The flora of Nova Scotia. Truro Printing and Publishing, Truro, NS. 552 pp.

Russell, W. E. 1979. The growth and reproductive characteristics and herbicidal control of Jerusalem artichoke (*Helianthus tuberosus*). Ph.D. thesis, Ohio State University. 86 pp.

Russell, W. E. and Stroube, E. W. 1979. Herbicidal control of Jerusalem artichoke. North Central Weed Control Conference **34:** 48–49.

Scoggan, H. J. 1979. Flora of Canada, Part 4-Dicotyledonae (Loasaceae to Compositae). National Museum of Natural Sciences Publications in Botany. National Museums of Canada, Ottawa, ON. 200 pp.

Seiler, G. J. 1988. Nitrogen and mineral content of selected wild and cultivated genotypes of Jerusalem artichoke. Agron. J. **80:** 681–687.

Seiler, G.J. 1990. Protein and mineral concentrations in tubers of selected genotypes of wild and cultivated Jerusalem-artichoke (*Helianthus tuberosus*, Asteraceae). Econ. Bot. **44:** 322–335.

Shane, W. W. and Baumer, J. S. 1984. Apical chlorosis and leaf spot of Jerusalem artichoke incited by *Pseudomonas syringae* pv *tagetis*. Plant Disease **68(3):** 257–260.

Shoemaker, M. D. 1927. The Jerusalem artichoke as a crop plant. USDA Tech. Bull. 33, 32 pp.

Simmonds, N. W. (ed). 1976. Evolution of Crop Plants. Longmans Press, New York, NY. 37 pp.

Stauffer, M. D., Chubey, B. B. and Dorrell, D. G. 1975. Jerusalem artichoke. Canadex No. 164, Canada Department of Agriculture Research Station, Morden, MB.

Stauffer, M. D., Chubey, B. B. and Dorrell, D. G. 1981. Growth, yield and compositional characteristics of Jerusalem artichoke as they relate to biomass production. Page 79 *in* Fuels from biomass and wastes. D. K. Klass and G. M. Emert, eds. Ann Arbor Science Publishers Inc., Ann Arbor, MI.

Sueldo, R., Gendraud, M. and Coudret, A. 1991. Water status and water movements in tubers of *Helianthus tuberosus* L. during dormancy and breaking of dormancy. Agronomie **11:** 65–74.

Swanton, C. J. 1982. Jerusalem artichoke — crop or weed? Highlights of Agricultural Research in Ontario **5(1):** 17–19.

Swanton, C. J. 1986. Ecological aspects of growth and development of Jerusalem artichoke (Helianthus tuberosus L.). Ph.D. thesis, University of Western Ontario.

Swanton, C. J. and Cavers, P. B. 1988. Regenerative capacity of rhizomes and tubers from two populations of Jerusalem artichoke (*Helianthus tuberosus*). Weed Res. **28:** 339–345.

Swanton, C. J. and Cavers, P. B. 1989. Biomass and nutrient allocation patterns in Jerusalem artichoke (*Helianthus tuberosus*). Can. J. Bot. **67:** 2880–2887.

Vanstone, D. E. and Chubey, B. B. 1978. Herbicides for control of volunteer Jerusalem artichoke. Can. J. Plant Sci. **58:** 571–572.

Wall, D. A. and Friesen, G. H. 1989. Volunteer Jerusalem artichoke (*Helianthus tuberosus*) interference and control in barley (*Hordeum vulgare*). Weed Tech. **3:** 170–172.

Wall, D. A., Kiehn, F. A. and Friesen, G. H. 1986. Control of Jerusalem artichoke (*Helianthus tuberosus*) in barley (*Hordeum vulgare*). Weed Sci. **34:** 761–764.

Wall, D. A., Kiehn, F. A. and Friesen, G. H. 1987. Tolerance of Columbia Jerusalem artichoke to selective herbicides. Can. J. Plant Sci. **67:** 835–837.

Waters, L., Jr., Davis, D. W., Riehle, J. and Weins, M. 1981. Jerusalem artichoke trials. Department of Horticulture, University of Minnesota.

Wilkinson, R. E. and Jaques, H. E. 1979. How to know the weeds. 3rd ed. Wm. C. Brown Company, Dubuque, IA. 235 pp.

Wright, L. C. and Raison, J. K. 1981. Correlation between changes in mitochondrial membranes of artichoke tubers and their hardening and dormancy. Plant Physiol. **68:** 919–923.

Wyse, D. L. and Wilfahrt, L. 1982. Today's weed: Jerusalem artichoke. Weeds Today. Spring 1982: 14–16.

Wyse, D. L. and Young, F. L. 1979. Jerusalem artichoke interference in corn and soybeans. North Central Weed Control Conference **34:** 48.

Wyse, D. L., Young, F. L. and Jones, R. J. 1986. Influence of Jerusalem artichoke (*Helianthus tuberosus*) density and duration of interference on soybean (*Glycine max*) growth and yield. Weed Sci. **34:** 243–247.

The biology of Canadian weeds. 102. *Gaultheria shallon* Pursh.

Lauchlan Fraser[1], Roy Turkington[1], and C. P. Chanway[2]

[1]*Botany Department, University of British Columbia, Vancouver, British Columbia, Canada V6T 1Z4; and* [2]*Department of Forest Sciences, University of British Columbia, Vancouver, British Columbia, Canada V6T 1Z4. Received 21 July 1992, accepted 24 March 1993.*

Fraser, L., Turkington, R. and Chanway, C. P. 1993. **The biology of Canadian weeds. 102.** *Gaultheria shallon* **Pursh.** Can. J. Plant Sci. **73**: 1233–1247. *Gaultheria shallon* Pursh., salal (Ericaceae), is a densely growing perennial evergreen shrub occurring only from the panhandle of Alaska along the entire coast of British Columbia to southern California; it is of native origin. Salal grows on a wide range of soil types and textures, and is abundant in open habitats near the coast particularly on rocky knolls and along bluffs. It is a persistent, pervasive woody perennial and is a serious competitor with coniferous species. The plant produces numerous seeds but the most significant and effective form of colonization is through vegetative spread. Several herbicides are recommended for control of the the weed but it is both resistant and resilient to many herbicides. This contribution summarizes the known biological data for this species.

Key words: *Gaultheria shallon*, salal, evergreen shrub, weed biology, competition

Fraser, L., Turkington, R. et Chanway, C. P. 1993. **Biologie des mauvaises herbes du Canada. 102.** *Gaultheria shallon* **Pursh.** Can. J. Plant Sci. **73**: 1233–1247. *Gaultheria shallon* Pursh., le salal (Ericacées), est un arbrisseau pérenne, touffu, à feuilles persistantes, que l'on ne retrouve, dans son habitat d'origine, que sur la côte du Pacifique, de la bande côtière sud (le "Manche-de-poêle") de l'Alaska à la Colombie-Britannique et jusqu'au sud de la Californie. Il pousse sur un vaste assortiment de types et de textures de sols. Il est abondant dans les habitats ouverts près de la côte, en particulier sur les buttes rocheuses et le long des escarpements. C'est une vivace ligneuses, persistante et envahissante, qui crée une grosse concurrence aux conifères. La production grainière est abondante, mais la plante se propage surtout par voie végétative. Plusieurs herbicides sont recommandés, mais la plante résiste à de nombreuses préparations. Le mémoire récapitule les données biologiques connues concernant cette espèce.

Mots clés: *Gaultheria shallon*, salal, arbrisseau à feuilles persistantes, biologie des mauvaises herbes, concurrence

1. Name

Gaultheria shallon Pursh. — **salal** (Scoggan 1978), **shallon** (Conners 1967), **lemon leaves** (Anonymous 1970); **wintergreen** genus, Ericaceae, Heath or Heather Family, (Hitchcock and Cronquist 1973), Éricacées.

2. Description and Account of Variation

(a) A sparse to densely growing perennial, evergreen shrub (Fig. 1) ranging from nearly prostrate to erect. *Gaultheria shallon* forms an extensive shallow root system with very fine roots (0.1-2.0 mm in diameter) and rhizomatous-like structures spreading from a central point. Stem 0.5–2.5 m high, creeping to upright, smooth, but may become scored with age. Twigs green when young, pilose to hirsute, and often glandular. Mature twigs red or brown. Buds 1.0–1.5 cm long, usually green but sometimes tinged red, ovoid and acute-tipped. Leaves alternate and petiolate; persistent, leathery and shiny; ovate to ovate-elliptic, 3-10 cm × 3-5 cm, sharply serrulate; margins often finely toothed. Petioles 2-4 mm long. Flowers 5–15 in terminal and sub-terminal bracteate racemes that appear one-sided because pedicels are deflexed; racemes usually 5–12 cm long. Bracts reddish,

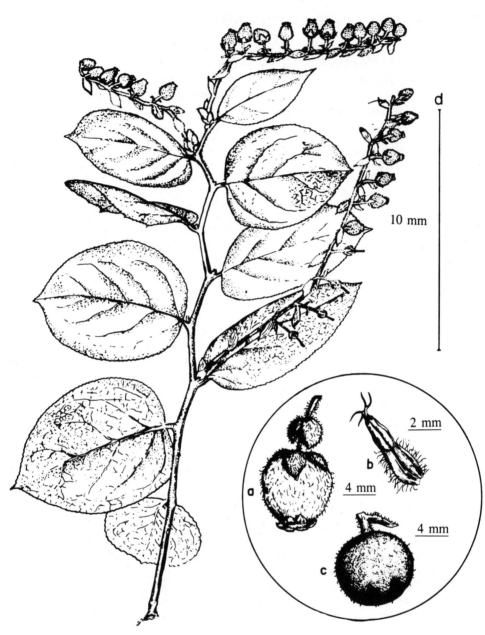

Fig. 1. *Gaultheria shallon* Pursh. (a) single flower (b) stamen (c) fruit (d) mature plant.

6–10 cm long and prominent. Calyx lobes triangular to lanceolate, glandular-pilose and red in color, usually 1/3 to 1/2 length of corolla, but often increasing in size with age.

Corolla white or pinkish, urn-shaped, with five short recurved lobes, glandular, and sticky, 6–11 mm. Stamens 10; filaments basally expanded; anthers with four slender apical awns, opening by terminal pores; superior ovary, multiple seeds. Fruit a depressed capsule 6–10 mm thick, purplish-black, berry-like because of the thickening of the calyx at its base, fleshy, pubescent (Szczawinski 1962; Hitchcock and Cronquist 1973). The chromosome base number is 11; the chromosome somatic number is 88 (Taylor and MacBryde 1977).

(b) The most distinguishing feature of salal is its large leaves which are ovate, shiny green and leathery. Leaves live for approximately 2-4 yr but can persist for as long as 6 yr (Koch 1983; Haeussler and Coates 1986). Another distinguishing feature is the hairy, dark purplish fruits. Fruits persist for several months after maturation (between August and October); eventually they dry up and drop off in December. However, some fruits can remain on the plant considerably longer. *Gaultheria miqueliana* Takeda is similar to salal but is found only in east Asia, and the westernmost Aleutian Islands (Scoggan 1978). *Gaultheria miqueliana* racemes with rarely over six flowers, these to about 5 mm, and with white fruit. *Gaultheria shallon* racemes are many-flowered, up to 8 mm long, and purplish black fruit.

(c) Variability of morphology has been reported for *G. shallon* in the size and shape of leaf, stem and rhizome. However, no subspecies or varieties have been described (Hitchcock and Cronquist 1973). The presence of altitudinal ecotypes is possible but not probable (Pojar 1974).

3. Economic Importance

(a) *Detrimental* — *Gaultheria shallon* is a persistent and pervasive plant and is considered a serious competitor with coniferous species, particularly Douglas-fir (*Pseudotsuga menziesii*) on semi-xeric sites in low-elevation coastal British Columbia (Tan et al. 1977; Stanek et al. 1979; Price et al. 1986). On wetter sites. *G. shallon* competes with young planted seedlings of western red cedar (*Thuja plicata*), western hemlock (*Tsuga heterophylla*), Pacific silver fir (*Abies amabilis*) and Sitka spruce (*Picea sitchensis*)

following clear-cut logging (Germain 1985; Weetman et al. 1990; Messier 1991). Harmful effects from salal on their neighbours vary from reduced growth to chlorosis of the needles and mortality of tree seedlings. Considering that in coastal British Columbia salal is dominant in at least 10 000 ha of cedar-hemlock forests (Barker et al. 1987; Weetman et al. 1990), and slightly fewer hectares of Douglas-fir forests (Nuszdorfer et al. 1991), the economic loss to the forest industry is potentially very high. Presently, the added expenditure of site preparation and management on salal-dominated sites is substantial (C. Fox, personal communication). In addition, salal can grow so rapidly that most plantable sites may become occupied and nearly impossible to clear manually.

(b) *Beneficial* — Salal forms a very large rooting system with many fine roots and associated microorganisms (mycorrhizae and rhizophere bacteria) in only a few years following clearcutting. Therefore, salal maintains nutrients in the system that would otherwise have been leached and lost. Furthermore, the roots may act to reduce soil erosion on recently disturbed sites and contribute to the organic matter content of the soil (Sabhasri 1961). The leaves of salal also contribute to the organic matter content of the soil, as well as cycling nutrients back into the soil. When salal is abundant, the leaf litter is very large and may serve as a mulch, thus reducing evapotranspiration. This trait is particularly useful in dry habitats. *Gaultheria shallon* has also been recommended for coastal sand dune stabilization (Brown and Hafenrichter 1962).

The young leaves, twigs and berries of salal are an important food source for many animals, in particular, for black-tailed deer, which is the major big game species of the Pacific Northwest (McTaggart-Cowan 1945; Singleton 1976; Crouch 1979; Jones and Bunnell 1984; Chambers 1988). Other animals which feed on salal include ruffed grouse, blue grouse and other birds (Martin et al. 1951; King 1969; Zwickel and Bendell 1972; Viereck and Little 1972; King and Bendell 1982), black bears, Roosevelt elk (Bailey

1966; Singleton 1976), mountain beaver (Banfield 1974), and small mammals (e.g. red squirrel (Dimock et al. 1974). Sheep will also eat young, tender salal leaves which has recently led to their introduction into salal-dominated areas.

Salal is a very attractive plant used by land-scapers and florists. Florists use the leaves as a foliage supplement (trade name "lemon leaves") for cut flower arrangements (Anonymous 1970). Salal is also grown commercially in greenhouses. In 1980 salal had an annual retail value of approximately $2 million in BC (Hunt 1980).

Salal berries are nutritious and plentiful and were known to be a staple food source for the native peoples of British Columbia (Turner

1975). The berry was prepared many ways but the main form was as a dried fruit for winter food. As well, native Indians smoked the leaves with kinnikinnick (*Arctostaphylos uva-ursi*) and used it for medicinal purposes (Gunther 1945).

4. Geographical Distribution

Gaultheria shallon occus from the panhandle of Alaska (56°N) along the entire British Columbia coast continuing to southern California (34.5°N) (Fig. 2). All recorded populations in BC occur west of the Coast Mountains except for a single isolated population along the east shore of southern Kootenay Lake (Szczawinski 1962; Calder and Taylor 1968). *Gaultheria shallon* has

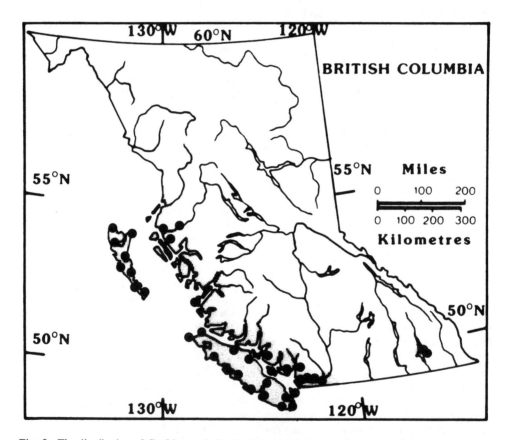

Fig. 2. The distribution of *Gaultheria shallon* in British Columbia (adapted from Szczawinski (1962), Haeussler et al. (1990), and Hultén (1968). The shaded area indicates the general distribution, while the individual points represent the locations where herbarium samples were collected.

been introduced to England, but is found nowhere else in the world.

Gaultheria shallon is found mainly at lower elevations. In its southern range it can be found up to approximately 800 m (Lyons 1952), in the north salal rarely exceeds 100-200 m elevation.

5. Habitat

(a) *Climatic requirements* — Salal is restricted to a humid to perhumid coastal climate with mild temperatures, little snow, and unfrozen soils in winter. It is abundant on open habitats near the coast particularly on rocky knolls and along bluffs (Calder and Taylor 1968), where it can withstand gale force winds. Salal is sensitive to frost (Paul Bavis, personal communication). Sabhasri (1961) observed that a short period of freezing temperature in the middle of May killed nearly all germinants. Although salal can grow under dense forest canopies in 0.3% full sunlight, the vigour, growth rate and flowering of salal increases as the light intensity increases (Sabhasri 1961; Stanek et al. 1979; Koch 1983; Messier et al. 1989; Bunnell 1990; Messier 1993). However, best growth is in partial shade rather than in full sunlight (Anonymous 1970; Dimock et al. 1974; Koch 1983).

Characteristic of many trees, shrubs, and herbaceous plants salal leaf morphology differs dramatically under different light intensities. Sun leaves develop in bright light, whereas shade leaves develop under low light levels. Sun leaves characteristically have prostrate stems and small, thick blades. Shade leaves are found on taller, more erect plants with larger but thinner blades. Smith (1991) found that sun leaves had a mean specific leaf area less than 90 cm^2 g^{-1}; and shade leaves were greater than 90 cm^2 g^{-1}. At 1.8% full sunlight (80% canopy cover), leaves were almost three times larger in area than they were in a clearing (Messier et al. 1989). Under deep shade (0.3% full sunlight), Messier et al. (1989) reported that leaves were similar in size to those in the clearing, but only half the dry weight. Smith (1991) reported that sun leaves of salal require at least 10% full photosynthetically active radiation (PAR), less than 10% of PAR will result in the formation of shade leaves.

(b) *Substratum - Gaultheria shallon* grows on a wide range of soil types and textures including peat, glacial till, sand dunes, and shallow rocky soils. It is most commonly found on Podzols, often with deep mor humus forms, but is also found on Folisolic, Brunisolic and organic soils (Klinka et al. 1979). Moist sandy or peaty soil is the best medium for cultivation. It does not grow well in alkaline soil conditions (Anonymous 1970). Salal exhibits vigorous upright growth in shaded conditions, good soil and plenty of moisture (Anonymous 1970). However, if the soil is poor salal often produces a low mat-forming habit. Salal can often be found growing in old stumps and decaying wood, and will also grow epiphytically on living trees in extremely humid climates (Anonymous 1970). Sabhasri (1961) has demonstrated that salal can survive and grow on soils of low fertility, but the addition of nutrients produces a definite growth response.

(c) *Communities in which the species occurs* — Using the biogeoclimatic classification for British Columbia (Krajina 1965), *G. shallon* occurs predominantly in the Coastal Western Hemlock and the Douglas-fir zones, i.e. lowland coniferous coastal forests. In the Douglas-fir zone, the species with which salal usually grows are *Pseudotsuga menziesii* var. *menziesii*, *Abies amabilis*, *Thuja plicata*, *Mahonia nervosa*, *Vaccinium parvifolium*, *Rosa gymnocarpa*, *Pteridium aquilinum*, *Rubus ursinus*, *Symphoricarpos mollis*, *Kinbergia oregana*, *Hylocomium splendens* and *Phytidiadelphus triquetrus* (Nuszdorfer et al. 1991). The species with which salal usually grows in the Coastal Western Hemlock zone are shown (Table 1).

6. History

Gaultheria shallon is of native origin throughout its present range. Salal is the Coastal Indian name for the plant. When David Douglas landed in Oregon in 1825, Haskin (1934; cited in Szczawinski 1962) reported

Table 1. Zonal vegetation of subzones of the Coastal Western Hemlock biogeoclimatic zone (adapted from Pojar et al. (1991)). vh, very wet hypermaritime; xm, very dry maritime; dm, dry maritime; mm, moist maritime; vm, very wet maritime. *Gaultheria shallon* is not present in the wh (wet hypermaritime), wm (wet maritime), ds (dry submaritime), ms (moist submaritime), and ws (wet submaritime) subzones. Percent cover classes, a — 0.1–1%, b — 2–5%, c — 6–10%, d — 11–25%, e — 26–99%

Botanical name	vh	xm	dm	mm	vm	Common name
Gaultheria shallon	**e**	**e**	**b**	**d**	**d**	**salal**
Abies amabilis	–	–	–	d	d	amabilis fir
Acer circinatum	–	–	b	–	–	vine maple
Achlys triphylla	–	b	–	b	–	vanilla-leaf
Blechnum spicatum	c	–	–	–	c	deer fern
Chamaecyparis nootkatensis	d	–	–	b	–	yellow-cedar
Chimaphila umbellata	–	a	–	a	–	prince's pine
Coptis aspleniifolia	a	–	–	–	–	fern-leaved goldthread
Cornus canadensis	b	–	–	b	b	bunchberry
Hylocominm spledens	d	d	c	b	b	step moss
Listera cordata	a	a	–	a	a	heart-leaved twayblade
Mahonia nervosa	–	c	–	a	–	dull Oregon grape
Maianthemum dilatatum	a	–	–	–	–	false lily-of-the-valley
Menziesia ferruginea	b	–	a	a	b	false azalea
Picea sitchensis	b	–	–	–	–	Sitka spruce
Plagiothecium undulatum	a	a	d	a	b	flat moss
Polystichum munitum	–	b	b	–	–	sword fern
Pseudotsuga menziesii	–	e	e	d	–	Douglas fir
Pteridium aquilinum	–	b	b	–	–	bracken fern
Rhytidiadelphus loreus	e	b	b	d	d	lanky moss
Rubus pedatus	–	–	–	a	–	five-leaved bramble
Rubus ursinus	–	a	a	–	–	trailing blackberry
Scapania bolanderi	b	–	–	–	–	
Thuja plicata	d	c	d	d	c	western redcedar
Tiarella trifoliata	–	–	–	a	–	three-leaved foamflower
Tsuga heterophylla	d	d	e	e	e	western hemlock
Vaccinium alaskaense	b	–	a	d	d	Alaskan blueberry
Vaccinium ovalifolium	a	–	–	a	b	oval-leafed blueberry

that "he was so impressed by the sight of salal he could scarcely see anything else. Throughout all his journey in the west, the salal was one of Douglas' favorites and he held great hopes of introducing it into England, and making of it a cultivated fruit."

7. Growth and Development

(a) *Morphology* — *Gaultheria shallon* has slow initial growth for approximately the first 2 yr, but once it is established it spreads vegetatively very rapidly by means of rhizomes (Messier 1991). The length and complexity of the rhizomes of an individual salal plant in an area dominated by salal has not been determined but Koch (1983) found new shoots up to 2 m from the parent plant. Bunnell (1990) observed a strong tendency for daughter shoots to be clumped around the mother shoot under sparse canopies, whereas daughter shoots were farther away from the oldest shoots under closed canopies. Salal accumulates considerable biomass in a growing season, but mainly through the expansion of rhizomes leading to the production of new shoots, not through significant increase in the height of pre-existing shoots (Sabhasri 1961).

Salal's ability to respond to a continuum of understory light conditions by producing either sun leaves or shade laves (Messier et al. 1989; Smith 1991) is important to its survival. Under dense stands salal can persist by forming shade leaves; in clearings or in openings of otherwise dense stands, salal forms sun leaves. Another important adaptive characteristic to capture light is stem elongation which responds to high red light levels

(Sabhasri 1961; Vales 1986) occurring in dense stands (Messier et al. 1989).

Leaves of *G. shallon* have a thin epicuticular layer that consists mostly of triterpenes, and always contains ursolic acid; this material also had traces of external flavonoid agylcones, namely galangin-3-methyl ether (Wollenweber and Kohorst 1984). Salasoo (1981, 1988) determined the patterns of alkane distribution in the epicuticular wax of *G. shallon* and detected rimuene. The wax was 28% hydrocarbon.

The pollen tetrad diameter of *Gaultheria shallon* has been calculated by Hebda (1978) from a sample size of 100 tetrads collected in Burns Bog, Delta, BC. The mean tetrad diameter is 46.97 μm, with a range of 41–53 μm and a standard deviation of 2.50. Hebda (1978) postulated that small tetrads (41–44.5 μm) indicate growth of salal in dry conditions, intermediate tetrads (44.6–49.5 μm) imply dry to intermediate habitats or fire, and large tetrads (49.6–53 μm) reflect wet sites.

(b) *Perennation* — Individual shoots may survive for 10–15 yr, but leaves are rarely older than 4 yr before senescence (Haeussler and Coates 1986). Shoots will bear leaves only during the first few years (Koch 1983). Rhizomes have the potential to continue reproducing vegetatively if there is sufficient light through the forest overstory (gaps and sunflecks) for shoot growth. Bunnell (1990) found extensive mats of salal rhizomes in conifer stands between 80 and 110 yr old, even when aboveground salal densities were low. During winter, salal is virtually dormant and is very sensitive to frozen soils and frost (Sabhasri 1961).

(c) *Physiological data* — Salal is at least a moderately shade-tolerant species (Sabhasri 1961; Koch 1983) but its photosynthetic and respiration characteristics are consistent with a shade-intolerant plant species (Sabhasri 1961). For an actively growing plant it was found that at low light intensities (6.06 μmol m^{-2} s^{-1}) respiration was greater than photosynthesis. Photosynthetic activity and seedling growth significantly increased with increased light intensities up to the maximum

level tested (24.24 μmol m^{-2} s^{-1}) (Sabhasri 1961). Maximum growth occurs under red light (Sabhasri 1961). Bunnell (1990) reported that the cost of flowering was shared across connected shoots of a plant, showing there is physiological integration between ramets.

(d) *Phenology* — The maximal growth of salal (roots, rhizomes, shoots and leaves) is between late April and August, peaking in early June. Vegetative buds burst in early April (Sabhasri 1961). Flowering can occur anytime between March and July depending on the area (Dimock et al. 1974). In Alaska, flowering occurs between March and June (Viereck and Little 1972). Near Vancouver, BC, Pojar (1974) reported flowering between 12 June and 4 July. In Washington state, flowering begins in the 3rd week of June. Fruits ripen between August and October and remain on the stem until December (Dimock et al. 1974).

(e) *Mycorrhizae* — Largent et al. (1980) reported that *G. shallon* can be associated with three different kinds of mycorrhizae: arbutoid, ericoid, and ectomycorrhizae. Three different fungal species have been identified, one is *Oidiodendron griseum* Robak and the taxonomic position of the other two species are being studied (Xiao and Berch 1992). This is the first report of *O. griseum* as an ericoid mycorrhizal fungus of *Gaultheria*.

8. Reproduction

(a) *Floral biology* — *Gaultheria shallon* flowers are pollinated by insects, primarily bumblebees and flies (Pojar 1974). The fruit is a many-seeded capsule, and each inflorescence has 5–15 capsules. However, Bunnell (1990) found that salal will flower only when two conditions are met: on vigorous stems greater than 4 yr old, and at a mean crown completeness (a measure of forest canopy closure) less than 30%. Hebda (1982) found that *Gaultheria shallon* contributed less than 2% of the pollen and spore rain in areas dominated by salal, indicating how little salal flowers.

(b) *Seed production and dispersal* — The fruits of salal remain on the stem until December and those seeds remaining are viable for up to 1 yr following ripening (Dimock et al. 1974). Fruits have an average of 126 seeds each. When conditions are suitable for flowering, heavy crops of fruit are produced on a regular basis (Haeussler et al. 1990). Seeds are dispersed mainly by the animals which feed upon the fruit: black-tailed deer, Roosevelt elk, mountain beaver, ruffed grouse, blue grouse, and other small mammals and birds (Halverson 1986).

(c) *Viability of seeds and germination* — Seeds can remain viable for several years in cold, dry storage, but the viability of seeds under natural conditions is generally much reduced (Dimock et al. 1974), Sabhasri (1961) stored seeds at 4.4°C for 1 yr and found a decline in germination from 31 to 21%. Seeds do not require chilling (Haeussler et al. 1990) or stratification (McKeever 1938) to induce germination. Successful germination requires moist, acidic sites under partial shade (Dimock et al. 1974) and light for 8 h or more per day is essential (McKeever 1938). In Washington, germination rates of 27–35% from fresh seed under lighted conditions were reported (Sabhasri 1961; Dimock et al. 1974). In British Columbia, Messier (personal communication) obtained germination rates of approximately 60% under the same conditions.

Despite the large quantity of seeds produced and the many seeds which germinate, seedling survival is very low (Haeussler et al. 1990). Sabhasri (1961) found that in Western Washington, seedling establishment is most successful in the understory of young Douglas-fir stands.

(d) *Vegetative reproduction* — The most significant and effective form of colonization is through vegetative spread, both in open habitats and in deep shade. Once salal is present on a site, further expansion is almost exclusively by vegetative means (Sabhasri 1961; Koch 1983; McGee 1988; Messier 1991) including layering and suckering from roots and stem bases. However, among the 54 naturally growing plants that Bunnell (1990) examined, no evidence of stem layering was found; rhizomes were the only means of producing new shoots. Bunnell (1990) forced stems into the organic mat and examined them 1 yr later to find that they had grown adventitious roots, and concluded that layering must also occur naturally. He found, while monitoring the colonization of salal, that 85% of the space occupied by salal after 9 yr of growth was occupied during the first 3 yr. Bunnell also observed that the vegetative reproduction of ramets was negatively associated with age ($r^2 = 0.95$) and that no new shoots were produced after an individual ramet reached 9 yr of age. Seed production may be significant in the initial colonization of a newly disturbed area (e.g. windthrow, clearcut), but considering that a plant must be at least 4 yr old before it will flower, and that most colonization of an area occurs within the first 3 yr, the vast majority of colonization occurs through vegetative spread. Bunnell (1990) found no seed production, only vegetative spread, at a mean crown completeness greater than 30%.

9. Hybrids

Gaultheria shallon does not naturally hybridize with any other species (Pojar 1974). However, an artificial hybrid between *G. shallon* and *Pernettya mucronata* has been produced in England (Dimock et al. 1974).

10. Population Dynamics

The rate of increase of salal populations depends largely on the stage of succession of the area. Messier (1991) proposed a general growth model based on the work of Messier (1991), Messier and Kimmins (1991), Messier et al. (1989), Vogt et al. (1987), and Vales (1986) (Fig. 3) of the development of salal over a 60-yr period following a major disturbance (e.g. clear-cutting and slashburning) of old-growth western red cedar and western hemlock forests on northern Vancouver Island. The development of the live fine-root, leaf, stem and rhizome biomass of salal has three different stages. Stage one is between

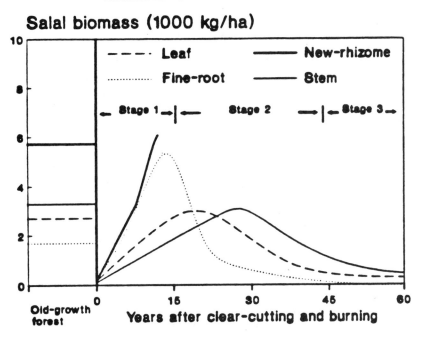

Salal biomass (1000 kg/ha)

Fig. 3. Hypothetical development of fine-root, leaf, stem and rhizome abundance of *Gaultheria shallon* over a 60-yr period following the clear-cutting and burning of old-growth forests of western redcedar and western hemlock on northern Vancouver Island (taken from Messier (1991)).

1 and 15 yr and is characterized by a rapid growth rate of rhizomes and fine-roots, in particular, between 8 and 15 yr. Stage two, approximately between 16 and 45 yr, begins with a rapid decline in salal live fine-root biomass followed by a more gradual decrease in leaf and stem biomass. The decline of the population is caused by shading due to an increase in the overstory tree canopy. There are no data for rhizome biomass in the 10- to 60-yr period, but it is believed to be high (Messier 1991). The final stage, occurring from 46 yr until the next major disturbance, is the virtual exclusion of salal by the dense overstory canopy. However, it is not completely excluded and can quickly re-establish following a disturbance.

Much research effort has been focused on the competitive interactions of salal and coniferous tree species in low-elevation coastal British Columbia forests (Tan et al. 1978; Black et al. 1980; Price et al. 1986; Weetman et al. 1989a; Klinka et al. 1989;

Bunnell et al. 1990; Messier et al. 1990; Messier 1991). The competitive influence of salal on the seedlings of Douglas-fir, western hemlock, and Sitka spruce is believed to be much stronger than on western red cedar and lodgepole pine (Bunnell et al. 1990). Competition is most severe during the early stages of stand development (Long 1977) but may continue through the rotation, in particular, if the canopy is open enough to allow a well-developed understory of salal to persist (Stanek et al. 1979).

Young stands of Douglas-fir on sub-xeric sites are limited by soil water potential (Tan et al. 1977). At low values of soil water potential, the reduction in stomatal conductance is greater for Douglas-fir than for salal, indicating that salal transpiration would account for a higher proportion of total stand transpiration (Tan et al. 1978). Price et al. (1986), found that the removal of the salal understory of thinned 32-yr-old Douglas-fir significantly increased rates of photosynthesis and tree growth due to an increase in the soil water potential. Other researchers have proposed that salal may be competing for nutrients in the Douglas-fir forests (Stanek et al. 1979; Haeussler and Coates 1986).

There is evidence to suggest that salal may also be competitive in moist ecosystems (Weetman et al. 1989b; Messier 1991). Two hypotheses have been proposed to account for this. First, is the resource exploitation hypothesis. Weetman et al. (1989a,b) have shown that on northern Vancouver Island western red cedar and western hemlock cutovers that are dominated with salal are nutrient deficient. Germain (1985) and Messier (1991) found that salal can have an impact on the nutrient budget for conifers. *Gaultheria shallon* forms three symbiotic fungal associations: ericoid-, arbutoid- and ecto-mycorrhizae (Largent et al. 1980), whereas western red cedar and western hemlock only form one fungal association each: endomycorrhizae and ectomycorrhizae, respectively. Therefore, *G. shallon* might be more efficient at extracting nutrients such as nitrogen and phosphorus at low pH, and accessing nutrients in complex organic forms (Xiao, Cade-Menum and Berch, personal communication). Parke et al. (1983) suggest that dense salal can lower soil temperatures causing reduced conifer growth by inhibiting root growth and mycorrhizal infection. The second hypothesis involves the possible allelopathic properties of salal. Del Moral and Cates (1971) did not find convincing evidence for allelopathy in salal, but Rose et al. (1983) have shown that allelochemicals in salal litter may inhibit seedling growth. It has been suggested that salal may have an allelopathic effect through the production of tannins and phenolic acids (de Montigny, personal communication).

Gaultheria shallon can be classified as a stress-tolerator with a low R (the level of resource below which the population is unable to maintain itself) (Messier 1991). Evidence that salal has a low R is its ability to maintain a higher stomatal conductance than Douglas-fir under a low soil water potential (Tan et al. 1978).

11. Response to Herbicides and Other Chemicals

In general salal is both resistant and resilient to many herbicides. The most successful herbicide in controlling salal is triclopyr ester (Garlon). Applying triclopyr ester at 4 kg a.i. ha^{-1} reduced salal cover by 78% (Barker 1988). Combining diesel with triclopyr ester effectively controlled salal for three seasons in a Douglas-fir salal ecosystem on the southeast coast of Vancouver Island (Dunsworth 1986). In an experiment conducted in a dry cedar–hemlock ecosystem, 4 kg a.i. ha^{-1} triclopyr ester in diesel oil at 100 L ha^{-1} in early spring or late summer reduced salal cover by 60-90%. When using mineral oil as the carrier instead of diesel oil, salal cover was reduced by only 40% (Haeussler et al. 1990).

Stewart (1974b) tested 10 herbicides mixed in diesel-oil carriers. Salal plants were sprayed on 1 April, when flower buds were swelling and vegetative buds were dormant. Silvex, dichlorprop, 2,4,5-T, and dicamba produced at least 80% topkill and a 50% reduction in salal cover with silvex showing the best control. Salal is resistant to these same herbicides when applied in water, or applied later in the growing season (Gratkowski 1970; Stewart 1974a).

Other herbicides which are less effective but have been reported to cause slight damage to salal are glyphosate and 2,4-D (Conard and Emmingham 1984). Results from hexazinone applications are variable; Newton and Knight (1981) and Boateng and Herring (1990) found it to be ineffective at controlling salal. However, Wellman and Harrison (1987) reported that an April ground application of 2 kg a.i. ha^{-1} granular hexazinone resulted in control of salal. Two years after herbicide application, salal biomass on the treated areas was about half that on the untreated areas.

In all of the herbicidal tests to control salal, little is known about how the below-ground plant portion responds. D'Anjou (cited by Haeussler et al (1990)) showed that although aboveground parts of salal were well controlled by triclopyr ester, living roots (dry weight basis) still comprised 89% of that in untreated controls, indicating that roots continue to survive despite substantial foliar control.

12. Responses to other Human Manipulations
Several studies have reported that salal will rapidly increase in cover and vigour following the removal or reduction of the forest canopy (Sabhasri 1961; Long and Turner 1975; Long 1977; Stanek et al. 1979; Black et al. 1980; Koch 1983; Gholz et al. 1985; Price et al. 1986; Vales and Bunnell 1988; Messier et al. 1989). Messier (1991) found that salal re-establishes relatively quickly below ground following clear-cut logging and slashburning, but the aboveground portion does not grow as rapidly and may take many years to become dominant.

Prescribed burning and logging can increase the growth of salal if the burn is light. Fire stimulates resprouting from roots and stem bases (Sabhasri 1961). Only severe burns that penetrate sufficiently deep to kill the roots can reduce salal cover. Vihanek (1985) reported that on dry sites on eastern Vancouver Island high severity burns decreased salal cover by 80% compared to adjacent unburned areas; whereas low to moderate burns decreased cover by only 40%.

Fertilizer application, particularly nitrogen-rich fertilizer, increases both above and below-ground growth of salal (Sabhasri 1961; Anonymous 1970). However, in forest stands, applications of fertilizer that result in an increased tree canopy density may cause a decline in the vigour and cover of the salal understory due to shading (Long an Turner 1975; Stanek et al. 1979).

Salal readily forms new plants from cuttings of the stem and roots (Sabhasri 1961), so it can be expected that any form of soil disturbance that causes mechanical damage to the plant, but that does not physically remove it from the site, will stimulate resprouting. However, it has been reported by Muller (1989, cited in Haeussler et al. (1990)) that heavy scarification on areas on southern Vancouver Island has resulted in very slow reinvasion of salal. Based on trials on

Table 2. The percentage of total number of leaves infected by commonly observed fungal taxa on 1240 leaf discs of *Gaultheria shallon* Pursh. (adapted from Petrini et al. (1980)).

Acremonium sp.	2.4
Geniculosporium sp.	8.4
Leptothyrium berberidis Cooke et Massee	3.6
Nodulisporium sp.	2.4
Pezicula sp.	6.4
Phialophora spp.	7.2
Phomopsis sp.	4.8
Phyllosticta pyrolae Ellis et Everh.	34.7
Phyllosticta vaccinii Earle	5.6
Ramularia sp.	4.8
Septogloeum sp.	4.4
Sigmoidea sp.	1.2
Xylaria hypoxylon (L. ex Fr.) Grev. anamorph	2.0

southern Vancouver Island, B. Green (personal communication) has speculated that heavy soil scarification (i.e. removing the organic layer) on dry sites causes mortality of salal rhizomes due to desiccation.

13. Responses to Parasites
Salal is infected by numerous fungal parasites. The most common and serious is the leaf spot fungus (*Mycosphaerella gaultheriae*) (Conners 1967; Haeussler et al. 1990). In a study conducted in western Oregon, Petrini et al. (1982) isolated 13 different species of endophytic fungi (Table 2). The most frequent was *Phyllosticta pyrolae* Ellis et Everh. which occurred on 34.7% of the observed leaves. They found that the frequency of endophyte infections diminishes with decreasing habitat moisture. Furthermore, rates of overall infection were higher in samples taken from densely wooded sites than in samples taken from more open sites. Other fungi reported on salal are *Asterella gaultheriae*, *Bulgaria melastoma*, *Lachnella gaultheriae*, *Leptosphaeria gaultheriae*, *Phacidium gaultheriae*, *Phyllosticta gaultheriae*, and *Poria ferrea* (Conners 1967). Linderman and Zeitoun (1977) found *Phytophthora cinnamomi* Rands, a very widespread fungus, occurring on nursery-grown salal. Apothecia of *Valdensinia heterodoxa* Peyr. (Sclerotiniaceae), have been found on fallen *G. shallon* leaves

(Redhead 1974). Salal is known to have at least one higher plant parasite, *Boschniakia hookeri* Walp. (Olsen and Olsen 1981; Kuijt and Toth 1985), a perennial root parasite. It is not known to what degree the parasite actually damages salal.

ACKNOWLEDGMENTS

This work was funded by a Natural Sciences and Engineering Research Council/Industry grant to C.P.C. and R.T. as part of the SCHIRP study.

Anonymous, 1970. *Gaultheria shallon* Pursh. Davidsonia **1**: 29–31.

Bailey, A. W. 1966. Forest associations and secondary plant succession in the southern Oregon Coast Range. Ph.D. thesis. Oregon State University, Corvallis, OR.

Banfield, A. W. F. 1974. The mammals of Canada. University Toronto Press, Toronto, ON.

Barker, J. E. 1988. Control of salal with Garlon (1988 update). Expert Committee on Weeds. Research report. p. 194. Western Canada Section Meeting. Winnipeg, MB.

Barker, J. E., Weetman, G. F. and Fournier, R. M. 1987. Growth and nutrition of sitka spruce, western hemlock and western red cedar following fertilization of coastal cedar/hemlock sites. Western Forest Products. Vancouver, BC. 14 pp.

Black, T. A., Tan, C. S. and Nnyamah, J. U. 1980. Transpiration rate of Douglas-fir trees in thinned and unthinned stands. Can. J. Soil Sci. **60**: 625–631.

Boateng, J. O. and Herring, L. 1990. Site preparation: Chemical. Pages 164–178 *in* D. P. Lavender, R. Parish, C. A. Johnson, G. Montgomery, A. Vyse, and R. Willis, eds. Regenerating British Columbia's forests. University of British Columbia Press, Vancouver, B.C.

Brown, R. L. and Hafenrichter, A. L. 1962. Stabilizing sand dunes on the Pacific coast with woody plants. USDA, Washington, DC. Misc. Publ. 892, 18 pp

Bunnell, R. L. 1990. 1990. Reproduction of salal (*Gaultheria shallon*) under forest canopy. Can. J. For. Res. **20**: 91–100.

Bunnell, F. L., McCann, R. K. Lindop, P. and Messier, C. 1990. Salal — a competitor? A field guide. Ministry of Forest and Lands, Victoria, BC.

Calder, J. A. and Taylor, R. L. 1968. Flora of the Queen Charlotte Islands. Part 1. Systematics of the vascular plants. Queen's Printer, Canadian Department of Agriculture, Ottawa, ON.

Chambers, M. 1988. Deer in British Columbia BC. Min. Environ., Fish Wildl. Br., Inf. and Education Section, Victoria, BC.

Conners, I. L. 1967. An annotated index of plant diseases in Canada and fungi recorded on plants in Alaska, Canada and Greeland. Canadian Department of Agriculture, Ottawa, ON. Publ. 1251. 381p.

Conard, S. G. and Emmingham, W. H. 1984. Herbicides for brush and fern control on forest sites in western Oregon and Washington. Special Publ. 8, For. Res. Lab., Oregon State University, Corvallis, OR.

Crouch, G. L. 1979. Food habits of black-tailed deer on forest habitats in the Pacific Northwest. Pages 53–59 *in* Wallmo, O. C. and Schoen, J. W. eds. Proceedings of a Conference on Sitka Black-tailed Deer. USDA Forest Service, Alaska Region, Juneau, AK.

Del Moral, R. and Cates, R. G. 1971. Allelopathic potential of the dominant vegetation of western Washington. Ecology **52**: 1030–1037.

Dimock II, E. J., Johnston, W. F. and Stein, W. I. 1974. *Gautheria* L., wintergreen. *In* S. C. Schopmeyer, ed. Seeds of woody plants of the United States. Agric. Hand. 450. USDA For. Ser., Washington, DC.

Dunsworth, B. G. 1986. Salal removal and its impact on crop tree performance. Expert Committee on Weeds. Research report, pp. 197. Western Canada Section Meeting. Saskatoon, SK.

Germain, A. 1985. Fertilization of stagnated Sitka spruce plantations on northern Vancouver Island. M.Sc thesis. University of British Columbia, Vancouver, BC.

Gholz, H. L., Hawk, G. M., Campbell, A., Cromack, JR., K. and Brown, A. T. 1985. Early vegetative recovery and element cycles on a clear-cut watershed in western Oregon. Can. J. For. Res. **15**: 400–409.

Gratkowski, H. 1970. Foliage sprays fail on salal. West. Soc. Weed Sci. Res. Prog. Rep. 1970: 18.

Gunther, E. 1945. Ethnobotany of Western Washington, University of Washing Press, Seattle, WA.

Haeussler, S. and Coates, D. 1986. Autecological characteristics of selected species that compete with conifers in B.C.: a literature review. Land Manage. Rep. No. 33 BC. Ministry of Forests, Victoria, BC.

Haeussler, S., Coates, D. and Mather, J. 1990. Autecology of common plants in British Columbia: a literature review. FRDA report #158, Victoria, BC.

Halverson, N. M. (ed). 1986. Major indicator shrubs and herbs on national forests of western Oregon and southwestern Washington. USDA For. Serv., Pacific NW Region.

Hebda, R. J. 1978. Size, productivity, and paleoecological implications of ericaceous pollen from Burns Bog, southern Fraser River Delta, British Columbia, Can. J. Bot. **57**: 1712–1717.

Hebda, R. J. 1982. Late-glacial and postglacial vegetation history at Bear Cove Bog, northeast Vancouver Island, British Columbia. Can. J. Bot. **61**: 3172–3192.

Hitchcock, C. L. and Cronquist, A. 1973. Flora of the Pacific Northwest. University of Washington Press, Seattle, WA.

Hulténe E. 1968. Flora of Alaska and neighbouring Territories: A manual of vascular plants. Stanford University Press, Stanford, CT.

Hunt, R. S. 1980 Rhytismataceae on salal leaves. Mycotaxonomy **11**: 233–240.

Jones, G. W. and Bunnell, F. L. 1984. Response of black-tailed deer to winters of different severity on northern Vancouver Island. Pages 385–396 *in* W. R. Meehan, T. R. Merrell, Jr., and T. A. Hanley, eds. Proceedings of a Symposium on Fish and Wildlife Relationships in Old-Growth Forests. Am. Inst. Fish. Res. Biol. Morehead City, NC.

King, R. D. 1969. Spring and summer foods of ruffed grouse on Vancouver Island. J. Wildl. Manage. **33**: 440-442.

King, R. D. and Bendell, J. F. 1982 Foods selected by blue grouse (*Dendragapus obscurus fuliginpsis*). Can. J. Zool. **60**: 3268–3281.

Klinka, K., Nuszdorfer, F. C. and Skoda, L. 1979. Biogeoclimatic units of central and southern Vancouver Island. BC Min. For., Victoria, BC.

Klinka, K., Carter, R. E., Feller, M. C. and Wang, Q. 1989. Relations between site index, salal, plant communities, and sites in coastal douglas-fir ecosystems. Northwest Sci. **63**(1): 19–28.

Koch, J. M. 1983. Salal plant structure, growth and allometric relationships under several forest stand densities in south coastal British Columbia, B.S.F. thesis, University of British Columbia, Vancouver, BC.

Krajina, V. J. 1965. Biogeoclimatic zones and classification of British Columbia. Ecol. West. N. Am. **1**: 1–17.

Kuijt, J. and Toth, R. 1985. Structure of the host-parasite interphace of *Boschniakia hookeri* Walpers (Orobanchaceae). Acta Bot. Neerl. **34**: 257–270.

Largent, D. L., Sugihara, N. and Wishner, C. 1980. Occurrence of mycorrhizae on ericaceous and pyrolaceous plants in northern California. Can. J. Bot. **58**: 2274–2279.

Linderman, R. G. and Zeitoun, F. 1977. *Pytophthora cinnamomi* causing root rot and wilt of nursery-grown native western azalea and salal. Plant Dis. Rep. **61**: 1045–1048.

Long, J. N. 1977. Trends in plant species diversity associated with development in a series of *Pseudotsuga menziesii/Gaultheria shallon* stands. Northwst Sci. **51**: 119–130.

Long, J. N. and Turner, J. 1975. Aboveground biomass of understory and overstory in an age sequence of four Douglas-fir stands, J. Appl. Ecol. **12**: 179–188.

Lyons, C. P. 1952. Trees, shrubs and flowers to know in British Columbia. J. M. Dent and Sons Ltd. Vancouver, BC.

Martin, A. C., ZIM, H. S. and Nelson, A. L. 1951. American wildlife and plants. McGraw-Hill Inc., New York, NY.

McGee, A. B. 1988. Effects of prescribed burning on vegetation and natural tree regeneration in mature cedar-hemlock forests in the Pacific Rim National Park. B.S.F. thesis. University of British Columbia, Vancouver, BC.

McKeever, D. G. 1938. The effect of various methods of treatment on the germination of seeds of some plants valuable for game and erosion purposes. M.Sc. thesis, University of Idaho, Moscow, ID.

McTaggart-Cowan, I. 1945. The ecological relationships of the food of the Columbia black-tailed deer, *Odocoileus hemionus columbianus* (Richardson), in the Coast Forest Region of southern Vancouver Island, British Columbia. Ecol. Monogr. **15**: 110–139.

Messier, C. 1991. Factors limiting early conifer growth in salal-dominated cutovers on northern Vancouver Island, British Columbia. Ph.D. thesis. University of British Columbia, Vancouver, BC.

Messier, C. 1993. Effects of neutral shade and growing media on growth, biomass allocation, and competitive ability of *Gaultheria shallon*. Can. J. Bot. **70**: 2271–2276.

Messier, C., Honer, T. W. and Kimmins, J. P. 1989. Photosynthetic photon flux density, red:far-red ratio, and minimum light requirements for survival of *Gaultheria shallon* in western red cedar/western hemlock stands in coastal British Columbia. Can. J For. Res. **19**: 1470–1477.

Messier, C., Kimmins, J. P., Bunnell, F. L. and McCann, R.K. 1990. Understanding salal as a competitor. *In* Vegetation management: An integrated approach. Proc. of the fourth annual BC Veg. Manag. Workshop. Victoria, BC.

Messier, C. and Kimmins, J. P. 1991. Above-and below-ground vegetation recovery in recently clear-cut and burned sites dominated by *Gaultheria shallon* in coastal British Columbia. For. Ecol. Man. **46**: 275–294.

Newton, M. and Knight, D. E. 1981. Handbook of weed and insect control chemicals for forest resource managers. Timber Press. Beaverton. OR.

Nuszdorfer, F. C., Klinka, K. and Demarchi, D. A. 1991. Coastal Douglas-fir zone. Ecosystems of British Columbia. D. Meidinger, and J. Pojar, eds. *In* Research Branch, Ministry of Forestry, Victoria, BC.

Olsen, S. and Olsen, I. D. 1981. Observations on the biology of *Boschniakia hookeri* (Oroban-chaceae). Nord. J. Bot. **1**: 585-594.

Parke, J. L., Linderman R. G. and Trappe, J. N. 1983. Effects of forest litter on mycorrhizal development and growth of Douglas-fir and western red cedar seedlings. Can. J. For. Res. **13**: 660-671.

Petrini, O., Stone, J. and Carroll, F. E. 1982. Endophytic fungi in evergreen shrubs in western Oregon: a preliminary study. Can. J. Bot. **60**: 789-796.

Pojar, J. 1974. The relation of the reproductive biology of plants to the structure and function of four plant communities. Ph.D. thesis. University of British Columbia, Vancouver, BC.

Pojar, J., Klinka, K. and Demarchi, D. A. 1991. Coastal western hemlock zone. *In* D. Meidinger and J. Pojar, eds. Ecosystems of British Columbia. Research Branch, Ministry of Forestry, Victoria, BC.

Price, D. T., Black, T. A. and Kelliher, F. M. 1986. Effects of salal understory removal on photosynthetic rate and stomatal conductance of young Douglas-fir trees. Can. J. For. Res. **16**: 90-97.

Redhead, S. 1974. Epistolae mycologicae IV. *Valdensinia heterodozoxa* Peyr. (Sclerotiniaceae). Syesis **7**: 235-238.

Rose, S. L., Perry, D. A. Pilz, D. and Schoeneberger, M. M. 1983. Allelopathic effects of litter on the growth and colonization of mycorrhizal fungi J. Chem. Ecol. **9**: 1153–1162.

Sabhasri, S. 1961. An ecological study of salal (*Gaultheria shallon*). Ph.D. thesis, University Washington, Seattle. WA.

Salasoo, I. 1981. Alkane distribution in epicuticular wax of some evergreen Ericaceae. Can. J. Bot. **59**: 1189–1191.

Salasoo, I. 1988. Epicuticular wax hydrocarbons of Ericaceae in the Pacific Northwest of U.S.A. Biochem. Syst, Ecol. **16**: 619–622.

Scoggan, H. J. 1978. The flora of Canada. Part 4. National Museum of Canada, Ottawa, ON.

Singleton, J. 1976. Food habits of wild ungulates in British Columbia: Bioliography and plant synopsis. BC Ministry of the Environment, Terrestrial Studies Branch, Victoria, BC.

Smith, N. J. 1991. Sun and shade leaves: clues to how salal (*Gaultheria shallon*) responds to overstory stand density. Can. J. For. Res. **21**: 300-305.

Stanek, W., Beddows, D. and State, D. 1979. Fertilization and thinning effects on a Douglas-fir ecosystem at Shawnigan Lake on Vancouver Island: some observations on salal and bracken fern undergrowth. Rep. BC-R-1, Canadian Forestry Service, Victoria, BC.

Stewart, R. E. 1974a. Foliage sprays for site preparation and release from six coastal brush species. Report PNW-172. USDA For. Ser. Portland, OR.

Stewart, R. E. 1974b. Budbreak sprays for site preparation and release from six coastal brush species, Report PNW-176. USDA For. Ser. Portland. OR.

Szczawinski, A. C. 1962. The heather family (Ericaceae) of British Columbia, BC Provincial Museum, Victoria, BC. Handb. No. 19.

Tan, C. S., Black, T. A. and Nnyamah, J. U. 1977. Characteristics of stomatal diffusion resistance in a Douglas-fir forest exposed to soil water deficits. Can. J. For. Res. **7**: 595–604.

Tan, C. S., Black, T. A. and Nnyamah, J. U. 1978. A simple diffusion model of transportation applied to a thinned Douglas-fir stand. Ecology **59**: 1221–1229.

Taylor, R. L. and MacBryde, B. 1977. Vascular plants of British Columbia: A descriptive resource inventory. The University of British Columbia Press, Vancouver, BC.

Turner, N. J. 1975. Food plants of British Columbia Indians. Handbook No. 34, BC, Provincial Museum, Victoria, BC.

Vales, D. J. 1986. Functional relationships between salal understory and overstory. M.Sc. thesis. University of British Columbia, Vancouver, BC.

Vales, D. J. and Bunnell, F. L. 1988. Relationships between transmission of solar radiation and forest stand characteristics. Agric. For. Meteorol. **43**: 201–223.

Viereck, L. A. and Little, E. L. 1972. Alaska trees and shrubs. Agric. Hand. 410. USDA For. Ser., Washington, DC.

Vihanek, R. E. 1985. The effects of slashburning on the growth and nutrition of young Douglas-fir plantations in some dry, salal dominated ecosystems. M.Sc. thesis, University of British Columbia, Vancouver, BC.

Vogt, K. A., Vogt, D. J., Moore, E. E., Fatuga, B. A., Redlin, M. R. and Edmons, R. L. 1987. Conifer and angiosperm fine-root biomass in relation to stand age and site productivity in Douglas-fir forests. J. Ecol. **75**: 857–870.

Weetman, G. F., Fournier, R., Barker, J., Schnorbus-Panozzo, E. and Germain, A. 1989a. Foliar analysis and response of fertilized chlorotic Sitka spruce plantations on salal-dominated cedar-hemlock cutovers on Vancouver Island. Can. For. Res., **12**: 1501–1511.

Weetman, G. F., Fournier, R., Barker, J. and Schnorbus-Panozzo, E. 1989b. Foliar analysis and response of fertilized chlorotic western hemlock and western red cedar reproduction on salal-dominatd cedar-hemlock cutovers on Vancouver Island. Can. For. Res. **12:** 1512–1520.

Weetman, G. F., Fournier, R. M., Schnborbus-Panozzo, E. and Barker, J. 1990. Post-burn nitrogen and phosphorous availability in coastal British Columbia cedar/hemlock forests and the use of fertilization and salal eradication to restore productivity. *In* S.P. Gessel, ed. Sustained productivity of forest lands. Proc. 7th North Amer. For. Soils Conf. Friesen Press, Vancouver, BC.

Wellman, R. and Harrison, C. 1987. Granular hexazinone site prep. Expert Committee on Weeds. Research report, p. 207. Western Canada Section Meeting, Victoria, BC.

Wollenweber, E. and Kohorst, G. 1984. Novel epicuticular leaf flavonoids from *Kalmia* and *Gaultheria* (Ericaceae). Z. Naturforsch **39c**: 710–713.

Xiao, G. and Berch, S. M. 1992. Ericoid mycorrhizal fungi of *Gaultheria shallon*. Mycologia **84**(3): 470–471.

Zwickel, F. C., and Bendell, J. F. 1972. Observations on food habits of incubating female blue grouse. Condor **74**: 493–494.

Index

Information about the Biology of Canadian Weeds series is available at:

http://www.nrc.ca/aic-journals/weeds.html